Common Core State Standards
Mathematics I
Integrated Pathway

Student Resource Book

WALCH EDUCATION

1   2   3   4   5   6   7   8   9   10
ISBN 978-0-8251-7102-4
Copyright © 2012
J. Weston Walch, Publisher
Portland, ME 04103
www.walch.com
Printed in the United States of America

Table of Contents

Introduction to the Program

Welcome to the *CCSS Integrated Pathway: Mathematics I Student Resource Book.* This book will help you learn how to use algebra, geometry, and data analysis to solve problems. Each lesson builds on what you have already learned. As you participate in classroom activities and use this book, you will master important concepts that will help to prepare you for the EOCT and for other mathematics assessments and courses.

This book is your resource as you work your way through the Math I course. It includes explanations of the concepts you will learn in class; math vocabulary and definitions; formulas and rules; and exercises so you can practice the math you are learning. Most of your assignments will come from your teacher, but this book will allow you to review what was covered in class, including terms, formulas, and procedures.

- In **Unit 1: Relationships Between Quantities**, you will learn first about structures of expressions, and then build on this knowledge by creating equations and inequalities in one variable and then in two variables. The unit focuses on real-world applications of linear equations, linear inequalities, and exponential equations. In addition to creating equations, you will also graph them. The unit concludes with manipulating formulas.

- In **Unit 2: Linear and Exponential Relationships**, you will be introduced to function notation, domain and range, rates of change, and sequences. The introduction of these concepts will allow you to deepen your study of linear and exponential functions in terms of comparing, building, and interpreting them. You will also perform operations and transformations on functions.

- In **Unit 3: Reasoning with Equations**, you will begin by solving linear equations and inequalities, as well as exponential equations. With this foundation for solving linear equations, you will move on to solving systems of equations using the substitution and elimination methods. Then, you will explore how to solve systems of linear equations by graphing.

- In **Unit 4: Descriptive Statistics**, you will start with single-measure variables and become fluent with summarizing, displaying, and interpreting data. Then you will build on these practices to include two-variable data. You will also be introduced to two-way frequency tables and fitting linear models to data. After learning how to fit functions to data, you will learn how to interpret the models, including evaluating the fit and learning the difference between correlation and causation.

- In **Unit 5: Congruence, Proof, and Constructions**, you will define transformations in terms of rigid motions. Geometry and algebra merge as you apply rotations, reflections, and translations to points and figures while using function notation. You will also explore triangle congruency, and construct lines, segments, angles, and polygons.

- In **Unit 6: Connecting Algebra and Geometry Through Coordinates**, your study of the links between the two math disciplines deepens as you use algebraic equations to prove geometric theorems involving distance and slope. You will create equations for parallel and perpendicular lines, and use the distance formula to find the perimeter and area of figures.

Each lesson is made up of short sections that explain important concepts, including some completed examples. Each of these sections is followed by a few problems to help you practice what you have learned. The "Words to Know" section at the beginning of each lesson includes important terms introduced in that lesson.

As you move through your Math I course, you will become a more confident and skilled mathematician. We hope this book will serve as a useful resource as you learn.

Unit 1
Relationships Between Quantities

Lesson 1: Interpreting Structure in Expressions

Common Core State Standards

A–SSE.1   Interpret expressions that represent a quantity in terms of its context.★

   a. Interpret parts of an expression, such as terms, factors, and coefficients.

   b. Interpret complicated expressions by viewing one or more of their parts as a single entity. *For example, interpret P(1 + r)ⁿ as the product of P and a factor not depending on P.*

Essential Questions

1. How are algebraic expressions different from algebraic equations?

2. How is the order of operations applied to expressions and simple formulas at specific values?

3. How are verbal phrases translated into algebraic expressions?

WORDS TO KNOW

algebraic expression	a mathematical statement that includes numbers, operations, and variables to represent a number or quantity
base	the factor being multiplied together in an exponential expression; in the expression a^b, a is the base
coefficient	the number multiplied by a variable in an algebraic expression
constant	a quantity that does not change
exponent	the number of times a factor is being multiplied together in an exponential expression; in the expression a^b, b is the exponent
factor	one of two or more numbers or expressions that when multiplied produce a given product
like terms	terms that contain the same variables raised to the same power

order of operations	the order in which expressions are evaluated from left to right (grouping symbols, evaluating exponents, completing multiplication and division, completing addition and subtraction)
term	a number, a variable, or the product of a number and variable(s)
variable	a letter used to represent a value or unknown quantity that can change or vary

Recommended Resources

- Math-Play.com. "Algebraic Expressions Millionaire Game."

  http://walch.com/rr/CAU1L1Expressions

  "Algebraic Expressions Millionaire Game" can be played alone or in two teams. For each question, players have to identify the correct mathematical expression that models a given expression.

- Quia. "Algebraic Symbolism Matching Game."

  http://walch.com/rr/CAU1L1AlgSymbolism

  In this matching game, players pair each statement with its algebraic interpretation. There are 40 matches to the provided game.

Lesson 1.1.1: Identifying Terms, Factors, and Coefficients

Introduction

Thoughts or feelings in language are often conveyed through expressions; however, mathematical ideas are conveyed through **algebraic expressions**. Algebraic expressions are mathematical statements that include numbers, operations, and variables to represent a number or quantity. **Variables** are letters used to represent values or unknown quantities that can change or vary. One example of an algebraic expression is $3x - 4$. Notice the variable, x.

Key Concepts

- Expressions are made up of **terms**. A term is a number, a variable, or the product of a number and variable(s). An addition or subtraction sign separates each term of an expression.

- In the expression $4x^2 + 3x + 7$, there are 3 terms: $4x^2$, $3x$, and 7.

- The **factors** of each term are the numbers or expressions that when multiplied produce a given product. In the example above, the factors of $4x^2$ are 4 and x^2. The factors of $3x$ are 3 and x.

- 4 is also known as the **coefficient** of the term $4x^2$. A coefficient is the number multiplied by a variable in an algebraic expression. The coefficient of $3x$ is 3.

- The term $4x^2$ also has an **exponent**. Exponents indicate the number of times a factor is being multiplied by itself. In this term, 2 is the exponent and indicates that x is multiplied by itself 2 times.

- Terms that do not contain a variable are called **constants** because the quantity does not change. In this example, 7 is a constant.

Expression	$4x^2 + 3x + 7$		
Terms	$4x^2$	$3x$	7
Factors	4 and x^2	3 and x	–
Coefficients	4	3	–
Constants	–	–	7

- Terms with the same variable raised to the same exponent are called **like terms**. In the example $5x + 3x - 9$, $5x$ and $3x$ are like terms. Like terms can be combined following the **order of operations** by evaluating grouping symbols, evaluating exponents, completing multiplication and division, and completing addition and subtraction from left to right. In this example, the sum of $5x$ and $3x$ is $8x$.

Guided Practice 1.1.1

Example 1

Identify each term, coefficient, constant, and factor of $2(3 + x) + x(1 - 4x) + 5$.

---

1. Simplify the expression.

   The expression can be simplified by following the order of operations and combining like terms.

$2(3 + x) + x(1 - 4x) + 5$	Distribute 2 over $3 + x$.
$6 + 2x + x(1 - 4x) + 5$	Distribute x over $1 - 4x$.
$6 + 2x + x - 4x^2 + 5$	Combine like terms: $2x$ and x; 6 and 5.
$11 + 3x - 4x^2$	

   It is common to rearrange the expression so the powers are in descending order, or go from largest to smallest power.

   $-4x^2 + 3x + 11$

---

2. Identify all terms.

   There are three terms in the expression: $-4x^2$, $3x$, and 11.

---

3. Identify any factors.

   The numbers or expressions that, when multiplied, produce the product $-4x^2$ are -4 and x^2. The numbers or expressions that, when multiplied, produce the product $3x$ are 3 and x.

---

4. Identify all coefficients.

   The number multiplied by a variable in the term $-4x^2$ is -4; the number multiplied by a variable in the term $3x$ is 3; therefore, -4 and 3 are coefficients.

---

5. Identify any constants.

   The number that does not change in the expression is 11; therefore, 11 is a constant.

Example 2

A smartphone is on sale for 25% off its list price. The sale price of the smartphone is $149.25. What expression can be used to represent the list price of the smartphone? Identify each term, coefficient, constant, and factor of the expression described.

1. Translate the verbal expression into an algebraic expression.

   Let x represent the unknown list price. Describe the situation. The list price is found by adding the discounted amount to the sale price:

   sale price + discount amount

   The discount amount is found by multiplying the discount percent by the unknown list price. The expression that represents the list price of the smartphone is $149.25 + 0.25x$.

2. Identify all terms.

   There are two terms described in the expression: the sale price of $149.25, and the discount of 25% off the list price, or 149.25 and $0.25x$.

3. Identify the factors.

   $0.25x$ is the product of the factors 0.25 and x.

4. Identify all coefficients.

   0.25 is multiplied by the variable, x; therefore, 0.25 is a coefficient.

5. Identify any constants.

   The number that does not change in the expression is 149.25; therefore, 149.25 is a constant.

Example 3

Helen purchased 3 books from an online bookstore and received a 20% discount. The shipping cost was $10 and was not discounted. Write an expression that can be used to represent the total amount Helen paid for 3 books plus the shipping cost. Identify each term, coefficient, constant, and factor of the expression described.

1. Translate the verbal expression into an algebraic expression.

   Let x represent the unknown price. The expression used to represent the total amount Helen paid for the 3 books plus shipping is $3x - 0.20(3x) + 10$.

2. Simplify the expression.

   The expression can be simplified by following the order of operations and combining like terms.

$3x - 0.20(3x) + 10$	Multiply 0.20 and $3x$.
$3x - 0.60x + 10$	Combine like terms: $3x$ and $-0.60x$.
$2.4x + 10$	

3. Identify all terms.

   There are two terms in the described expression: the product of 2.4 and x, and the shipping charge of $10: 2.4x$ and 10.

4. Identify the factors.

   $2.4x$ is the product of the factors 2.4 and x.

5. Identify all coefficients.

   2.4 is multiplied by the variable, x; therefore, 2.4 is a coefficient.

6. Identify any constants.

   The number that does not change in the expression is 10; therefore, 10 is a constant.

UNIT 1 • RELATIONSHIPS BETWEEN QUANTITIES
Lesson 1: Interpreting Structure in Expressions

Practice 1.1.1: Identifying Terms, Factors, and Coefficients

For problems 1–3, identify the terms, coefficients, constants, and factors of the given expressions.

1. $8x^2 - 3x + 6x^2 + 5x - 9$

2. $5(2x + 4) + 3x$

3. $\dfrac{4x^3}{5} + 9x$

For problems 4 and 5, translate each verbal expression to an algebraic expression then identify the terms, coefficients, and constants of the given expressions.

4. 4 more than the quotient of x squared and 3

5. the sum of x to the sixth power and 3 times x

6. Write an expression with 5 terms, containing the coefficients 12, 15, 18, and 21.

UNIT 1 • RELATIONSHIPS BETWEEN QUANTITIES
Lesson 1: Interpreting Structure in Expressions

For problems 7–10, write an algebraic expression to describe each situation, and then identify the terms, coefficients, constants, and factors.

7. Colin bought 2 theater tickets and paid a service charge of 5% for buying them from a ticket broker. Write an algebraic expression to represent the total cost of the tickets. Let x represent the cost of each ticket.

8. Eddie purchased 4 packages of light bulbs and received a 15% discount. He also paid $4.85 in taxes on his purchase. Write an algebraic expression to represent the total amount Eddie paid. Let x represent the cost of each package purchased.

9. The perimeter of a rectangle is found by finding the sum of all the sides. Write an expression to represent the perimeter of a rectangle with length x meters and width 4 meters shorter.

10. Write an algebraic expression that represents $\frac{5}{9}$ of the difference of a given Fahrenheit temperature and 32.

Lesson 1.1.2: Interpreting Complicated Expressions

Introduction

Algebraic expressions, used to describe various situations, contain variables. It is important to understand how each term of an expression works and how changing the value of variables impacts the resulting quantity.

Key Concepts

- If a situation is described verbally, it is often necessary to first translate each expression into an algebraic expression. This will allow you to see mathematically how each term interacts with the other terms.

- As variables change, it is important to understand that constants will always remain the same. The change in the variable will not change the value of a given constant.

- Similarly, changing the value of a constant will not change terms containing variables.

- It is also important to follow the order of operations, as this will help guide your awareness and understanding of each term.

Guided Practice 1.1.2

Example 1

A new car loses an average value of $1,800 per year for each of the first six years of ownership. When Nia bought her new car, she paid $25,000. The expression $25,000 - 1800y$ represents the current value of the car, where y represents the number of years since she bought it. What effect, if any, does the change in the number of years since Nia bought the car have on the original price of the car?

> 1. Refer to the expression given: $25,000 - 1800y$.
>
>   The term $1800y$ represents the amount of value the car loses each year, y. As y increases, the product of 1800 and y also increases.

> 2. 25,000 represents the price of the new car.
>
>   As y increases and the product of 1800 and y increases, the original cost is not affected. 25,000 is a constant and remains unchanged.

Example 2

To calculate the perimeter of an isosceles triangle, the expression $2s + b$ is used, where s represents the length of the two congruent sides and b represents the length of the base. What effect, if any, does increasing the length of the congruent sides have on the expression?

> 1. Refer to the expression given: $2s + b$.
>
>   Changing only the length of the congruent sides, s, will not impact the length of base b since b is a separate term.

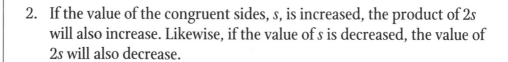

> 2. If the value of the congruent sides, s, is increased, the product of $2s$ will also increase. Likewise, if the value of s is decreased, the value of $2s$ will also decrease.

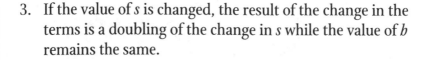

> 3. If the value of s is changed, the result of the change in the terms is a doubling of the change in s while the value of b remains the same.

Example 3

Money deposited in a bank account earns interest on the initial amount deposited as well as any interest earned as time passes. This compound interest can be described by the expression $P(1 + r)^n$, where P represents the initial amount deposited, r represents the interest rate, n represents the number of months that pass. How does a change in each variable affect the value of the expression?

1. Refer to the given expression: $P(1 + r)^n$.

   Notice the expression is made up of one term containing the factors P and $(1 + r)^n$.

2. Changing the value of P does not change the value of the factor $(1 + r)^n$, but it will change the value of the expression by a factor of P. In other words, the change in P will multiply by the result of $(1 + r)^n$.

3. Similarly, changing r changes the **base** of the exponent (the number that will be multiplied by itself), but does not change the value of P. This change will affect the value of the overall expression.

4. Changing n changes the number of times $(1 + r)$ will be multiplied by itself, but does not change the value of P. This change will affect the value of the overall expression.

UNIT 1 • RELATIONSHIPS BETWEEN QUANTITIES
Lesson 1: Interpreting Structure in Expressions

Practice 1.1.2: Interpreting Complicated Expressions

Use your understanding of terms, coefficients, factors, exponents, and the order of operations to answer each of the following questions.

1. Explain why the expression $7 \cdot 3^x$ is not equal to the expression 21^x.

2. Explain why the expression $(5 \cdot 2)^x$ is equal to the expression 10^x.

3. Julio and his sister bought 8 books and m number of magazines and split the cost. The amount of money that Julio spent is represented by the expression $\frac{1}{2}(8+m)$. Does the number of books purchased affect the value of m?

4. Satellite Cell Phone company bills on a monthly basis. Each bill includes a $19.95 service fee for 500 minutes plus a $3.95 communication tax and $0.15 for each minute over 500 minutes. The following expression describes the cost of the cellphone service per month: $23.90 + 0.15m$. If Satellite Cell Phone lowers its service fee, how will the expression change?

5. The expression $\frac{9}{x}$ is given. Describe the value of this expression if the value of x is less than 1, but greater than 0.

continued

6. For what values of x will the result of 0.5^x be greater than 1?

7. A bank account balance for an account with an initial deposit of P dollars earns interest at an annual rate of r. The amount of money in the account after n years is described using the following expression: $P(1 + r)^n$. What effect, if any, does increasing the value of r have on the amount of money after n years?

8. The effectiveness of an initial dose, d, of a particular medicine decreases over a period of time, t, at a rate, r. This situation can be described using the expression: $d(1 - r)^t$. What effect, if any, does decreasing the value of r have on the value of d?

9. The population of a town changes at a rate of r each year. To determine the number of people after n years, the following expression is used: $P(1 + r)^n$, where P represents the initial population, r represents the rate, and n represents the number of years. If the population were declining, what values would you expect for the factor $(1 + r)$?

10. The fine print on the back of a gift card states that a 1% inactivity fee will be deducted each month from the remaining balance if the card has never been used. The expression $x(0.99)^y$ describes this situation. Does the number of months that the gift card remains inactive affect the rate at which the amount is deducted?

Lesson 2: Creating Equations and Inequalities in One Variable

Common Core State Standards

N–Q.2   Define appropriate quantities for the purpose of descriptive modeling.★

N–Q.3   Choose a level of accuracy appropriate to limitations on measurement when reporting quantities.★

A–CED.1   Create equations and inequalities in one variable and use them to solve problems. *Include equations arising from linear and quadratic functions, and simple rational and exponential functions.*★

Essential Questions

1. How are quantities modeled with equations and inequalities?

2. How are equations and inequalities alike and different?

3. What makes creating an exponential equation different from creating a linear equation?

WORDS TO KNOW

equation	a mathematical sentence that uses an equal sign (=) to show that two quantities are equal
exponential decay	an exponential equation with a base, b, that is between 0 and 1 ($0 < b < 1$); can be represented by the formula $y = a(1 - r)^t$, where a is the initial value, $(1 - r)$ is the decay rate, t is time, and y is the final value
exponential equation	an equation that has a variable in the exponent; the general form is $y = a \cdot b^x$, where a is the initial value, b is the base, x is the time, and y is the final output value. Another form is $y = ab^{\frac{x}{t}}$, where t is the time it takes for the base to repeat.
exponential growth	an exponential equation with a base, b, greater than 1 ($b > 1$); can be represented by the formula $y = a(1 + r)^t$, where a is the initial value, $(1 + r)$ is the growth rate, t is time, and y is the final value

inequality	a mathematical sentence that shows the relationship between quantities that are not equivalent
linear equation	an equation that can be written in the form $ax + by = c$, where a, b, and c are rational numbers
quantity	something that can be compared by assigning a numerical value
rate	a ratio that compares different kinds of units
solution	a value that makes the equation true
solution set	the value or values that make a sentence or statement true
unit rate	a rate per one given unit
variable	a letter used to represent a value or unknown quantity that can change or vary

Recommended Resources

- APlusMath. "Algebra Planet Blaster."

  http://walch.com/rr/CAU1L2LinEquations

  Players solve each multi-step linear equation to find the correct planet to "blast." Incorrect answers cause players to destroy their own ship.

- Figure This! Math Challenges for Families. "Challenge 24: Gasoline Tanks."

  http://walch.com/rr/CAU1L2Rates

  This website features a description of the math involved, related occupations, a hint to get started, complete solutions, and a "Try This" section, as well as additional related problems with answers, questions to think about, and resources for further exploration.

- Purplemath.com. "Exponential Functions: Introduction."

  http://walch.com/rr/CAU1L2ExpEquations

  This website gives an introduction of exponential equations and provides a few examples of tables of input and output values, with integers as inputs. The introduction goes into more depth about the shapes of the graphs of exponential functions and continues on to develop the concept of compound interest. It also introduces the number e.

Lesson 1.2.1: Creating Linear Equations in One Variable

Introduction

Creating equations from context is important since most real-world scenarios do not involve the equations being given. An **equation** is a mathematical sentence that uses an equal sign (=) to show that two quantities are equal. A **quantity** is something that can be compared by assigning a numerical value. In this lesson, contexts will be given and equations must be created from them and then used to solve the problems. Since these problems are all in context, units are essential because without them, the numbers have no meaning.

Key Concepts

- A **linear equation** is an equation that can be written in the form $ax + b = c$, where a, b, and c are rational numbers. Often, the most difficult task in turning a context into an equation is determining what the variable is and how to represent that variable.

- The variables are letters used to represent a value or unknown quantity that can change or vary. Once the equation is determined, solving for the variable is straightforward.

- The **solution** will be the value that makes the equation true.

- In some cases the solution will need to be converted into different units. Multiplying by a unit rate or a ratio can do this.

- A **unit rate** is a rate per one given unit, and a **rate** is a ratio that compares different kinds of units.

- Use units that make sense, such as when reporting time; for example, if the time is less than 1 hour, report the time in minutes.

- Think about rounding and precision. The more numbers you list to the right of the decimal place, the more precise the number is.

- When using measurement in calculations, only report to the nearest decimal place of the least accurate measurement. See Guided Practice Example 5.

Creating Equations from Context

1. Read the problem statement first.

2. Reread the scenario and make a list or a table of the known quantities.

3. Read the statement again, identifying the unknown quantity or variable.

4. Create expressions and inequalities from the known quantities and variable(s).

5. Solve the problem.

6. Interpret the solution of the equation in terms of the context of the problem and convert units when appropriate, multiplying by a unit rate.

Guided Practice 1.2.1

Example 1

James earns $15 per hour as a teller at a bank. In one week he pays 17% of his earnings in state and federal taxes. His take-home pay for the week is $460.65. How many hours did James work?

1. Read the statement carefully.

2. Reread the scenario and make a list of the known quantities.

    James earns $15 per hour.

    James pays 17% of his earning in taxes.

    His pay for the week is $460.65.

3. Read the statement again and look for the unknown or the variable.

    The scenario asks for James's hours for the week. The variable to solve for is hours.

4. Create expressions and inequalities from the known quantities and variable(s).

    James's pay for the week was $460.65.

    _____ = 460.65

    He earned $15 an hour. Let h represent hours.

    $15h$

    He paid 17% in taxes.

    $-0.17(15h)$

    Put this information all together.

    $15h - 0.17(15h) = 460.65$

5. Solve the equation.

$$15h - 0.17(15h) = 460.65 \qquad \text{Multiply } -0.17 \text{ and } 15h.$$

$$15h - 2.55h = 460.65 \qquad \text{Combine like terms } 15h \text{ and } -2.55h.$$

$$12.45h = 460.65 \qquad \text{Divide both sides by } 12.45.$$

$$\frac{12.45h}{12.45} = \frac{460.65}{12.45}$$

$$h = 37 \text{ hours}$$

James worked 37 hours.

6. Convert to the appropriate units if necessary.

The scenario asked for hours and the quantity given was in terms of hours. No unit conversions are necessary.

Example 2

Brianna has saved $600 to buy a new TV. If the TV she wants costs $1,800 and she saves $20 a week, how many years will it take her to buy the TV?

1. Read the statement carefully.

2. Reread the scenario and make a list of the known quantities.

The TV costs $1,800.

Brianna saved $600.

Brianna saves $20 per week.

3. Read the statement again and look for the unknown or the variable.

The scenario asks for the number of years. This is tricky because the quantity is given in terms of weeks. The variable to solve for first, then, is weeks.

4. Create expressions and inequalities from the known quantities and variable(s).

Brianna needs to reach $1,800.

$$\underline{\hspace{1.5cm}} = 1800$$

Brianna has saved $600 so far and has to save more to reach her goal.

$$600 + \underline{\hspace{1.5cm}} = 1800$$

Brianna is saving $20 a week for some unknown number of weeks to reach her goal. Let x represent the number of weeks.

$$600 + 20x = 1800$$

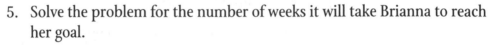

5. Solve the problem for the number of weeks it will take Brianna to reach her goal.

$$600 + 20x = 1800$$
$$\underline{-600 \qquad\quad -600}$$
$$20x = 1200$$
$$\frac{20x}{20} = \frac{1200}{20}$$
$$x = 60 \text{ weeks}$$

Brianna will need 60 weeks to save for her TV.

6. Convert to the appropriate units.

The problem statement asks for the number of years it will take Brianna to save for the TV. There are 52 weeks in a year.

$$\frac{1 \text{ year}}{52 \text{ weeks}}$$

$$60 \text{ weeks} \bullet \frac{1 \text{ year}}{52 \text{ weeks}}$$

$$60 \ \cancel{\text{weeks}} \bullet \frac{1 \text{ year}}{52 \ \cancel{\text{weeks}}} \approx 1.15 \text{ years}$$

Brianna will need approximately 1.15 years, or a little over a year, to save for her TV.

Example 3

Suppose two brothers who live 55 miles apart decide to have lunch together. To prevent either brother from driving the entire distance, they agree to leave their homes at the same time, drive toward each other, and meet somewhere along the route. The older brother drives cautiously at an average speed of 60 miles per hour. The younger brother drives faster, at an average speed of 70 mph. How long will it take the brothers to meet each other?

1. Read the statement carefully.

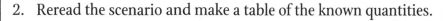

2. Reread the scenario and make a table of the known quantities.

    Problems involving "how fast," "how far," or "how long" require the distance equation, $d = rt$, where d is distance, r is rate of speed, and t is time.

    Complete a table of the known quantities.

	Rate (r)	Distance (d)
Older brother	60 mph	55 miles
Younger brother	70 mph	55 miles

3. Read the statement again and look for the unknown or the variable.

    The scenario asks for how long, so the variable is time, t.

4. Create expressions and inequalities from the known quantities and variable(s).

Step 2 showed that the distance equation is $d = rt$ or $rt = d$. Together the brothers will travel a distance, d, of 55 miles.

(older brother's rate)(t) + (younger brother's rate)(t) = 55

The rate r of the older brother = 60 mph and the rate of the younger brother = 70 mph.

$60t + 70t = 55$

Expand the table from step 2 to see this another way.

	Rate (r)	Time (t)	Distance (d)
Older brother	60 mph	t	$d = 60t$
Younger brother	70 mph	t	$d = 70t$

Together, they traveled 55 miles, so add the distance equations based on each brother's rate.

$60t + 70t = 55$

5. Solve the problem for the time it will take for the brothers to meet each other.

$60t + 70t = 55$

$130t = 55$

$$\frac{130t}{130} = \frac{55}{130}$$

$t \approx 0.42$ hours

It will take the brothers 0.42 hours to meet each other.

Note: The answer was rounded to the nearest hundredth of an hour because any rounding beyond the hundredths place would not make sense. Most people wouldn't be able to or need to process that much precision. When talking about meeting someone, it is highly unlikely that anyone would report a time that is broken down into decimals, which is why the next step will convert the units.

6. Convert to the appropriate units if necessary.

Automobile speeds in the United States are typically given in miles per hour (mph). Therefore, this unit of measurement is appropriate.

However, typically portions of an hour are reported in minutes unless the time given is $\frac{1}{2}$ of an hour.

Convert 0.42 hours to minutes using 60 minutes = 1 hour.

$$60\,\text{min} = 1\,\text{hr}$$

$$0.42\,\text{hr} \cdot \frac{60\,\text{min}}{1\,\text{hr}}$$

$$0.42\,\cancel{\text{hr}} \cdot \frac{60\,\text{min}}{1\,\cancel{\text{hr}}} = 25.2\,\text{minutes}$$

Here again, rarely would a person report that they are meeting someone in 25.2 minutes. In this case, there is a choice of rounding to either 25 or 26 minutes. Either answer makes sense.

The two brothers will meet each other in 25 or 26 minutes.

Example 4

Think about the following scenarios. In what units should they be reported? Explain the reasoning.

a. Water filling up a swimming pool

A swimming pool, depending on the size, has between several gallons and hundreds of thousands of gallons of water.

Think about water flowing out of a faucet and picture filling up a milk jug. How long does it take? Less than a minute? The point is that gallons of water can be filled in minutes.

Report the filling of a swimming pool in terms of gallons per minute.

b. The cost of tiling a kitchen floor

Think about how big rooms are. They can be small or rather large, but typically they are measured in feet. When calculating the area, the measurement units are square feet.

Tiles cost in the dollar range.

Report the cost of tiling a kitchen floor in dollars per square foot.

c. The effect of gravity on a falling object

Think about how fast an object falls when you drop it from shoulder-height. How far is it traveling from your shoulder to the ground? It travels several feet (or meters).

How long does it take before the object hits the ground? It only takes a few seconds.

Report gravity in terms of feet or meters per second.

d. A snail traveling across the sidewalk

The context of the problem will determine the correct units. Think about how slowly a snail moves. Would a snail be able to travel at least one mile in an hour? Perhaps it makes more sense to report the distance in a smaller unit. Report the snail traveling across the sidewalk in feet per minute.

If comparing speeds of other animals to the snail's rate, and the animals' rates are being reported in miles per hour, then it makes sense to report the snail's rate in miles per hour, too.

e. Painting a room

Think about how long it takes to paint a room. It takes longer than several minutes. It would probably take hours.

How is the surface area of a wall typically measured? It's usually measured in square feet.

Report the painting of a room in square feet per hour.

Example 5

Ernesto built a wooden car for a soap box derby. He is painting the top of the car blue and the sides black. He already has enough black paint, but needs to buy blue paint. He needs to know the approximate area of the top of the car to determine the size of the container of blue paint he should buy. He measured the length to be 9 feet $11\frac{1}{4}$ inches, and the width to be $\frac{1}{2}$ inch less than 3 feet. What is the surface area of the top of the car? What is the most accurate area Ernesto can use to buy his paint?

1. Read the statement carefully.

2. Reread the scenario and make a list of the known quantities.
 	
    Length = 9 feet 11.25 inches
 	
    Width = 35.5 inches (3 feet = 36 inches; $36 - \frac{1}{2}$ inch = 35.5 inches)

3. Read the statement again and look for the unknown or the variable.
 	
    The scenario asks for the surface area of the car's top.
 	
    Work with the accuracy component after calculating the surface area.

4. Create expressions and inequalities from the known quantities and variable(s).

The surface area will require some assumptions. A soap box derby car is tapered, meaning it is wider at one end than it is at another. To be sure Ernesto has enough paint, he assumes the car is rectangular with the width being measured at the widest location.

$A = \text{length} \times \text{width} = lw$

For step 2, we listed length and width, but they are not in units that can be multiplied.

Convert the length to inches.

Length = 9 feet 11.25 inches = 9(12) + 11.25 = 119.25 inches

Width = 35.5 inches

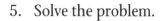

5. Solve the problem.

Substitute length and width into the formula $A = lw$.

$A = lw$

$A = 119.25 \cdot 35.5 = 4233.375$

This gives a numerical result for the surface area, but the problem asks for the most accurate surface area measurement that can be calculated based on Ernesto's initial measurements. Since Ernesto only measured to the hundredths place, the answer can only be reported to the hundredths place.

The surface area of the top of Ernesto's car is 4,233.38 square inches.

6. Convert to the appropriate units if necessary.

    When buying paint, the hardware store associate will ask how many square feet need to be covered. Ernesto has his answer in terms of square inches. Convert to square feet.

    There are 144 square inches in a square foot.

    $$1\,\text{ft}^2 = 144\,\text{in}^2$$

    $$4233.38\,\text{in}^2 \bullet \frac{1\,\text{ft}^2}{144\,\text{in}^2}$$

    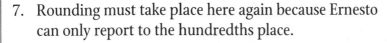

    $$4233.38\,\cancel{\text{in}^2} \bullet \frac{1\,\text{ft}^2}{144\,\cancel{\text{in}^2}} = 29.398472\,\text{ft}^2$$

7. Rounding must take place here again because Ernesto can only report to the hundredths place.

    Ernesto's surface area = 29.40 ft²

UNIT 1 • RELATIONSHIPS BETWEEN QUANTITIES
Lesson 2: Creating Equations and Inequalities in One Variable

Practice 1.2.1: Creating Linear Equations in One Variable

For the problem below, read each scenario and give the units you would use to work with each situation.

1. What units would you use to write equations for each scenario that follows?

   a. jogging

   b. speed of a giant tortoise on land

   c. speed of light

   d. cost of mailing a package

Read each scenario, write an equation, and then solve the problem. Remember to include the appropriate units.

2. The radius of a sphere is measured to be 3.12 cm. What is the most accurate volume of the sphere you can report?

3. The length of a dance floor to be replaced is 1 foot shorter than twice than width. You measured the width to be 12.25 feet. What is the area and what is the most accurate area you can report?

4. Leah's dog consumes four times as many calories a day as her cat. Her cat consumes 240 calories per day. How many calories per day does her dog consume?

continued

5. It costs Marcus an access fee for each visit to his gym, plus it costs him $3 in gas for each trip to the gym and back. This month it cost Marcus $108 for 6 trips to his gym. How much is Marcus's access fee per visit?

6. Rebecca bought x pairs of socks and received a 20% discount. Each pair of socks cost her $4.99. Her total cost without tax was $29.94. How many pairs of socks did Rebecca buy?

7. Amelia and 2 of her friends went out to lunch. Each girl ordered exactly the same meal. The total cost was $55.08, which included an 8% tax. What was the price of each meal, not including tax?

8. Alan mowed the lawn and trimmed the hedges in his yard. The amount of time he spent trimming the hedges was $\dfrac{1}{3}$ the amount of time it took him to mow the lawn. If it took him 1 hour and 15 minutes to mow the lawn, how long did it take him to trim the hedges?

9. The area of a football field is about $\dfrac{3}{4}$ the size of an international soccer field. The area of a football field, including the end zones, is 57,600 square feet. What is an approximate area of an international soccer field?

10. Alex and Brian park their bikes side-by-side. Alex leaves to visit friends, and Brian leaves 30 minutes later, headed for the same destination. Alex pedals 5 miles per hour slower than Brian. After 1 hour, Brian passes Alex. At what speed are they each pedaling?

Lesson 1.2.2: Creating Linear Inequalities in One Variable

Introduction

Inequalities are similar to equations in that they are mathematical sentences. They are different in that they are not equal all the time. An inequality has infinite solutions, instead of only having one solution like a linear equation. Setting up the inequalities will follow the same process as setting up the equations did. Solving them will be similar, with two exceptions, which will be described later.

Key Concepts

- The prefix *in-* in the word *inequality* means "not." Inequalities are sentences stating that two things are not equal. Remember earlier inequalities such as $12 > 2$ and $1 < 7$.

- Remember that the symbols $>$, $<$, $\geq$, $\leq$, and $\neq$ are used with inequalities.

- Use the table below to review the meanings of the inequality symbols and the provided examples with their **solution sets,** or the value or values that make a sentence or statement true.

Symbol	Description	Example	Solution set
$>$	greater than, more than	$x > 3$	all numbers greater than 3; does not include 3
$\geq$	greater than or equal to, at least	$x \geq 3$	all numbers greater than or equal to 3; includes 3
$<$	less than	$x < 3$	all numbers less than 3; does not include 3
$\leq$	less than or equal to, no more than	$x \leq 3$	all numbers less than or equal to 3; includes 3
$\neq$	not equal to	$x \neq 3$	includes all numbers except 3

- Solving a linear inequality is similar to solving a linear equation. The processes used to solve inequalities are the same processes that are used to solve equations.

- Multiplying or dividing both sides of an inequality by a negative number requires reversing the inequality symbol. On the next page, there is a number line to show the process.

- First, look at the example of the inequality 2 < 4.

$$2 < 4$$

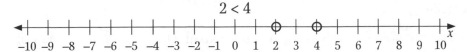

- Multiply both sides by –2 and the inequality becomes 2(–2) < 4(–2) or –4 < –8.

- Is –4 really less than –8?

- To make the statement true, you must reverse the inequality symbol: –4 > –8

$$-4 > -8$$

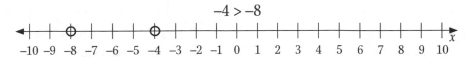

Creating Inequalities from Context

1. Read the problem statement first.

2. Reread the scenario and make a list or a table of the known quantities.

3. Read the statement again, identifying the unknown quantity or variable.

4. Create expressions and inequalities from the known quantities and variable(s).

5. Solve the problem.

6. Interpret the solution of the inequality in terms of the context of the problem.

Guided Practice 1.2.2

Example 1

Juan has no more than $50 to spend at the mall. He wants to buy a pair of jeans and some juice. If the sales tax on the jeans is 4% and the juice with tax costs $2, what is the maximum price of jeans Juan can afford?

1. Read the problem statement first.

2. Reread the scenario and make a list or a table of the known quantities.

   Sales tax is 4%.

   Juice costs $2.

   Juan has no more than $50.

3. Read the statement again, identifying the unknown quantity or variable.

   The unknown quantity is the cost of the jeans.

4. Create expressions and inequalities from the known quantities and variable(s).

   The price of the jeans + the tax on the jeans + the price of the juice must be less than or equal to $50.

   $x + 0.04x + 2 \leq 50$

5. Solve the problem.

$$x + 0.04x + 2 \le 50 \qquad \text{Add like terms.}$$

$$1.04x + 2 \le 50 \qquad \text{Subtract 2 from both sides.}$$

$$1.04x \le 48 \qquad \text{Divide both sides by 1.04.}$$

$$x \le 46.153846$$

Normally, the answer would be rounded down to 46.15. However, when dealing with money, round up to the nearest whole cent as a retailer would.

$$x \le 46.16$$

6. Interpret the solution of the inequality in terms of the context of the problem.

Juan should look for jeans that are priced at or below $46.16.

Example 2

Alexis is saving to buy a laptop that costs $1,100. So far she has saved $400. She makes $12 an hour babysitting. What's the least number of hours she needs to work in order to reach her goal?

1. Read the problem statement first.

2. Reread the scenario and make a list or a table of the known quantities.

   Alexis has saved $400.

   She makes $12 an hour.

   She needs at least $1,100.

3. Read the statement again, identifying the unknown quantity or variable.

   You need to know the least number of hours Alexis must work to make enough money. Solve for hours.

4. Create expressions and inequalities from the known quantities and variable(s).

   Alexis's saved money + her earned money must be greater than or equal to the cost of the laptop.

   $400 + 12h \geq 1100$

5. Solve the problem.

$400 + 12h \geq 1100$	Subtract 400 from both sides.
$12h \geq 700$	Divide both sides by 12.
$h \geq 58.3\overline{3}$	

6. Interpret the solution of the inequality in terms of the context of the problem.

   In this situation, it makes sense to round up to the nearest half hour since babysitters usually get paid by the hour or half hour. Therefore, Alexis needs to work at least 58.5 hours to make enough money to save for her laptop. ✔

Example 3

A radio station is giving away concert tickets. There are 40 tickets to start. They give away 1 pair of tickets every hour for a number of hours until they have at most 4 tickets left for a grand prize. If the contest runs from 11:00 A.M. to 1:00 P.M. each day, for how many days will the contest last?

1. Read the problem statement first.

2. Reread the scenario and make a list or a table of the known quantities.

   The contest starts with 40 tickets.

   The station gives away 2 tickets every hour.

   The contest ends with at most 4 tickets left.

3. Read the statement again, identifying the unknown quantity or variable(s).

   For how many days will the contest last?

   This is tricky because the tickets are given away in terms of hours.

   First, solve for hours.

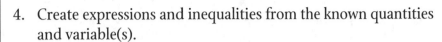

4. Create expressions and inequalities from the known quantities and variable(s).

   40 tickets – 2 tickets given away each hour must be less than or equal to 4 tickets.

   $$40 - 2h \leq 4$$

5. Solve the problem.

$40 - 2h \leq 4$	Subtract 40 from both sides.
$-2h \leq -36$	Divide both sides by –2 and switch the inequality symbol.
$h \geq 18$	

6. Interpret the solution of the inequality in terms of the context of the problem.

   The inequality is solved for the number of hours the contest will last. The contest will last at least 18 hours, or 18 hours or more.

   The problem asks for the number of days the contest will last. If the contest lasts from 11:00 A.M. to 1:00 P.M. each day, that is 3 hours per day. Convert the units.

   1 day = 3 hours

   $$18 \text{ hours} \cdot \frac{1 \text{ day}}{3 \text{ hours}}$$

   $$18 \text{ hours} \cdot \frac{1 \text{ day}}{3 \text{ hours}} = 6 \text{ days}$$

   The contest will run for 6 days or more.

Practice 1.2.2: Creating Linear Inequalities in One Variable

Translate each phrase into an algebraic inequality.

1. An amusement park ride can hold 8 passengers.

2. An auditorium can seat 250 people or fewer.

3. The maximum weight an elevator can hold is 2,400 pounds.

Read each scenario, write an inequality to model the scenario, and then use the inequality to solve the problem.

4. Jeff is saving to purchase a new basketball that will cost at least $88. He has already saved $32. At least how much more does he need to save for the basketball?

5. Suppose you earn $15 per hour working part time as a carpenter. This month, you want to earn at least $950. How many hours must you work?

6. Mackenzie earned a score of 79 on her semester biology test. She needs to have a total of at least 160 points from her semester and final tests to receive a B for her grade. What score must Mackenzie earn on her final test to ensure her B?

continued

UNIT 1 • RELATIONSHIPS BETWEEN QUANTITIES
Lesson 2: Creating Equations and Inequalities in One Variable

7. Arianna buys computer games from an online store. Each game she orders costs $22, and shipping for her total order is $9. Arianna can spend no more than $75. How many computer games can Arianna buy?

8. A recreation center holds a lacrosse game every Saturday morning for young adults. The group agreed that at least 6 players are needed on each team. One team started out with 16 players. After an hour of playing, 2 players from that team started leaving every 7 minutes. For at least how long can they remain playing?

9. A radio station has no more than $25,000 to give away. They have decided to give away $1,000 three times a day every day until they have at least $4,000 left to award as a grand prize. How many days will the contest run?

For problem 10, create your own context for the given inequality, and then solve the inequality. Be sure to express your solution in terms of the context of the problem.

10. $3x - 3 > 6$

Lesson 1.2.3: Creating Exponential Equations

Introduction

Exponential equations are equations that have the variable in the exponent. Exponential equations are found in science, finance, sports, and many other areas of daily living. Some equations are complicated, but some are not.

Key Concepts

- The general form of an exponential equation is $y = a \cdot b^x$, where a is the initial value, b is the base, and x is the time. The final output value will be y.

- Since the equation has an exponent, the value increases or decreases rapidly.

- The base, b, must always be greater than 0 ($b > 0$).

- If the base is greater than 1 ($b > 1$), then the exponential equation represents **exponential growth**.

- If the base is between 0 and 1 ($0 < b < 1$), then the exponential equation represents **exponential decay**.

- If the time is given in units other than 1 (e.g., 1 month, 1 hour, 1 minute, 1 second), use the equation $y = ab^{\frac{x}{t}}$, where t is the time it takes for the base to repeat.

- Another form of the exponential equation is $y = a(1 \pm r)^t$, where a is the initial value, r is the rate of growth or decay, and t is the time.

- Use $y = a(1 + r)^t$ for exponential growth (notice the plus sign). For example, if a population grows by 2% then r is 0.02, but this is less than 1 and by itself does not indicate growth.

- Substituting 0.02 for b into the formula $y = a \cdot b^x$ requires the expression $(1 + r)$ to arrive at the full growth rate of 102%, or 1.02.

- Use $y = a(1 - r)^t$ for exponential decay (notice the minus sign). For example, if a population decreases by 3%, then 97% is the factor being multiplied over and over again. The population from year to year is always 97% of the population from the year before (a 3% decrease). Think of this as 100% minus the rate, or in decimal form $(1 - r)$.

- Look for words such as *double, triple, half, quarter*—such words give the number of the base. For example, if an experiment begins with 1 bacterium that doubles (splits itself in two) every hour, determining how many bacteria will be present after x hours is solved with the following equation: $y = (1)2^x$, where 1 is the starting value, 2 is the rate, x is the number of hours, and y is the final value.

- Look for the words *initial* or *starting* to substitute in for a.

- Look for the words *ended with* and *after*—these words will be near the final value given.

- Follow the same procedure as with setting up linear equations and inequalities in one variable:

Creating Exponential Equations from Context

1. Read the problem statement first.

2. Reread the scenario and make a list or a table of the known quantities.

3. Read the statement again, identifying the unknown quantity or variable.

4. Create expressions and inequalities from the known quantities and variable(s).

5. Solve the problem.

6. Interpret the solution of the exponential equation in terms of the context of the problem.

Guided Practice 1.2.3

Example 1

A population of mice quadruples every 6 months. If a mouse nest started out with 2 mice, how many mice would there be after 2 years? Write an equation and then use it to solve the problem.

---

1. Read the scenario and then reread it again, this time identifying the known quantities.

   The initial number of mice = 2.

   The base = quadruples, so that means 4.

   The amount of time = every 6 months for 2 years.

---

2. Read the statement again, identifying the unknown quantity or variable.

   The unknown quantity is the number of mice after 2 years. Solve for the final amount of mice after 2 years.

---

3. Create expressions and equations from the known quantities and variable(s).

   The general form of the exponential equation is $y = a \cdot b^x$, where y is the final value, a is the initial value, b is the base, and x is the time.

   $a = 2$

   $b = 4$

   x = every 6 months for 2 years

   Since the problem is given in months, you need to convert 2 years into 6-month time periods. How many 6-month time periods are there in 2 years?

   To determine this, think about how many 6-month time periods there are in 1 year. There are 2. Multiply that by 2 for each year. Therefore, there are four 6-month time periods in 2 years.

   (continued)

Another way to determine the period is to set up ratios.

$$2 \text{ years} \cdot \frac{12 \text{ months}}{1 \text{ year}} = 24 \text{ months}$$

$$24 \text{ months} \cdot \frac{1 \text{ time period}}{6 \text{ months}} = 4 \text{ time periods}$$

Therefore, $x = 4$.

4. Substitute the values into the general form of the equation $y = a \cdot b^x$.

$$y = a \cdot b^x \qquad \text{OR} \qquad y = ab^{\frac{x}{t}}$$

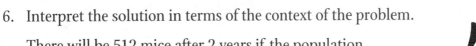

$$y = (2) \cdot (4)^4 \qquad \text{OR} \qquad y = (2)(4)^{\frac{24}{6}}$$

5. Follow the order of operations to solve the problem.

$y = (2) \cdot (4)^4$ Raise 4 to the 4th power.

$y = (2) \cdot 256$ Multiply 2 and 256.

$y = 512$

6. Interpret the solution in terms of the context of the problem.

There will be 512 mice after 2 years if the population quadruples every 6 months.

Example 2

In sporting tournaments, teams are eliminated after they lose. The number of teams in the tournament then decreases by half with each round. If there are 16 teams left after 3 rounds, how many teams started out in the tournament?

1. Read the scenario and then reread it again, this time identifying the known quantities.

   The final number of teams = 16.

   The reduction = $\dfrac{1}{2}$.

   The amount of time = 3 rounds.

2. Read the statement again, identifying the unknown quantity or variable.

   The unknown quantity is the number of teams with which the tournament began. Solve for the initial or starting value, a.

3. Create expressions and equations from the known quantities and variable(s).

   The general form of the exponential equation is $y = a \cdot b^x$, where y is the final value, a is the initial value, b is the rate of decay or growth, and x is the time.

   $y = 16$

   $b = \dfrac{1}{2}$

   $x = 3$ rounds

4. Substitute the values into the general form of the equation $y = a \cdot b^x$.

   $y = a \cdot b^x$

   $16 = a \cdot \left(\dfrac{1}{2}\right)^3$

5. Follow the order of operations to solve the problem.

$$16 = a \cdot \left(\frac{1}{2}\right)^3 \qquad \text{Raise the base to the power of 3.}$$

$$16 = a \cdot \frac{1}{8} \qquad \text{Multiply by the reciprocal.}$$

$$a = 128$$

6. Interpret the solution in terms of the context of the problem.

The tournament started with 128 teams.

Example 3

The population of a small town is increasing at a rate of 4% per year. If there are currently about 6,000 residents, about how many residents will there be in 5 years at this growth rate?

1. Read the scenario and then reread it again, this time identifying the known quantities.

The initial number of residents = 6,000.

The growth = 4%.

The amount of time = 5 years.

2. Read the statement again, identifying the unknown quantity or variable.

The unknown quantity is the number of residents after 5 years. Solve for the final value after 5 years.

3. Create expressions and equations from the known quantities and variable(s).

The general form of the exponential growth equation with a percent increase is $y = a(1 + r)^t$, where y is the final value, a is the initial value, r is the rate of growth, and t is the amount of time.

$a = 6000$

$r = 4\% = 0.04$

$t = 5$ years

4. Substitute the values into the general form of the equation $y = a(1 + r)^t$.

$y = a(1 + r)^t$

$y = 6000(1 + 0.04)^5$

5. Follow the order of operations to solve the problem.

$y = 6000(1 + 0.04)^5$ Add inside the parentheses first.

$y = 6000(1.04)^5$ Raise the base to the power of 5.

$y = 6000(1.21665)$ Multiply.

$y \approx 7300$

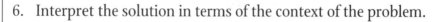

6. Interpret the solution in terms of the context of the problem.

If this growth rate continues for 5 years, the population will increase by more than 1,000 residents to about 7,300 people.

Example 4

You want to reduce the size of a picture to place in a small frame. You aren't sure what size to choose on the photocopier, so you decide to reduce the picture by 15% each time you scan it until you get it to the size you want. If the picture was 10 inches long at the start, how long is it after 3 scans?

1. Read the scenario and then reread it again, this time identifying the known quantities.

   The initial length = 10 inches.

   The reduction = 15% = 0.15.

   The amount of time = 3 scans.

2. Read the statement again, identifying the unknown quantity or variable.

   The unknown quantity is the length of the picture after 3 scans. Solve for the final value after 3 scans.

3. Create expressions and equations from the known quantities and variable(s).

   The general form of the exponential growth equation with a percent decrease is $y = a(1 - r)^t$, where y is the final value, a is the initial value, r is the rate of decay, and t is the amount of time.

   $a = 10$

   $r = 15\% = 0.15$

   $t = 3$ scans

4. Substitute the values into the general form of the equation $y = a(1 - r)^t$.

   $y = a(1 - r)^t$

   $y = 10(1 - 0.15)^3$

5. Follow the order of operations to solve the problem.

$y = 10(1 - 0.15)^3$ Subtract inside the parentheses first.

$y = 10(0.85)^3$ Raise the base to the power of 3.

$y = 10(0.614125)$ Multiply.

$y \approx 6.14$

6. Interpret the solution in terms of the context of the problem.

After 3 scans, the length of the picture is about 6 inches.

UNIT 1 • RELATIONSHIPS BETWEEN QUANTITIES
Lesson 2: Creating Equations and Inequalities in One Variable

Practice 1.2.3: Creating Exponential Equations

Use what you know about linear and exponential equations to complete problems 1–3.

1. Determine whether each scenario can be modeled by a linear or an exponential equation.

   a. The price of a gallon of gas increases by $0.75 every 2 months.

   b. Every 2 months, a gallon of gas costs three times as much as it did before.

2. Determine whether each scenario can be modeled by a linear or an exponential equation.

   a. A piece of jewelry appreciates (increases in value) so that after 20 years it's worth twice what you paid for it.

   b. A piece of jewelry appreciates so that its value doubles every 20 years.

3. Determine whether each scenario can be modeled by a linear or an exponential equation.

   a. A town's population declines by 3% each year.

   b. About 200 residents leave town each year.

For problems 4–10, write an equation to model each scenario. Then use the equation to solve the problem.

4. If you end with 1,920 bacteria in a Petri dish and the population doubled every hour, how many bacteria did you start with 6 hours ago?

UNIT 1 • RELATIONSHIPS BETWEEN QUANTITIES
Lesson 2: Creating Equations and Inequalities in One Variable

5. An investment doubles in value every 9 years. What was the starting value of the investment if it is worth $4,800 after 27 years?

6. An insect population triples every 4 months. If the population started out with 24 insects, how many insects would there be in 16 months?

7. The half-life of a radioactive substance is the time it takes for half of the substance to decay. The half-life of one form of rhodium, Rh-106, is about 30 seconds. If you start with 100 grams of Rh-106, how much will be left after 4 minutes?

8. The NCAA Division I Basketball tournament begins each year with a certain number of teams. After each round of games, the losing teams are cut from the tournament, so that each round has half as many teams playing as the previous round. After 3 rounds 8 teams are left. How many teams started out in the tournament?

9. A city's population grows by about 1% each year. If the city's population is 63,000 people now, what will the population be in 4 years?

10. A town's population decreases each year by about 1%. If the town's population is 3,000 now, what will the population be in 5 years? In 10 years?

Lesson 3: Creating and Graphing Equations in Two Variables

Common Core State Standards

A–CED.2 Create equations in two or more variables to represent relationships between quantities; graph equations on coordinate axes with labels and scales.★

N–Q.1 Use units as a way to understand problems and to guide the solution of multi-step problems; choose and interpret units consistently in formulas; choose and interpret the scale and the origin in graphs and data displays.★

Essential Questions

1. What do the graphs of equations in two variables represent?

2. How do you determine the scales to use for the *x*- and *y*-axes on any given graph?

3. How do the graphs of linear equations and exponential equations differ? How are they similar?

4. How can graphing equations help you to make decisions?

WORDS TO KNOW

coordinate plane	a set of two number lines, called the axes, that intersect at right angles
dependent variable	labeled on the *y*-axis; the quantity that is based on the input values of the independent variable
exponential decay	an exponential equation with a base, b, that is between 0 and 1 ($0 < b < 1$); can be represented by the formula $y = a(1 - r)^t$, where a is the initial value, $(1 - r)$ is the decay rate, t is time, and y is the final value
exponential equation	an equation that has a variable in the exponent; the general form is $y = a \cdot b^x$, where a is the initial value, b is the base, x is the time, and y is the final output value. Another form is $y = ab^{\frac{x}{t}}$, where t is the time it takes for the base to repeat.

exponential growth	an exponential equation with a base, b, greater than 1 ($b > 1$); can be represented by the formula $y = a(1 + r)^t$, where a is the initial value, $(1 + r)$ is the growth rate, t is time, and y is the final value
independent variable	labeled on the x-axis; the quantity that changes based on values chosen
linear equation	an equation that can be written in the form $ax + by = c$, where a, b, and c are rational numbers; can also be written as $y = mx + b$, in which m is the slope, b is the y-intercept, and the graph is a straight line
slope	the measure of the rate of change of one variable with respect to another variable; slope $= \dfrac{y_2 - y_1}{x_2 - x_1} = \dfrac{\Delta y}{\Delta x} = \dfrac{\text{rise}}{\text{run}}$
***x*-intercept**	the point at which the line intersects the x-axis at $(x, 0)$
***y*-intercept**	the point at which the line intersects the y-axis at $(0, y)$

Recommended Resources

- Math-Play.com. "Hoop Shoot."

  http://walch.com/rr/CAU1L3SlopeandIntercept

  This one- or two-player game includes 10 multiple-choice questions about slope and y-intercept. Correct answers result in a chance to make a 3-point shot in a game of basketball.

- Oswego City School District Regents Exam Prep Center. "Equations and Graphing."

  http://walch.com/rr/CAU1L3GraphLinear

  This site contains a thorough summary of the methods used to graph linear equations.

- Ron Blond Mathematics Applets. "The Exponential Function $y = ab^x$."

  http://walch.com/rr/CAU1L3ExponentialFunction

  This applet provides sliders for the variables a and b, and shows how changing the values of these variables results in changes in the graph.

Lesson 1.3.1: Creating and Graphing Linear Equations in Two Variables

Introduction

Many relationships can be represented by linear equations. Linear equations in two variables can be written in the form $y = mx + b$, where m is the slope and b is the y-intercept. The slope of a linear graph is a measure of the rate of change of one variable with respect to another variable. The y-intercept of the equation is the point at which the graph crosses the y-axis and the value of x is zero.

Creating a linear equation in two variables from context follows the same procedure at first for creating an equation in one variable. Start by reading the problem carefully. Once you have created the equation, the equation can be graphed on the coordinate plane. The **coordinate plane** is a set of two number lines, called the axes, that intersect at right angles.

Key Concepts

Reviewing Linear Equations:

- The slope of a linear equation is also defined by the ratio of the rise of the graph compared to the run. Given two points on a line, (x_1, y_1) and (x_2, y_2), the slope is the ratio of the change in the y-values of the points (rise) to the change in the corresponding x-values of the points (run).

$$\text{slope} = \frac{\text{rise}}{\text{run}} = \frac{y_2 - y_1}{x_2 - x_1}$$

- The slope-intercept form of an equation of a line is often used to easily identify the slope and **y-intercept**, which then can be used to graph the line. The slope-intercept form of an equation is shown below, where m represents the slope of the line and b represents the y-value of the point where the line intersects the y-axis at point $(0, y)$.

$$y = mx + b$$

- Horizontal lines have a slope of 0. They have a run but no rise. Vertical lines have no slope.

- The **x-intercept** of a line is the point where the line intersects the x-axis at $(x, 0)$.

- If a point lies on a line, its coordinates make the equation true.

- The graph of a line is the collection of all points that satisfy the equation. The graph of the linear equation $y = -2x + 2$ is shown on the following page, with its x- and y-intercepts plotted.

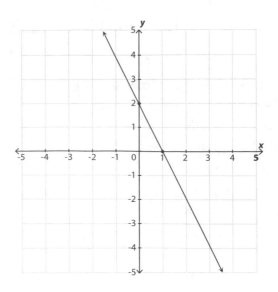

Creating Equations

1. Read the problem statement carefully before doing anything.

2. Look for the information given and make a list of the known quantities.

3. Determine which information tells you the rate of change, or the slope, m. Look for words such as *each*, *every*, *per*, or *rate*.

4. Determine which information tells you the y-intercept, or b. This could be an initial value or a starting value, a flat fee, and so forth.

5. Substitute the slope and y-intercept into the linear equation formula, $y = mx + b$.

Determining the Scale and Labels When Graphing:

- If the slope has a rise and run between −10 and 10 and the y-intercept is 10 or less, use a grid that has squares equal to 1 unit.

- Adjust the units according to what you need. For example, if the y-intercept is 10,000, each square might represent 2,000 units on the y-axis. Be careful when plotting the slope to take into account the value each grid square represents.

- Sometimes you need to skip values on the y-axis. It makes sense to do this if the y-intercept is very large (positive) or very small (negative). For example, if your y-intercept is 10,000, you could start your y-axis numbering at 0 and "skip" to 10,000 at the next y-axis number. Use a short, zigzag line starting at 0 to about the first grid line to show that you've skipped values. Then continue with the correct numbering for the rest of the axis. For an illustration, see Guided Practice Example 3, step 4.

- Only use x- and y-values that make sense for the context of the problem. Ask yourself if negative values make sense for the x-axis and y-axis labels in terms of the context. If negative values don't make sense (for example, time and distance can't have negative values), only use positive values.

- Determine the independent and dependent variables.

- The independent variable will be labeled on the x-axis. The **independent variable** is the quantity that changes based on values you choose.

- The dependent variable will be labeled on the y-axis. The **dependent variable** is the quantity that is based on the input values of the independent variable.

Graphing Equations Using a Table of Values

Using a table of values works for any equation when graphing. For an example, see Guided Practice Example 1, step 7.

1. Choose inputs or values of x.

2. Substitute those values in for x and solve for y.

3. The result is an ordered pair (x, y) that can be plotted on the coordinate plane.

4. Plot at least 3 ordered pairs on the line.

5. Connect the points, making sure that they lie in a straight line.

6. Add arrows to the end(s) of the line to show when the line continues infinitely (if continuing infinitely makes sense in terms of the context of the problem).

7. Label the line with the equation.

Graphing Equations Using the Slope and y-intercept

For an example, see Guided Practice Example 2, step 6.

1. Plot the y-intercept first. The y-intercept will be on the y-axis.

2. Recall that slope is $\dfrac{\text{rise}}{\text{run}}$. Change the slope into a fraction if you need to.

3. To find the rise when the slope is positive, count up the number of units on your coordinate plane the same number of units in your rise. (So, if your slope is $\dfrac{3}{5}$, you count up 3 on the y-axis.)

(continued)

4. For the run, count over to the right the same number of units on your coordinate plane in your run, and plot the second point. (For the slope $\frac{3}{5}$, count 5 to the right and plot your point.)

5. To find the rise when the slope is negative, count down the number of units on your coordinate plane the same number of units in your rise. For the run, you still count over to the right the same number of units on your coordinate plane in your run and plot the second point. (For a slope of $-\frac{4}{7}$, count down 4, right 7, and plot your point.)

6. Connect the points and place arrows at one or both ends of the line when it makes sense to have arrows within the context of the problem.

7. Label the line with the equation.

Graphing Equations Using a TI-83/84:

Step 1: Press [Y=] and key in the equation using [X, T, θ, n] for x.

Step 2: Press [WINDOW] to change the viewing window, if necessary.

Step 3: Enter in appropriate values for Xmin, Xmax, Xscl, Ymin, Ymax, and Yscl, using the arrow keys to navigate.

Step 4: Press [GRAPH].

Graphing Equations Using a TI-Nspire:

Step 1: Press the home key.

Step 2: Arrow over to the graphing icon (the picture of the parabola or the U-shaped curve) and press [enter].

Step 3: At the blinking cursor at the bottom of the screen, enter in the equation and press [enter].

Step 4: To change the viewing window: press [menu], arrow down to number 4: Window/Zoom, and click the center button of the navigation pad.

Step 5: Choose 1: Window settings by pressing the center button.

Step 6: Enter in the appropriate XMin, XMax, YMin, and YMax fields.

Step 7: Leave the XScale and YScale set to auto.

Step 8: Use [tab] to navigate among the fields.

Step 9: Press [tab] to "OK" when done and press [enter].

Guided Practice 1.3.1

Example 1

A local convenience store owner spent $10 on pencils to resell at the store. What is the equation of the store's revenue if each pencil sells for $0.50? Graph the equation.

1. Read the problem and then reread the problem, determining the known quantities.

   Initial cost of pencils: $10

   Charge per pencil: $0.50

2. Identify the slope and the y-intercept.

   The slope is a rate. Notice the word "each."

   Slope = 0.50

   The y-intercept is a starting value. The store *paid* $10. The starting revenue then is –$10.

   y-intercept = –10

3. Substitute the slope and y-intercept into the equation $y = mx + b$, where m is the slope and b is the y-intercept.

   $m = 0.50$

   $b = -10$

   $y = 0.50x - 10$

4. Change the slope into a fraction in preparation for graphing.

   $$0.50 = \frac{50}{100} = \frac{1}{2}$$

5. Rewrite the equation using the fraction.

$$y = \frac{1}{2}x - 10$$

6. Set up the coordinate plane and identify the independent and dependent variables.

In this scenario, x represents the number of pencils sold and is the independent variable. The x-axis label is "Number of pencils sold."

The dependent variable, y, represents the revenue the store will make based on the number of pencils sold. The y-axis label is "Revenue in dollars ($)."

Determine the scales to be used. Since the slope's rise and run are within 10 units and the y-intercept is –10 units, a scale of 1 on each axis is appropriate. Label the x-axis from 0 to 10, since you will not sell a negative amount of pencils. Label the y-axis from –15 to 15, to allow space to plot the $10 the store owner paid for the pencils (–10).

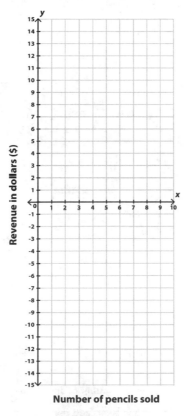

7. Plot points using a table of values.

Substitute x values into the equation $y = \frac{1}{2}x - 10$ and solve for y.

Choose any values of x to substitute. Here, it's easiest to use values of x that are even since after substituting you will be multiplying by $\frac{1}{2}$. Using even-numbered x values will keep the numbers whole after you multiply.

x	y
0	$\frac{1}{2}(0) - 10 = -10$
2	-9
4	-8
6	-7

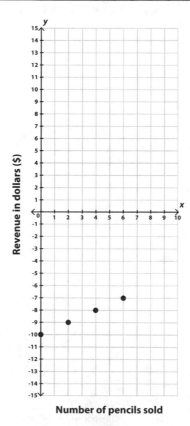

8. Connect the points with a line and add an arrow to the right end of the line to show that the line of the equation goes on infinitely in that direction. Be sure to write the equation of the line next to the line on the graph.

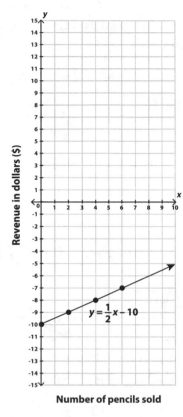

Revenue in dollars ($)

Number of pencils sold

$y = \dfrac{1}{2}x - 10$

Example 2

A taxi company in Kansas City charges $2.50 per ride plus $2 for every mile driven. Write and graph the equation that models this scenario.

1. Read the problem statement and then reread the problem, determining the known quantities.

   Initial cost of taking a taxi: $2.50

   Charge per mile: $2

⬇

2. Identify the slope and the y-intercept.

   The slope is a rate. Notice the word "every."

   Slope = 2

   The y-intercept is a starting value. It costs $2.50 initially to hire a cab driver.

   y-intercept = 2.50

⬇

3. Substitute the slope and y-intercept into the equation $y = mx + b$, where m is the slope and b is the y-intercept.

   $m = 2$

   $b = 2.50$

   $y = 2x + 2.50$

⬇

4. Set up the coordinate plane.

   In this scenario, *x* represents the number of miles traveled in the cab and is the independent variable. The *x*-axis label is "Miles traveled."

   The dependent variable, *y*, represents the cost of taking a cab based on the number of miles traveled. The *y*-axis label is "Cost in dollars ($)."

   Determine the scales to be used. Since the slope's rise and run are within 10 units and the *y*-intercept is within 10 units of 0, a scale of 1 on each axis is appropriate. Label the *x*-axis from 0 to 10, since miles traveled will only be positive. Label the *y*-axis from 0 to 10, since cost will only be positive.

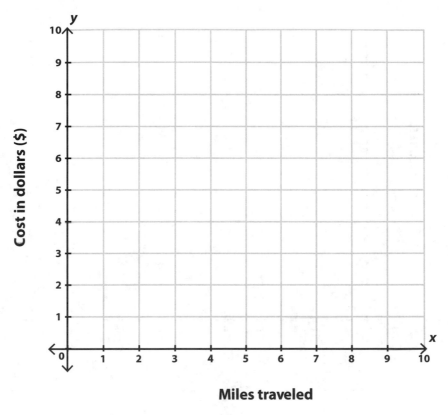

5. Graph the equation using the slope and *y*-intercept. Plot the *y*-intercept first.

The *y*-intercept is 2.5. Remember that the *y*-intercept is where the graph crosses the *y*-axis and the value of *x* is 0. Therefore, the coordinate of the *y*-intercept will always have 0 for *x*. In this case, the coordinate of the *y*-intercept is (0, 2.5).

To plot points that lie in between grid lines, use estimation. Since 2.5 is halfway between 2 and 3, plot the point halfway between 2 and 3 on the *y*-axis. Estimate the halfway point.

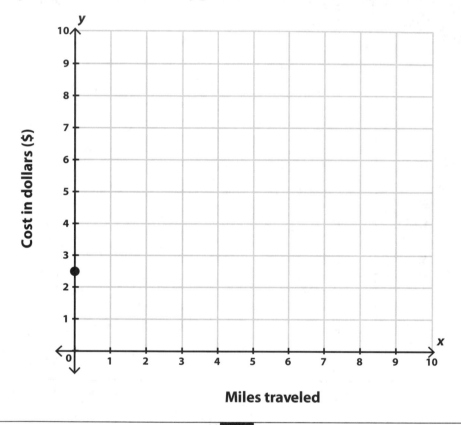

6. Graph the equation using the slope and *y*-intercept. Use the slope to find the second point.

Remember that the slope is $\dfrac{\text{rise}}{\text{run}}$. In this case, the slope is 2. Write 2 as a fraction.

$$2=\dfrac{2}{1}=\dfrac{\text{rise}}{\text{run}}$$

The rise is 2 and the run is 1.

Point your pencil at the *y*-intercept. Move the pencil up 2 units, since the slope is positive. Remember that the *y*-intercept was halfway between grid lines. Be sure that you move your pencil up 2 complete units by first going to halfway between 3 and 4 (3.5) and then halfway between 4 and 5 (4.5) on the *y*-axis.

Now, move your pencil to the right 1 unit for the run and plot a point. This is your second point.

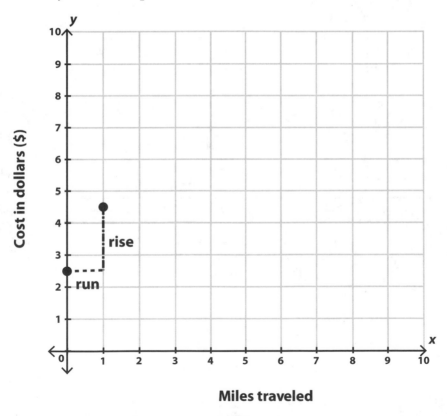

7. Connect the points and extend the line. Then, label your line.

Draw a line through the two points and add arrows to the right end of the line to show that the line continues infinitely in that direction. Label the line with the equation, $y = 2x + 2.5$.

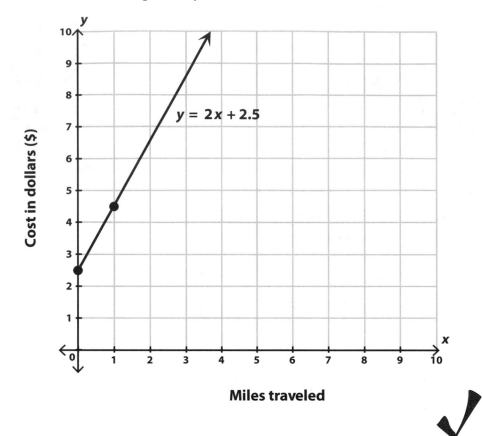

Example 3

Miranda gets paid $300 a week to deliver groceries. She also earns 5% commission on any orders she collects while out on her delivery run. Write an equation that represents her weekly pay and then graph the equation.

1. Read the problem statement and then reread the problem, determining the known quantities.

   Weekly payment: $300

   Commission: 5% = 0.05

2. Identify the slope and the y-intercept.

   The slope is a rate. Notice the symbol "%," which means *percent*, or *per 100*.

   Slope = 0.05

   The y-intercept is a starting value. She gets paid $300 a week to start with before taking any orders.

   y-intercept = 300

3. Substitute the slope and y-intercept into the equation $y = mx + b$, where m is the slope and b is the y-intercept.

   $m = 0.05$

   $b = 300$

   $y = 0.05x + 300$

4. Set up the coordinate plane.

In this scenario, x represents the amount of money in orders Miranda gets. The x-axis label is "Orders in dollars ($)."

The dependent variable, y, represents her total earnings in a week. The y-axis label is "Weekly earnings in dollars ($)."

Determine the scales to be used. The y-intercept is in the hundreds and the slope is in decimals. Work with the slope first. The slope is 0.05 or $\dfrac{5}{100}$. The rise is a small number, but the run is big. The run is shown on the x-axis, so that will need to be in increments of 100. Start at −100 or 0, since the order amounts will be positive, and continue to 1,000. The rise is shown on the y-axis and is small, but remember that the y-intercept is $300. Since there's such a large gap before the y-intercept, the y-axis will need to skip values so the graph doesn't become too large. Start the y-axis at 0, then skip to 250 and label the rest of the axis in increments of 5 until you reach 450. Use the zigzag line to show you skipped values between 0 and 250.

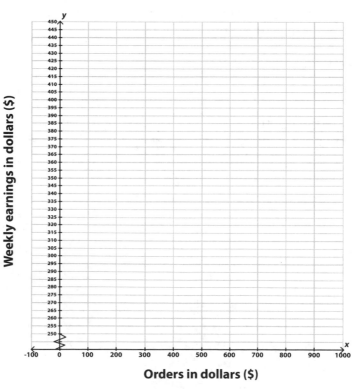

5. Graph the equation using the slope and y-intercept. Plot the y-intercept first.

   The y-intercept is 300. Remember that the y-intercept is where the graph crosses the y-axis and the value of x is 0. Therefore, the coordinate of the y-intercept will always have 0 for x. In this case, the coordinate of the y-intercept is (0, 300).

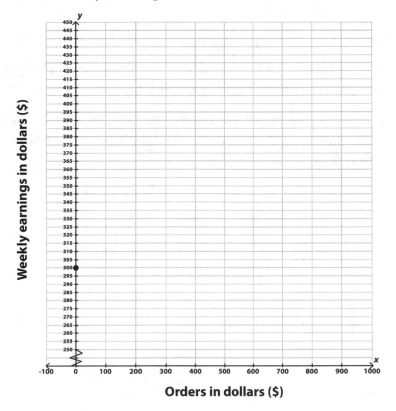

6. Graph the equation using the slope and y-intercept. Use the slope to find the second point.

Remember that the slope is $\dfrac{\text{rise}}{\text{run}}$. In this case the slope is 0.05. Rewrite 0.05 as a fraction.

$$0.05 = \frac{5}{100} = \frac{\text{rise}}{\text{run}}$$

The rise is 5 and the run is 100.

Point your pencil at the y-intercept. Move the pencil up 5 units, since the slope is positive. On this grid, 5 units is one tick mark.

Now, move your pencil to the right 100 units for the run and plot a point. On this grid, 100 units to the right is one tick mark. This is your second point.

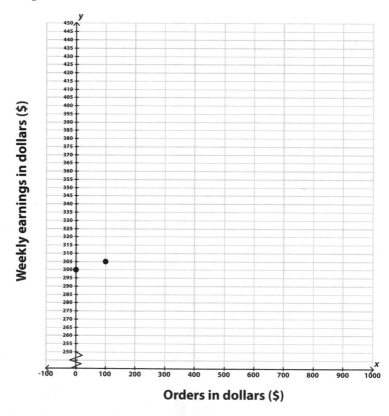

7. Connect the points and extend the line. Then, label your line.

Draw a line through the two points and add an arrow to the right end of the line to show that the line continues infinitely in that direction. Label your line with the equation, $y = 0.05x + 300$.

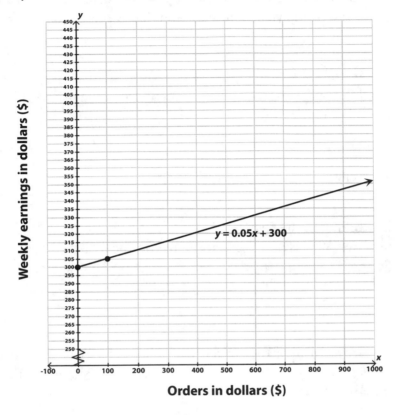

Example 4

The velocity (or speed) of a ball thrown directly upward can be modeled with the following equation: $v = -gt + v_0$, where v is the speed, g is the acceleration due to gravity, t is the elapsed time, and v_0 is the initial velocity at time 0. If the acceleration due to gravity is equal to 32 feet per second per second, and the initial velocity of the ball is 96 feet per second, what is the equation that represents the velocity of the ball? Graph the equation.

---

1. Read the problem statement and then reread the problem, determining the known quantities.

    Initial velocity: 96 ft/s

    Acceleration due to gravity: 32 ft/s²

    Notice that in the given equation, the acceleration due to gravity is negative. This is due to gravity acting on the ball, pulling it back to Earth and slowing the ball down from its initial velocity.

⬇

2. Identify the slope and the y-intercept.

    Notice the form of the given equation for velocity is the same form as $y = mx + b$, where $y = v$, $m = -g$, $x = t$, and $b = v_0$. Therefore, the slope $= -32$ and the y-intercept $= 96$.

⬇

3. Substitute the slope and y-intercept into the equation $y = mx + b$, where m is the slope and b is the y-intercept.

    $m = -g = -32$

    $b = v_0 = 96$

    $y = -32x + 96$

⬇

4. Set up the coordinate plane.

   In this scenario, x represents the time passing after the ball was dropped. The x-axis label is "Time in seconds."

   The dependent variable, y, represents the velocity, or speed, of the ball. The y-axis label is "Velocity in ft/s."

   Determine the scales to be used. The y-intercept is close to 100 and the slope is 32. Notice that 96 (the y-intercept) is a multiple of 32. The y-axis can be labeled in units of 32. Since the x-axis is in seconds, it makes sense that these units are in increments of 1. Since time cannot be negative, use only a positive scale for the x-axis.

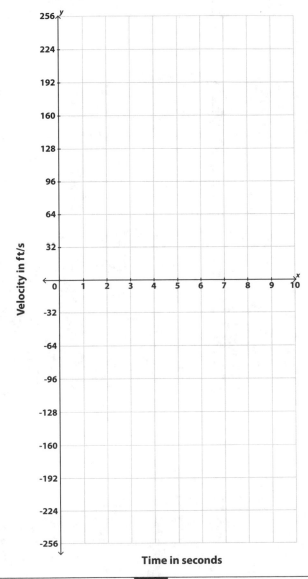

5. Graph the equation using the slope and *y*-intercept. Plot the *y*-intercept first.

The *y*-intercept is 96. Remember that the *y*-intercept is where the graph crosses the *y*-axis and the value of *x* is 0. Therefore, the coordinate of the *y*-intercept will always have 0 for *x*. In this case, the coordinate of the *y*-intercept is (0, 96).

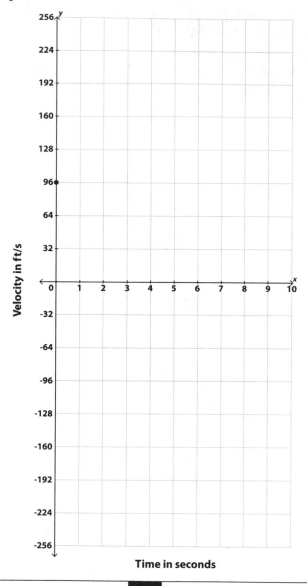

6. Graph the equation using the slope and *y*-intercept. Use the slope to find the second point.

Remember that the slope is $\dfrac{\text{rise}}{\text{run}}$. In this case, the slope is –32. Rewrite –32 as a fraction.

$$-32 = \dfrac{-32}{1} = \dfrac{\text{rise}}{\text{run}}$$

The rise is –32 and the run is 1.

Point your pencil at the *y*-intercept. Move the pencil down 32 units, since the slope is negative. On this grid, 32 units is one tick mark.

Now, move your pencil to the right 1 unit for the run and plot a point. This is your second point.

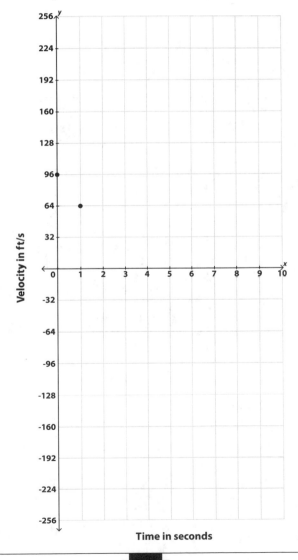

7. Connect the points and extend the line. Then, label your line.

Draw a line through the two points and add an arrow to the right end of the line to show that the line continues infinitely in that direction. Label your line with the equation, $y = -32x + 96$.

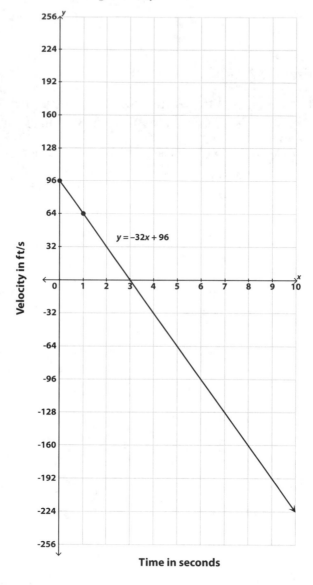

Example 5

A Boeing 747 starts out a long flight with about 57,260 gallons of fuel in its tank. The airplane uses an average of 5 gallons of fuel per mile. Write an equation that models the amount of fuel in the tank and then graph the equation using a graphing calculator.

1. Read the problem statement and then reread the problem, determining the known quantities.

   Starting fuel tank amount: 57,260 gallons

   Rate of fuel consumption: 5 gallons per mile

2. Identify the slope and the y-intercept.

   The slope is a rate. Notice the word "per" in the phrase "5 gallons of fuel per mile." Since the total number of gallons left in the fuel tank is decreasing at this rate, the slope is negative.

   Slope = –5

   The y-intercept is a starting value. The airplane starts out with 57,260 gallons of fuel.

   y-intercept = 57,260

   Substitute the slope and y-intercept into the equation $y = mx + b$, where m is the slope and b is the y-intercept.

   $m = 5$

   $b = 57,260$

   $y = -5x + 57,260$

3. Graph the equation on your calculator.

On a TI-83/84:

Step 1: Press [Y=].

Step 2: At Y_1, type in [(–)][5][X, T, θ, n][+][57260].

Step 3: Press [WINDOW] to change the viewing window.

Step 4: At Xmin, enter [0] and arrow down 1 level to Xmax.

Step 5: At Xmax, enter [3000] and arrow down 1 level to Xscl.

Step 6: At Xscl, enter [100] and arrow down 1 level to Ymin.

Step 7: At Ymin, enter [40000] and arrow down 1 level to Ymax.

Step 8: At Ymax, enter [58000] and arrow down 1 level to Yscl.

Step 9: At Yscl, enter [1000].

Step 10: Press [GRAPH].

On a TI-Nspire:

Step 1: Press the [home] key.

Step 2: Arrow over to the graphing icon and press [enter].

Step 3: At the blinking cursor at the bottom of the screen, enter in the equation [(–)][5][x][+][57260] and press [enter].

Step 4: Change the viewing window by pressing [menu], arrowing down to number 4: Window/Zoom, and clicking the center button of the navigation pad.

Step 5: Choose 1: Window settings by pressing the center button.

Step 6: Enter in the appropriate XMin value, [0], then press [tab].

Step 7: Enter in the appropriate XMax value, [3000], then press [tab].

Step 8: Leave the XScale set to "Auto." Press [tab] twice to navigate to YMin and enter [40000].

Step 9: Press [tab] to navigate to YMax. Enter [58000]. Press [tab] twice to leave YScale set to "auto" and to navigate to "OK."

Step 10: Press [enter].

Step 11: Press [menu] and select 2: View and 5: Show Grid.

4. Redraw the graph on graph paper.

   On the TI-83/84, the scale was entered in [WINDOW] settings. The X scale was 100 and the Y scale was 1000. Set up the graph paper using these scales. Label the *y*-axis "Fuel used in gallons." Show a break in the graph from 0 to 40,000 using a zigzag line. Label the *x*-axis "Distance in miles." To show the table on the calculator so you can plot points, press [2nd][GRAPH]. The table shows two columns with values; the first column holds the *x*-values, and the second column holds the *y*-values. Pick a pair to plot, and then connect the line. To return to the graph, press [GRAPH]. Remember to label the line with the equation. (*Note:* It may take you a few tries to get the window settings the way you want. The graph that follows shows an X scale of 200 so that you can easily see the full extent of the graphed line.)

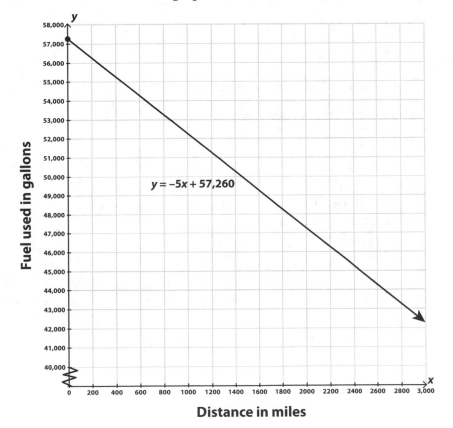

$$y = -5x + 57{,}260$$

(*continued*)

If you used a TI-Nspire, determine the scale that was used by counting the dots on the grid from your minimum y-value to your maximum y-value. In this case, there are 18 dots vertically between 40,000 and 58,000. The difference between the YMax and YMin values is 18,000. Divide that by the number of dots (18). The result (1,000) is the scale.

$$\frac{Y\,Max - Y\,Min}{Number\,of\,dots} = \frac{58,000 - 40,000}{18} = \frac{18,000}{18} = 1000$$

This means each dot is worth 1,000 units vertically. Label the y-axis "Fuel used in gallons." Use a zigzag line to show a break in the graph from 0 to 40,000.

Repeat the same process for determining the x-axis scale. The XMin = 0 and XMax = 3000. The number of dots = 30.

$$\frac{X\,Max - X\,Min}{Number\,of\,dots} = \frac{3000 - 0}{30} = \frac{3000}{30} = 100$$

This means each dot is worth 100 units horizontally.

Set up your graph paper accordingly. Label the x-axis "Distance in miles."

On your calculator, you need to show the table in order to plot points. To show the table, press [tab][T]. To navigate within the table, use the navigation pad. The table shows two columns with values; the first column holds the x-values, and the second column holds the y-values. Pick a pair to plot and then connect the line. Remember to label the line with the equation. To hide the table, navigate back to the graph by pressing [ctrl][tab]. Then press [ctrl][T].

UNIT 1 • RELATIONSHIPS BETWEEN QUANTITIES
Lesson 3: Creating and Graphing Equations in Two Variables

Practice 1.3.1: Creating and Graphing Linear Equations in Two Variables

Graph each equation on graph paper.

1. $y = -x - 2$

2. $y = -x + 2$

3. $y = \frac{1}{2}x + 4$

4. A gear on a machine turns at a rate of $\frac{1}{2}$ revolution per second. Let x = time in seconds and y = number of revolutions. What is the equation that models the number of revolutions over time? Graph this equation.

5. The formula for converting temperature from degrees Fahrenheit to degrees Celsius is linear. To convert from Fahrenheit to Celsius, subtract 32 from the Fahrenheit temperature and then multiply by a rate of five-ninths. What is the equation that models the conversion of degrees Fahrenheit to degrees Celsius? Graph this equation.

6. A limousine company charges an initial rate of $50.00 and $75.00 for each hour. What is the equation that models the fee for hiring this limousine company? Graph this equation.

7. Angela receives a base weekly salary of $100 plus a commission of $65 for each computer she installs. What is the equation that models her weekly pay? Graph this equation.

8. A cable company charges a monthly fee of $59.00 plus $8 for each on-demand movie watched. What is the equation that models the company's total fees? Graph this equation.

9. Garrett borrowed $500 from his aunt. She doesn't charge any interest, and he makes $15 payments each month. What is the equation that models the amount Garrett owes? Graph this equation.

10. A small newspaper company is downsizing and has lost employees at a steady rate. Twelve months ago they had 65 employees, and now they have 29. What is the equation that models the loss of employees over time? Graph this equation.

Lesson 1.3.2: Creating and Graphing Exponential Equations

Introduction

Exponential equations in two variables are similar to linear equations in two variables in that there is an infinite number of solutions. The two variables and the equations that they are in describe a relationship between those two variables. Exponential equations are equations that have the variable in the exponent. This means the final values of the equation are going to grow or decay very quickly.

Key Concepts

Reviewing Exponential Equations:

- The general form of an exponential equation is $y = a \bullet b^x$, where a is the initial value, b is the rate of decay or growth, and x is the time. The final output value will be y.

- Since the equation has an exponent, the value increases or decreases rapidly.

- The base, b, must always be greater than 0 ($b > 0$).

- If the base is greater than 1 ($b > 1$), then the exponential equation represents exponential growth.

- If the base is between 0 and 1 ($0 < b < 1$), then the exponential equation represents exponential decay.

- If the base repeats after anything other than 1 unit (e.g., 1 month, 1 week, 1 day, 1 hour, 1 minute, 1 second), use the equation $y = ab^{\frac{x}{t}}$, where t is the time when the base repeats. For example, if a quantity doubles every 3 months, the equation would be $y = 2^{\frac{x}{3}}$.

- Another formula for exponential growth is $y = a(1 + r)^t$, where a is the initial value, $(1 + r)$ is the growth rate, t is time, and y is the final value.

- Another formula for exponential decay is $y = a(1 - r)^t$, where a is the initial value, $(1 - r)$ is the decay rate, t is time, and y is the final value.

Introducing the Compound Interest Formula:

- The general form of the compounding interest formula is $A = P\left(1 + \dfrac{r}{n}\right)^{nt}$, where A is the initial value, r is the interest rate, n is the number of times the investment is compounded in a year, and t is the number of years the investment is left in the account to grow.

- Use this chart for reference:

Compounded...	n (number of times per year)
Yearly/annually	1
Semi-annually	2
Quarterly	4
Monthly	12
Weekly	52
Daily	365

- Remember to change the percentage rate into a decimal by dividing the percentage by 100.

- Apply the order of operations and divide r by n, then add 1. Raise that value to the power of the product of nt. Multiply that value by the principal, P.

Graphing Exponential Equations Using a Table of Values

1. Create a table of values by choosing x-values and substituting them in and solving for y.

2. Determine the labels by reading the context. The x-axis will most likely be time and the y-axis will be the units of the final value.

3. Determine the scales. The scale on the y-axis will need to be large since the values will grow or decline quickly. The value on the x-axis needs to be large enough to show the growth rate or the decay rate.

Graphing Equations Using a TI-83/84:

Step 1: Press [Y=] and key in the equation using [^] for the exponent and [X, T, θ, n] for x.

Step 2: Press [WINDOW] to change the viewing window, if necessary.

Step 3: Enter in appropriate values for Xmin, Xmax, Xscl, Ymin, Ymax, and Yscl, using the arrow keys to navigate.

Step 4: Press [GRAPH].

Graphing Equations Using a TI-Nspire:

Step 1: Press the home key.

Step 2: Arrow over to the graphing icon (the picture of the parabola or the U-shaped curve) and press [enter].

Step 3: At the blinking cursor at the bottom of the screen, enter in the equation using [^] before entering the exponents, and press [enter].

Step 4: To change the viewing window: press [menu], arrow down to number 4: Window/Zoom and click the center button of the navigation pad.

Step 5: Choose 1: Window settings by pressing the center button.

Step 6: Enter in the appropriate XMin, Xmax, YMin, and YMax fields.

Step 7: Leave the XScale and YScale set to auto.

Step 8: Use [tab] to navigate among the fields.

Step 9: Press [tab] to "OK" when done and press [enter].

Guided Practice 1.3.2

Example 1

If a pendulum swings to 90% of its height on each swing and starts out at a height of 60 cm, what is the equation that models this scenario? What is its graph?

1. Read the problem statement and then reread the scenario, identifying the known quantities.

   Initial height = 60 cm

   Decay rate = 90% or 0.90

2. Substitute the known quantities into the general form of the exponential equation $y = ab^x$, where a is the initial value, b is the rate of decay, x is time (in this case swings), and y is the final value.

   $a = 60$

   $b = 0.90$

   $y = ab^x$

   $y = 60(0.90)^x$

3. Create a table of values.

x	y
0	60
1	54
2	48.6
3	43.74
5	35.43
10	20.92
20	7.29
40	0.89

4. Set up the coordinate plane.

Determine the labels by reading the problem again. The independent variable is the number of swings. That will be the label of the *x*-axis. The *y*-axis label will be the height. The height is the dependent variable because it depends on the number of swings.

To determine the scales, examine the table of values. The *x*-axis needs a scale that goes from 0 to 40. Counting to 40 in increments of 1 would cause the axis to be very long. Use increments of 5. For the *y*-axis, start with 0 and go to 60 in increments of 5. This will make plotting numbers like 43.74 a little easier than if you chose increments of 10.

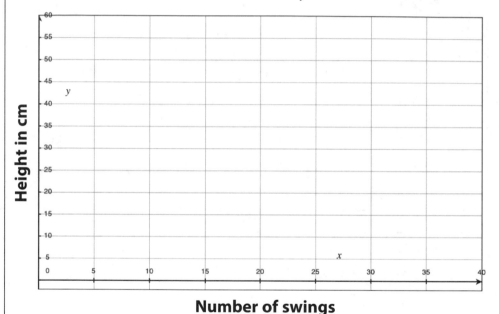

5. Plot the points on the coordinate plane and connect the points with a line (curve).

When the points do not lie on a grid line, use estimation to approximate where the point should be plotted. Add an arrow to the right end of the line to show that the curve continues in that direction toward infinity.

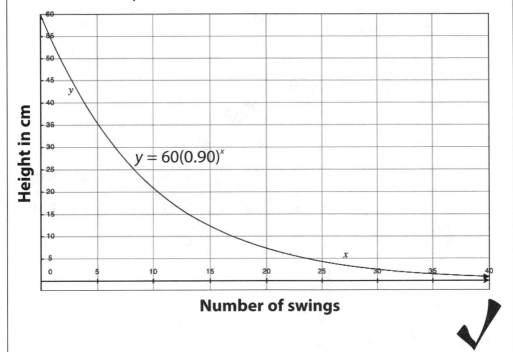

Height in cm

$$y = 60(0.90)^x$$

Number of swings

Example 2

The bacteria *Streptococcus lactis* doubles every 26 minutes in milk. If a container of milk contains 4 bacteria, write an equation that models this scenario and then graph the equation.

1. Read the problem statement and then reread the scenario, identifying the known quantities.

   Initial bacteria count = 4

   Base = 2

   Time period = 26 minutes

2. Substitute the known quantities into the general form of the exponential equation $y = ab^x$, for which a is the initial value, b is the base, x is time (in this case 1 time period is 26 minutes), and y is the final value. Since the base is repeating in units other than 1, use the equation $y = ab^{\frac{x}{t}}$, where $t = 26$.

   $a = 4$

   $b = 2$

   $y = ab^{\frac{x}{26}}$

   $y = 4(2)^{\frac{x}{26}}$

3. Create a table of values.

x	y
0	4
26	8
52	16
78	32
104	64

4. Set up the coordinate plane.

Determine the labels by reading the problem again. The independent variable is the number of time periods. The time periods are in number of minutes. Therefore, "Minutes" will be the x-axis label. The y-axis label will be the "Number of bacteria." The number of bacteria is the dependent variable because it depends on the number of minutes that have passed.

The x-axis needs a scale that reflects the time period of 26 minutes and the table of values. The table of values showed 4 time periods. One time period = 26 minutes and so 4 time periods = 4(26) = 104 minutes. This means the x-axis scale needs to go from 0 to 104. Use increments of 26 for easy plotting of the points. For the y-axis, start with 0 and go to 65 in increments of 5. This will make plotting numbers like 32 a little easier than if you chose increments of 10.

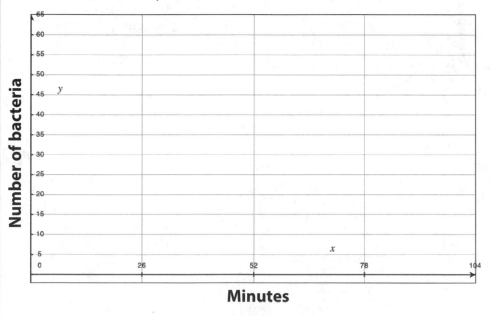

5. Plot the points on the coordinate plane and connect the points with a line (curve).

When the points do not lie on a grid line, use estimation to approximate where the point should be plotted. Add an arrow to the right end of the line to show that the curve continues in that direction toward infinity.

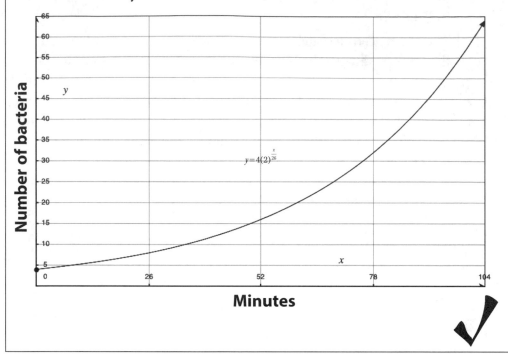

Minutes

Example 3

An investment of $500 is compounded monthly at a rate of 3%. What is the equation that models this situation? Graph the equation.

1. Read the problem statement and then reread the scenario, identifying the known quantities.

   Initial investment = $500

   $r = 3\%$

   Compounded monthly = 12 times a year

2. Substitute the known quantities into the general form of the compound interest formula, $A = P\left(1 + \dfrac{r}{n}\right)^{nt}$, for which P is the initial value, r is the interest rate, n is the number of times the investment is compounded in a year, and t is the number of years the investment is left in the account to grow.

   $P = 500$

   $r = 3\% = 0.03$

   $n = 12$

   $$A = P\left(1 + \frac{r}{n}\right)^{nt}$$

   $$A = 500\left(1 + \frac{0.03}{12}\right)^{12t}$$

   $$A = 500(1.0025)^{12t}$$

   Notice that, after simplifying, this form is similar to $y = ab^x$. To graph on the x- and y-axes, put the compounded interest formula into this form, where $A = y$, $P = a$, $\left(1 + \dfrac{r}{n}\right) = b$, and $t = x$.

   $A = 500(1.0025)^{12t}$ becomes $y = 500(1.0025)^{12x}$.

3. Graph the equation using a graphing calculator.

    On a TI-83/84:

    Step 1: Press [Y=].

    Step 2: Type in the equation as follows: [500][×][1.0025][^][12][X, T, θ, *n*]

    Step 3: Press [WINDOW] to change the viewing window.

    Step 4: At Xmin, enter [0] and arrow down 1 level to Xmax.

    Step 5: At Xmax, enter [10] and arrow down 1 level to Xscl.

    Step 6: At Xscl, enter [1] and arrow down 1 level to Ymin.

    Step 7: At Ymin, enter [500] and arrow down 1 level to Ymax.

    Step 8: At Ymax, enter [700] and arrow down 1 level to Yscl.

    Step 9: At Yscl, enter [15].

    Step 10: Press [GRAPH].

    On a TI-Nspire:

    Step 1: Press the [home] key.

    Step 2: Arrow over to the graphing icon and press [enter].

    Step 3: At the blinking cursor at the bottom of the screen, enter in the equation [500][×][1.0025][^][12x] and press [enter].

    Step 4: To change the viewing window: press [menu], arrow down to number 4: Window/Zoom, and click the center button of the navigation pad.

    Step 5: Choose 1: Window settings by pressing the center button.

    Step 6: Enter in the appropriate XMin value, [0], and press [tab].

    Step 7: Enter in the appropriate XMax value, [10], and press [tab].

    Step 8: Leave the XScale set to "Auto." Press [tab] twice to navigate to YMin and enter [500].

    Step 9: Press [tab] to navigate to YMax. Enter [700]. Press [tab] twice to leave YScale set to "Auto" and to navigate to "OK."

    Step 10: Press [enter].

    Step 11: Press [menu] and select 2: View and 5: Show Grid.

    Note: To determine the *y*-axis scale, show the table to get an idea of the values for *y*. To show the table, press [ctrl] and then [T]. To turn the table off, press [ctrl][tab] to navigate back to the graphing window and then press [ctrl][T] to turn off the table.

4. Transfer your graph from the screen to graph paper.

   Use the same scales that you set for your viewing window.

   The x-axis scale goes from 0 to 10 years in increments of 1 year.

   The y-axis scale goes from $500 to $700 in increments of $15. You'll need to show a break in the graph from 0 to 500 with a zigzag line.

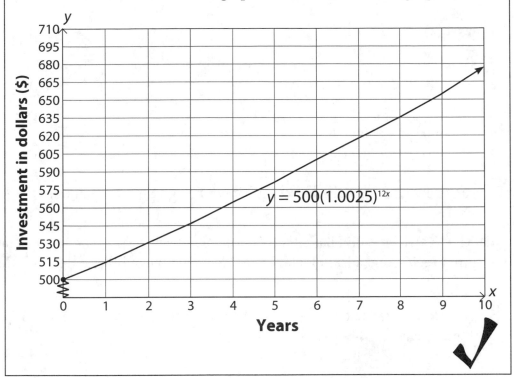

UNIT 1 • RELATIONSHIPS BETWEEN QUANTITIES
Lesson 3: Creating and Graphing Equations in Two Variables

Practice 1.3.2: Creating and Graphing Exponential Equations

Use a table of values to graph the following exponential equations.

1. $y = 3(2)^x$

2. $y = 30(0.95)^x$

3. $y = 800(1.00267)^{12x}$

Write an equation to model each scenario, and then graph the equation.

4. The NCAA Division I Basketball Tournament begins each year with 64 teams. After each round a team is eliminated, reducing the number of teams by half.

5. A type of bacteria doubles every 36 hours. A Petri dish starts out with 16 of these bacteria.

6. The population of a town is increasing by 1.7% per year. The current population is 9,000 people.

7. The population of a town is decreasing by 2.2% per year. The current population is 15,000 people.

8. An investment of $2,500 earns 2.3% interest and is compounded monthly.

9. An investment of $300 earns 3.1% interest and is compounded weekly.

10. An investment of $500 earns 1.9% interest and is compounded daily.

Lesson 4: Representing Constraints

Common Core State Standard

A–CED.3 Represent constraints by equations or inequalities, and by systems of equations and/or inequalities, and interpret solutions as viable or nonviable options in a modeling context. *For example, represent inequalities describing nutritional and cost constraints on combinations of different foods.*★

Essential Questions

1. How can you model real-world applications using equations?
2. How can you solve real-world applications by graphing systems of equations?
3. How can you model real-world applications using inequalities?
4. Why are there constraints when solving and graphing real-world applications?

WORDS TO KNOW

algebraic inequality	an inequality that has one or more variables and contains at least one of the following symbols: $<$, $>$, $\leq$, $\geq$, or $\neq$
constraint	a restriction or limitation on either the input or output values
inequality	a mathematical sentence that shows the relationship between quantities that are not equivalent
solution set	the value or values that make a sentence or statement true
system of equations	a set of equations with the same unknowns
system of inequalities	a set of inequalities with the same unknowns

Recommended Resources

- NCTM Illuminations. "Dirt Bike Dilemma."

  http://walch.com/rr/CAU1L4SysEquations

  Students use a system of equations to maximize profits for a dirt bike manufacturer.

- Purplemath.com. "Linear Programming: Word Problems."

  http://walch.com/rr/CAU1L4SysInequalities

  This site offers a review of systems of inequalities and constraints associated with real-world situations. It also includes graphs of feasible regions.

Lesson 1.4.1: Representing Constraints

Introduction

Situations in the real world often determine the types of values we would expect as answers to equations and inequalities. When an inequality has one or more variables and contains at least one inequality symbol ($<$, $>$, $\leq$, $\geq$, or $\neq$), it is called an **algebraic inequality**.

Sometimes there are limits or restrictions on the values that can be substituted into an equation or inequality; other times, limits or restrictions are placed on answers to problems involving equations or inequalities. These limits or restrictions are called **constraints**.

Key Concepts

- Many real-world situations can be modeled using an equation, an inequality, or a **system of equations** or **inequalities**. A system is a set of equations or inequalities with the same unknowns.

- When creating a system of equations or inequalities, it is important to understand that the solution set is the value or values that make each sentence in the system a true statement.

- Being able to translate real-world situations into algebraic sentences will help with the understanding of constraints.

Guided Practice 1.4.1

Example 1

Determine whether the coordinate $(-2, 9)$ is a solution to the inequality $y \leq 5x + 6$.

1. Substitute the values for x and y into the original inequality.

    $y \leq 5x + 6$

    $9 \leq 5(-2) + 6$

2. Simplify the sentence.

    $9 \leq 5(-2) + 6$ Multiply 5 and –2.

    $9 \leq -10 + 6$ Add –10 and 6.

    $9 \leq -4$

3. Interpret the results.

    9 is NOT less than or equal to –4; therefore, $(-2, 9)$ is not a solution to the inequality $y \leq 5x + 6$.

Example 2

A taxi company charges $2.50 plus $1.10 for each mile driven. Write an equation to represent this situation. Use this equation to determine how far you can travel if you have $10.00. What is the minimum amount of money you will spend?

1. Translate the verbal description into an algebraic equation. Let m represent the number of miles driven and let C represent the total cost of the trip.

    $2.50 + 1.10m = C$

2. The total cost of the trip can't be more than $10.00 because that is all you have to spend. Substitute this amount in for C.

    $2.50 + 1.10m = 10.00$

3. Although you have $10.00 to spend, you could also spend less than that. Change the equal sign to a less than or equal to sign (≤).

$$2.50 + 1.10m \le 10.00$$

4. Solve the inequality by isolating the variable.

$2.50 + 1.10m \le 10.00$	Subtract 2.50 from both sides.
$1.10m \le 7.50$	Divide both sides by 1.10.
$m \le 6.82$	

You can travel up to 6.82 miles and not pay more than $10.00. Because the company charges by the mile, you can travel no more than 6 miles.

5. The minimum the taxi driver charges is $2.50, but it is unlikely that he or she will charge you if you get in the cab and get right back out without going anywhere. You will pay $1.10 if you travel 1 mile or less; add this to the minimum charge of $2.50 to arrive at $3.60.

6. You will spend a minimum of $3.60, but no more than $10.00.

Example 3

A school supply company produces wooden rulers and plastic rulers. The rulers must first be made, and then painted.

- It takes 20 minutes to make a wooden ruler. It takes 15 minutes to make a plastic ruler. There is a maximum amount of 480 minutes per day set aside for making rulers.

- It takes 5 minutes to paint a wooden ruler. It takes 2 minutes to paint a plastic ruler. There is a maximum amount of 180 minutes per day set aside for painting rulers.

Write a system of inequalities that models the making and then painting of wooden and plastic rulers.

1. Identify the information you know.

   There is a maximum of 480 minutes for making rulers.

   - It takes 20 minutes to make a wooden ruler.
   - It takes 15 minutes to make a plastic ruler.

   There is a maximum of 180 minutes for painting rulers.

   - It takes 5 minutes to paint a wooden ruler.
   - It takes 2 minutes to paint a plastic ruler.

2. Write an inequality to represent the amount of time needed to make the rulers. Let w represent the wooden rulers and p represent the plastic rulers.

   $20w + 15p \leq 480$

3. Write an inequality to represent the amount of time needed to paint the rulers. Use the same variables to represent wooden and plastic rulers.

   $5w + 2p \leq 180$

4. Now consider the constraints on this situation. It is not possible to produce a negative amount of either wooden rulers or plastic rulers; therefore, you need to limit the values of w and p to values that are greater than or equal to 0.

   $w \geq 0$

   $p \geq 0$

5. Combine all the inequalities related to the situation and list them in a brace, {. These are the constraints of your scenario.

   $$\begin{cases} 20w + 15p \leq 480 \\ 5w + 2p \leq 180 \\ w \geq 0 \\ p \geq 0 \end{cases}$$

Example 4

Use the system of inequalities created in Example 3 to give a possible solution to the system.

1. We know from this situation that you cannot produce a negative amount of rulers, so none of our solutions can be negative.

2. In future lessons, we discuss more precise ways of determining the solution set to a system. For now, we can use our knowledge of numbers and ability to solve algebraic sentences to find possible solutions.

3. Choose a value for w.

   Let $w = 0$. Substitute 0 for each occurrence of w in the system and solve for p.

   $20w + 15p \leq 480$

   $20(0) + 15p \leq 480$ Substitute 0 for w.

   $15p \leq 480$ Divide both sides by 15.

   For the first inequality, $p \leq 32$.

   $5w + 2p \leq 180$

   $5(0) + 2p \leq 180$ Substitute 0 for w.

   $2p \leq 180$ Divide both sides by 2.

   For the second inequality, $p \leq 90$.

4. Interpret the results.

   In 480 minutes, the company can make no more than 32 plastic rulers if 0 wooden rulers are produced.

   In 180 minutes, the company can paint no more than 90 plastic rulers if there are no wooden rulers to paint.

UNIT 1 • RELATIONSHIPS BETWEEN QUANTITIES
Lesson 4: Representing Constraints

Practice 1.4.1: Representing Constraints

Determine whether each coordinate listed below is a solution to the given algebraic sentence.

1. Is the coordinate (3, 1) a solution to the equation $y = -15x + 14$?

2. Is the coordinate (2, 5) a solution to the inequality $y \le 11x - 7$?

3. Is the coordinate (1, 3) a solution to the inequality $y < 6x - 3$?

Read each scenario and use it to complete the parts that follow.

4. Given the inequalities $y < -2x + 8$ and $y \ge 4x + 1$, find a point that

   a. satisfies both inequalities.

   b. satisfies neither inequality.

   c. satisfies one inequality, but not the other.

5. A water company charges a monthly fee of $7.90 plus a usage fee of $2.60 per 1,000 gallons used.

   a. Write an equation to find the total monthly charges, including the number of gallons used.

   b. Use your equation to determine the maximum number of gallons you can use each month if you have budgeted $30 a month for water.

continued

UNIT 1 • RELATIONSHIPS BETWEEN QUANTITIES
Lesson 4: Representing Constraints

Use the information in each scenario to complete problems 6–10.

6. A clothing store is selling graphic tees for $7.50 and solid tees for $5.00. You have $30. Write an inequality to represent this situation. What can you buy?

7. A store offers two rental options for a television. Plan A charges an up-front fee of $15 plus another $7 each month. Plan B charges $20 up front plus $5 each month. Write a system of equations that represents the cost of renting a television under both plans. Be sure to include any necessary constraints.

8. You have 200 feet of fence to create a rectangular garden. The width of the garden can't be more than 20 feet. What constraints represent this situation?

9. The local bakery never has more than a combined total of 32 strawberry cakes and carrot cakes and never more than 6 carrot cakes. Write a system of inequalities that represents this situation. Be sure to include all constraints.

10. Emilee wants to restock her fish tank. She can add no more than 15 new fish, and she wants to include Tiger Barbs and catfish. She would like to have at least 4 catfish. Write a system of inequalities that represents this situation. Be sure to include all constraints.

Lesson 5: Rearranging Formulas

Common Core State Standard

A–CED.4   Rearrange formulas to highlight a quantity of interest, using the same reasoning as in solving equations. *For example, rearrange Ohm's law V = IR to highlight resistance R.*★

Essential Questions

1. How is solving a literal equation or formula for a specific variable similar to solving an equation with one variable?

2. How could solving a literal equation or formula for a specific variable be helpful?

3. How do you determine for which variable a literal equation or formula should be solved?

WORDS TO KNOW

formula	a literal equation that states a specific rule or relationship among quantities
inverse	a number that when multiplied by the original number has a product of 1
literal equation	an equation that involves two or more variables
reciprocal	a number that when multiplied by the original number has a product of 1

Recommended Resources

- CRCTLessons.com. "Solving Equations Game."

  http://walch.com/rr/CAU1L5SolvingEquations

  Practice solving equations for a given variable with this online basketball game.

- Purplemath.com. "Solving Literal Equations."

  http://walch.com/rr/CAU1L5LitEquations

  This site has an overview of literal equations, with worked examples on how to solve equations and formulas for a given variable.

Lesson 1.5.1: Rearranging Formulas

Introduction

Literal equations are equations that involve two or more variables. Sometimes it is useful to rearrange or solve literal equations for a specific variable in order to find a solution to a given problem. In this lesson, literal equations and **formulas**, or literal equations that state specific rules or relationships among quantities, will be examined.

Key Concepts

- It is important to remember that both literal equations and formulas contain an equal sign indicating that both sides of the equation must remain equal.

- Literal equations and formulas can be solved for a specific variable by isolating the specified variable.

- To isolate the specified variable, use inverse operations. When coefficients are fractions, multiply both sides of the equation by the **reciprocal**. The reciprocal of a number, also known as the **inverse** of a number, can be found by flipping a number. Think of an integer as a fraction with a denominator of 1. To find the reciprocal of the number, flip the fraction. The number 2 can be thought of as the fraction $\frac{2}{1}$. To find the reciprocal, flip the fraction: $\frac{2}{1}$ becomes $\frac{1}{2}$. You can check if you have the correct reciprocal because the product of a number and its reciprocal is always 1.

Guided Practice 1.5.1

Example 1

Solve $6y - 12x = 18$ for y.

1. Begin isolating y by adding $12x$ to both sides.

$$6y - 12x = 18$$
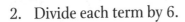
$$\underline{+\ 12x \qquad\quad +\ 12x}$$
$$6y = 18 + 12x$$

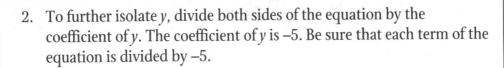

2. Divide each term by 6.

$$\frac{6y}{6} = \frac{18}{6} + \frac{12x}{6}$$

$$y = 3 + 2x$$

Example 2

Solve $15x - 5y = 25$ for y.

1. Begin isolating y by subtracting $15x$ from both sides of the equation.

$$15x - 5y = 25$$
$$\underline{-15x \qquad\quad -15x}$$
$$-5y = 25 - 15x$$

2. To further isolate y, divide both sides of the equation by the coefficient of y. The coefficient of y is -5. Be sure that each term of the equation is divided by -5.

$$\frac{-5y}{-5} = \frac{25 - 15x}{-5}$$

$$\frac{-5y}{-5} = \frac{25}{-5} - \frac{15x}{-5}$$

$$y = -5 + 3x$$

Example 3

Solve $4y + 3x = 16$ for y.

1. Begin isolating y by subtracting $3x$ from both sides of the equation.

$$4y + 3x = 16$$
$$\underline{-3x \qquad -3x}$$
$$4y = 16 - 3x$$

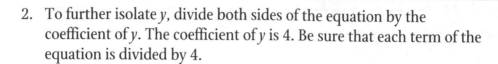

2. To further isolate y, divide both sides of the equation by the coefficient of y. The coefficient of y is 4. Be sure that each term of the equation is divided by 4.

$$\frac{4y}{4} = \frac{16 - 3x}{4}$$

$$y = \frac{16}{4} - \frac{3x}{4}$$

$$y = 4 - \frac{3}{4}x$$

Example 4

The formula for finding the area of a triangle is $A = \frac{1}{2}bh$, where b is the length of the base and h is the height of the triangle. Suppose you know the area and height of the triangle, but need to find the length of the base. In this case, solving the formula for b would be helpful.

1. Begin isolating b by multiplying both sides of the equation by the reciprocal of $\frac{1}{2}$, or 2.

$$A = \frac{1}{2}bh$$

$$2 \bullet A = 2 \bullet \left(\frac{1}{2}bh \right)$$

$$2A = bh$$

Multiplying both sides of the equation by the reciprocal is the same as dividing both sides of the equation by $\frac{1}{2}$. The result will be the same.

2. To further isolate b, divide both sides of the equation by h.

$$\frac{2A}{h} = \frac{bh}{h} \text{ or } b = \frac{2A}{h}$$

$$\frac{2A}{h} = b$$

3. The formula for finding the length of the base of a triangle can be found by doubling the area and dividing the result by the height of the triangle.

Example 5

The distance, d, that a train can travel is found by multiplying the rate of speed, r, by the amount of time that it is travelling, t, or $d = rt$. Solve this formula for t to find the amount of time the train will travel given a specific distance and rate of speed.

1. Isolate t by dividing both sides of the equation by r.

$$\frac{d}{r} = \frac{rt}{r}$$

$$t = \frac{d}{r}$$

2. The formula for finding the amount of time it will take a train to travel a given distance at a given speed is $t = \dfrac{d}{r}$.

Practice 1.5.1: Rearranging Equations and Formulas

For problems 1–4, solve each equation for y.

1. $4y + 24 = 40x$

2. $7y + 14x = 63$

3. $24x - 72 = 8y$

4. $39 - 3y = 15x$

Read each scenario and solve for the given variable.

5. The formula $C = \pi d$ is used to calculate the circumference of a circle. Solve this formula for d.

6. The formula for calculating distance given rate of speed and time is $d = rt$. Solve this formula for r.

7. The formula for calculating simple interest is $I = prt$. Solve this formula for t.

8. The formula for calculating the surface area of a right square pyramid is $A = s^2 + 2sl$. Solve this formula for l.

9. The formula for converting degrees Fahrenheit to degrees Celsius is $C = \dfrac{5}{9}(F - 32)$. Solve this formula for F.

10. The formula for calculating the volume of a square pyramid is $V = \dfrac{1}{3}b^2 h$. Solve this formula for h.

Unit 2
Linear and Exponential Relationships

Lesson 1: Graphs As Solution Sets and Function Notation

Common Core State Standards

A–REI.10   Understand that the graph of an equation in two variables is the set of all its solutions plotted in the coordinate plane, often forming a curve (which could be a line).

A–REI.11   Explain why the x-coordinates of the points where the graphs of the equations $y = f(x)$ and $y = g(x)$ intersect are the solutions of the equation $f(x) = g(x)$; find the solutions approximately, e.g., using technology to graph the functions, make tables of values, or find successive approximations. Include cases where $f(x)$ and/or $g(x)$ are linear, polynomial, rational, absolute value, exponential, and logarithmic functions. ★

F–IF.1   Understand that a function from one set (called the domain) to another set (called the range) assigns to each element of the domain exactly one element of the range. If f is a function and x is an element of its domain, then $f(x)$ denotes the output of f corresponding to the input x. The graph of f is the graph of the equation $y = f(x)$.

F–IF.2   Use function notation, evaluate functions for inputs in their domains, and interpret statements that use function notation in terms of a context.

Essential Questions

1. How can we represent the set of all solutions of a function?

2. What condition must be met for $y = f(x)$ and $y = g(x)$ to intersect?

3. What is the relationship between the domain and range of a function?

4. What does it mean to evaluate a function?

5. What does it mean to evaluate a function over a given domain?

WORDS TO KNOW

curve	the graphical representation of the solution set for $y = f(x)$; in the special case of a linear equation, the curve will be a line
dependent variable	the output variable of a function

domain	the set of all inputs of a function; the set of *x*-values that are valid for the function
function	a relation in which every element of the domain is paired with exactly one element of the range; that is, for every value of *x*, there is exactly one value of *y*.
function notation	a way to name a function using $f(x)$ instead of *y*
independent variable	the input variable of a function
linear equation	an equation that can be written in the form $ax + by = c$, where *a*, *b*, and *c* are rational numbers; can also be written as $y = mx + b$, in which *m* is the slope, *b* is the *y*-intercept, and the graph is a straight line. The solutions to the linear equation are the infinite set of points on the line.
ordered pair	a pair of values (x, y) where the order is significant
range	the set of all outputs of a function; the set of *y*-values that are valid for the function
relation	a relationship between two sets of elements
solution set	the set of ordered pairs that represent all of the solutions to an equation or a system of equations
system	a set of more than one equation

Recommended Resources

- Algebrahelp.com. "Function Graphing Calculator."

  http://walch.com/rr/CAU3L1FunctionGrapher

  Users can enter a function, specify a domain and range, and see the function graphed.

- Interactivate. "Sequencer."

  http://walch.com/rr/CAU3L1Sequencer

  This activity allows users to devise multiple sequences by changing the starting number, multiplier, and add-on values. The Sequencer will then calculate the sequence and show its graph.

- MathPlayground. "Function Machine."

  http://walch.com/rr/CAU3L1FunctionMachine

  Users can input values into the function machine, which shows the correct output. Users then determine the function rule that produced the output.

Lesson 2.1.1: Graphing the Set of All Solutions

Introduction

In an equation with one variable, x, the solution will be the value that makes the equation true. For example:

> 1 is the solution for the equation $x = 1$.

> 2 is the solution for the equation $2^x = 4$.

The solution of an equation with two variables x and y is the pair of values (x, y) that make the equation true. For example:

> $(1, 2)$ is a solution to the equation $y = 2x$ because the statement $2 = 2$ is true.

> $(1, 3)$ is not a solution for $y = 2x$ because the statement $3 = 2$ is false.

The pairs of values (x, y) are called **ordered pairs**, and the set of all ordered pairs that satisfy the equation is called the **solution set**. Each ordered pair in the solution set represents a point in the coordinate plane. When we plot these points, they will begin to form a curve. A **curve** is a graphical representation of the solution set for the equation. In the special case of a linear equation, the curve will be a straight line. A **linear equation** is an equation that can be written in the form $ax + by = c$, where a, b, and c are rational numbers. It can also be written as $y = mx + b$, in which m is the slope, and b is the y-intercept.

It is important to understand that the solution set for most equations is infinite; therefore, it is impossible to plot every point. There are several reasons the solution set is infinite; one reason is that there is always a number between any two numbers x_1 and x_2, and for that number there will be a y that satisfies the equation. So when we graph the solution set for an equation, we plot several points and then connect them with the appropriate curve. The curve that connects the points represents the infinite solution set to the equation.

Key Concepts

- A solution to an equation with two variables is an ordered pair, written (x, y).

- Ordered pairs can be plotted in the coordinate plane.

- The path the plotted ordered pairs describe is called a curve.

- A curve may be without curvature, and therefore is a line.

- An equation whose graph is a line is a linear equation.

- The solution set of an equation is infinite.

- When we graph the solution set of an equation, we connect the plotted ordered pairs with a curve that represents the complete solution set.

Guided Practice 2.1.1

Example 1

Graph the solution set for the linear equation $-3x + y = -2$.

---

1. Solve the equation for y.

   $-3x + y = -2$

   $y = 3x - 2$

---

2. Make a table. Choose at least 3 values for x and find the corresponding values of y using the equation.

x	y
−2	−8
−1	−5
0	−2
1	1
2	4

---

3. Plot the ordered pairs on the coordinate plane.

   Notice that the points fall in a straight line.

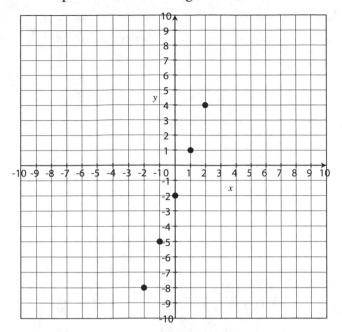

4. Connect the points by drawing a line through them. Use arrows at each end of the line to show that the line continues indefinitely in each direction. This represents all of the solutions for the equation.

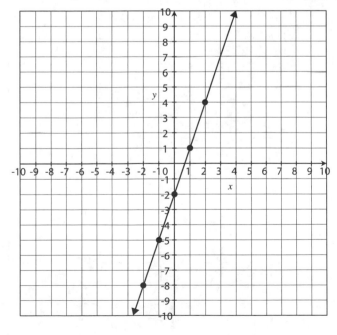

Example 2

Graph the solution set for the equation $y = 3^x$.

1. Make a table. Choose at least 3 values for x and find the corresponding values of y using the equation.

x	y
-2	$\dfrac{1}{9}$
-1	$\dfrac{1}{3}$
0	1
1	3
2	9

2. Plot the ordered pairs in the coordinate plane.

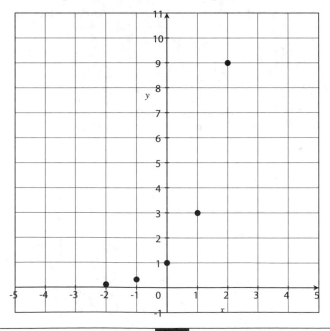

3. Notice the points do not fall on a line. The solution set for $y = 3^x$ is an exponential curve. Connect the points by drawing a curve through them. Use arrows at each end of the line to demonstrate that the curve continues indefinitely in each direction. This represents all of the solutions for the equation.

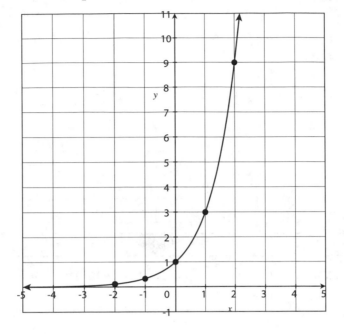

Example 3

The Russell family is driving 1,000 miles to the beach for vacation. They are driving at an average rate of 60 miles per hour. Write an equation that represents the distance remaining in miles and the time in hours they have been driving, until they reach the beach. They plan on stopping 4 times during the trip. Draw a graph that represents all of the possible distances and times they could stop on their drive.

1. Write an equation to represent the distance from the beach.

   Let $d = 1000 - 60t$, where d is the distance remaining in miles and t is the time in hours.

2. Make a table. Choose values for *t* and find the corresponding values of *d*.

    The trip begins at time 0. Let 0 = the first value of *t*.

    The problem states that the Russells plan to stop 4 times on their trip. Choose 4 additional values for *t*. Let's use 2, 5, 10, and 15.

    Use the equation $d = 1000 - 60t$ to find *d* for each value of *t*. Fill in the table.

t	d
0	1000
2	880
5	700
10	400
15	100

3. Plot the ordered pairs on a coordinate plane.

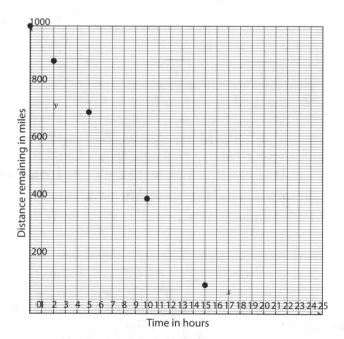

Distance remaining in miles

Time in hours

4. Connect the points by drawing a line. Do not use arrows at each end of the line because the line does not continue in each direction. This represents all of the possible stopping points in distance and time.

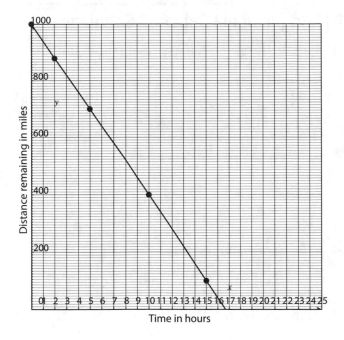

UNIT 2 • LINEAR AND EXPONENTIAL RELATIONSHIPS
Lesson 1: Graphs As Solution Sets and Function Notation

Practice 2.1.1: Graphing the Set of All Solutions

For problems 1–4, draw the graph that represents the solution set of the equation.

1. $3x + 2y = 2$

2. $x - y = 4$

3. $y = 3^x$

4. $y = \left(\dfrac{1}{4}\right)^x$

For problems 5 and 6, use the given graph to find three solutions that will satisfy the equation.

5. $-3x + 2y = 4$

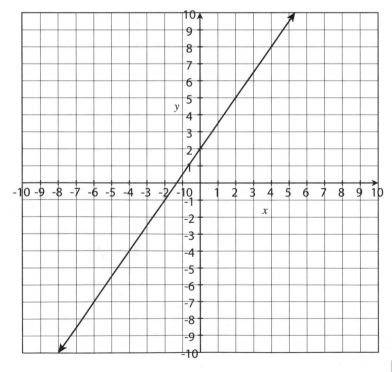

continued

6. $y = \left(\dfrac{1}{3}\right)^x$

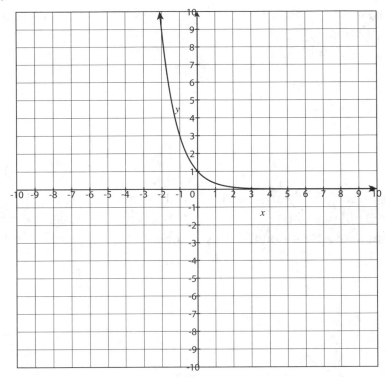

For problems 7–10, use the given information to answer the questions.

7. A house painter starts a job with 65 gallons of paint, and uses 5 gallons every hour. Draw the graph of all solutions for this situation. If he started 6 hours ago, how many gallons of paint should he have left?

8. A certain bacteria in the science lab grows at the rate of $y = (\text{mass in grams}) \cdot 2^{\frac{x}{15}}$, where x is in hours. If there were 0.1 grams of bacteria to start with, how many grams of bacteria were there 60 hours later? Draw the graph of all solutions for this situation.

9. Enrico wants to bike twice as far he did the previous day for 5 days straight. If he biked 3 miles the first day, how many miles must he go on the fifth day? Draw the graph of all solutions for this situation.

10. Mr. Samuelson spent $3,000 on a new, more efficient air conditioning unit for his large house. He hopes to save 35% each month on his electricity bill, which averages $350 a month. The equation $y = 3000 - (0.35)(350)x$, where x is in months and y is in dollars, represents this situation. How many months will it take for his total savings to be greater than the $3,000 he spent? Draw the graph of all solutions for this situation.

Lesson 2.1.2: Intersecting Graphs

Introduction

Recall that the graph of an equation, such as $y = x + 1$, is the complete set of solutions for that equation. The values for y are the result of a process being done to x. To make a general statement, we call the process by a letter, such as f, and we can call the results of that process "f of x." We write "f of x" as $f(x)$. The process f is a function; in a **function**, every element of the domain is paired with exactly one element of the range. That is, for every value of x, there is exactly one value of y. Both y and $f(x)$ represent the outcome of the function f on x. So, for the equation $y = x + 1$, adding 1 to x is the function f. Therefore, $f(x)$ is $x + 1$ and $y = f(x)$. Writing equations this way is called function notation. **Function notation** is a way to name a function using $f(x)$ instead of y. Using function notation, we can graph more than one function at a time. A set of more than one equation is called a **system**. If we call one function f and another g, then we can graph $y = f(x)$ and $y = g(x)$ on the same coordinate plane. By graphing the functions f and g on the same plane, we can more easily see the functions' differences or similarities. Functions can be named using any letter, though f and g are used often. In this lesson, we will work with pairs of equations, $f(x)$ and $g(x)$, attempting to find a solution set where $f(x) = g(x)$. In other words, we want to find all values for x where $f(x)$ and $g(x)$ are the same.

Key Concepts

Graphing Solutions of Functions

- In the graph of the functions $f(x)$ and $g(x)$, the set of solutions for $f(x) = g(x)$ will be where the two graphs intersect.

- If $f(x) = g(x) = b$ for a particular value of x, say a, then the point (a, b) will be on the curve defined by f and will also fall on the curve defined by g.

- Since (a, b) falls on both curves, they must intersect at point (a, b).

- In the graphs of $f(x)$ and $g(x)$, look for the point(s) where the curves intersect.

- Substitute the x-value from the point into the functions to see if it is, or is close to, a solution.

- Note that it is possible for a system of equations to intersect at more than one point, at only one point, or to not intersect at all.

Points of Intersection

More than one	One	None
Both points of intersection are solutions to the system.	The point of intersection is the system's only solution.	There is no solution to the system.

Using a Table of Values to Find Solutions

- Making a table of values for a system of two equations means listing the inputs for each equation and then comparing the outputs.

- List the values of x to substitute into the first column.

- List the first equation in the second column and the corresponding outputs, which are the resulting values after substituting in the x-values chosen in the first column.

- List the second equation in the third column and the corresponding outputs, which are the resulting values after substituting in the x-values chosen in the first column.

- In the fourth column, list the difference of the first functions' outputs minus the second equations' outputs.

- Look for where the difference is the smallest in absolute value and for a sign change event.

- A sign change event is where the values of $f(x) - g(x)$ change from negative to positive (or positive to negative).

- The solution(s) to the system are where the sign change occurs and the difference in the two outputs is smallest in absolute value.

- If the difference between the outputs is 0, the value of x that was substituted is the x-coordinate of the solution and the corresponding output is the y-coordinate of the solution.

Guided Practice 2.1.2

Example 1

Use a graph to approximate the solutions for the following system of equations. Find the difference in outputs, $f(x) - g(x)$, for your estimates.

$$f(x) = \frac{1}{2}x + 1$$

$$g(x) = -2x + 9$$

1. Graph $f(x) = \frac{1}{2}x + 1$ and $g(x) = -2x + 9$ on the same coordinate plane.

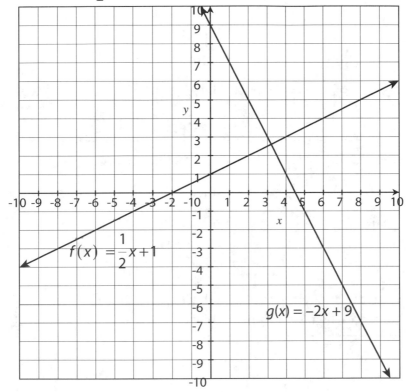

2. Approximate the values for x where $f(x) = g(x)$.

   From the graph, $x = 3$ should be a good estimate.

3. Evaluate $f(x) = \dfrac{1}{2}x + 1$ for $x = 3$.

$$y = \dfrac{1}{2}x + 1 \qquad\qquad \text{Change "} f(x) = \text{" to "} y =\text{."}$$

$$y = \dfrac{1}{2}(3) + 1 \qquad\qquad \text{Substitute 3 for } x.$$

$$y = 1.5 + 1 = 2.5 \qquad\qquad \text{Simplify.}$$

4. Evaluate $g(x) = -2x + 9$ for $x = 3$.

$$y = -2x + 9 \qquad\qquad \text{Change "} g(x) = \text{" to "} y =\text{."}$$

$$y = -2(3) + 9 \qquad\qquad \text{Substitute 3 for } x.$$

$$-6 + 9 = 3 \qquad\qquad \text{Simplify.}$$

5. Find the difference of the y-values of the equations.

$$f(x) - g(x) \qquad\qquad \text{Subtract } g(x) \text{ from } f(x).$$

$$2.5 - 3 = -0.5 \qquad\qquad \text{Substitute the calculated values for } f(x) \text{ and } g(x) \text{ and subtract.}$$

Since the difference is close to 0, we can say the functions intersect when x is approximately equal to 3.

Example 2

Use a graph to approximate the solutions for the following system of equations. Find $f(x) - g(x)$ for your estimates.

$$f(x) = 2^x$$

$$g(x) = x + 2$$

1. Graph $f(x) = 2^x$ and $g(x) = x + 2$ on the same coordinate plane.

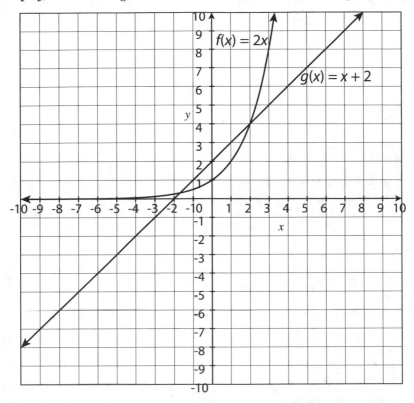

2. Approximate the values for x where $f(x) = g(x)$.

   From the graph, -2 and 2 should be good estimates.

3. Evaluate $f(x) = 2^x$ and $g(x) = x + 2$ for $x = 2$.

   Change "$f(x) =$" and "$g(x) =$" to "$y =$" and substitute 2 for x.

   $y = 2^x = 2^{(2)} = 4$

   $y = x + 2 = (2) + 2 = 4$

4. Find the difference in the y-values for the equations.

   $4 - 4 = 0$; therefore, $x = 2$ satisfies $f(x) = g(x)$ and is a solution to the system.

   The point $(2, 4)$ is a solution for both graphs.

5. Evaluate $f(x) = 2^x$ and $g(x) = x + 2$ for $x = -2$.

   Change "$f(x) =$" and "$g(x) =$" to "$y =$" and substitute -2 for x.

   $y = 2^x = 2^{(-2)} = 0.25$

   $y = x + 2 = (-2) + 2 = 0$

6. Find the difference in the y-values for the equations.

   $0.25 - 0 = 0.25$

   0.25 is very close to 0; therefore, $f(x) = g(x)$ when x is approximately equal to -2.

Example 3

Use a table of values to approximate the solutions for the following system of equations:

$f(x) = 3^x$

$g(x) = 2^x + 1$

1. Create a table of values.

x	$f(x) = 3^x$	$g(x) = 2^x + 1$	$f(x) - g(x)$
-1	$0.3\overline{3}$	1.5	-1.17
0	1	2	-1
1	3	3	0
2	9	5	4
3	27	9	18

2. In column $f(x) - g(x)$, look for sign changes.

   There is a sign change from $x = 0$ to $x = 2$, and at $x = 1$, $f(x) - g(x) = 0$. This tells us the curves f and g intersect at $x = 1$.

UNIT 2 • LINEAR AND EXPONENTIAL RELATIONSHIPS
Lesson 1: Graphs As Solution Sets and Function Notation

Practice 2.1.2: Intersecting Graphs

Use what you know about graphing functions to answer the questions.

1. If $f(x) = g(x)$ for some value of x, what does this imply about where the graphs of f and g will intersect?

2. If you are using the graphs of $y = f(x)$ and $y = g(x)$ to estimate x where $f(x) = g(x)$, and you see that the graphs do not cross, how many values of x should you attempt to find?

3. If you are trying to estimate x where $f(x) = g(x)$ using a table of values, and all the values for $f(x) - g(x)$ are negative, what does this imply?

4. When using a table of values to estimate the solutions to a system, what does a sign change in the $f(x) - g(x)$ column mean?

5. Estimate the solution(s) to the following system by graphing.

   $f(x) = 3x - 2$

   $g(x) = \dfrac{1}{2}x + 3$

6. Estimate the solution(s) to the following system by graphing.

   $h(x) = 2^x$

   $k(x) = x$

7. Use a table of values to estimate the solution(s) to the following system on the interval $3 \le x \le 8$.

   $r(x) = x - 6$

   $s(x) = \left(\dfrac{1}{4}\right)^x$

continued

UNIT 2 • LINEAR AND EXPONENTIAL RELATIONSHIPS
Lesson 1: Graphs As Solution Sets and Function Notation

8. Use a table of values to estimate the solution(s) to the following system on the interval $-3 \le x \le 1$.

$$f(x) = x + 7$$

$$g(x) = \left(\frac{1}{3}\right)^x + 3$$

9. Alanna leaves a small airport in a single-engine airplane traveling at 190 nautical miles per hour, or knots. A half hour later, her brother Josiah leaves the same airport heading in the same direction in a turbo-prop airplane at 225 knots. Using a graph, estimate how many minutes it will take Josiah to catch Alanna and how many nautical miles they will be from the airport. The equations for the flights are as follows ($A(x)$ = Alanna and $J(x)$ = Josiah):

$$A(x) = \frac{190}{60}x$$

$$J(x) = \frac{225}{60}(x - 30)$$

10. Shaina and Aaron are growing bacteria for a science experiment. Shaina starts with 2 cells and expects to see the cells double every 3 days. Her bacteria's growth can be modeled by $S(x) = 2(2)^{\frac{x}{3}}$. Aaron's bacteria culture starts out with 4 cells and is expected to double every 4 days. His bacteria's growth can be modeled by $A(x) = 4(2)^{\frac{x}{4}}$. After how many days should they expect to see the same number of cells in their cultures?

Lesson 2.1.3: Domain and Range

Introduction

Earlier we saw that the graph of $y = f(x)$ is the set of all solutions to the function f. We also found that when $f(x) = g(x)$, the functions f and g share a common solution and the graphs of these functions will intersect at that point. In this lesson, we learn what defines a function and the properties of a function.

Before we define what it is to be a function, we must first define a relation. A **relation** is a relationship between two sets of data. If you pair any two sets of data, you create a relation between the sets. For example, you could define a relation between the neighbors on your block and the cars they drive such that if you are given a neighbor's name, you can properly assign that person to his or her car. And, you could define another relation between the same sets such that if you are given a car's make and model, you can assign that car to the correct neighbor.

Remember that a function is a special relation in which each input is mapped to only one output. So, as with the first example, say we are given a name of a neighbor and we assign that neighbor to a make and model of a car. Even if some of your neighbors drive the same make and model car, each person's name is assigned to only one type of car. This relation is a function. But, what if we go the other way and look at the make and model of the cars and map them to the neighbors who drive them? Then a particular make and model of a car may be assigned to two or more neighbors. Both relations are pictured below:

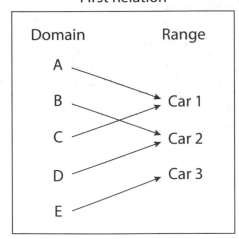

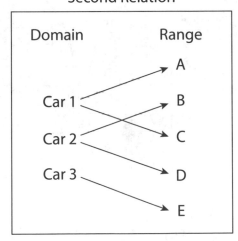

In the first relation, neighbors A and C are both mapped to Car 1 and neighbors B and D are mapped to Car 2. But what is important is that all the neighbors A–E are each mapped to only one car; therefore, this relation is a function. In the second relation, we see Car 1 is mapped to neighbors A and C, and Car 2 is mapped to neighbors B and D. The second relation is not a function.

We call the set of all potential inputs the **domain** of the function. We call the set of potential outputs the **range** of the function. So a function f takes an element x from the domain and creates $f(x)$, an element in the range. It is important to understand that $f(x)$ is strictly one value; each element in the domain of a function can be mapped to exactly one element in the range. That is, for every value of x, there is exactly one value of $f(x)$.

One way to determine whether a relation is a function is to graph the relation and perform a vertical line test. A vertical line in the coordinate plane is described by $x = a$, where a is the value of x where the line crosses the x-axis. So, if a vertical line crosses a graph at two unique points, this implies the graphed relation has two unique values for $f(a)$. In other words, if the vertical line crosses the graph in only one place, the graph is a function. If the line crosses the graph in two or more places, it is not a function.

Take a look at the following graph of a complete circle. If we draw a vertical line where $x = -2$, we see that the line crosses the graph at two points. This means the relation that describes this graph will map $x = -2$ to more than one value. Therefore, the graph is not a function.

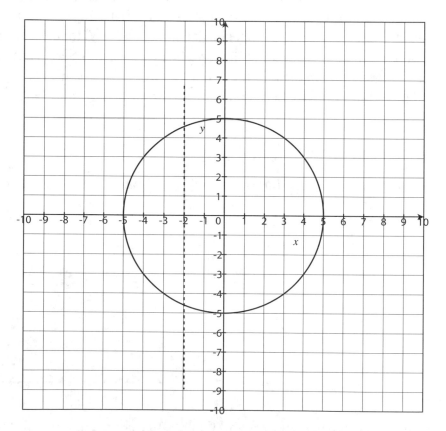

The graphs on the following page are very similar, but the graph on the left fails the vertical line test and the graph on the right passes the vertical line test. Therefore, the graph on the left is not a function and the graph on the right is a function.

Is not a function:	**Is a function:**

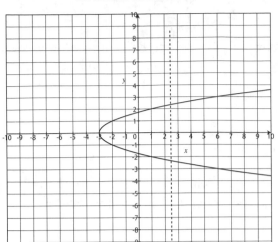 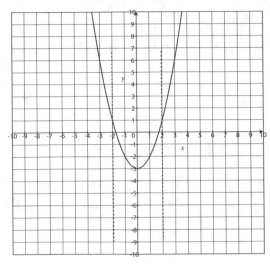

Key Concepts

- The domain is the set of x-values that are valid for the function.

- The range is the set of y-values that are valid for the function.

- A function maps elements from the domain of the function to the range of the function.

- Each x in the domain of a function can be mapped to one $f(x)$ in the range only.

- If an element in the domain maps to more than one element in the range, then the relation is not a function.

- To create a mapping, list the domain in one column and the range in a second column. Then draw lines that match the elements in the domain to the corresponding elements in the range.

- In the mapping, if one line goes from one x-value to only one y-value, then the relation is a function.

- If more than one line goes from an element in the domain (x-values) to multiple elements in the range (y-values), then the relation is not a function.

- The vertical line test can also be used to determine if a relation is a function. If you pass an imaginary vertical line across the graph, look to see if the line ever crosses more than one point on the graph at a time.

- If a vertical line that sweeps across the graph crosses only one point on the graph, then the relation is a function.

- If a vertical line that sweeps across the graph crosses more than one point on the graph at the same time, then the relation is not a function.

Guided Practice 2.1.3

Example 1

Is the relation below a function? Use a mapping diagram to determine your answer.

$$\{(-2, 4), (-1, 1), (0, 0), (1, 1), (2, 4), (3, 9)\}$$

---

1. Find the domain of the first relation.

   The domain is the set of *x*-values of the relation. List the domain in numerical order. If any of the values repeat, list them only once.

   Domain: {−2, −1, 0, 1, 2, 3}

---

2. Find the range of the relation.

   The range is the set of *y*-values of the relation. List the range in numerical order. If any of the values repeat, list them only once.

   Range: {0, 1, 4, 9}

   The *y*-values 1 and 4 each appear in more than one of the ordered pairs, but they are only listed once.

---

3. Map the elements in the domain to the corresponding elements in the range.

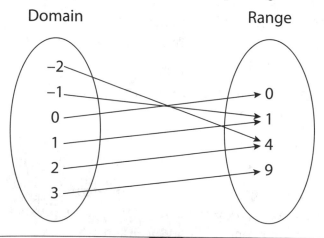

---

4. Analyze the mapping.

If there is only one line coming from each element of the domain, the relation is a function. In this case, each element of the domain is paired with exactly one element in the range, so the relation is a function. Notice that some elements in the range have two arrows coming to them. The relation is still a function because each element in the domain has only one line from it.

Example 2

Is the relation below a function? Use a mapping diagram to determine your answer.

$$\{(4, -5), (1, -3), (0, 0), (1, 1), (4, 5), (9, 3)\}$$

1. Find the domain of the relation.

The domain is the set of x-values of the relation. List the domain in numerical order. List repeating values only once.

Domain: {0, 1, 4, 9}

1 and 4 repeat, but they are only listed once.

2. Find the range of the relation.

The range is the set of y-values of the relation. List the range in numerical order. List repeating values only once.

Range: {−5, −3, 0, 1, 3, 5}

3. Map the elements in the domain to the corresponding elements in the range.

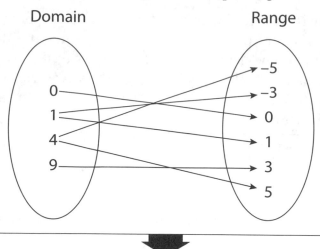

4. Analyze the mapping.

   If there is only one line coming from each element of the domain, the relation is a function. In this case, two elements of the domain have multiple lines going to elements in the range. The relation is not a function.

Example 3

Use the vertical line test to determine if each relation is a function.

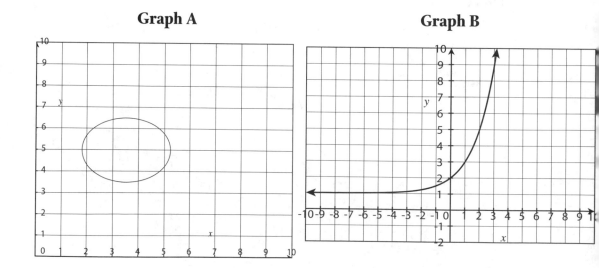

1. Pass a vertical line over the figure in Graph A. Notice that the line crosses two points on the figure at the same time. The relation is not a function.

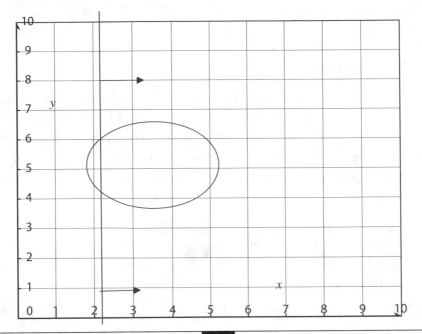

2. Pass a vertical line over the curve in Graph B. Notice that at any time the vertical line only crosses 1 point on the curve at a time. The relation is a function.

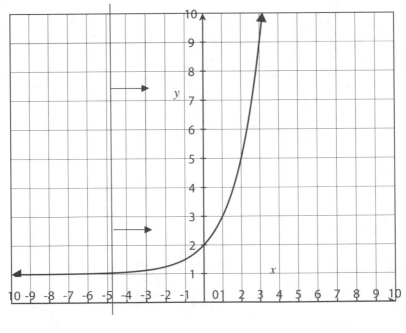

Example 4

Omar has decided to take yoga classes for one year. The yoga studio costs $10 to join and then each yoga class is $5. Omar's fees can be represented by the function $f(x) = 5x + 10$. What are the domain and range of the function?

1. Identify the domain.

    The domain is the set of x-values that are valid for the function. Omar can take 0, 1, 2, 3, 4, ... etc., classes up to infinity. However, it is unlikely that Omar would take any more than 1 yoga class per day. If Omar never takes a class, the lowest value in the domain would be 0. If Omar takes a class every day for a year, the highest value in the domain would be 365.

    Domain: {0, 1, 2, 3, ..., 363, 364, 365}

2. Identify the range.

    The range is the values of y that are valid for the function. The y-values will be the solutions to the function when the domain is substituted. The function is $f(x) = 5x + 10$. Substitute domain values for x in the function to find values for the range.

    Range: {10, 15, 20, 25, 35, ..., 1825, 1830, 1835}

Example 5

Identify the domain and range of the function $f(x) = 2^x$. Use the graph below.

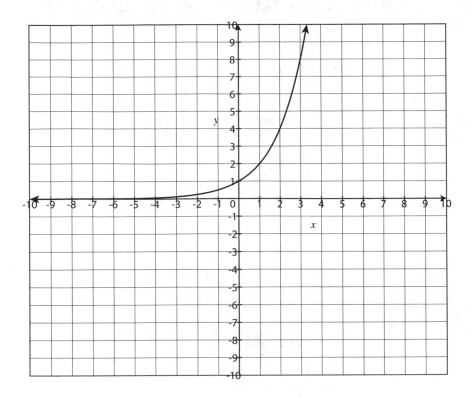

1. Identify the domain.

   The domain is the set of x-values that are valid for the function. This graph goes on infinitely; so, the domain can be any real x-value.

   Domain: {all real numbers}

2. Identify the range.

   The range is the set of y-values that are valid for the function.

   The range will never go below 0. In fact, the range never actually reaches 0. The upper end of the range, however, is limitless.

   Range: {$x > 0$}

UNIT 2 • LINEAR AND EXPONENTIAL RELATIONSHIPS
Lesson 1: Graphs As Solution Sets and Function Notation

Practice 2.1.3: Domain and Range

Use what you know about functions, domain, and range to answer each question.

1. Could the table below represent a function? Why or why not?

x	y
10	1
20	2
30	3
10	4
20	5
30	6

2. Could the table below represent a function? Why or why not?

x	y
1	0
2	1
4	2
8	3
16	4
32	5

3. Could the graph shown below be a function? Why or why not?

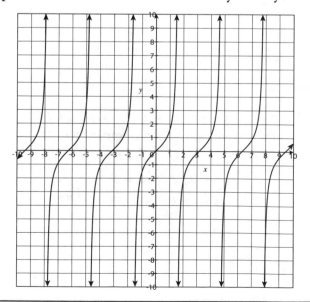

continued

4. Could the graph shown below be a function? Why or why not?

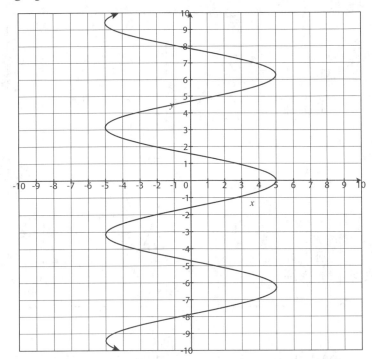

5. Given the following set of points, is there a relation? If so, is the relation a function? Why or why not?

$\{(1, 4), (2, 4), (3, 4), (4, 4), (5, 4), (6, 4)\}$

6. Given the following set of points, is there a relation? If so, is the relation a function? Why or why not?

$\{(2, 4), (2, 6), (2, 8), (2, 10), (2, 12), (2, 14)\}$

7. What are the domain and range of the function graphed below?

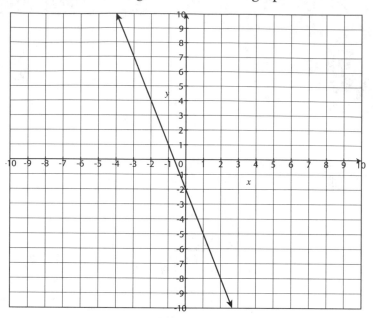

8. What are the domain and range of the function graphed below?

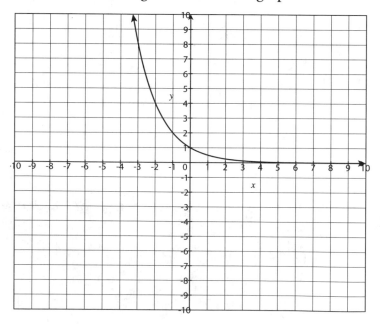

continued

9. Imani is selling T-shirts for a student council fund-raiser. She spent $100 on 25 T-shirts. She plans to sell the T-shirts for $12 each. The function of her revenues can be modeled by $r(x) = 12x - 100$. What are the domain and range of the function?

10. There are 16 bands competing in a battle of the bands to play at the next school dance. After each round, half of the bands are eliminated. This situation can be represented by the function $f(x) = 16\left(\dfrac{1}{2}\right)^x$. What are the domain and range of the function?

Lesson 2.1.4: Function Notation and Evaluating Functions

Introduction

So far we have seen a function f of a variable x represented by $f(x)$. We have graphed $f(x)$ and learned that its range is dependent on its domain. But, can a function be applied to expressions other than x? What would it mean if we wrote $f(2x)$ or $f(x + 1)$? In this lesson, we will explore function notation and the versatility of functions.

For example, let f be a function with the domain $\{1, 2, 3\}$ and let $f(x) = 2x$. To evaluate f over the domain $\{1, 2, 3\}$, we would write the following equations by substituting each value in the domain for x:

$$f(1) = 2(1) = 2$$

$$f(2) = 2(2) = 4$$

$$f(3) = 2(3) = 6$$

$\{2, 4, 6\}$ is the range of $f(x)$.

Key Concepts

- Functions can be evaluated at values and variables.

- To evaluate a function, substitute the values for the domain for all occurrences of x.

- To evaluate $f(2)$ in $f(x) = x + 1$, replace all x's with 2 and simplify: $f(2) = (2) + 1 = 3$. This means that $f(2) = 3$.

- $(x, (f(x)))$ is an ordered pair of a function and a point on the graph of the function.

Guided Practice 2.1.4

Example 1

Evaluate $f(x) = 4x - 7$ over the domain {1, 2, 3, 4}. What is the range?

1. To evaluate $f(x) = 4x - 7$ over the domain {1, 2, 3, 4}, substitute the values from the domain into $f(x) = 4x - 7$.

2. Evaluate $f(1)$.

   $f(x) = 4x - 7$ Original function

   $f(1) = 4(1) - 7$ Substitute 1 for x.

   $f(1) = 4 - 7 = -3$ Simplify.

3. Evaluate $f(2)$.

   $f(x) = 4x - 7$ Original function

   $f(2) = 4(2) - 7$ Substitute 2 for x.

   $f(2) = 8 - 7 = 1$ Simplify.

4. Evaluate $f(3)$.

   $f(x) = 4x - 7$ Original function

   $f(3) = 4(3) - 7$ Substitute 3 for x.

   $f(3) = 12 - 7 = 5$ Simplify.

5. Evaluate $f(4)$.

   $f(x) = 4x - 7$ Original function

   $f(4) = 4(4) - 7$ Substitute 4 for x.

   $f(4) = 16 - 7 = 9$ Simplify.

6. Collect the set of outputs from the inputs.

   The range is {–3, 1, 5, 9}.

Example 2

Evaluate $g(x) = 3^x + 1$ over the domain $\{0, 1, 2, 3\}$. What is the range?

1. To evaluate $g(x) = 3^x + 1$ over the domain $\{0, 1, 2, 3\}$, substitute the values from the domain into $g(x) = 3^x + 1$.

2. Evaluate $g(0)$.

   $g(x) = 3^x + 1$ Original function

   $g(0) = 3^0 + 1$ Substitute 0 for x.

   $g(0) = 1 + 1 = 2$ Simplify.

3. Evaluate $g(1)$.

   $g(x) = 3^x + 1$ Original function

   $g(1) = 3^1 + 1$ Substitute 1 for x.

   $g(1) = 3 + 1 = 4$ Simplify.

4. Evaluate $g(2)$.

   $g(x) = 3^x + 1$ Original function

   $g(2) = 3^2 + 1$ Substitute 2 for x.

   $g(2) = 9 + 1 = 10$ Simplify.

5. Evaluate $g(3)$.

   $g(x) = 3^x + 1$ Original function

   $g(3) = 3^3 + 1$ Substitute 3 for x.

   $g(3) = 27 + 1 = 28$ Simplify.

6. Collect the set of outputs from the inputs.

   The range is $\{2, 4, 10, 28\}$.

Example 3

Raven started an online petition calling for more vegan options in the school cafeteria. So far, the number of signatures has doubled every day. She started with 32 signatures on the first day. Raven's petition can be modeled by the function $f(x) = 32(2)^x$. Evaluate $f(3)$ and interpret the results in terms of the petition.

1. Evaluate the function.

    $f(x) = 32(2)^x$ Original function

    $f(3) = 32(2)^3$ Substitute 3 for x.

    $f(3) = 32(8)$ Simplify as needed.

    $f(3) = 256$

2. Interpret the results.

    On day 3, the petition has 256 signatures. This is a point on the graph, (3, 256), of the function $f(x) = 32(2)^x$.

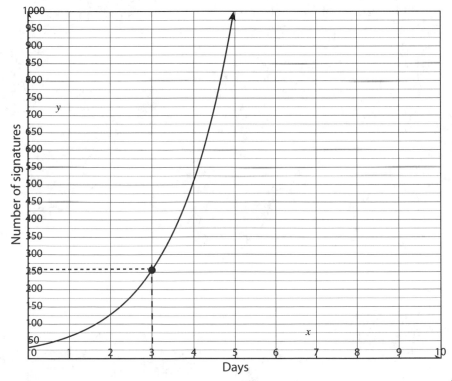

UNIT 2 • LINEAR AND EXPONENTIAL RELATIONSHIPS
Lesson 1: Graphs As Solution Sets and Function Notation

Practice 2.1.4: Function Notation and Evaluating Functions

Evaluate the given functions and determine the range of each.

1. Evaluate $f(x) = 3x + 10$ over the domain {0, 6, 12, 24}. What is the range of $f(x)$?

2. Evaluate $g(x) = 2x - 7$ over the domain {2, 4, 6, 8}. What is the range of $g(x)$?

3. Evaluate $f(x) = 4^x + 3$ over the domain {–1, 0, 1, 3}. What is the range of $f(x)$?

4. Given $r(x) = 2^x + 2$, evaluate r over the domain {0, 1, 3, 5}. What is the range of $r(x)$?

Use what you know about function notation and graphing functions to complete problems 5–10.

5. Given the graph of $f(x)$ below, what is $f(-4)$?

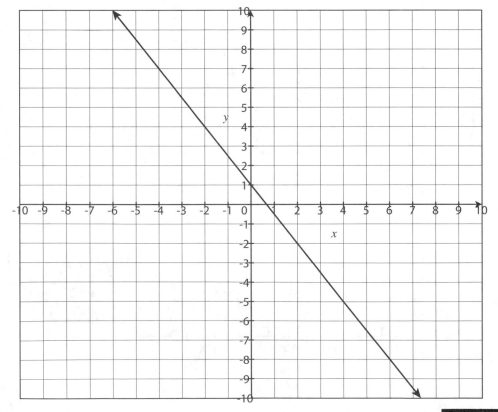

continued

UNIT 2 • LINEAR AND EXPONENTIAL RELATIONSHIPS
Lesson 1: Graphs As Solution Sets and Function Notation

6. Given the graph of $f(x)$ below, what is $f(-2)$?

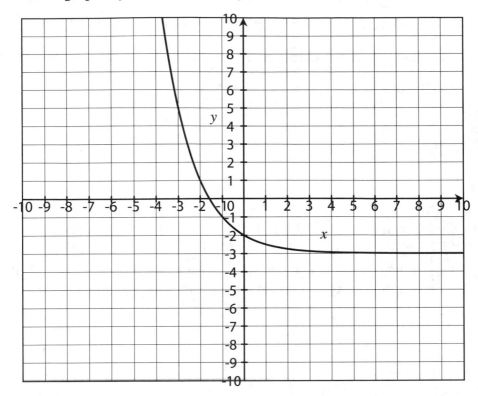

7. A bookstore has seen a steady decline in sales. As a result, the store is laying off employees at a steady rate. The function of the decline in employees is $g(x) = -2x + 56$, where x is in months. Evaluate the function over the domain {3, 6, 18, 24}. Interpret the results and use a graph to explain your answer.

continued

UNIT 2 • LINEAR AND EXPONENTIAL RELATIONSHIPS
Lesson 1: Graphs As Solution Sets and Function Notation

8. A population of rabbits doubles every 2 years. A farm started with 4 rabbits. The function of the rabbits' population growth can be modeled by the function $b(x) = 4(2)^{\frac{x}{2}}$. Evaluate the function over the domain {2, 6, 14} and interpret the results.

9. Carlos is taking a road trip. So far he has traveled 120 miles at a constant speed of 60 mph. His distance can be modeled by the function $d(x) = 60x + 120$, where x is in hours. How many miles will he have traveled after 3, 5, and 8 more hours? Interpret the results in terms of the context of the function.

10. A small manufacturing town is declining in population since a factory shut down. The population decline can be modeled by the function $p(x) = 6000(0.99)^x$. Economists want to project what the population will be in 1, 2, 5, and 10 years. Write four statements using function notation that evaluate the function given the years economists want to know about. Interpret the results in terms of the context of the function.

Lesson 2: Solving Linear Inequalities in Two Variables and Systems of Inequalities

Common Core State Standard

A–REI.12   Graph the solutions to a linear inequality in two variables as a half-plane (excluding the boundary in the case of a strict inequality), and graph the solution set to a system of linear inequalities in two variables as the intersection of the corresponding half-planes.

Essential Questions

1. How do you represent the solution to a linear inequality in two variables?

2. How do you graph the boundary of a linear inequality in two variables?

3. How are linear equations and inequalities in two variables similar? How are they different?

4. How do you represent the solution to a system of inequalities?

5. How are systems of linear equations and inequalities similar? How are they different?

WORDS TO KNOW

half plane	a region containing all points that has one boundary, a straight line that continues in both directions infinitely
inclusive	a graphed line or boundary is part of an inequality's solution
intercept	the point at which the line intersects the x- or y-axis
non-inclusive	a graphed line or boundary is not part of an inequality's solution
solution to a system of linear inequalities	the intersection of the half planes of the inequalities; the solution is the set of all points that make all the inequalities in the system true.

system of inequalities	two or more inequalities in the same variables that work together
x-intercept	the point at which the line intersects the *x*-axis at $(x, 0)$
y-intercept	the point at which the line intersects the *y*-axis at $(0, y)$

Recommended Resources

- Math Planet. "Systems of Linear Inequalities."

  http://walch.com/rr/CAU2L3GraphingSystems

  This site gives an overview of graphing systems of linear inequalities. It includes a short video clip with an example of how to graph one of these systems.

- Monterey Institute. "Algebra IA: Systems of Linear Inequalities."

  http://walch.com/rr/CAU2L3SystemsLesson

  This site goes through a lesson on systems of linear inequalities. It includes a warm-up, a lesson, and practice with multiple-choice problems that can be submitted and scored by the computer with feedback. The lesson ends with a practice test. Site contains audio.

- Purplemath.com. "Graphing Linear Inequalities: $y > mx + b$."

  http://walch.com/rr/CAU2L3GraphingInequalities

  This site includes brief instruction and examples of graphing linear inequalities in forms such as $y > mx + b$.

- Quia.com. "Rags to Riches."

  http://walch.com/rr/CAU2L3InequalityGame

  Players match the given inequality with the graph in this quiz show-style game. The game provides extra practice and immediate feedback.

Lesson 2.2.1: Solving Linear Inequalities in Two Variables

Introduction

Solving a linear inequality in two variables is similar to graphing a linear equation, with a few extra steps that will be explained below. Remember that inequalities have infinitely many solutions and all the solutions need to be represented. This will be done through the use of shading.

Key Concepts

- A linear inequality in two variables has a half plane as the set of solutions.

- A **half plane** is a region containing all points that has one boundary, which is a straight line that continues in both directions infinitely.

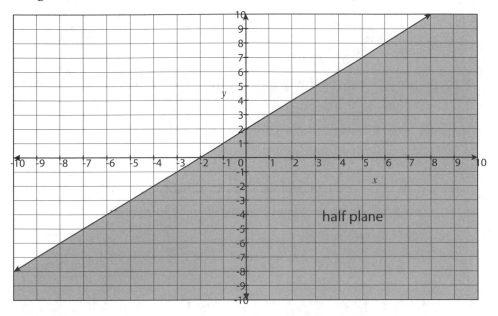

- To determine the solution set, first graph the inequality as a line.

- Sometimes the line or the boundary is part of the solution; this means it's **inclusive**. Inequalities that have "greater than or equal to" ($\geq$) or "less than or equal to" ($\leq$) symbols are inclusive.

- Use a solid line when graphing the solution to inclusive inequalities.

- Other times the line or boundary is NOT part of the solution; in other words, it's **non-inclusive**. Inequalities that have "greater than" ($>$) or "less than" ($<$) symbols are non-inclusive.

- Use a dashed line when graphing the solution to non-inclusive inequalities.

- Either all the points above the line or all the points below the line will be part of the solution. To find out which side of the line contains the solutions, choose a point that is clearly on one side of the line or the other.

- Substitute the test point into the inequality.

- If the test point makes the inequality true, shade the side of the line (half plane) that contains the test point. If it does not make the inequality true, shade the opposite side of the line. Shading indicates that all points in that region are solutions.

Graphing Equations Using a TI-83/84:

Step 1: Press [Y=] and arrow over to the left two times so that the cursor is blinking on the "\".

Step 2: Press [ENTER] two times for the greater than icon " ◥ " and three times for the less than icon " ◣ ".

Step 3: Arrow over to the right two times so that the cursor is blinking after the equal sign.

Step 4: Key in the equation using [X, T, θ, n] for x.

Step 5: Press [WINDOW] to change the viewing window, if necessary.

Step 6: Enter in appropriate values for Xmin, Xmax, Xscl, Ymin, Ymax, and Yscl, using the arrow keys to navigate.

Step 7: Press [GRAPH].

Graphing Equations Using a TI-Nspire:

> Step 1: Press the home key.
>
> Step 2: Arrow over to the graphing icon (the picture of the parabola or the U-shaped curve) and press [enter].
>
> Step 3: At the blinking cursor at the bottom of the screen, press once the backspace key (a left facing arrow). A menu pops up that gives choices for less than or equal to (≤), less than (<), greater than (>), and greater than or equal to (≥). Choose the appropriate symbol by using the arrow keys to navigate to the desired symbol and press the center button of the navigation pad. Alternatively, enter the number that is associated with the symbol.
>
> Step 4: Enter in the equation and press [enter].
>
> Step 5: To change the viewing window: press [menu], arrow down to number 4: Window/Zoom, and click the center button of the navigation pad.
>
> Step 6: Choose 1: Window settings by pressing the center button.
>
> Step 7: Enter in the appropriate XMin, XMax, YMin, and YMax fields.
>
> Step 8: Leave the XScale and YScale set to auto.
>
> Step 9: Use [tab] to navigate among the fields.
>
> Step 10: Press [tab] to "OK" when done and press [enter].

Graphing a Linear Inequality in Two Variables

1. Determine the symbolic representation (write the inequality using symbols) of the scenario if given a context.

2. Graph the inequality as a linear equation.

3. If the inequality is inclusive (≤ or ≥), use a solid line.

4. If the inequality is non-inclusive (< or >), use a dashed line.

5. Pick a test point above or below the line.

6. If the test point makes the inequality true, shade the half plane that contains the test point.

7. If the test point makes the inequality false, shade the half plane that does NOT contain the test point.

Standard Form of Linear Equations and Inequalities

- Linear equations can also be written as $ax + by = c$, where a, b, and c are real numbers.

- Similarly, an inequality can be written in the same form but with an inequality symbol ($<$, $>$, $\leq$, or $\geq$) instead of an equal sign.

- To convert to slope-intercept form ($y = mx + b$), solve the equation or inequality for y.

- Remember to switch the inequality symbol if you multiply or divide by a negative.

Intercepts

- An **intercept** is the point at which the line intersects (or intercepts) the x- or y-axis.

- You have dealt with the **y-intercept**, which is the point at which the line intersects the y-axis. When an equation is in slope-intercept form, $y = mx + b$, b is the y-intercept.

- The general coordinates for the y-intercept are $(0, y)$. Notice the x-coordinate of the y-intercept is 0.

- To solve for the x-intercept in an equation, set $x = 0$ and solve for y.

- The **x-intercept** is the point at which the line intersects the x-axis.

- The general coordinates for the x-intercept are $(x, 0)$.

- To solve for the x-intercept in an equation, set $y = 0$ and solve for x.

- You can plot a line using the intercepts. Find the x- and y-intercepts and then connect the points.

- Plotting a line using the intercepts is helpful in linear inequalities that are in context.

- Generally, linear inequalities in context have the constraint that the variables can't be negative. This means the line will stop at the intercepts.

Guided Practice 2.2.1

Example 1

Graph the solutions to the following inequality.

$$y > x + 3$$

1. Graph the inequality as a linear equation. Since the inequality is non-inclusive, use a dashed line.

   $$y = x + 3$$

   To graph the line, plot the y-intercept first, (0, 3). Then use the slope to find a second point. The slope is 1. Count up one unit and to the right one unit and plot a second point. Connect the two points and extend the line to the edges of the coordinate plane.

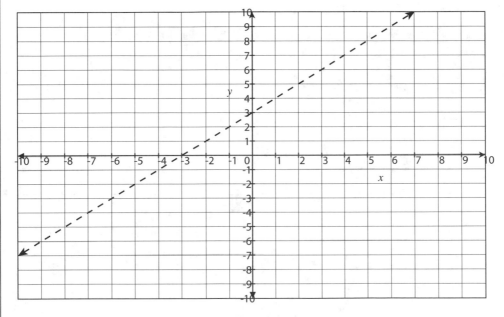

2. Pick a test point above or below the line and substitute the point into the inequality.

   Choose (0, 0) because this point is easy to substitute into the inequality.

   $y > x + 3$

   $(0) > (0) + 3$

   $0 > 3$ This is false!

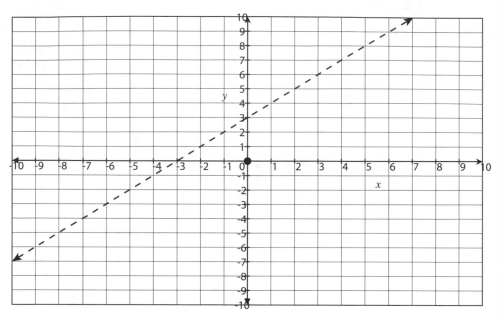

3. Shade the appropriate half plane.

   Since the test point makes the inequality false, all points on that side of the line make the inequality false. Shade above the line instead; this is the half plane that does NOT contain the point.

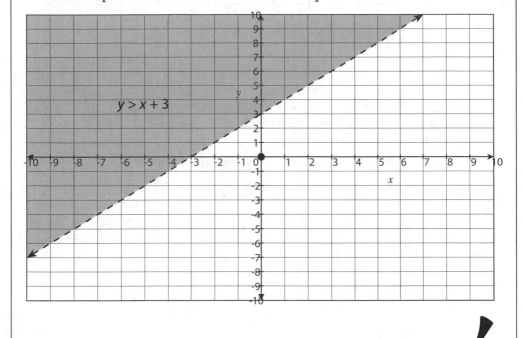

Example 2

Graph the solution to the following inequality.

$$y \leq -3x + 7$$

1. Graph the inequality as a linear equation. Since the inequality is inclusive, use a solid line.

   $$y = -3x + 7$$

   To graph the line, plot the *y*-intercept first, (0, 7). Then use the slope to find a second point. The slope is −3. Count down 3 units and to the right one unit and plot a second point. Connect the two points and extend the line to the edges of the coordinate plane.

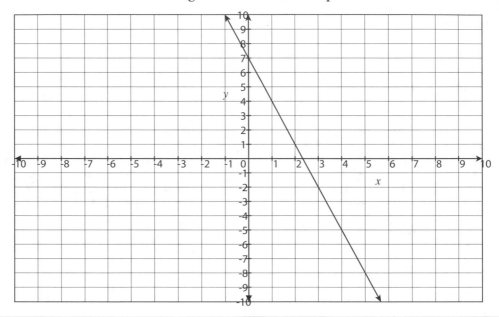

2. Pick a test point above or below the line and substitute the point into the inequality.

Choose (0, 0) because this point is easy to substitute into the inequality.

$y \leq -3x + 7$

$(0) \leq -3(0) + 7$

$0 \leq 7$ This is true!

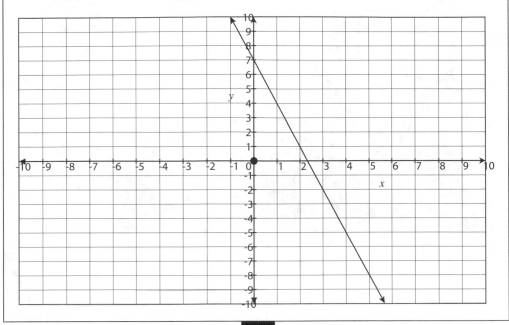

3. Shade the appropriate half plane.

Since the test point makes the inequality true, that means all points on that side of the line make the inequality true. Shade the half plane that contains the test point.

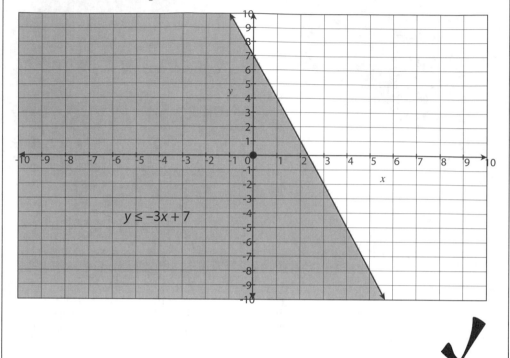

$y \leq -3x + 7$

Example 3

A company that manufactures MP3 players needs to hire more workers to keep up with an increase in orders. Some workers will be assembling the players and others will be packaging them. The company can hire no more than 15 new employees. Write and graph an inequality that represents the number of workers who can be hired.

1. Create an inequality from the context.

   There are two jobs to perform.

   Let x = the number of workers who will assemble the MP3 players.

   Let y = the number of workers who will package the MP3 players.

   $x + y \leq 15$

2. Graph the inequality as a linear equation. Since the inequality is inclusive, use a solid line.

   $x + y = 15$

   To graph the line, convert the standard form of the equation to slope-intercept form.

   $y = -x + 15$

   Plot the y-intercept first, (0, 15). Then use the slope to find a second point. The slope is -1. Count down one unit and to the right one unit and plot a second point. Connect the two points and extend the line.

3. Determine where to stop the line.

   Stop the line at the intercepts because there cannot be negative employees.

   To find the y-intercept, look at the equation in slope-intercept form. The y-intercept is 15. The y-intercept coordinates are (0, 15).

   To find the x-intercept, use the standard form of the equation and set $y = 0$.

   $x + y = 15$

   $x + (0) = 15$

   $x = 15$

   The coordinates of the x-intercept are (15, 0).

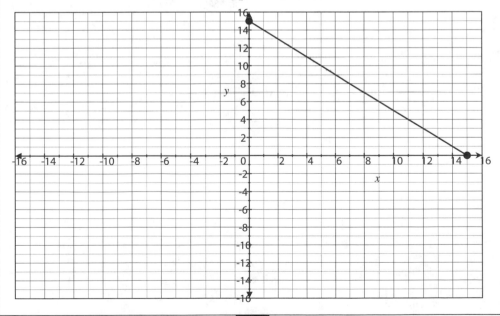

4. Pick a test point above or below the line and substitute the point into the inequality.

Choose (0, 0) because this point is easy to substitute into the inequality.

$x + y \leq 15$

$(0) + (0) \leq 15$

$0 \leq 15$ This is true!

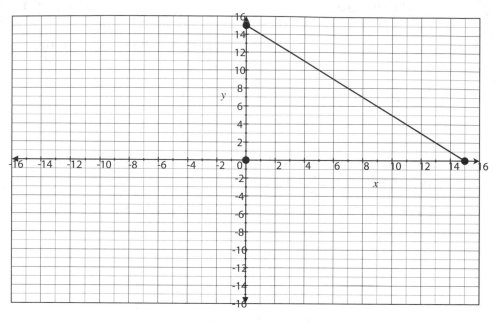

5. Shade the appropriate half plane.

Since the test point makes the inequality true, that means all points on that side of the line make the inequality true. Shade the half plane that contains the test point.

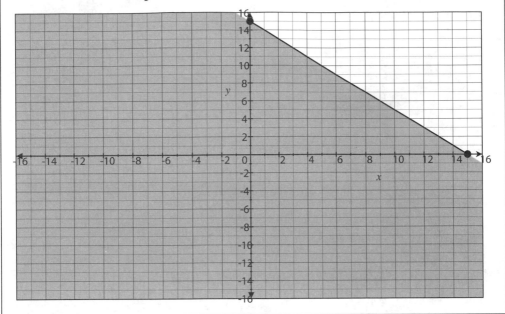

6. Reduce the shading to fit the context of the problem and add labels.

   Having negative employees doesn't make sense. Stop the shading at the
   x-axis, the y-axis, and the boundary line so that the shading ends at
   (0, 15) and (15, 0).

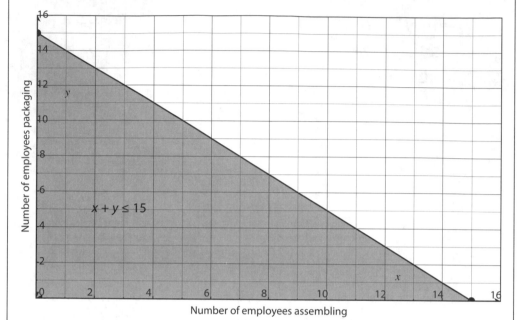

UNIT 2 • LINEAR AND EXPONENTIAL RELATIONSHIPS
Lesson 2: Solving Linear Inequalities in Two Variables and Systems of Inequalities

Practice 2.2.1: Solving Linear Inequalities in Two Variables

Graph the solution to each inequality.

1. $y < 3x - 2$

2. $y > x - 4$

3. $y < 2x - 4$

4. $y \leq x$

5. $2x + 3y \geq -3$

6. $4x + y > 3$

7. $y \leq 2$

Read each scenario. Then write an inequality and graph the solutions.

8. Adult tickets for the high school musical, *Oklahoma!*, are $12 and student tickets are $8. The drama club needs to sell at least $3,000 worth of tickets to break even on the production. What inequality represents the number of tickets that need to be sold? What is the graph of the solutions?

9. Rowan needs to gather pledges for his walk-a-thon to benefit cancer research. People can pledge either a flat donation or a rate per mile walked. Rowan has a goal of getting more than 200 pledges total. What inequality represents the number of pledges Rowan wants? What is the graph of the solutions?

10. Lisette has 45 minutes or less to complete her homework. She must study for her biology quiz and finish her math homework. What inequality represents the time she has to complete these two tasks? What is the graph of the solutions?

Lesson 2.2.2: Solving Systems of Linear Inequalities

Introduction

Finding the solutions to a system of linear equations requires graphing multiple linear inequalities on the same coordinate plane. Most real world applications dealing with linear inequalities are actually systems of linear inequalities where at least one of the conditions is that one of the variables must be greater than 0.

Key Concepts

- A **system of inequalities** is two or more inequalities in the same variables that work together.

- The **solution to a system of linear inequalities** is the intersection of the half planes of the inequalities. The solution will be the set of all points that make all the inequalities in the system true.

- Graph each inequality and include the correct shading.

- Look for the area where the shading of the inequalities overlaps; this is the solution.

- Remember to add constraints to the system that aren't explicitly stated in the problem context but that make sense for the problem.

Guided Practice 2.2.2

Example 1

Solve the following system of inequalities graphically:

$$\begin{cases} x + y > 10 \\ 2x - 4y > 5 \end{cases}$$

1. Graph the line $x + y = 10$. Use a dashed line because the inequality is non-inclusive (greater than).

2. Shade the solution set. First pick a test point. Choose a point that is on either side of the line.

   Test point: $(0, 0)$

3. Then, substitute that point into the inequality $x + y > 10$. If the test point makes the inequality true, shade the region that contains that point. If the test point makes the inequality false, shade on the opposite side of the line.

   $x + y > 10$

   $(0) + (0) \overset{?}{>} 10$

   $0 \not> 10$

4. Since the point $(0, 0)$ makes the inequality false, shade the opposite side of the line. The shaded region represents the solutions for $x + y > 10$.

5. Graph the line $2x - 4y = 5$ on the same coordinate plane. Use a dashed line because the inequality is non-inclusive (greater than).

6. Shade the solution set. First pick a test point. Choose a point that is on either side of the line.

   Test point: $(0, 0)$

7. Then, substitute that point into the inequality $2x - 4y > 5$. If the test point makes the inequality true, shade the region that contains that point. If the test point makes the inequality false, shade on the opposite side of the line.

$$2x - 4y > 5$$
$$2(0) - 4(0) > 5$$
$$0 \not> 5$$

8. Since the point (0, 0) makes the inequality false, shade the opposite side of the line. The second shaded region represents the solutions for $2x - 4y > 5$.

9. Find the solutions to the system. The overlap of the two shaded regions, which is darker, represents the solutions to the system

$$\begin{cases} x + y > 10 \\ 2x - 4y > 5 \end{cases}.$$

A possible solution to this system is (14, 2) because it satisfies both inequalities.

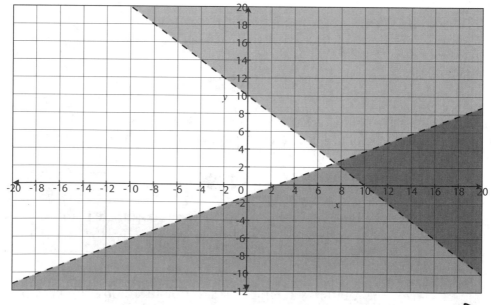

Example 2

Solve the following system of inequalities graphically:

$$\begin{cases} -4x + 2y \geq 20 \\ x - y \geq 10 \end{cases}$$

---

1. Graph the line $-4x + 2y = 20$. Use a solid line because the inequality is inclusive (greater than *or* equal to).

2. Shade the solution set. First, pick a test point. Choose a point that is on either side of the line.

   Test point: $(0, 0)$

3. Then, substitute that point into the inequality $-4x + 2y \geq 20$. If the test point makes the inequality true, shade the region that contains that point. If the test point makes the inequality false, shade on the opposite side of the line.

   $-4x + 2y \geq 20$

   $-4(0) + 2(0) \geq 20$

   $0 \ngeq 20$

4. Since the point $(0, 0)$ makes the inequality false, shade the opposite side of the line. The second shaded region represents the solutions for $-4x + 2y \geq 20$.

5. Graph the line $x - y = 10$. Use a solid line because the inequality is inclusive (greater than *or* equal to).

6. Shade the solution set. First, pick a test point. Choose a point that is on either side of the line.

   Test point: $(0, 0)$

7. Then, substitute that point into the inequality $x - y \geq 10$. If the test point makes the inequality true, shade the region that contains that point. If the test point makes the inequality false, shade on the opposite side of the line.

$$x - y \geq 10$$

$$(0) - (0) \geq 10$$

$$0 \ngeq 10$$

8. Since the point $(0, 0)$ makes the inequality false, shade the opposite side of the line. The second shaded region represents the solutions for $x - y \geq 10$.

9. Find the intersection of the two shaded regions. The overlap of the first two shaded regions, which is darker, represents the solutions to

the system $\begin{cases} -4x + 2y \geq 20 \\ x - y \geq 10 \end{cases}$. A possible solution is $(-24, -36)$.

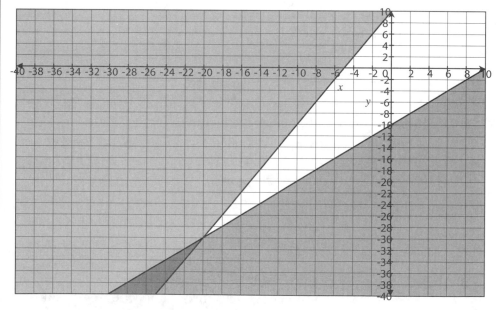

Example 3

Solve the following system of inequalities graphically:

$$\begin{cases} y \le x + 2 \\ y \ge 2x - 10 \\ x \le 0 \\ y \ge 0 \end{cases}$$

1. Graph the line $y = x + 2$. Use a solid line because the inequality is inclusive (less than *or* equal to).

2. Shade the solution set. First, pick a test point. Choose a point that is on either side of the line.

   Test point: (0, 0)

3. Then, substitute that point into the inequality $y \le x + 2$. If the test point makes the inequality true, shade the region that contains that point. If the test point makes the inequality false, shade on the opposite side of the line.

   $y \le x + 2$

   $0 \le 0 + 2$

   $0 \le 2$

4. Since the point (0, 0) makes the inequality true, shade the region that contains the point. The shaded region represents $y - x + 2$.

5. Graph the line $y \ge 2x - 10$. Use a solid line because the inequality is inclusive (greater than *or* equal to).

6. Shade the solution set. First, pick a test point. Choose a point that is on either side of the line.

   Test point: (0, 0)

7. Then, substitute that point into the inequality $y \geq 2x - 10$. If the test point makes the inequality true, shade the region that contains that point. If the test point makes the inequality false, shade on the opposite side of the line.

$$y \geq 2x - 10$$
$$(0) \geq 2(0) - 10$$
$$0 \geq -10$$

8. Since the point $(0, 0)$ makes the inequality true, shade the region that contains the point.

9. Find the intersection of the two shaded regions. The dark gray region represents where solutions to $y \leq x + 2$ and $y \geq 2x - 10$ overlap.

10. You also have the constraints of $x \leq 0$ and $y \geq 0$. This decreases the size of the dark gray region that will satisfy all inequalities in the system.

$$\begin{cases} y \leq x + 2 \\ y \geq 2x - 10 \\ x \leq 0 \\ y \geq 0 \end{cases}$$

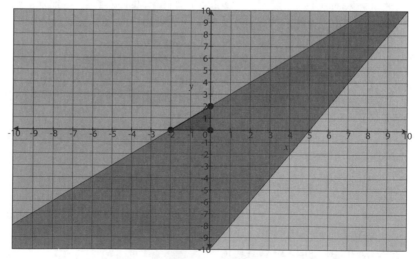

Therefore, the solutions to the system are within the dark triangular region bounded by points $(-2, 0)$, $(0, 0)$, and $(0, 2)$. A possible solution to this system is $(-0.5, 0.5)$.

Example 4

An artist wants to analyze the time that he spends creating his art. He makes oil paintings and watercolor paintings. The artist takes 8 hours to paint an oil painting. He takes 6 hours to paint a watercolor painting. He has set aside a maximum of 24 hours per week to paint his paintings. The artist then takes 2 hours to frame and put the final touches on his oil paintings. He takes 3 hours to frame and put the final touches on his watercolor paintings. He has set aside a maximum of 12 hours per week for framing and final touch-ups. Write a system of inequalities that represents the time the artist has to complete his paintings. Graph the solution.

1. Create the system of inequalities.

   Let x = the number of oil paintings he makes.

   Let y = the number of watercolor paintings he makes.

   It might be helpful to create a table:

	Oil (x)	Watercolor (y)	Total
Paint	8	6	24
Frame	2	3	12

   $$\begin{cases} 8x+6y\leq24 \\ 2x+3y\leq12 \end{cases}$$

   Now, think about what must always be true of creating the paintings: there will never be negative paintings. Add these two constraints to the system: $x \geq 0$ and $y \geq 0$.

   $$\begin{cases} 8x+6y\leq24 \\ 2x+3y\leq12 \\ x\geq0 \\ y\geq0 \end{cases}$$

2. Graph the system on the same coordinate plane.

Start by graphing the first two inequalities.

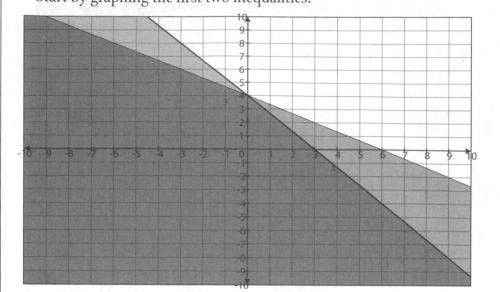

Now apply the last two constraints: $x \geq 0$ and $y \geq 0$. This means the solution lies in the first quadrant.

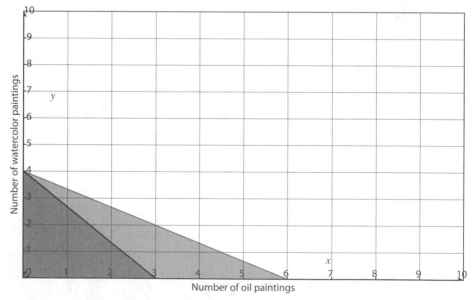

The solution is the darker shaded region; any points that lie within it are solutions to the system. The point (1, 1) is a solution because it satisfies both inequalities. The artist can create 1 oil painting and 1 watercolor painting given the time constraints he has. Or, he can create no oil paintings and 4 watercolor paintings, (0, 4). However, he cannot create 4 oil paintings and 1 watercolor painting, because the point (4, 1) only satisfies one inequality and does not lie in the darker shaded region.

UNIT 2 • LINEAR AND EXPONENTIAL RELATIONSHIPS
Lesson 2: Solving Linear Inequalities in Two Variables and Systems of Inequalities

Practice 2.2.2: Solving Systems of Linear Inequalities

Solve the systems graphically.

1. $\begin{cases} y > 2x \\ y > -2x \end{cases}$

2. $\begin{cases} y \geq 4x \\ y \geq -4x \end{cases}$

3. $\begin{cases} y > x - 2 \\ y < x + 12 \end{cases}$

4. $\begin{cases} y > x - 5 \\ y > -4x + 8 \end{cases}$

5. $\begin{cases} x + y \leq 4 \\ 3x + y \geq 0 \\ x \leq 0 \\ y \geq 0 \end{cases}$

6. $\begin{cases} 2x - y \leq 1 \\ 4x - y > 0 \\ x \geq 0 \\ y \leq 0 \end{cases}$

7. $\begin{cases} 2x + y \leq 14 \\ 2x - y \leq 14 \\ x \geq 0 \\ y \leq 0 \end{cases}$

continued

UNIT 2 • LINEAR AND EXPONENTIAL RELATIONSHIPS
Lesson 2: Solving Linear Inequalities in Two Variables and Systems of Inequalities

Read each scenario and answer the questions that follow.

8. Barry is working hard to earn the rank of Eagle Scout. His project is to build wooden benches and planters for a local children's hospital. It takes 1 hour to cut the pieces of wood for each bench, and 0.5 hours to cut out the pieces for each planter. Barry plans to spend no more than 8 hours cutting out pieces.

   After Barry has all the pieces cut out, he can build and sand each item. It takes 4 hours to build and sand each bench, and 2 hours to build and sand each planter. Barry plans to spend no more than 16 hours building and sanding each item.

   a. What is the system of inequalities that models this scenario?

   b. What is the graph of the solution to this system?

9. Camryn is making puppets for theater class. It takes 1 hour to sew a cloth puppet body, and 5 hours to build a wooden puppet body. She has less than 15 hours set aside for these tasks.

   After Camryn makes the puppet bodies, she has to decorate them. It takes 3 hours to sew decorations onto a cloth puppet, and 2 hours to paint a wooden puppet. Camryn plans to spend no more than 12 hours decorating each puppet.

   a. What is the system of inequalities that represents this situation?

   b. What is the graph of the solutions?

10. Jerrod is a freelancer who writes articles for two different magazines. It takes him 2 hours to research an article for a lifestyle magazine, and 3 hours to research an article for a finance magazine. He plans to spend no more than 15 hours per week on research.

    After Jerrod finishes his research, he has to write and revise each article. Lifestyle articles are usually shorter than finance articles, so he plans to spend 2 hours writing and revising each lifestyle article and 5 hours writing and revising each finance article. He spends 20 hours per week on writing and revision.

    a. What is the system of inequalities that models this scenario?

    b. What is the graph of the solutions?

Lesson 3: Sequences As Functions

Common Core State Standard

F–IF.3   Recognize that sequences are functions, sometimes defined recursively, whose domain is a subset of the integers. *For example, the Fibonacci sequence is defined recursively by $f(0) = f(1) = 1, f(n + 1) = f(n) + f(n – 1)$ for $n \geq 1$.*

Essential Questions

1. What determines the nth term in a sequence?

2. Is a sequence a function?

3. What is the domain of a sequence?

4. What is recursion?

5. Can you add and subtract sequences?

6. Can sequences be scaled?

WORDS TO KNOW

discrete	individually separate and distinct
explicit formula	a formula used to find the nth term of a sequence; the explicit formula for an arithmetic sequence is $a_n = a_1 + (n – 1)d$; the explicit formula for a geometric sequence is $a_n = a_1 \cdot r^{n-1}$
natural numbers	the set of positive integers $\{1, 2, 3, ..., n\}$
recursive formula	a formula used to find the next term of a sequence when the previous term or terms are known; the recursive formula for an arithmetic sequence is $a_n = a_{n-1} + d$; the recursive formula for a geometric sequence is $a_n = a_{n-1} \cdot r$
sequence	an ordered list of numbers

Recommended Resources

- MathIsFun Advanced. "Sequences."

  http://walch.com/rr/CAU3L2Sequences

  This site introduces and defines arithmetic and geometric sequences, and illustrates notation of sequences.

- OEIS.org. "The On-Line Encyclopedia of Integer Sequences."

  http://walch.com/rr/CAU3L2SequencesEncyclopedia

  This quirky site will complete and define an entered sequence of integers. It will also provide any historical or quasi-relevant links to the defined sequence.

- Purplemath.com. "Sequences and Series."

  http://walch.com/rr/CAU3L2SequencesAndSeries

  This site provides a more in-depth look at sequences and series.

Lesson 2.3.1: Sequences As Functions

Introduction

A **sequence** is an ordered list of numbers. The numbers, or terms, in the ordered list are determined by a formula that is a function of the position of the term in the list. So if we have a sequence A determined by a function f, the terms of the sequence will be:

$$A = a_1, a_2, a_3, ..., a_n, \text{ where } a_1 = f(1), a_2 = f(2), a_3 = f(3), ..., a_n = f(n)$$

Unlike a typical function on a variable, there are no fractional terms between the first and second term, between the second and third term, etc. Each term is a whole number. Just like no one can place 1.23rd in a race, there is no 1.23rd term in a sequence. Therefore, the domain of f is at most $\{1, 2, 3, ..., n\}$. This sub-set of the integers is called the **natural number** system. Natural numbers are the numbers we use for counting. Because every element of the domain of a sequence is individually separate and distinct, we say a sequence is a **discrete** function.

Key Concepts

- Sequences are ordered lists determined by functions.

- The domain of the function that generates a sequence is all natural numbers.

- A sequence is itself a function.

- There are two ways sequences are generally defined—recursively and explicitly.

- An **explicit formula** is a formula used to find the nth term of a sequence. If a sequence is defined explicitly (that is, with an explicit formula), the function is given.

- A **recursive formula** is a formula used to find the next term of a sequence when the previous term or terms are known. If the sequence is defined recursively (that is, with a recursive formula), the next term is based on the term before it and the commonality between terms.

- For this lesson, sequences have a common difference or a common ratio.

- To determine the common difference, subtract the second term from the first term. Then subtract the third term from the second term and so on.

- If a common difference exists, $a_n - a_{n-1} = \text{constant}$. So, $a_4 - a_3 = a_3 - a_2 = a_2 - a_1$.

- If the difference is not constant, then the commonality might be a ratio between terms. To find a common ratio, divide the second term by the first term. Then, divide the third term by the second term, and so on.

- If a common ratio exists, then $\dfrac{a_n}{a_{n-1}} = \text{constant}$. So, $\dfrac{a_4}{a_3} = \dfrac{a_3}{a_2} = \dfrac{a_2}{a_1}$.

Explicit Sequences

- Explicitly defined sequences provide the function that will generate each term. For example: $a_n = 2n + 3$ or $b_n = 5(3)^n$.

- In each case, we simply plug in the n representing the nth term and we get a_n or b_n.

Recursive Sequences

- The second way a sequence may be defined is recursively. In a recursive sequence, each term is a function of the term, or terms, that came before it. For example: $a_n = a_{n-1} + 2$ or $b^n = b^{n-1} \cdot 3$, where n is the number of the term.

Graphing Sequences

- Sequences can be graphed with a domain of natural numbers. Compare the following graphs. The first graph is of a sequence, $a_n = n - 1$, while the second graph is of the line $f(x) = x - 1$.

Sequence graph

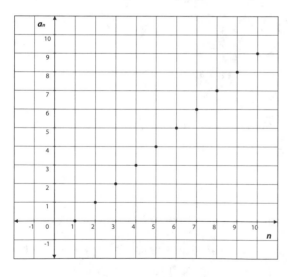

Line graph

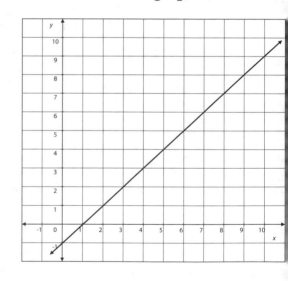

- Notice the sequence only has values where $n = 1, 2, 3, 4$, etc. Also notice the labels on the axes of each graph. The sequence is in terms of n and a_n, while the line is in terms of x and y.

Guided Practice 2.3.1

Example 1

Complete the sequence by using recursion. What are the fifth, sixth, and tenth terms of the sequence?

$$A = \{5, 9, 13, 17, a_5, a_6, 29, 33, 37, a_{10}\}$$

1. First, determine the pattern.

   Is there a common difference or a common ratio? Subtract the second term from the first term and then continue that pattern to see if the difference between each pair of terms is the same.

   $a_2 - a_1 = 9 - 5 = 4$

   $a_3 - a_2 = 13 - 9 = 4$

   $a_4 - a_3 = 17 - 13 = 4$

   $a_8 - a_7 = 33 - 29 = 4$

   $a_9 - a_8 = 37 - 33 = 4$

   The common difference is 4.

2. Think about what it takes to get from one term to the next.

   The common difference is 4. This means that to get to the next term, add 4.

   $a_n = a_{n-1} + 4$

3. Use the recursive formula to calculate the fifth, sixth, and tenth terms in the sequence using the terms just before them.

   $a_5 = a_4 + 4 = 17 + 4 = 21$

   $a_6 = a_5 + 4 = 21 + 4 = 25$

   $a_{10} = a_9 + 4 = 37 + 4 = 41$

   The fifth, sixth, and tenth terms of the sequence are 21, 25, and 41.

Example 2

Find the missing terms in the sequence using recursion.

$$A = \{8, 13, 18, 23, a_5, a_6, a_7\}$$

1. First look for the pattern. Is there a common difference or common ratio?

   $$a_2 - a_1 = 5$$

   $$a_3 - a_2 = 5$$

   $$a_4 - a_3 = 5$$

   The terms are separated by a common difference of 5.

   From this, we can deduce $a_n = a_{n-1} + 5$.

2. Use the formula to find the missing terms.

   $$a_n = a_{n-1} + 5$$

   $$a_5 = a_4 + 5 = 23 + 5 = 28$$

   $$a_6 = a_5 + 5 = 28 + 5 = 33$$

   $$a_7 = a_6 + 5 = 33 + 5 = 38$$

   The missing terms are 28, 33, and 38.

Example 3

Find the missing terms in the sequence using recursion.

$$B = \{6, 18, 54, 162, b_5, b_6, 4374, b_8\}$$

---

1. First, determine the pattern.

   Is there a common difference or a common ratio?

   Subtract the second term from the first term and then continue that pattern to see if the difference between each pair of terms is the same.

   $$b_2 - b_1 = 18 - 6 = 12$$

   $$b_3 - b_2 = 54 - 18 = 36$$

   $$b_4 - b_3 = 162 - 54 = 108$$

   We can quickly see there is not a common difference; but, is there a common ratio?

   Divide each term by the term that precedes it to determine if there's a common ratio.

   $$\frac{b_2}{b_1} = \frac{18}{6} = 3$$

   $$\frac{b_3}{b_2} = \frac{54}{18} = 3$$

   $$\frac{b_4}{b_3} = \frac{162}{54} = 3$$

   The terms share a common ratio of 3.

---

2. Consider what function is performed to get from one term to the next.

   The common ratio is 3.

   The terms increase in value as the sequence progresses.

   To get to the next term, multiply by 3.

   $$b_n = b_{n-1} \cdot 3$$

3. Use the recursive formula to find b_5, b_6, and b_8:

$$b_5 = b_4 \bullet 3 = 162 \bullet 3 = 486$$

$$b_6 = b_5 \bullet 3 = 486 \bullet 3 = 1458$$

$$b_8 = b_7 \bullet 3 = 4374 \bullet 3 = 13{,}122$$

The missing terms in the sequence are 486, 1,458, and 13,122.

Example 4

Find the ninth term in the sequence given by $a_n = 3n + 1$. Then, graph the first 5 terms in the sequence.

1. Substitute 9 for n.

$$a_n = 3n + 1$$

$$a_9 = 3(9) + 1$$

$$a_9 = 27 + 1$$

$$a_9 = 28$$

2. Generate the first 5 terms of the sequence.

$$a_n = 3n + 1$$

$$a_1 = 3(1) + 1 = 4$$

$$a_2 = 3(2) + 1 = 7$$

$$a_3 = 3(3) + 1 = 10$$

$$a_4 = 3(4) + 1 = 13$$

$$a_5 = 3(5) + 1 = 16$$

3. Create ordered pairs from the sequence.

   n corresponds to x, and a_n corresponds to y.

   (n, a_n)

   $(1, 4)$

   $(2, 7)$

   $(3, 10)$

   $(4, 13)$

   $(5, 16)$

4. Plot the ordered pairs. Do not connect the points.

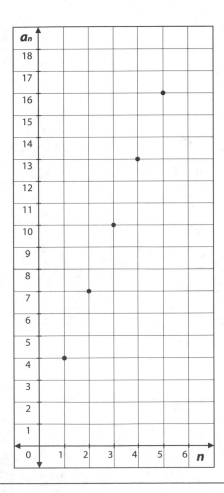

Example 5

Find the seventh term in the sequence given by $a_n = 3 \cdot 2^{n-1}$. Then, graph the first 5 terms in the sequence.

1. Substitute 7 for n.

   $a_n = 3 \cdot 2^{n-1}$

   $a_7 = 3 \cdot 2^{(7)-1} = 3 \cdot 2^6 = 3 \cdot 64 = 192$

2. Generate the first 5 terms of the sequence.

   $a_n = 3 \cdot 2^{n-1}$

   $a_1 = 3 \cdot 2^{(1)-1} = 3 \cdot 2^0 = 3 \cdot 1 = 3$

   $a_2 = 3 \cdot 2^{(2)-1} = 3 \cdot 2^1 = 3 \cdot 2 = 6$

   $a_3 = 3 \cdot 2^{(3)-1} = 3 \cdot 2^2 = 3 \cdot 4 = 12$

   $a_4 = 3 \cdot 2^{(4)-1} = 3 \cdot 2^3 = 3 \cdot 8 = 24$

   $a_5 = 3 \cdot 2^{(5)-1} = 3 \cdot 2^4 = 3 \cdot 16 = 48$

3. Create the ordered pairs from the sequence.

   n corresponds to x, and a_n corresponds to y.

   (n, a_n)

   $(1, 3)$

   $(2, 6)$

   $(3, 12)$

   $(4, 24)$

   $(5, 48)$

4. Plot the ordered pairs. Do not connect the points.

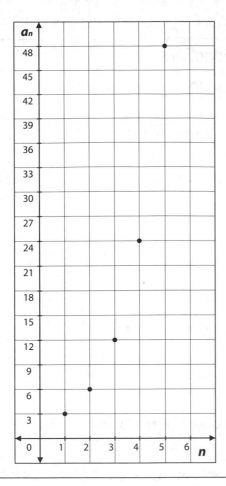

UNIT 2 • LINEAR AND EXPONENTIAL RELATIONSHIPS
Lesson 3: Sequences As Functions

Practice 2.3.1: Sequences As Functions

Use what you know about sequences to answer each question.

1. What is the third term in the sequence given by $a_n = 7n + 11$?

2. Find the sixth term in the sequence given by $a_n = 4n - 2$ and graph the first 6 terms.

3. Find the fifth term in the sequence given by $a_n = 13n - 12$ and graph the first 5 terms.

4. What is the third term in the sequence given by $a_n = 3n + 4n$?

5. What is the fifth term in the sequence given by $a_n = 2(2)^{n-1}$?

6. What is the fourth term in the sequence given by $a_n = 11(3)^{n-1}$?

7. Complete and graph the sequence: 5, 9, 13, 17, a_5, a_6.

8. Complete and graph the sequence: 1, 2, 4, 8, 16, a_6, a_7, 128.

9. Morgan despises waking up early in the morning, but she has an 8 A.M. class this semester and must reluctantly set her alarm for 5:23 A.M. Morgan's alarm has a 6-minute snooze function, and on this particular morning she uses it 5 times before getting out of bed. What time did Morgan get out of bed?

10. Ezra has a set of 5 storage containers. Each container after the largest one is half the size of the previous container. If the middle container holds 8 gallons, how many gallons do the largest and smallest containers hold?

Lesson 4: Interpreting Graphs of Functions

Common Core State Standards

F–IF.4	For a function that models a relationship between two quantities, interpret key features of graphs and tables in terms of the quantities, and sketch graphs showing key features given a verbal description of the relationship. *Key features include: intercepts; intervals where the function is increasing, decreasing, positive, or negative; relative maximums and minimums; symmetries; end behavior; and periodicity.* ★
F–IF.5	Relate the domain of a function to its graph and, where applicable, to the quantitative relationship it describes. *For example, if the function h(n) gives the number of person-hours it takes to assemble n engines in a factory, then the positive integers would be an appropriate domain for the function.* ★
F–IF.6	Calculate and interpret the average rate of change of a function (presented symbolically or as a table) over a specified interval. Estimate the rate of change from a graph. ★
F–LE.1	Distinguish between situations that can be modeled with linear functions and with exponential functions. ★

    a. Prove that linear functions grow by equal differences over equal intervals, and that exponential functions grow by equal factors over equal intervals.

    b. Recognize situations in which one quantity changes at a constant rate per unit interval relative to another.

    c. Recognize situations in which a quantity grows or decays by a constant percent rate per unit interval relative to another.

Essential Questions

1. How can maximum and minimum values of a function be applied to a real-world context?

2. What is the purpose of using the rate of change to analyze real-world data?

3. For what types of real-world data can you find the rate of change?

4. Why might you find the rate of change?

WORDS TO KNOW

asymptote	a line that a graph gets closer and closer to, but never crosses or touches
continuous	having no breaks
domain	the set of all inputs of a function
extrema	the minima and maxima of a function
integer	a number that is not a fraction or a decimal
intercept	the point at which a line intersects the x- or y-axis
interval	a continuous series of values
irrational numbers	numbers that cannot be written as $\dfrac{a}{b}$, where a and b are integers and $b \neq 0$; any number that cannot be written as a decimal that ends or repeats
natural numbers	the set of positive integers $\{1, 2, 3, ..., n\}$
negative function	a portion of a function where the y-values are less than 0 for all x-values
positive function	a portion of a function where the y-values are greater than 0 for all x-values
rate of change	a ratio that describes how much one quantity changes with respect to the change in another quantity; also known as the slope of a line
ratio	the relation between two quantities; can be expressed in words, fractions, decimals, or as a percent
rational number	a number that can be written as $\dfrac{a}{b}$, where a and b are integers and $b \neq 0$; any number that can be written as a decimal that ends or repeats
real numbers	the set of all rational and irrational numbers
relative maximum	the greatest value of a function for a particular interval of the function
relative minimum	the least value of a function for a particular interval of the function

slope	the measure of the rate of change of one variable with respect to another variable; $\text{slope} = \dfrac{y_2 - y_1}{x_2 - x_1} = \dfrac{\Delta y}{\Delta x} = \dfrac{\text{rise}}{\text{run}}$
slope-intercept method	the method used to graph a linear equation; with this method, draw a line using only two points on the coordinate plane
undefined slope	the slope of a vertical line
whole numbers	the set of natural numbers that also includes 0: {0, 1, 2, 3, ...}
_x_-intercept	the point at which the line intersects the _x_-axis at $(x, 0)$

Recommended Resources

- National Council of Teachers of Mathematics. "Changing Cost per Minute."

  http://walch.com/rr/CAU3L3ChangingCost

  This interactive graphical representation of cell phone charges allows users to view how changing the graph of the cost per minute affects the graph of the total cost.

- National Council of Teachers of Mathematics. "Constant Cost per Minute."

  http://walch.com/rr/CAU3L3ConstantCost

  This interactive graphical representation of cell phone charges allows users to view how the total cost of service changes when a constant cost per minute is manipulated.

- Oswego City School District Regents Exam Prep Center. "Exponential Growth and Decay."

  http://walch.com/rr/CAU3L3ExponentialDecay

  This site summarizes exponential growth and decay using various examples to describe the key features of graphs including rates of change.

Lesson 2.4.1: Identifying Key Features of Linear and Exponential Graphs

Introduction

Real-world contexts that have two variables can be represented in a table or graphed on a coordinate plane. There are many characteristics of functions and their graphs that can provide a great deal of information. These characteristics can be analyzed and the real-world context can be better understood.

Key Concepts

- One of the first characteristics of a graph that we can observe are the **intercepts**, where a function crosses the *x*-axis and *y*-axis.

  - The *y*-intercept is the point at which the graph crosses the *y*-axis, and is written as $(0, y)$.

  - The ***x*-intercept** is the point at which the graph crosses the *x*-axis, and is written as $(x, 0)$.

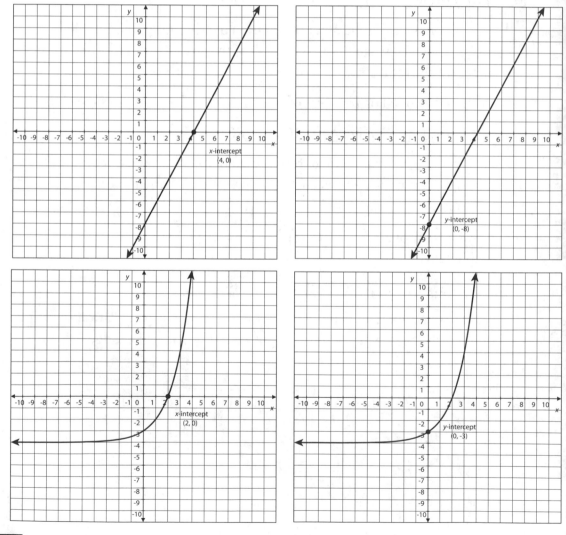

- Another characteristic of graphs that we can observe is whether the graph represents a function that is increasing or decreasing.

- When determining whether intervals are increasing or decreasing, focus just on the *y*-values.

- Begin by reading the graph from left to right and notice what happens to the graphed line. If the line goes up from left to right, then the function is increasing. If the line is going down from left to right, then the function is decreasing.

- A function is said to be constant if the graphed line is horizontal, neither rising nor falling.

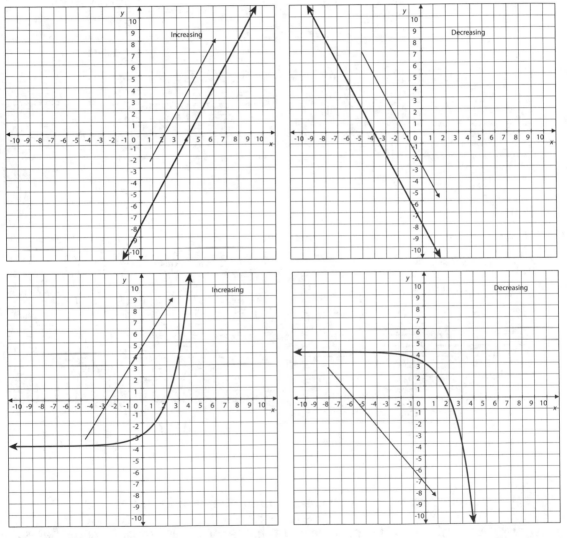

- An **interval** is a continuous series of values. (**Continuous** means "having no breaks.") A function is **positive** on an interval if the *y*-values are greater than zero for all *x*-values in that interval.

- A function is positive when its graph is above the *x*-axis.

- Begin by looking for the *x*-intercepts of the function.

- Write the *x*-values that are greater than zero using inequality notation.

- A function is **negative** on an interval if the *y*-values are less than zero for all *x*-values in that interval.

- The function is negative when its graph is below the *x*-axis.

- Again, look for the *x*-intercepts of the function.

- Write the *x*-values that are less than zero using inequality notation.

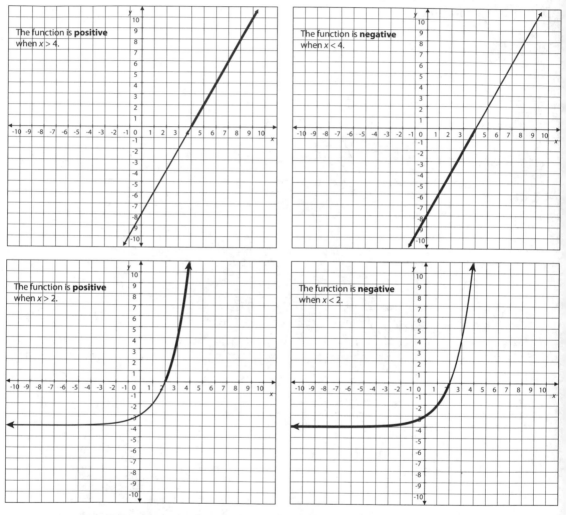

The function is **positive** when $x > 4$.

The function is **negative** when $x < 4$.

The function is **positive** when $x > 2$.

The function is **negative** when $x < 2$.

- Graphs may contain **extrema**, or minimum or maximum points.

- A **relative minimum** is the point that is the lowest, or the *y*-value that is the least for a particular interval of a function.

- A **relative maximum** is the point that is the highest, or the *y*-value that is the greatest for a particular interval of a function.

- Linear and exponential functions will only have a relative minimum or maximum if the domain is restricted.

- The **domain** of a function is the set of all inputs, or *x*-values of a function.

- Compare the following two graphs. The graph on the left is of the function $f(x) = 2x - 8$. The graph on the right is of the same function, but the domain is for $x \geq 1$. The minimum of the function is -6.

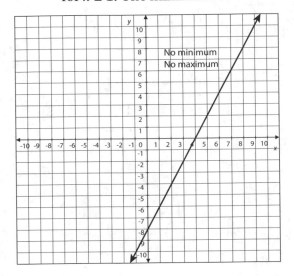

No minimum
No maximum

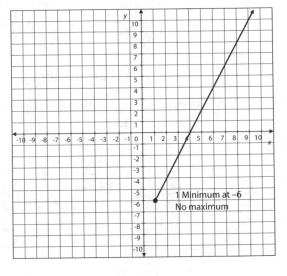

1 Minimum at -6
No maximum

- Functions that represent real-world scenarios often include domain restrictions. For example, if we were to calculate the cost to download a number of e-books, we would not expect to see negative or fractional downloads as values for *x*.

- There are several ways to classify numbers. The following table lists the most commonly used classifications when defining domains.

Natural numbers	1, 2, 3, ...
Whole numbers	0, 1, 2, 3, ...
Integers	..., –3, –2, –1, 0, 1, 2, 3, ...
Rational numbers	numbers that can be written as $\dfrac{a}{b}$, where *a* and *b* are integers and $b \neq 0$; any number that can be written as a decimal that ends or repeats

(continued)

Irrational numbers	numbers that cannot be written as $\dfrac{a}{b}$, where a and b are integers and $b \neq 0$; any number that cannot be written as a decimal that ends or repeats
Real numbers	the set of all rational and irrational numbers

- An exponential function in the form $f(x) = a^x$, where $a > 0$ and $a \neq 1$, has an **asymptote**, or a line that the graph gets closer and closer to, but never crosses or touches.

- The function in the following graph has a horizontal asymptote at $y = -4$.

- It may appear as though the graphed line touches $y = -4$, but it never does.

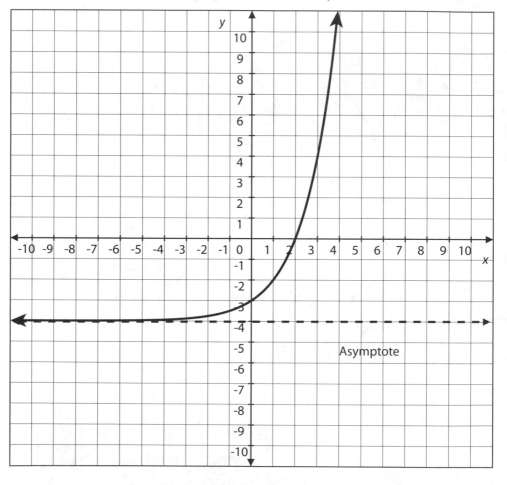

- Fairly accurate representations of functions can be sketched using the key features we have just described.

Guided Practice 2.4.1

Example 1

A taxi company in Atlanta charges $2.75 per ride plus $1.50 for every mile driven. Determine the key features of this function.

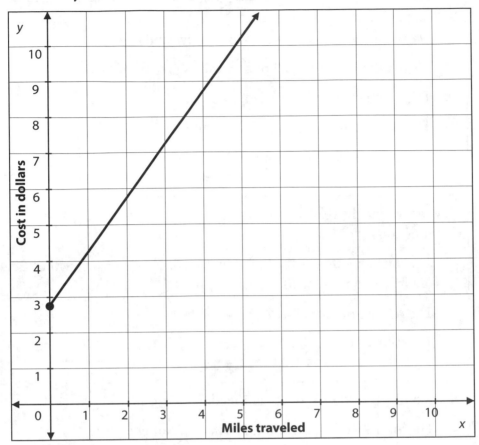

1. Identify the type of function described.

   We can see by the graph that the function is increasing at a constant rate.

   The function is linear.

2. Identify the intercepts of the graphed function.

   The graphed function crosses the y-axis at the point (0, 2.75).

   The y-intercept is (0, 2.75).

   The function does not cross the x-axis.

   There is not an x-intercept.

3. Determine whether the graphed function is increasing or decreasing.

    Reading the graph left to right, the y-values are increasing.

    The function is increasing.

4. Determine where the function is positive and negative.

    The y-values are positive for all x-values greater than 0.

    The function is positive when $x > 0$.

    The y-values are never negative in this scenario.

    The function is never negative.

5. Determine the relative minimum and maximum of the graphed function.

    The lowest y-value of the function is 2.75. This is shown with the closed dot at the coordinate (0, 2.75).

    The relative minimum is 2.75.

    The values increase infinitely; therefore, there is no relative maximum.

6. Identify the domain of the graphed function.

    The lowest x-value is 0 and it increases infinitely.

    x can be any real number greater than or equal to 0.

    The domain can be written as $x \geq 0$.

7. Identify any asymptotes of the graphed function.

    The graphed function is a linear function, not an exponential; therefore, there are no asymptotes for this function.

Example 2

A pendulum swings to 90% of its height on each swing and starts at a height of 80 cm. The height of the pendulum in centimeters, y, is recorded after x number of swings. Determine the key features of this function.

Number of swings (x)	Height in cm (y)
0	80
1	72
2	64.8
3	58.32
5	47.24
10	27.89
20	9.73
40	1.18
60	0.14
80	0.02

1. Identify the type of function described.

   The scenario described here is that of an exponential function.

   We can be certain of this because the pendulum swings at 90% of its height in each swing; also, we can see from the table that the values for y do not decrease at a constant rate.

2. Identify the intercepts of the function based on the information in the table.

   The function crosses the y-axis at the point (0, 80) as indicated in the table.

   The y-intercept is (0, 80).

   As the x-values increase, the y-values get closer and closer to 0, but do not seem to reach 0; therefore, there is not an x-intercept.

3. Determine whether the function is increasing or decreasing.

   As the x-values increase, the y-values decrease.

   The function is decreasing.

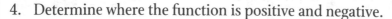

4. Determine where the function is positive and negative.

   The y-values are positive for all x-values greater than 0.

   The function is positive when $x > 0$.

   The y-values are never negative in this scenario.

   The function is never negative.

5. Determine the relative minimum and maximum of the function.

   The data in the table do not change at a constant rate; therefore, the function is not linear.

   Based on the information given in the problem and the values in the table, we know that this is an exponential function.

   Exponential functions do not have a relative minimum because the graph continues to become infinitely smaller.

   The height of the pendulum never goes higher than its initial height; therefore, the relative maximum of this function is (0, 80).

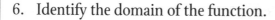

6. Identify the domain of the function.

   The lowest x-value is 0 and it increases infinitely.

   x can be any real number greater than or equal to 0, but cannot be a partial swing.

   The domain is all whole numbers.

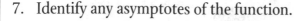

7. Identify any asymptotes of the function.

   The points approach 0, but never actually reach 0.

   The asymptote of this function is $y = 0$.

Example 3

A ringtone company charges $15 a month plus $2 for each ringtone downloaded. Create a graph and then determine the key features of this function.

1. Create a function to represent this scenario.

    Let x represent the number of ringtones downloaded and $f(x)$ represent the total monthly fee.

    $f(x) = 15 + 2x$.

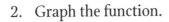

2. Graph the function.

    When creating the graph of the function, consider the domain of the function.

    In past lessons, we have graphed the equations of functions. In this lesson, and in the future, we want to consider the function as it relates to the scenario.

    We can't download a partial ringtone, and can't be charged for a partial download.

    It does not make sense to consider values for x other than those that are whole numbers.

    (continued)

Notice the points in the graph are not connected.

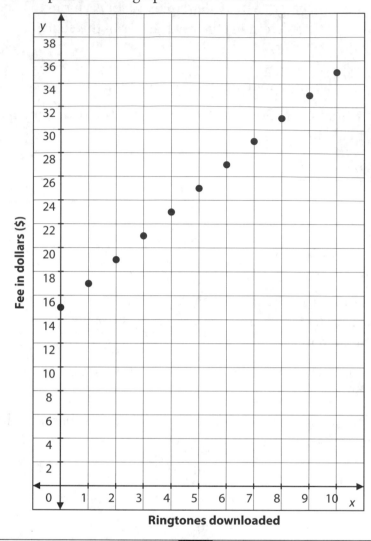

3. Identify the type of function described.

The function is still a linear function; it just has a restricted domain. We can see this in the function $f(x) = 15 + 2x$ and in the graph of the function.

4. Identify the intercepts of the graphed function.

   The graphed function crosses the *y*-axis at the point (0, 15).

   The *y*-intercept is (0, 15).

   The function does not cross the *x*-axis.

   There is no *x*-intercept.

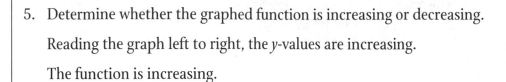

5. Determine whether the graphed function is increasing or decreasing.

   Reading the graph left to right, the *y*-values are increasing.

   The function is increasing.

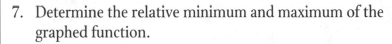

6. Determine where the function is positive and negative.

   The *y*-values are positive for all *x*-values greater than or equal to 0.

   The function is positive when $x \geq 0$.

   The *y*-values are never negative in this scenario.

   The function is never negative.

7. Determine the relative minimum and maximum of the graphed function.

   The lowest *y*-value of the function is 15. This is shown with the dot at the coordinate (0, 15).

   The relative minimum is 15.

   The *x*-values increase infinitely; therefore there is not a relative maximum.

8. Identify the domain of the graphed function.

The lowest *x*-value is 0 and it increases infinitely, but for only whole-number values.

x can be any whole number greater than or equal to 0.

9. Identify any asymptotes of the graphed function.

The graphed function is a linear function, not an exponential; therefore, there are no asymptotes for this function.

UNIT 2 • LINEAR AND EXPONENTIAL RELATIONSHIPS
Lesson 4: Interpreting Graphs of Functions

Practice 2.4.1: Identifying Key Features of Linear and Exponential Graphs

Determine the domain of each function, and then graph the function on graph paper.

1. A company started with 4 employees and steadily grew by 3 employees each month. The number of employees can be modeled by the function $f(x) = 4 + 3x$.

2. The half-life of a type of rhodium, Rh-106, is about 30 seconds. You start an experiment with 300 grams. The grams of rhodium can be modeled by the function $f(x) = 300(0.5)^x$, for which x is in 30-second increments.

For the following problems, determine the key features of each function. Include the x- and y-intercepts, whether the function is increasing or decreasing, whether the function is negative or positive, the minimum and maximum, asymptotes, and domain. Find the asymptotes as if the domain were all real numbers.

3. A small bookstore is downsizing and has lost employees at a steady rate. The company started with 30 employees, but has lost 3 employees each month for the past 4 months. Identify the key features of the graph of this function.

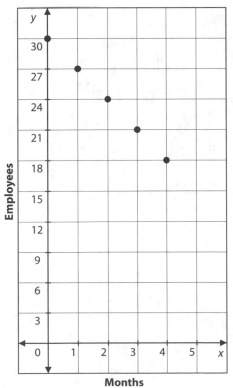

4. Manny borrowed $750 from his uncle. He doesn't have to pay any interest, and he makes $25 payments each month. Identify the key features of the graph of this function.

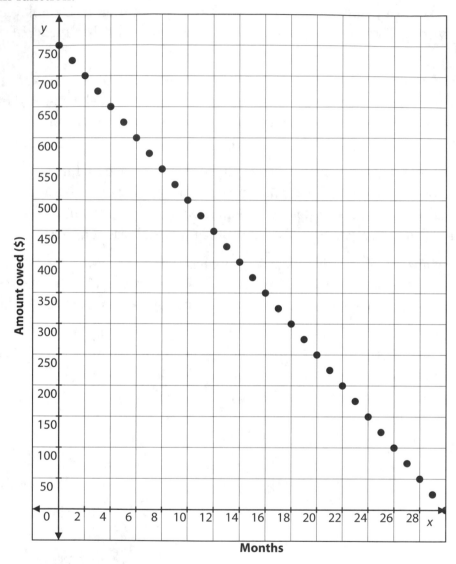

continued

5. A gear on a machine turns at a rate of $\frac{1}{3}$ revolution per second. Identify the key features of the graph of this function.

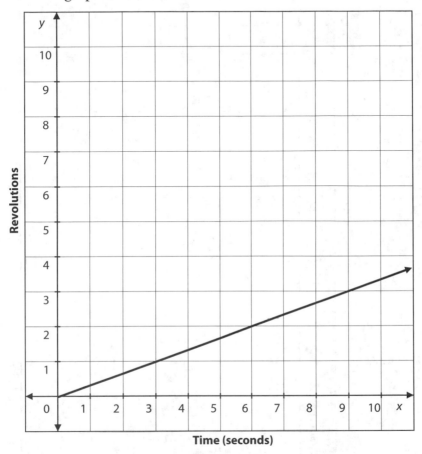

6. Alice receives a base weekly salary of $150 plus a commission of $45 for each computer she installs. Identify the key features of this function.

Number of computer installations (x)	Weekly earnings in dollars ($f(x)$)
0	150
1	195
2	240
3	285
4	330
5	375

continued

UNIT 2 • LINEAR AND EXPONENTIAL RELATIONSHIPS
Lesson 4: Interpreting Graphs of Functions

7. A golf tournament begins with 32 teams. Each round, half the teams are eliminated. Identify the key features of the graph of this function.

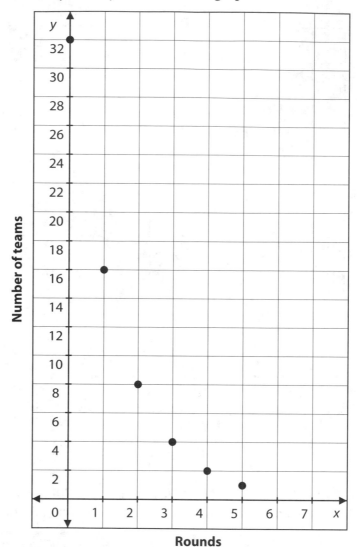

continued

8. A type of bacteria doubles every 12 hours. A Petri dish starts out with 8 of these bacteria. Identify the key features of the graph of this function.

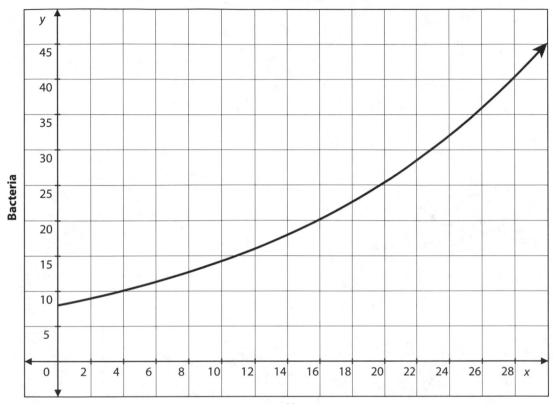

UNIT 2 • LINEAR AND EXPONENTIAL RELATIONSHIPS
Lesson 4: Interpreting Graphs of Functions

9. An investment of $1,500 earns 2.4% interest and is compounded monthly. Identify the key features of the graph of this function.

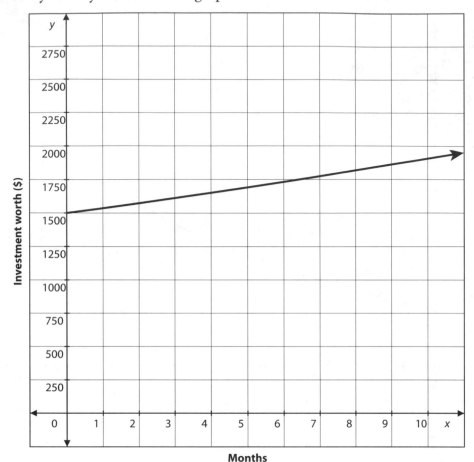

10. An investment of $750 earns 2.1% interest and is compounded daily. Identify the key features of this function.

Year (x)	Investment value in dollars (f(x))
0	750
1	763.81
2	777.88
3	792.21
4	806.80
5	821.66
6	836.79

Lesson 2.4.2: Proving Average Rate of Change

Introduction

In previous lessons, we have found the **slope** of linear equations and functions using the slope formula, $\dfrac{y_2 - y_1}{x_2 - x_1}$. We have also identified the slope of a line from a given equation by rewriting the equation in slope-intercept form, $y = mx + b$, where m is the slope of the line. By calculating the slope, we are able to determine the **rate of change**, or the ratio that describes how much one quantity changes with respect to the change in another quantity of the function. The rate of change can be determined from graphs, tables, and equations themselves. In this lesson, we will extend our understanding of the slope of linear functions to that of intervals of exponential functions.

Key Concepts

- The rate of change is a ratio describing how one quantity changes as another quantity changes.

- Slope can be used to describe the rate of change.

- The slope of a line is the ratio of the change in y-values to the change in x-values.

- A positive rate of change expresses an increase over time.

- A negative rate of change expresses a decrease over time.

- Linear functions have a constant rate of change, meaning values increase or decrease at the same rate over a period of time.

- Not all functions change at a constant rate.

- The rate of change of an **interval**, or a continuous portion of a function, can be calculated.

- The rate of change of an interval is the average rate of change for that period.

- Intervals can be noted using the format $[a, b]$, where a represents the initial x value of the interval and b represents the final x value of the interval. Another way to state the interval is $a \le x \le b$.

- A function or interval with a rate of change of 0 indicates that the line is horizontal.

- Vertical lines have an **undefined slope**. An undefined slope is not the same as a slope of 0. This occurs when the denominator of the ratio is 0.

Calculating Rate of Change from a Table
1. Choose two points from the table.
2. Assign one point to be (x_1, y_1) and the other point to be (x_2, y_2).
3. Substitute the values into the slope formula.
4. The result is the rate of change for the interval between the two points chosen.

- The rate of change between any two points of a linear function will be equal.

- The rate of change between any two points of any other function will not be equal, but will be an average for that interval.

Calculating Rate of Change from an Equation of a Linear Function
1. Transform the given linear function into slope-intercept form, $f(x) = mx + b$.
2. Identify the slope of the line as m from the equation.
3. The slope of the linear function is the rate of change for that function.

Calculating Rate of Change of an Interval from an Equation of an Exponential Function
1. Determine the interval to be observed.
2. Determine (x_1, y_1) by identifying the starting x-value of the interval and substituting it into the function.
3. Solve for y.
4. Determine (x_2, y_2) by identifying the ending x-value of the interval and substituting it into the function.
5. Solve for y.
6. Substitute (x_1, y_1) and (x_2, y_2) into the slope formula to calculate the rate of change.
7. The result is the rate of change for the interval between the two points identified.

Guided Practice 2.4.2

Example 1

Janie invests \$1,300 at a rate of 2.6%, compounded monthly. The function that models this situation is $f(x)=1300\left(1+\dfrac{0.026}{12}\right)^{12x}$, where x represents time in years. What is the rate of change for the interval [1, 4]?

---

1. Determine the interval to be observed.

    The interval to be observed is [1, 4], or the interval where $1 \le x \le 4$.

---

2. Determine (x_1, y_1).

    The initial x-value is 1.

    Substitute the value 1 into the given function.

    $$f(x)=1300\left(1+\frac{0.026}{12}\right)^{12x} \qquad \text{Given function}$$

    $$f(1)=1300\left(1+\frac{0.026}{12}\right)^{12(1)} \qquad \text{Substitute 1 for the value of } x.$$

    $$f(1)=1300\left(1+\frac{0.026}{12}\right)^{12} \qquad \text{Simplify as needed.}$$

    $$f(1) = 1300(1.002)^{12}$$

    $$f(1) \approx 1334.21$$

    (x_1, y_1) is (1, 1334.21).

3. Determine (x_2, y_2) by identifying the ending x-value of the interval and substituting it into the function.

The ending x-value is 4.

Substitute the value 4 into the given function.

$$f(x) = 1300\left(1 + \frac{0.026}{12}\right)^{12x} \quad\quad \text{Given function}$$

$$f(4) = 1300\left(1 + \frac{0.026}{12}\right)^{12(4)} \quad\quad \text{Substitute 4 for the value for } x.$$

$$f(4) = 1300\left(1 + \frac{0.026}{12}\right)^{48} \quad\quad \text{Simplify as needed.}$$

$$f(4) \approx 1442.32$$

(x_2, y_2) is (4, 1442.32).

4. Substitute (x_1, y_1) and (x_2, y_2) into the slope formula to calculate the rate of change.

$$\frac{y_2 - y_1}{x_2 - x_1} \quad\quad \text{Slope formula}$$

$$= \frac{1442.32 - 1334.21}{4 - 1} \quad\quad \begin{array}{l}\text{Substitute (1, 1334.21) and}\\ \text{(4, 1442.32) for } (x_1, y_1) \text{ and } (x_2, y_2).\end{array}$$

$$= \frac{108.11}{3} \quad\quad \text{Simplify as needed.}$$

$$\approx 36.04$$

The rate of change for the interval [1, 4] is \$36.04 per year.

Example 2

In 2008, about 66 million U.S. households had both landline phones and cell phones. This number decreased by an average of 5 million households per year. Use the table below to calculate the rate of change for the interval [2008, 2011].

Year (x)	Households in millions ($f(x)$)
2008	66
2009	61
2010	56
2011	51

1. Determine the interval to be observed.

   The interval to be observed is [2008, 2011], or where $2008 \leq x \leq 2011$.

2. Determine (x_1, y_1).

   The initial x-value is 2008 and the corresponding y-value is 66; therefore, (x_1, y_1) is (2008, 66).

3. Determine (x_2, y_2).

   The ending x-value is 2011 and the corresponding y-value is 51; therefore, (x_2, y_2) is (2011, 51).

4. Substitute (x_1, y_1) and (x_2, y_2) into the slope formula to calculate the rate of change.

   $$\frac{y_2 - y_1}{x_2 - x_1}$$ Slope formula

   $$= \frac{51 - 66}{2011 - 2008}$$ Substitute (2008, 66) and (2011, 51) for (x_1, y_1) and (x_2, y_2).

   $$= \frac{-15}{3}$$ Simplify as needed.

   $$= -5$$

   The rate of change for the interval [2008, 2011] is 5 million households per year.

Example 3

A type of bacteria doubles every 36 hours. A Petri dish starts out with 12 of these bacteria. Use the table below to calculate the rate of change for the interval [2, 5].

Days (x)	Amount of bacteria (f(x))
0	12
1	19
2	30
3	48
4	76
5	121
6	192

1. Determine the interval to be observed.

   The interval to be observed is [2, 5], or where $2 \leq x \leq 5$.

2. Determine (x_1, y_1).

   The initial x-value is 2 and the corresponding y-value is 30; therefore, (x_1, y_1) is (2, 30).

3. Determine (x_2, y_2).

   The ending x-value is 5 and the corresponding y-value is 121; therefore, (x_2, y_2) is (5, 121).

4. Substitute (x_1, y_1) and (x_2, y_2) into the slope formula to calculate the rate of change.

$$\frac{y_2 - y_1}{x_2 - x_1}$$ Slope formula

$$= \frac{121 - 30}{5 - 2}$$ Substitute (2, 30) and (5, 121) for (x_1, y_1) and (x_2, y_2).

$$= \frac{91}{3}$$ Simplify as needed.

$$\approx 30.3$$

   The rate of change for the interval [2, 5] is approximately 30.3 bacteria per day.

Practice 2.4.2: Proving Average Rate of Change

Calculate the rate of change for each scenario described.

1. The fuel capacity of a popular hybrid car is 11.9 gallons. The function for this situation is $f(x) = -0.02x + 11.9$, where x represents miles and $f(x)$ represents the amount of fuel remaining. What is the rate of change for this scenario?

2. The cost of videotaping a basketball tournament is modeled by the function $f(x) = 20x + 350$, where x represents the cost of each video. What is the rate of change for this scenario?

3. An investment of $750 is invested at a rate of 3.5%, compounded monthly. The function that models this situation is $f(x) = 750\left(1 + \dfrac{0.035}{12}\right)^{12x}$, where x represents time in years. What is the rate of change for the interval $[2, 7]$?

4. The price of a stock started out at $23 and has declined to 25% of its value every 2 weeks. The function that models this decline is $f(x) = 150(0.25)^{\frac{x}{2}}$, where x represents time in weeks. What is the rate of change for the interval $[3, 6]$?

5. The conversion of inches to centimeters follows a function. Several conversions are listed in the table below. What is the rate of change for this function?

Inches (x)	Centimeters ($f(x)$)
5	12.7
10	25.4
15	38.1
20	50.8
25	63.5

UNIT 2 • LINEAR AND EXPONENTIAL RELATIONSHIPS
Lesson 4: Interpreting Graphs of Functions

The table below represents the total cost to ship a package based on the package's weight in pounds. Use the table to answer questions 6 and 7.

Number of pounds (x)	Total cost in dollars ($f(x)$)
0	5.25
5	5.90
10	6.55
15	7.20
20	7.85

6. What is the rate of change for this function over the interval [0, 10]?

7. What is the rate of change for this function over the interval [10, 20]?

8. A Petri dish starts out with 9 bacteria. The number of bacteria doubles every 3 minutes. Use the table below to calculate the rate of change for the interval [3, 12].

Minutes (x)	Number of bacteria ($f(x)$)
0	9
3	18
6	36
9	72
12	144

continued

UNIT 2 • LINEAR AND EXPONENTIAL RELATIONSHIPS
Lesson 4: Interpreting Graphs of Functions

The table below represents the worth each year of an initial investment of $650 that earns 3.4% interest compounded quarterly. Use the table to answer questions 9 and 10.

Years (x)	Investment value in dollars ($f(x)$)
0	650
2	862.56
4	1144.64
6	1518.96
8	2015.70

9. What is the rate of change for this function over the interval [0, 6]?

10. What is the rate of change for this function over the interval [4, 8]?

Lesson 2.4.3: Recognizing Average Rate of Change

Introduction

Previously, we calculated the rate of change of linear functions as well as intervals of exponential functions. We observed that the rate of change of exponential functions changed if we focused on different intervals of the function. Here, we will focus on graphs of linear and exponential functions and learn how to estimate the rates of change.

Key Concepts

- To determine the rate of change of a function, first identify the coordinates of the interval being observed.

- Sometimes it is necessary to estimate the values for y.

- The resulting calculation may be an estimation of the rate of change for the interval identified for the given function.

Estimating Rate of Change from a Graph
1. Determine the interval to be observed.
2. Identify (x_1, y_1) as the starting point of the interval.
3. Identify (x_2, y_2) as the ending point of the interval.
4. Substitute (x_1, y_1) and (x_2, y_2) into the slope formula to calculate the rate of change.
5. The result is the estimated rate of change for the interval between the two points identified.

Guided Practice 2.4.3

Example 1

The graph below compares the distance a small motor scooter can travel in miles to the amount of fuel used in gallons. What is the rate of change for this scenario?

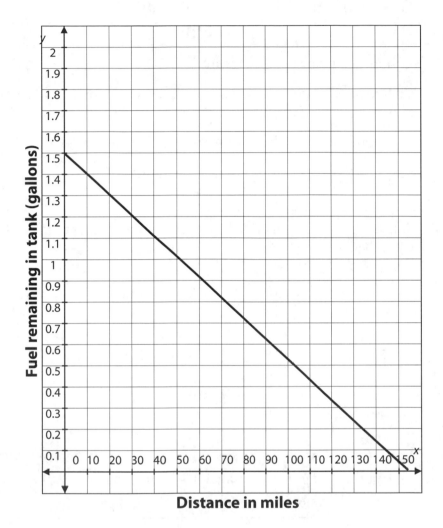

1. Determine the interval to be observed.

   The function is linear, so the rate of change will be constant for any interval of the function.

2. Choose a starting point of the interval.

   Choose a point on the graph with coordinates that are easy to estimate.

   It appears as though the line crosses the y-axis at the point (0, 1.5).

   Let (0, 1.5) be the starting point of the interval.

3. Choose an ending point of the interval.

   Choose another point on the graph with coordinates that are easy to estimate.

   It appears as though the line crosses the x-axis at the point (155, 0).

   Let (155, 0) be the ending point of the interval.

4. Substitute (0, 1.5) and (155, 0) into the slope formula to calculate the rate of change.

   $$\frac{y_2 - y_1}{x_2 - x_1}$$

   Slope formula

   $$= \frac{0 - 1.5}{155 - 0}$$

   Substitute (0, 1.5) and (155, 0) for (x_1, y_1) and (x_2, y_2).

   $$= \frac{-1.5}{155}$$

   Simplify as needed.

   $$\approx -0.01$$

   The rate of change for this function is approximately –0.01 gallons per mile. The amount of fuel decreases by 0.01 gallons per mile.

Example 2

Jasper has invested an amount of money into a savings account. The graph below shows the value of his investment over a period of time. What is the rate of change for the interval [1, 3]?

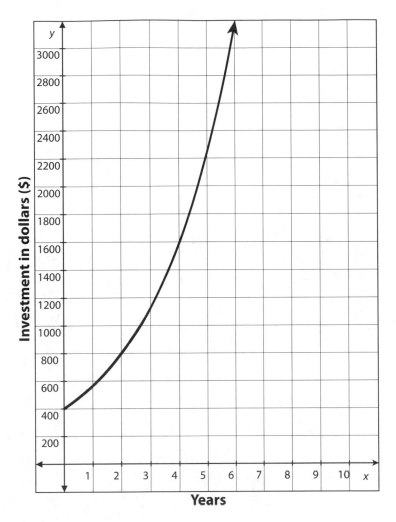

1. Determine the interval to be observed.

   The interval to observe is [1, 3], or where $1 \leq x \leq 3$.

2. Identify the starting point of the interval.

   The x-value of the starting point is 1. The corresponding y-value is approximately 550.

   The starting point of the interval is (1, 550).

3. Identify the ending point of the interval.

The *x*-value for the ending point is 3. The corresponding *y*-value is approximately 1,100.

The ending point of the interval is (3, 1100).

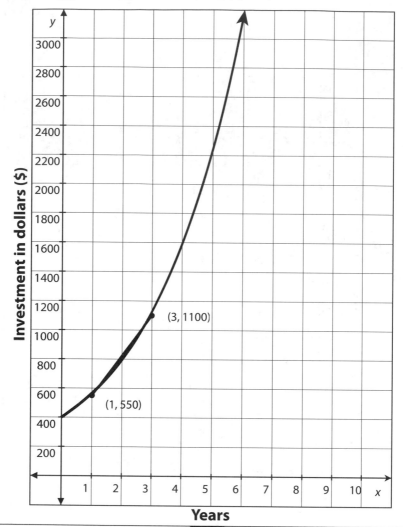

4. Substitute (1, 550) and (3, 1100) into the slope formula to calculate the rate of change.

$$\frac{y_2 - y_1}{x_2 - x_1}$$ Slope formula

$$= \frac{1100 - 550}{3 - 1}$$ Substitute (1, 550) and (3, 1100) for (x_1, y_1) and (x_2, y_2).

$$= \frac{550}{2}$$ Simplify as needed.

$$= 275$$

The rate of change for this function over the interval [1, 3] is approximately \$275 per year.

Example 3

Jasper is curious about how the rate of change differs for the interval [3, 6]. Calculate the rate of change using the graph from Example 2.

1. Determine the interval to be observed.

   The interval to observe is [3, 6], or where $3 \le x \le 6$.

2. Identify the starting point of the interval.

   The x-value of the starting point is 3. The corresponding y-value is approximately 1,100.

   The starting point of the interval is (3, 1100).

3. Identify the ending point of the interval.

The x-value for the ending point is 6. The corresponding y-value is approximately 3,100.

The ending point of the interval is (6, 3100).

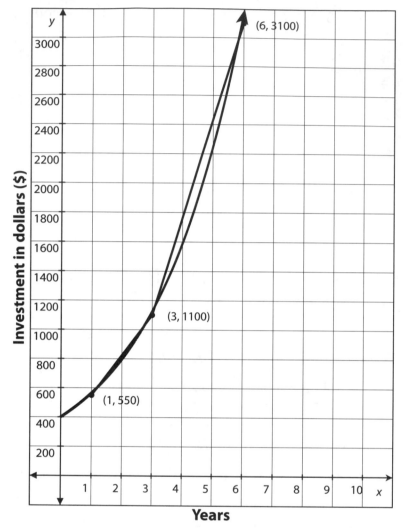

4. Substitute (3, 1100) and (6, 3100) into the slope formula to calculate the rate of change.

$$\frac{y_2 - y_1}{x_2 - x_1}$$
Slope formula

$$= \frac{3100 - 1100}{6 - 3}$$
Substitute (3, 1100) and (6, 3100) for (x_1, y_1) and (x_2, y_2).

$$= \frac{2000}{3}$$
Simplify as needed.

$$\approx 666.67$$

The rate of change for this function over the interval [3, 6] is approximately $666.67 per year.

Notice that the rate of change for the interval [3, 6] is much steeper than that of the interval [1, 3].

UNIT 2 • LINEAR AND EXPONENTIAL RELATIONSHIPS
Lesson 4: Interpreting Graphs of Functions

Practice 2.4.3: Recognizing Average Rate of Change

The graph below shows the amount of paint needed to paint the doors of a house. Use the graph to answer questions 1 and 2.

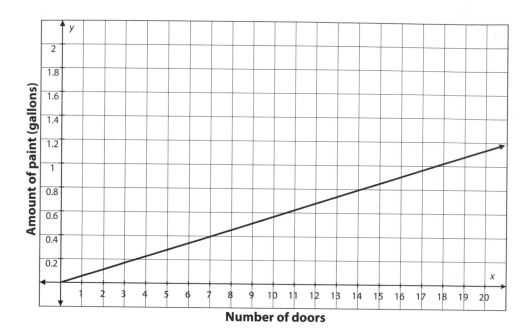

1. What is the approximate rate of change for the interval [2, 7]?

2. What is the approximate rate of change for the interval [12, 19]?

continued

UNIT 2 • LINEAR AND EXPONENTIAL RELATIONSHIPS
Lesson 4: Interpreting Graphs of Functions

The graph below shows the value of the U.S. dollar compared to the value of the Australian dollar on a specific day. Use the graph to answer questions 3–5.

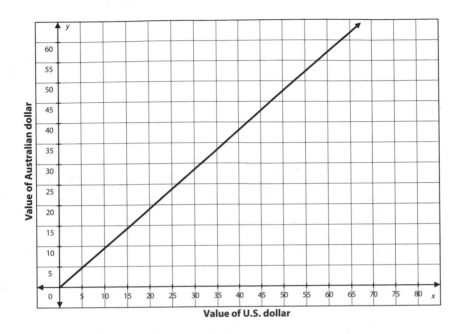

3. What is the approximate rate of change for the interval [10, 25]?

4. What is the approximate rate of change for the interval [30, 65]?

5. Could you predict the rate of change for a third interval on the same graph? If so, what is your prediction?

UNIT 2 • LINEAR AND EXPONENTIAL RELATIONSHIPS
Lesson 4: Interpreting Graphs of Functions

Each year, volunteers at a three-day music festival record the number of people who camp on the festival grounds. The graph below shows the number of campers for each of the last 20 years. Use the graph to answer questions 6 and 7.

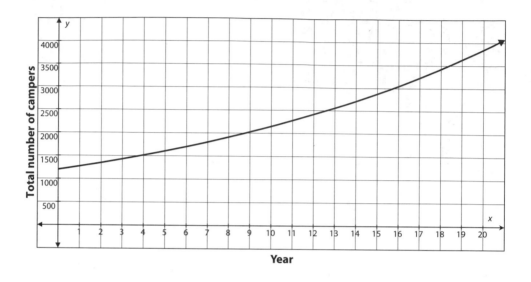

6. What is the approximate rate of change for the interval [3, 9]?

7. What is the approximate rate of change for the interval [9, 16]?

continued

UNIT 2 • LINEAR AND EXPONENTIAL RELATIONSHIPS
Lesson 4: Interpreting Graphs of Functions

The graph below shows the yearly population of a small town. Use the graph to answer questions 8–10.

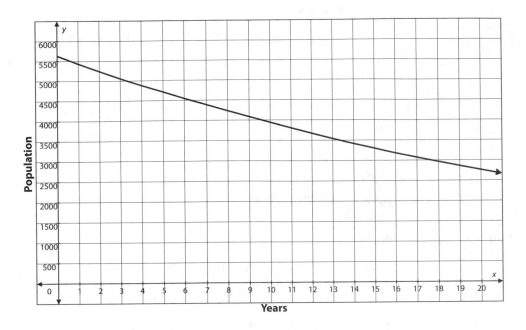

8. What is the approximate rate of change for the interval [1, 6]?

9. What is the approximate rate of change for the interval [10, 20]?

10. How does the rate of change differ for each interval?

Lesson 5: Analyzing Linear and Exponential Functions

Common Core State Standards

F–IF.7   Graph functions expressed symbolically and show key features of the graph, by hand in simple cases and using technology for more complicated cases. ★

a. Graph linear and quadratic functions and show intercepts, maxima, and minima.

e. Graph exponential and logarithmic functions, showing intercepts and end behavior, and trigonometric functions, showing period, midline, and amplitude.

Essential Questions

1. What are the key features of a linear function?

2. What are the key features of an exponential function?

3. How can technology be used to graph complex models?

4. How can linear and exponential functions be used to model real-world scenarios?

WORDS TO KNOW

asymptote	a line that a graph gets closer and closer to, but never crosses or touches
end behavior	the behavior of the graph as x approaches positive infinity and as x approaches negative infinity
exponential function	a function that has a variable in the exponent; the general form is $f(x) = ab^x$, where a is the initial value, b is the rate of decay or growth, x is the time, and $f(x)$ is the final output value
linear function	a function that can be written in the form $f(x) = mx + b$, in which m is the slope, b is the y-intercept, and the graph is a straight line
y-intercept	the point at which a line or curve intersects the y-axis at $(0, y)$

Recommended Resources

- AnalyzeMath.com. "Exponential Functions."

  http://walch.com/rr/CAU3L4ExpFunctionApplet

  This site links to an applet that allows users to change the values of the variables of an exponential function and observe its effects on the associated graph.

- Math Open Reference. "Linear Function Explorer."

  http://walch.com/rr/CAU3L4LinFunctionApplet

  Use the sliders to observe the changes in the slope and intercepts of a linear function.

Lesson 2.5.1: Graphing Linear Functions

Introduction

In this lesson, different methods will be used to graph lines and analyze the features of the graph. In a **linear function**, the graph is a straight line with a constant slope. All linear functions have a y-intercept. The **y-intercept** is where the graph crosses the y-axis. If a linear equation has a slope other than 0, then the function also has an x-intercept. The x-intercept is where the function crosses the x-axis.

Key Concepts

- To find the y-intercept in function notation, evaluate $f(0)$.

- The y-intercept has the coordinates $(0, f(0))$.

- To locate the y-intercept of a graphed function, determine the coordinates of the function where the line crosses the y-axis.

- To find the x-intercept in function notation, set $f(x) = 0$ and solve for x.

- The x-intercept has the coordinates $(x, 0)$.

- To locate the x-intercept of a graphed function, determine the coordinates of the line where the line crosses the x-axis.

- To find the slope of a linear function, pick two coordinates on the line and substitute the points into the equation $m = \dfrac{y_2 - y_1}{x_2 - x_1}$, where m is the slope, y_2 is the y-coordinate of the second point, y_1 is the y-coordinate of the first point, x_2 is the x-coordinate of the second point, and x_1 is the x-coordinate of the first point.

- If the line is in slope-intercept form, the slope is the x coefficient.

Graphing Equations Using a TI-83/84:

Step 1: Press [Y=].

Step 2: Key in the equation using [X, T, θ, n] for x.

Step 3: Press [WINDOW] to change the viewing window, if necessary.

Step 4: Enter in appropriate values for Xmin, Xmax, Xscl, Ymin, Ymax, and Yscl, using the arrow keys to navigate.

Step 5: Press [GRAPH].

Graphing Equations Using a TI-Nspire:

Step 1: Press the home key.

Step 2: Arrow over to the graphing icon (the picture of the parabola or the U-shaped curve) and press [enter].

Step 3: Enter in the equation and press [enter].

Step 4: To change the viewing window: press [menu], arrow down to number 4: Window/Zoom, and click the center button of the navigation pad.

Step 5: Choose 1: Window settings by pressing the center button.

Step 6: Enter in the appropriate XMin, XMax, YMin, and YMax fields.

Step 7: Leave the XScale and YScale set to auto.

Step 8: Use [tab] to navigate among the fields.

Step 9: Press [tab] to "OK" when done and press [enter].

Guided Practice 2.5.1

Example 1

Given the function $f(x) = \dfrac{3}{2}x - 6$, use a table of values to graph and identify the x- and y-intercepts.

1. Create a table of values.

   Choose values for x and determine the corresponding $f(x)$ values.

x	$f(x)$
−2	−9
0	−6
2	−3
4	0
6	3

2. Plot two points from the table.

   The points (6, 3) and (−2, −9) are shown plotted in the graph below.

   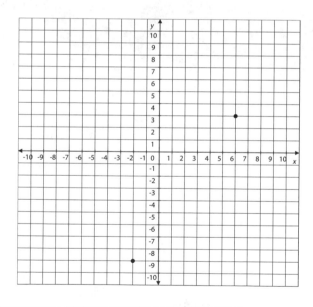

3. Draw the line connecting the two points. Be sure to extend the line so that it crosses both the x- and y-axes.

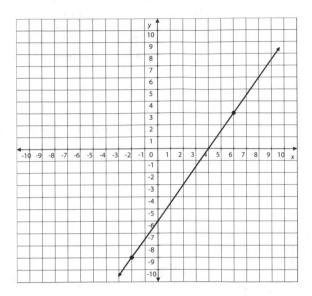

4. Identify the x-intercept.

   The x-intercept is where the line crosses the x-axis.

   The x-intercept is (4, 0).

5. Identify the y-intercept.

   The y-intercept is where the line crosses the y-axis.

   The y-intercept is (0, –6).

Example 2

Given the function $f(x)=-\dfrac{1}{5}x+2$, use the slope and y-intercept to identify the x-intercept of the function.

---

1. Identify the slope and y-intercept.

    The function $f(x)=-\dfrac{1}{5}x+2$ is written in $f(x) = mx + b$ form, where m is the slope and b is the y-intercept.

    The slope of the function is $-\dfrac{1}{5}$.

    The y-intercept is 2.

---

2. Graph the function on a coordinate plane.

    Use the y-intercept, $(0, 2)$, and slope to graph the function.

    Be sure to extend the line to cross both the x- and y-axes.

    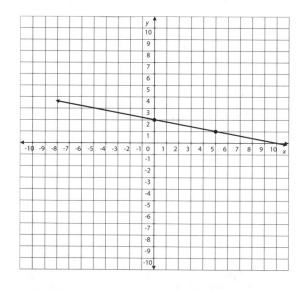

---

3. Identify the x-intercept.

    The x-intercept is where the line crosses the x-axis.

    The x-intercept is $(10, 0)$.

Example 3

Given the function $f(x)=-\dfrac{4}{3}x+4$, solve for the x- and y-intercepts. Use the intercepts to graph the function.

1. Find the x-intercept.

   Substitute 0 for f(x) in the equation and solve for x.

$f(x)=-\dfrac{4}{3}x+4$	Original function
$0=-\dfrac{4}{3}x+4$	Substitute 0 for f(x).
$-4=-\dfrac{4}{3}x$	Subtract 4 from both sides.
$x=3$	Divide both sides by $-\dfrac{4}{3}$.

   The x-intercept is (3, 0).

2. Find the y-intercept.

   Substitute 0 for x in the equation and solve for f(x).

$f(x)=-\dfrac{4}{3}x+4$	Original function
$f(x)=-\dfrac{4}{3}(0)+4$	Substitute 0 for x.
$f(x)=0+4$	Simplify as needed.
$f(x)=4$	

   The y-intercept is (0, 4).

3. Graph the function.

   Plot the *x*- and *y*-intercepts.

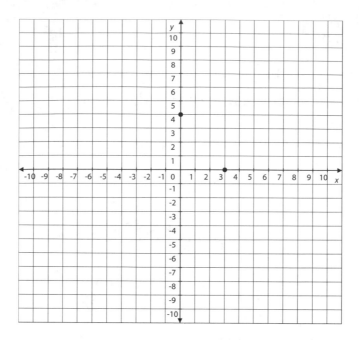

Draw a line connecting the two points.

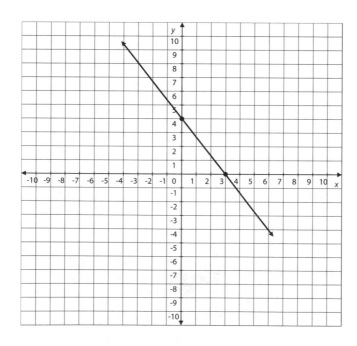

Example 4

Given the function $f(x)=-\dfrac{1}{8}x+20$, graph the function using technology. Identify the intercepts.

1. Set the viewing window of the graphing calculator.

   Use the following settings:

Xmin = –20	Ymax = 30
Xmax = 20	Yscal = 2
Xscl = 2	Xres = 1
Ymin = –20	

   To Set the Window on a TI-83/84:

   Step 1: Press [WINDOW].

   Step 2: Change values accordingly. Use the arrow keys to navigate.

   Step 3: Press [ENTER].

   To Set the Window on a TI-Nspire:

   Step 1: Press [menu], arrow down to number 4: Window/Zoom, and click the center button of the navigation pad.

   Step 2: Choose 1: Window settings by pressing the center button.

   Step 3: Enter in the appropriate XMin, XMax, YMin, and YMax fields.

   Step 4: Leave the XScale and YScale set to auto.

   Step 5: Use [tab] to navigate among the fields.

   Step 6: Press [tab] to "OK" when done and press [enter].

2. Graph the function.

   Graphing Equations Using a TI-83/84:

   Step 1: Press [Y=].

   Step 2: Key in the equation using [X, T, θ, n] for x, [–1/8x+20].

   Step 3: Press [GRAPH].

   (continued)

Graphing Equations Using a TI-Nspire:

Step 1: Press the home key.

Step 2: Arrow over to the graphing icon (the picture of the parabola or the U-shaped curve) and press [enter].

Step 3: Enter in the equation [−1/8x+20] and press [enter].

Step 4: Press [tab] to "OK" when done and press [enter].

3. Find the intercepts using technology.

Finding the Intercepts Using a TI-83/84:

Step 1: Press [2nd] and [TRACE].

Step 2: Press 1: value.

Step 3: Type [0] and press [ENTER].

Step 4: Record the y-value. This is the y-intercept.

Step 5: Press [2nd] and [TRACE].

Step 6: Type 2: zero.

Step 7: Move the cursor so it is to the left of the x-intercept and press [ENTER].

Step 8: Move the cursor so it is to the right of the x-intercept and press [ENTER].

Step 9: Press [ENTER].

Step 10: Record the x-value. This is the x-intercept.

(continued)

Finding the Intercepts Using a TI-Nspire:

Step 1: Press [menu].

Step 2: Press 6: Analyze Graph.

Step 3: Press 1: Zero.

Step 4: Move the hand to a point on the graph to the left of the *x*-intercept.

Step 5: Press [enter].

Step 6: Record the *x*-value. This is the *x*-intercept.

Step 7: Press [menu].

Step 8: Press 5: Trace.

Step 9: Press 1: Graph Trace.

Step 10: Move the cursor so it is on the *y*-axis. Use the arrow keys to navigate.

Step 11: Record the *y*-value. This is the *y*-intercept.

The *x*-intercept is (160, 0) and the *y*-intercept is (0, 20).

UNIT 2 • LINEAR AND EXPONENTIAL RELATIONSHIPS
Lesson 5: Analyzing Linear and Exponential Functions

Practice 2.5.1: Graphing Linear Functions

Use what you know about linear functions to complete the following problems.

1. Given the function $f(x)=-\dfrac{2}{3}x-4$, use the slope and y-intercept to graph the function. Identify the x- and y-intercepts.

2. Given the function $f(x) = -3x + 9$, use the slope and y-intercept to graph the function. Identify the x- and y-intercepts.

3. Given the table of values, graph the function and identify the x- and y-intercepts.

x	$f(x)$
−7	−6
−5	0
−3	6
0	15

4. Given the table of values, graph the function and identify the x- and y-intercepts.

x	$f(x)$
−2	−8
0	−4
2	0
3	2

5. Given the function $f(x)=\dfrac{7}{3}x+7$, solve for the x- and y-intercepts. Use the intercepts to graph the function.

6. Given the function $f(x) = -8x - 16$, solve for the x- and y-intercepts. Use the intercepts to graph the function.

continued

7. Chris is collecting cans and bottles to raise money for his baseball team. He gets $6 for each bag of bottles collected and $5 for each bag of cans collected. Chris needs to collect $30 worth of cans and bottles. Write a function to represent how many bags of cans and bottles Chris needs to collect. Draw the graph of the function. If Chris collects only bottles, how many bags of bottles does he need to collect? If he collects only cans, how many bags of cans does he need to collect?

8. Ashlyn makes leather handbags and belts to sell online. The belts require 50 square inches of leather and the handbags require 350 square inches of leather. Ashlyn has 700 square inches of leather available. Write a function to represent the combination of belts and handbags she can make. Draw the graph of the function. If Ashlyn makes only belts, how many can she make? If she makes only handbags, how many can she make?

9. A farmer grows corn and wheat. Each acre of corn requires takes 40 hours to plant. Each acre of wheat takes 120 hours to plant. The farmer has 360 hours to plant the crops. Write a function to represent the combination of wheat and corn that the farmer can plant. Draw the graph of the function. If the farmer grows only corn, how many acres can he plant? If the farmer plants only wheat, how many acres can he plant?

10. The graph of a function is shown below. Write a scenario that could be represented by the graph.

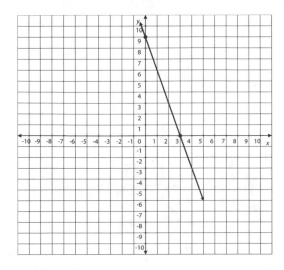

Lesson 2.5.2: Graphing Exponential Functions

Introduction

In this lesson, different methods will be used to graph exponential functions and analyze the key features of the graph. In an **exponential function**, the graph is a smooth line with a rounded curve. All exponential functions have an **asymptote**, or a line that the graph gets closer and closer to, but never crosses or touches. Every exponential function has a y-intercept, where the graph crosses the y-axis. There is, at most, one x-intercept, where the function crosses the x-axis.

Key Concepts

- To find the y-intercept of an exponential function, evaluate $f(0)$.

- The y-intercept has the coordinates $(0, f(0))$.

- To locate the y-intercept of a graphed function, determine the coordinates of the function where the line crosses the y-axis.

- To find the x-intercept in function notation, set $f(x) = 0$ and solve for x.

- The x-intercept has the coordinates $(x, 0)$.

- To locate the x-intercept of a graphed function, determine the coordinates of the line where the line crosses the x-axis.

- Not all exponential functions cross the x-axis.

- The asymptote of exponential functions of the form $f(x) = ab^x$ is always the x-axis, or $y = 0$.

- If the exponential function is of the form $f(x) = ab^x + k$, then the function will be shifted vertically by the same number of units as k.

- The asymptote is then $y = k$.

- The **end behavior**, or the behavior of the graph as x becomes larger or smaller, will always be one of three descriptions: infinity, negative infinity, or the asymptote.

- It is easiest to first graph the function and then observe what happens to the value of y as the value of x increases and decreases.

- Graph complex exponential models using technology as values can become quite large or small very quickly.

Graphing Equations Using a TI-83/84:

Step 1: Press [Y=].

Step 2: Key in the equation using [X, T, θ, *n*] for *x*.

Step 3: Press [WINDOW] to change the viewing window, if necessary.

Step 4: Enter in appropriate values for Xmin, Xmax, Xscl, Ymin, Ymax, and Yscl, using the arrow keys to navigate.

Step 5: Press [GRAPH].

Graphing Equations Using a TI-Nspire:

Step 1: Press the home key.

Step 2: Arrow over to the graphing icon (the picture of the parabola or the U-shaped curve) and press [enter].

Step 3: Enter in the equation and press [enter].

Step 4: To change the viewing window: press [menu], arrow down to number 4: Window/Zoom, and click the center button of the navigation pad.

Step 5: Choose 1: Window settings by pressing the center button.

Step 6: Enter in the appropriate XMin, XMax, YMin, and YMax fields.

Step 7: Leave the XScale and YScale set to auto.

Step 8: Use [tab] to navigate among the fields.

Step 9: Press [tab] to "OK" when done and press [enter].

Guided Practice 2.5.2

Example 1

Create a table of values for the exponential function $f(x) = 3(2)^x + 4$. Identify the asymptote and y-intercept of the function. Plot the points and sketch the graph of the function, and describe the end behavior.

---

1. Create a table of values.

   Choose values of x and solve for the corresponding values of $f(x)$.

x	$f(x)$
-4	4.1875
-2	4.75
0	7
2	16
4	52

---

2. Identify the asymptote of the function.

   The asymptote of the function is always the constant, k.

   In the function $f(x) = 3(2)^x + 4$, the value of k is 4.

   The asymptote of the function is $y = 4$.

---

3. Determine the y-intercept of the function.

   The y-intercept of the function is the value of $f(x)$ when x is equal to 0.

   It can be seen in the table that when $x = 0$, $f(x) = 7$.

   The y-intercept is (0, 7).

---

4. Graph the function.

   Use the table of values to create a graph of the function.

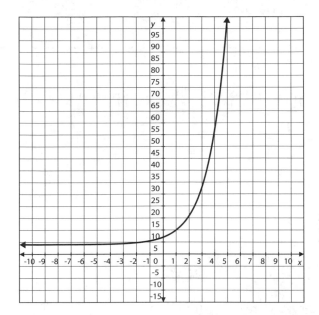

5. Describe the end behavior of the graph.

   The end behavior is what happens at the ends of the graph.

   As x becomes larger, the value of the function approaches infinity.

   As x becomes smaller, the value of the function approaches the asymptote, 4.

   Since the function approaches infinity as x becomes larger, the graph shows exponential growth.

Example 2

Create a table of values for the exponential function $f(x) = -1(3)^x - 2$. Identify the asymptote and y-intercept of the function. Plot the points and sketch the graph of the function, and describe the end behavior.

1. Create a table of values.

   Choose values of x and solve for the corresponding values of $f(x)$.

x	$f(x)$
−1	−2.33
0	−3
1	−5
2	−11
3	−29

2. Identify the asymptote of the function.

   The asymptote of the function is always the constant, k.

   In the function $f(x) = -1(3)^x - 2$, the value of k is −2.

   The asymptote of the function is $y = -2$.

3. Determine the y-intercept of the function.

   The y-intercept of the function is the value of $f(x)$ when x is equal to 0.

   It can be seen in the table that when $x = 0$, $f(x) = -3$.

   The y-intercept is $(0, -3)$.

4. Graph the function.

   Use the table of values to create a graph of the function.

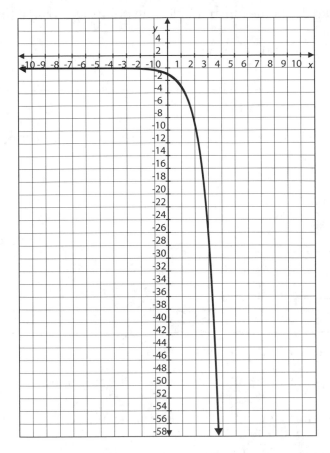

5. Describe the end behavior of the graph.

   The end behavior is what happens at the ends of the graph.

   As x becomes larger, the value of the function approaches negative infinity.

   As x becomes smaller, the value of the function approaches the asymptote, –2.

Example 3

Create a table of values for the exponential function $f(x) = 4\left(\dfrac{2}{3}\right)^x - 3$. Identify the asymptote and y-intercept of the function. Plot the points and sketch the graph of the function, and describe the end behavior.

1. Create a table of values.

   Choose values of x and solve for the corresponding values of $f(x)$.

x	$f(x)$
–4	17.25
–2	6
0	1
2	–1.22
4	–2.2099

2. Identify the asymptote of the function.

   The asymptote of the function is always the constant, k.

   In the function $f(x) = 4\left(\dfrac{2}{3}\right)^x - 3$, the value of k is –3.

   The asymptote of the function is $y = -3$.

3. Determine the y-intercept of the function.

   The y-intercept of the function is the value of $f(x)$ when x is equal to 0.

   It can be seen in the table that when $x = 0$, $f(x) = 1$.

   The y-intercept is (0, 1).

4. Graph the function.

Use the table of values to create a graph of the function.

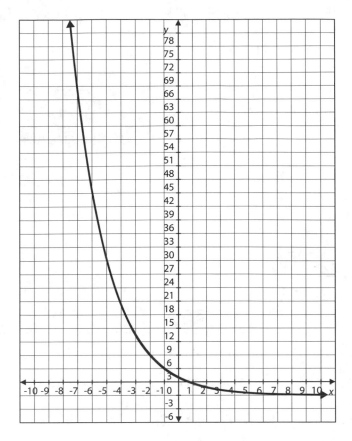

5. Describe the end behavior of the graph.

The end behavior is what happens at the ends of the graph.

As x becomes larger, the value of the function approaches the asymptote, –3.

As x becomes smaller, the value of the function approaches infinity.

Since the function approaches infinity as x becomes smaller, the graph shows exponential decay.

Example 4

Create a table of values for the exponential function $f(x)=-2\left(\dfrac{1}{4}\right)^{x}+5$. Identify the asymptote and y-intercept of the function. Plot the points and sketch the graph of the function, and describe the end behavior.

1. Create a table of values.

   Choose values of x and solve for the corresponding values of $f(x)$.

x	$f(x)$
−2	−27
−1	−3
0	3
1	4.5
2	4.875

2. Identify the asymptote of the function.

   The asymptote of the function is always the constant, k.

   In the function $f(x)=-2\left(\dfrac{1}{4}\right)^{x}+5$, the value of k is 5.

   The asymptote of the function is $y = 5$.

3. Determine the y-intercept of the function.

   The y-intercept of the function is the value of $f(x)$ when x is equal to 0.

   It can be seen in the table that when $x = 0$, $f(x) = 3$.

   The y-intercept is (0, 3).

4. Graph the function.

   Use the table of values to create a graph of the function.

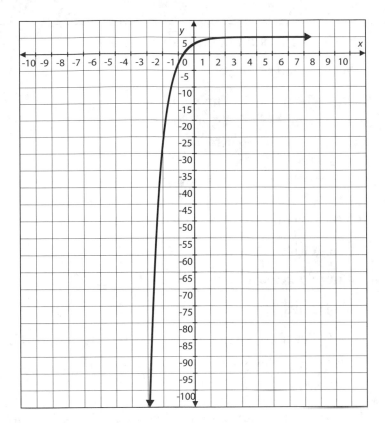

5. Describe the end behavior of the graph.

   The end behavior is what happens at the ends of the graph.

   As *x* becomes larger, the value of the function approaches the asymptote, 5.

   As *x* becomes smaller, the value of the function approaches negative infinity.

Example 5

Use technology to identify the *y*-intercept of the function $f(x) = -2\left(\dfrac{1}{4}\right)^x + 5$.

---

1. Set the viewing window of the graphing calculator.

    Use the following settings:

Xmin = –5	Ymax = 10
Xmax = 5	Yscal = 5
Xscl = 1	Xres = 1
Ymin = –100	

---

2. Graph the function on a graphing calculator.

    Use the following steps:

    ### Graphing Equations Using a TI-83/84:

    Step 1: Press [Y=].

    Step 2: Key in the equation using [X, T, θ, *n*] for *x*, [–2(1/4)^x + 5].

    Step 3: Press [WINDOW] to change the viewing window, if necessary.

    Step 4: Enter in appropriate values for Xmin [–5], Xmax [5], Xscl [1], Ymin [–100], Ymax [10], and Yscl [5], using the arrow keys to navigate.

    Step 5: Press [GRAPH].

    ### Graphing Equations Using a TI-Nspire:

    Step 1: Press the home key.

    Step 2: Arrow over to the graphing icon (the picture of the parabola or the U-shaped curve) and press [enter].

    Step 3: Enter in the equation [–2(1/4)^x + 5] and press [enter].

    Step 4: To change the viewing window: press [menu], arrow down to number 4: Window/Zoom, and click the center button of the navigation pad.

    (continued)

Step 5: Choose 1: Window settings by pressing the center button.

Step 6: Enter in the appropriate XMin [–5], XMax [5], YMin [–100], and YMax [10] fields.

Step 7: Leave the XScale and YScale set to auto.

Step 8: Use [tab] to navigate among the fields.

Step 9: Press [tab] to "OK" when done and press [enter].

3. Find the *y*-intercept of the function.

Use the following steps:

Finding the Value When *x* = 0 Using a TI-83/84:

Step 1: Press [2nd] [CALC].

Step 2: Select 1: value.

Step 3: Type [5] and press [ENTER].

Step 4: Record the value, *y* = 3.

Finding the Value When *x* = 0 Using a TI-Nspire:

Step 1: Press [menu].

Step 2: Select 5: Trace.

Step 3: Select 1: Graph Trace.

Step 4: Record the *y*-value, 3.

Practice 2.5.2: Graphing Exponential Functions

Use what you know about exponential functions to complete the problems that follow.

1. Given the function $f(x) = -5(2)^x + 3$, identify the y-intercept and describe the end behavior. Justify your answer with a graph.

2. Given the function $f(x) = 2\left(\dfrac{1}{4}\right)^x + 20$, identify the y-intercept and describe the end behavior. Justify your answer with a graph.

3. Given the function $f(x) = 4(6)^x + 2$, identify the y-intercept and describe the end behavior. Justify your answer with a graph.

4. Given the function $y = 4\left(\dfrac{1}{3}\right)^x$, identify the y-intercept and describe the end behavior. Justify your answer with a graph.

5. Given the function $f(x) = -2(4)^x - 5$, identify the y-intercept and describe the end behavior.

6. Given the function $f(x) = 10(3^x) - 8$, identify the y-intercept and describe the end behavior.

7. A certain radioactive isotope has a half-life of 8 hours. The starting amount is 55 grams. Write an exponential function to model this scenario. How much of the isotope remains after 24 hours?

8. You are growing bacteria for a science experiment. The number of organisms quadruples every 13 hours. You begin the experiment with 10 organisms. Write an exponential function to model this scenario. How many organisms will you have in 26 hours?

continued

UNIT 2 • LINEAR AND EXPONENTIAL RELATIONSHIPS
Lesson 5: Analyzing Linear and Exponential Functions

9. Connor invests $250 in an account that earns 3.7% interest per year. Write an exponential function to represent this scenario. How much money is in the account after 3 years?

10. The graph of a function is shown below. Write a scenario that could be represented by the graph.

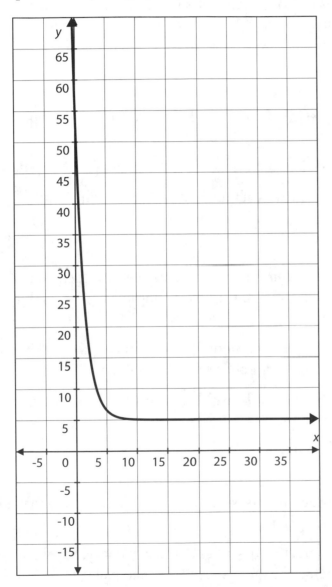

Lesson 6: Comparing Functions

Common Core State Standards

F–IF.9 Compare properties of two functions each represented in a different way (algebraically, graphically, numerically in tables, or by verbal descriptions). *For example, given a graph of one quadratic function and an algebraic expression for another, say which has the larger maximum.*

F–LE.3 Observe using graphs and tables that a quantity increasing exponentially eventually exceeds a quantity increasing linearly, quadratically, or (more generally) as a polynomial function. ★

Essential Questions

1. What different interpretations can be made from different representations of functions?

2. Why is comparing functions important?

3. How can you use characteristics of functions to compare functions?

WORDS TO KNOW

exponential function	a function that has a variable in the exponent; the general form is $f(x) = ab^x$, where a is the initial value, b is the rate of decay or growth, x is the time, and $f(x)$ is the final output value
factor	one of two or more numbers or expressions that when multiplied produce a given product
growth factor	the multiple by which a quantity increases or decreases over time
interval	a continuous series of values
linear function	a function that can be written in the form $f(x) = mx + b$, in which m is the slope, b is the y-intercept, and the graph is a straight line
rate of change	a ratio that describes how much one quantity changes with respect to the change in another quantity; also known as the slope of a line

slope	the measure of the rate of change of one variable with respect to another variable; slope $= \dfrac{y_2 - y_1}{x_2 - x_1} = \dfrac{\Delta y}{\Delta x} = \dfrac{\text{rise}}{\text{run}}$
***x*-intercept**	the point at which the line intersects the *x*-axis; written as $(x, 0)$
***y*-intercept**	the point at which the line intersects the *y*-axis; written as $(0, y)$

Recommended Resources

- Algebra 4 All. "Exponential Functions."

  http://walch.com/rr/CAU3L5ExponentialFunctions

  This site provides links to several applets that allow users to explore exponential functions.

- Interactivate. "Graphit."

  http://walch.com/rr/CAU3L5Graphit

  This interactive applet allows users to compare functions using tables, graphs, and/or equations.

- Math Open Reference. "Linear Function Explorer."

  http://walch.com/rr/CAU3L5LinearFunctions

  Users of this interactive applet can change the values of the variables *a* and *b* to observe the changes in a given graph of linear functions.

Lesson 2.6.1: Comparing Linear Functions

Introduction

Remember that **linear functions** are functions that can be written in the form $f(x) = mx + b$, where m is the slope and b is the y-intercept. The slope of a linear function is also the **rate of change** and can be calculated using the formula slope $= \dfrac{y_2 - y_1}{x_2 - x_1}$. The y-intercept is the point at where the function crosses the y-axis and has the point $(0, y)$. The x-intercept, if it exists, is the point where the graph crosses the x-axis and has the point $(x, 0)$. Slope and both intercepts can be determined from tables, equations, and graphs. These features are used to compare linear functions to one another.

Key Concepts

- Linear functions can be represented in words or as equations, graphs, or tables.

- To compare linear functions, determine the rate of change and intercepts of each function.

- Review the following processes for identifying the rate of change and y-intercept of a linear function.

Identifying the Rate of Change and the y-intercept from Context
1. Read the problem statement carefully.
2. Look for the information given and make a list of the known quantities.
3. Determine which information tells you the rate of change, or the slope, m. Look for words such as *each*, *every*, *per*, or *rate*.
4. Determine which information tells you the y-intercept, or b. This could be an initial value or a starting value, a flat fee, and so forth.

Identifying the Rate of Change and the y-intercept from an Equation
1. Simplify linear functions to follow the form $f(x) = mx + b$.
2. Identify the rate of change, or the slope, m, as the coefficient of x.
3. Identify the y-intercept, or b, as the constant in the function.

Identifying the Rate of Change and the *y*-intercept from a Table

1. Choose two points from the table.

2. Assign one point to be (x_1, y_1) and the other point to be (x_2, y_2).

3. Substitute the values into the slope formula, $\dfrac{y_2 - y_1}{x_2 - x_1}$.

4. Identify the *y*-intercept as the coordinate in the form $(0, y)$. If this coordinate is not given, substitute the rate of change and one coordinate into the form $f(x) = mx + b$ and solve for b.

Identifying the Rate of Change and the *y*-intercept from a Graph

1. Choose two points from the graph.

2. Assign one point to be (x_1, y_1) and the other point to be (x_2, y_2).

3. Substitute the values into the slope formula, $\dfrac{y_2 - y_1}{x_2 - x_1}$.

4. Identify the *y*-intercept as the coordinate of the line that intersects with the *y*-axis.

- When presented with functions represented in different ways, it is helpful to rewrite the information using function notation.

- You can compare the functions once you have identified the rate of change and the *y*-intercept of each function.

- Linear functions are increasing if the rate of change is a positive value.

- Linear functions are decreasing if the rate of change is a negative value.

- The greater the rate of change, the steeper the line will appear on the graph.

- A rate of change of 0 appears as a horizontal line on a graph.

Guided Practice 2.6.1

Example 1

The functions $f(x)$ and $g(x)$ are described below. Compare the properties of each.

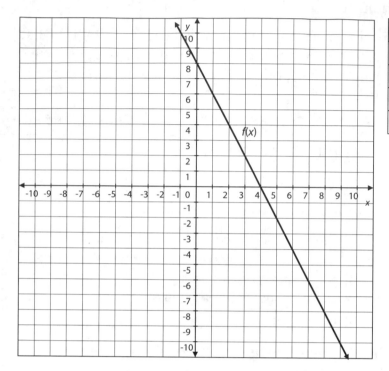

x	$g(x)$
-2	-10
-1	-8
0	-6
1	-4

1. Identify the rate of change for the first function, $f(x)$.

   Let $(0, 8)$ be (x_1, y_1) and $(4, 0)$ be (x_2, y_2).

   Substitute the values into the slope formula.

   $\dfrac{y_2 - y_1}{x_2 - x_1}$ Slope formula

   $\dfrac{0-8}{4-0}$ Substitute $(0, 8)$ and $(4, 0)$ for (x_1, y_1) and (x_2, y_2).

   $\dfrac{-8}{4}$ Simplify as needed.

   -2

   The rate of change for this function is -2.

2. Identify the rate of change for the second function, $g(x)$.

Choose two points from the table. Let $(-2, -10)$ be (x_1, y_1) and let $(-1, -8)$ be (x_2, y_2).

Substitute the values into the slope formula.

$\dfrac{y_2 - y_1}{x_2 - x_1}$ Slope formula

$\dfrac{(-8) - (-10)}{(-1) - (-2)}$ Substitute $(-2, -10)$ and $(-1, -8)$ for (x_1, y_1) and (x_2, y_2).

$\dfrac{2}{1}$ Simplify as needed.

2

The rate of change for this function is 2.

3. Identify the y-intercept of the first function, $f(x)$.

The graph crosses the y-axis at $(0, 8)$, so the y-intercept is 8.

4. Identify the y-intercept of the second function, $g(x)$.

From the table, we can determine that the function would intersect the y-axis where the x-value is 0. This happens at the point $(0, -6)$. The y-intercept is -6.

5. Compare the properties of each function.

The rate of change for the first function is -2 and the rate of change for the second function is 2. The first function is decreasing and the second is increasing, but the rates of change are equal in value.

The y-intercept of the first function is 8, but the y-intercept of the second function is -6. The graph of the second function crosses the y-axis at a lower point.

Example 2

Your employer has offered two pay scales for you to choose from. The first option is to receive a base salary of $250 a week plus 15% of the price of any merchandise you sell. The second option is represented in the graph below. Compare the properties of the functions.

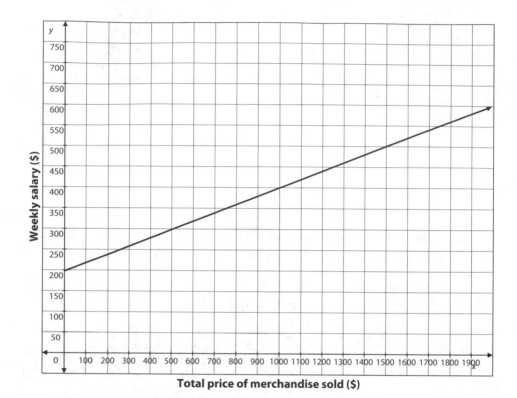

Total price of merchandise sold ($)

1. Identify the rate of change for the first function.

   Determine which information tells you the rate of change, or the slope, m.

   You are told that your employer will pay you 15% of the price of the merchandise you sell.

   This information is the rate of change for this function and can be written as 0.15.

2. Identify the y-intercept for the first function.

   Your employer has offered a base salary of $250 per week.

   250 is the y-intercept of the function.

3. Identify the rate of change for the second function.

   Let (0, 200) be (x_1, y_1) and (500, 300) be (x_2, y_2).

   Substitute the values into the slope formula.

   $\dfrac{y_2 - y_1}{x_2 - x_1}$ Slope formula

   $\dfrac{300 - 200}{500 - 0}$ Substitute (0, 200) and (500, 300) for (x_1, y_1) and (x_2, y_2).

   $\dfrac{100}{500}$ Simplify as needed.

   $\dfrac{1}{5} = 0.2$

   The rate of change for this function is 0.2.

4. Identify the y-intercept as the coordinate of the line that intersects the y-axis.

   The graph intersects the y-axis at (0, 200). The y-intercept is 200.

5. Compare the properties of each function.

   The rate of change for the second function is greater than the first function. You will get paid more for the amount of merchandise you sell.

   The y-intercept of the first function is greater than the second. You will get a higher base pay with the first function.

   In the first function, you would receive a higher base salary, but get paid less for the amount of merchandise you sell.

   In the second function, you would receive a lower base salary, but get paid more for the merchandise you sell.

Example 3

Two airplanes are in flight. The function $f(x) = 400x + 1200$ represents the altitude, $f(x)$, of one airplane after x minutes. The graph below represents the altitude of the second airplane. Compare the properties of the functions.

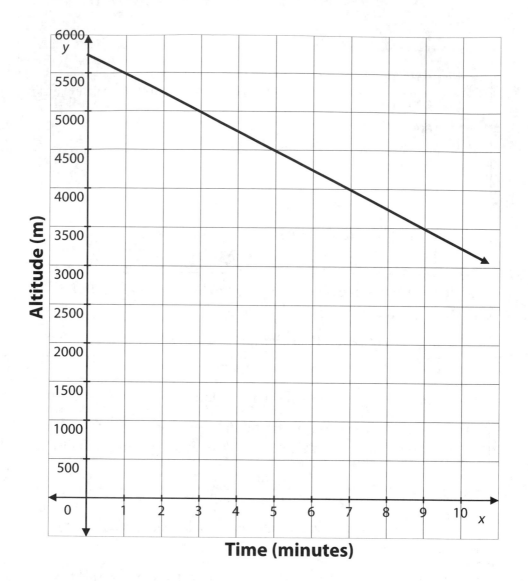

1. Identify the rate of change for the first function.

   The function is written in $f(x) = mx + b$ form; therefore, the rate of change for the function is 400.

2. Identify the *y*-intercept for the first function.

   The *y*-intercept of the first function is 1,200, as stated in the equation.

3. Identify the rate of change for the second function.

   Choose two points from the graph.

   Let (0, 5750) be (x_1, y_1) and (5, 4500) be (x_2, y_2).

   Substitute the values into the slope formula.

   $$\frac{y_2 - y_1}{x_2 - x_1}$$ Slope formula

   $$\frac{4500 - 5750}{5 - 0}$$ Substitute (0, 5750) and (5, 4500) for (x_1, y_1) and (x_2, y_2).

   $$\frac{-1250}{5}$$ Simplify as needed.

   -250

   The rate of change for this function is −250.

4. Identify the *y*-intercept of the second function as the coordinate of the line that intersects with the *y*-axis.

   The graph intersects the *y*-axis at (0, 5750).

5. Compare the properties of each function.

   The rate of change for the first function is greater than the second function. The rate of change for the first function is also positive, whereas the rate of change for the second function is negative. The first airplane is ascending at a faster rate than the second airplane is descending.

   The *y*-intercept of the second function is greater than the first. The second airplane is higher in the air than the first airplane at that moment.

UNIT 2 • LINEAR AND EXPONENTIAL RELATIONSHIPS
Lesson 6: Comparing Functions

Practice 2.6.1: Comparing Linear Functions

Compare the properties of the linear functions.

1. Which function has a greater rate of change? Which function has the greater *y*-intercept? Explain how you know.

Function A

x	f(x)
−3	−14
0	−5
2	1
5	10

Function B

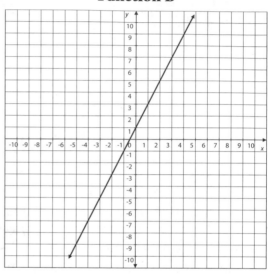

2. Which function has a greater rate of change? Which function has the greater *y*-intercept?

Function A

x	f(x)
−14	−2
−7	−3
0	−4
7	−5

Function B

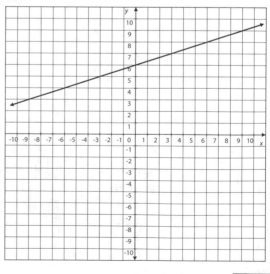

continued

3. Compare the properties of each function.

Function A

$$f(x) = \frac{2}{3}x + 9$$

Function B

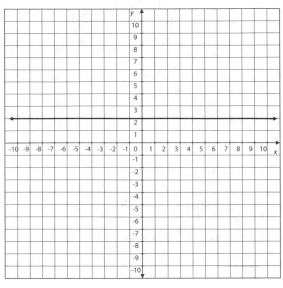

4. Compare the properties of each function.

Function A

$$f(x) = 3x$$

Function B

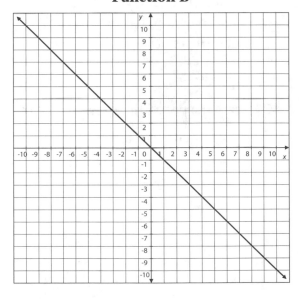

continued

5. Compare the properties of each function.

Function A	**Function B**

Function A

The table describes the profit in dollars made on ice creams sold by a street vendor.

Number of ice creams sold (x)	Profit ($f(x)$)
0	0
20	4.60
40	9.20
60	13.80

Function B

For each hot dog sold, the same vendor makes a profit of $0.20.

6. Compare the properties of each function.

Function A

The local community magazine began with a circulation of 3,400 subscribers in its first year. Since then, its circulation has increased by 175 subscribers per year.

Function B

The function $f(x) = 95x + 2200$ represents the circulation of another magazine in a nearby community, where $f(x)$ represents total subscriptions and x represents the number of years since it began its circulation.

7. Compare the properties of each function.

Function A

A game store charges $3.50 to rent a video game for one night, plus an additional $2 per day thereafter.

Function B

The table shows the total cost to rent the same game at a different rental store, where $f(x)$ represents the total cost in dollars after x days.

x	$f(x)$
2	6.00
3	8.50
4	11.00
5	13.50

continued

8. Compare the properties of each function.

Function A

The table below shows the remaining balance, $f(x)$, of the cost of pool repairs after x months.

x	$f(x)$
0	1200
2	1050
4	900
6	750

Function B

The graph below shows the remaining balance, $g(x)$, of the cost of pool repairs after x months.

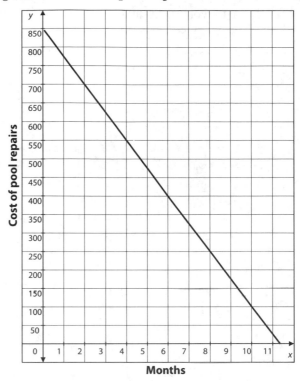

9. Compare the properties of each function. What do the rate of change and y-intercept mean in terms of the scenarios?

Function A

The function $f(x) = 12.5 - 0.32x$ represents $f(x)$, the amount of cat food remaining in pounds when a cat is fed the same amount each day for x days.

Function B

The table represents $g(x)$, the amount of cat food remaining in pounds when a cat is fed the same amount each day for x days.

x	$g(x)$
3	9.04
4	8.72
5	8.40
6	8.08

continued

UNIT 2 • LINEAR AND EXPONENTIAL RELATIONSHIPS
Lesson 6: Comparing Functions

10. Compare the properties of each function. What do the rate of change and *y*-intercept mean in terms of the scenarios?

Function A	**Function B**

Function A

Sophie ran 8 miles last week and plans to run 2 miles each additional week.

Function B

The graph below represents Kaelina's running plan.

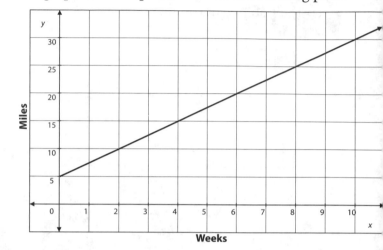

Lesson 2.6.2: Comparing Exponential Functions

Introduction

Exponential functions are functions that can be written in the form $f(x) = ab^x$, where a is the initial value, b is the rate of decay or growth, x is the time, and $f(x)$ is the final output value. The **growth factor** is the multiple by which a quantity increases or decreases over time. The **rate of change** of an exponential function can be calculated using the formula $slope = \dfrac{y_2 - y_1}{x_2 - x_1}$, over a specified interval. An interval is a continuous series of values. The y-intercept is the point at which the function crosses the y-axis and has the point $(0, y)$. Both the rate of change and y-intercept can be determined from tables, equations, and graphs. Exponential functions can also be compared to one another using these features.

Key Concepts

- Exponential functions can be represented in words or as equations, graphs, or tables.

- To compare exponential functions, determine the rate of change and the intercepts of each function.

- Review the following processes for identifying the rate of change and the y-intercept of an exponential function.

Identifying the Rate of Change and the y-intercept from Context
1. Determine the interval to be observed.
2. Create a table of values by choosing appropriate x-values, substituting them, and solving for $f(x)$.
3. Choose two points from the table.
4. Assign one point to be (x_1, y_1) and the other point to be (x_2, y_2).
5. Substitute the values into the slope formula, $\dfrac{y_2 - y_1}{x_2 - x_1}$.
6. The result is the rate of change for the interval between the two points chosen.
7. Determine which information tells you the y-intercept, or b. This could be an initial value or a starting value, a flat fee, and so forth.

Identifying the Rate of Change and the y-intercept from Exponential Equations

1. Determine the interval to be observed.

2. Determine (x_1, y_1) by identifying the starting x-value of the interval and substituting it into the function.

3. Solve for $f(x)$.

4. Determine (x_2, y_2) by identifying the ending x-value of the interval and substituting it into the function.

5. Solve for $f(x)$.

6. Substitute (x_1, y_1) and (x_2, y_2) into the slope formula, $\dfrac{y_2 - y_1}{x_2 - x_1}$, to calculate the rate of change.

7. Determine the y-intercept by substituting 0 for x and solving for $f(x)$.

Identifying the Rate of Change and the y-intercept from a Table

1. Determine the interval to be observed.

2. Assign one point to be (x_1, y_1) and the other point to be (x_2, y_2).

3. Substitute the values into the slope formula, $\dfrac{y_2 - y_1}{x_2 - x_1}$.

4. The result is the rate of change for the interval between the two points chosen.

5. Identify the y-intercept as the coordinate in the form $(0, y)$.

Identifying the Rate of Change and the y-intercept from a Graph

1. Determine the interval to be observed.

2. Identify (x_1, y_1) as the starting point of the interval.

3. Identify (x_2, y_2) as the ending point of the interval.

4. Substitute (x_1, y_1) and (x_2, y_2) into the slope formula, $\dfrac{y_2 - y_1}{x_2 - x_1}$, to calculate the rate of change.

5. Identify the y-intercept as the coordinate in the form $(0, y)$.

- You can compare the functions once you have identified the rate of change and the y-intercept of each function.

- Exponential functions are increasing if the rate of change is a positive value.

- Exponential functions are decreasing if the rate of change is a negative value.

- The greater the rate of change, the steeper the line connecting the points of the interval will appear on the graph.

Guided Practice 2.6.2

Example 1

Compare the properties of each of the following two functions over the interval [0, 16].

Function A

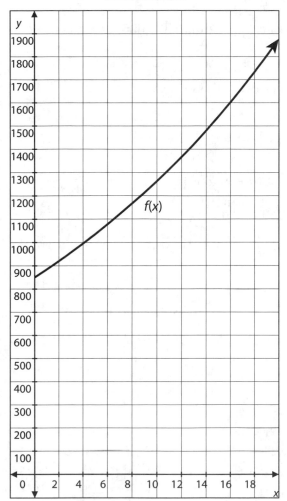

f(x)

Function B

x	$g(x)$
0	850
4	976.55
8	1121.94
12	1288.98
16	1480.88

1. Compare the *y*-intercepts of each function.

   Identify the *y*-intercept of the graphed function, $f(x)$.

   The graphed function appears to cross the *y*-axis at the point (0, 850).

   According to the table, the second function, $g(x)$ has a *y*-intercept of (0, 850).

   Both functions have a *y*-intercept of (0, 850).

2. Compare the rate of change for each function over the interval [0, 16].

Calculate the rate of change over the interval [0, 16] for $f(x)$.

Let $(x_1, y_1) = (0, 850)$.

Determine (x_2, y_2) from the graph.

The value of y when x is 16 is approximately 1,600.

Let $(x_2, y_2) = (16, 1600)$.

Calculate the rate of change using the slope formula.

$\dfrac{y_2 - y_1}{x_2 - x_1}$ Slope formula

$\dfrac{1600 - 850}{16 - 0}$ Substitute (0, 850) and (16, 1600) for (x_1, y_1) and (x_2, y_2).

$\dfrac{750}{16}$ Simplify as needed.

46.875

The rate of change for the graphed function is approximately 47.

Calculate the rate of change over the interval [0, 16] for $g(x)$.

Let $(x_1, y_1) = (0, 850)$.

Determine (x_2, y_2) from the table.

The value of y when x is 16 is 1,480.88.

Let $(x_2, y_2) = (16, 1480.88)$.

(continued)

Calculate the rate of change using the slope formula.

$$\frac{y_2 - y_1}{x_2 - x_1}$$ Slope formula

$$\frac{1480.88 - 850}{16 - 0}$$ Substitute (0, 850) and (16, 1480.88) for (x_1, y_1) and (x_2, y_2).

$$\frac{630.88}{16}$$ Simplify as needed.

39.43

The rate of change for $g(x)$ is 39.43.

The rate of change for the graphed function, $f(x)$, is greater over the interval [0, 16] than the rate of change for the function in the table, $g(x)$.

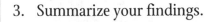

3. Summarize your findings.

The y-intercepts of both functions are the same; however, the graphed function has a greater rate of change over the interval [0, 16].

Example 2

A Petri dish contains 8 bacteria that double every 15 minutes. Compare the properties of the function that represents this situation to another population of bacteria, graphed below, that starts with 8 organisms over the interval [150, 210].

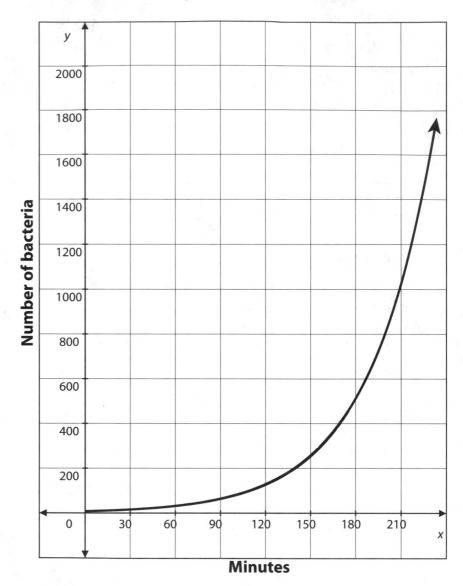

1. Compare the *y*-intercepts of each function.

   According to the scenario, the starting number of bacteria for both functions is 8; therefore, the *y*-intercept is (0, 8).

2. Compare the rate of change for each function over the interval [150, 210].

Calculate the rate of change over the interval [150, 210] for the graphed function.

Determine (x_1, y_1) from the graph.

The value of y when x is 150 is approximately 275.

Let $(x_1, y_1) = (150, 275)$.

Determine (x_2, y_2) from the graph.

The value of y when x is 210 is approximately 1,000.

Let $(x_2, y_2) = (210, 1000)$.

Calculate the rate of change using the slope formula.

$$\frac{y_2 - y_1}{x_2 - x_1}$$ Slope formula

$$\frac{1000 - 275}{210 - 150}$$ Substitute (150, 275) and (210, 1000) for (x_1, y_1) and (x_2, y_2).

$$\frac{725}{60}$$ Simplify as needed.

$$\approx 12$$

The rate of change for the graphed function is approximately 12 bacteria per minute.

To determine the rate of change for the function in the scenario, first write a function rule to represent the situation.

$$f(x) = 8(2)^{\frac{x}{15}}$$

Determine the value for y when x is 150 using the function.

$$f(x) = 8(2)^{\frac{x}{15}}$$ Original function

$$f(x) = 8(2)^{\frac{150}{15}}$$ Substitute 150 for x.

$$f(150) = 8(2)^{10}$$ Simplify as needed.

(*continued*)

$f(150) = 8(1024)$

$f(150) = 8192$

$(x_1, y_1) = (150, 8192)$

Determine the value for y when x is 210 using the function.

$f(x) = 8(2)^{\frac{x}{15}}$ Original function

$f(x) = 8(2)^{\frac{210}{15}}$ Substitute 210 for x.

$f(210) = 8(2)^{14}$ Simplify as needed.

$f(210) = 8(16,384)$

$f(210) = 131,072$

$(x_2, y_2) = (210, 131,072)$

Calculate the rate of change using the slope formula.

$\dfrac{y_2 - y_1}{x_2 - x_1}$ Slope formula

$\dfrac{131,072 - 8192}{210 - 150}$ Substitute (150, 8192) and (210, 131,072) for (x_1, y_1) and (x_2, y_2).

$\dfrac{122,880}{60}$ Simplify as needed.

2048

The rate of change for the function in the table is 2,048 bacteria per minute.

The rate of change for the graphed function is less steep over the interval [150, 210] than the rate of change for the scenario function.

3. Summarize your findings.

The y-intercepts of both functions are the same; however, the graphed function is less steep over the interval [150, 210]. The bacteria in the graphed function are doubling at a slower rate than the first function described.

Example 3

A pendulum swings to 90% of its previous height. Pendulum A starts at a height of 50 centimeters. Its height at each swing is modeled by the function $f(x) = 50(0.90)^x$. The height after every fifth swing of Pendulum B is recorded in the following table. Compare the properties of each function over the interval [5, 15].

x	$f(x)$
0	100
5	59.05
10	34.87
15	20.59
20	12.16

1. Compare the y-intercepts of each function.

   Identify the y-intercept of Pendulum A.

   The problem states that the pendulum starts at a height of 50 centimeters.

   The y-intercept of the function is (0, 50).

   Identify the y-intercept of Pendulum B.

   The value of $f(x)$ is 100 when x is 0.

   The y-intercept of the function is (0, 100).

2. Compare the rate of change for each function over the interval [5, 15].

Calculate the rate of change over the interval [5, 15] for Pendulum A.

Determine (x_1, y_1) from the function.

$f(x) = 50(0.90)^x$ — Original function

$f(5) = 50(0.90)^5$ — Substitute 5 for x.

$f(5) = 29.52$ — Simplify as needed.

Let $(x_1, y_1) = (5, 29.52)$.

Determine (x_2, y_2) from the function.

$f(x) = 50(0.90)^x$ — Original function

$f(15) = 50(0.90)^{15}$ — Substitute 15 for x.

$f(15) \approx 10.29$ — Simplify as needed.

The value of y when x is 15 is approximately 10.29.

Let $(x_2, y_2) = (15, 10.29)$.

Calculate the rate of change using the slope formula.

$$\frac{y_2 - y_1}{x_2 - x_1}$$ — Slope formula

$$\frac{10.29 - 29.52}{15 - 5}$$ — Substitute (5, 29.52) and (15, 10.29) for (x_1, y_1) and (x_2, y_2).

$$\frac{-19.23}{10} = -1.923$$ — Simplify as needed.

The rate of change for Pendulum A's function is approximately −1.923 centimeters per swing.

(*continued*)

Calculate the rate of change over the interval [5, 15] for Pendulum B.

Let $(x_1, y_1) = (5, 59.05)$.

Let $(x_2, y_2) = (15, 20.59)$.

Calculate the rate of change using the slope formula.

$$\frac{y_2 - y_1}{x_2 - x_1}$$ Slope formula

$$\frac{20.59 - 59.05}{15 - 5}$$ Substitute (5, 59.05) and (15, 20.59) for (x_1, y_1) and (x_2, y_2).

$$\frac{-38.46}{10} = -3.846$$ Simplify as needed.

The rate of change for Pendulum B's function is approximately −3.846 centimeters per swing.

The rate of change for Pendulum B is greater over the interval [5, 15] than the rate of change for Pendulum A.

3. Summarize your findings.

The y-intercept of Pendulum A is less than the y-intercept of Pendulum B. This means that Pendulum B begins higher than Pendulum A. The rate of change for Pendulum A is less than the rate of change for Pendulum B. This means that Pendulum B is losing height faster than Pendulum A.

UNIT 2 • LINEAR AND EXPONENTIAL RELATIONSHIPS
Lesson 6: Comparing Functions

Practice 2.6.2: Comparing Exponential Functions

Compare the properties of the exponential functions.

1. Which function has a greater rate of change over the interval [3, 6]? Which function has the greater *y*-intercept? Explain how you know.

Function A

x	*f(x)*
0	25
3	1600
4	6400
6	102,400

Function B

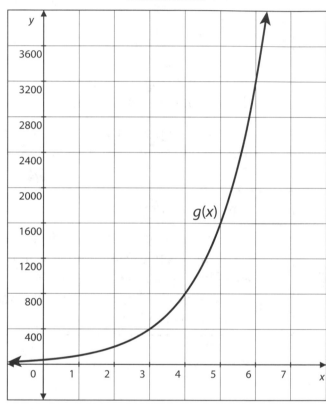

2. Which function has a greater rate of change over the interval [0, 4]? Which function has the greater *y*-intercept?

Function A

$$f(x) = 3^x$$

Function B

$$g(x) = \left(\frac{1}{3}\right)^x$$

continued

3. Compare the properties of each function over the interval [4, 10].

Function A

$$f(x) = 250\left(1 + \frac{0.05}{12}\right)^{12x}$$

Function B

x	$g(x)$
0	300
2	324.94
4	351.96
6	381.22
8	412.92
10	447.25
12	484.44

4. Compare the properties of each function over the interval [1, 4].

Function A

$$f(x) = 4\left(\frac{5}{2}\right)^x$$

Function B

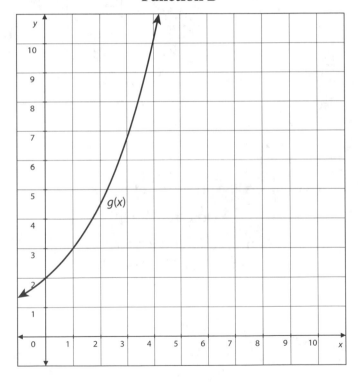

continued

UNIT 2 • LINEAR AND EXPONENTIAL RELATIONSHIPS
Lesson 6: Comparing Functions

5. Compare the properties of each exponential function over the interval [0,5].

Function A

Geoff and Hazel bought a new car for $25,000. The car loses approximately 15% of its value each year.

Function B

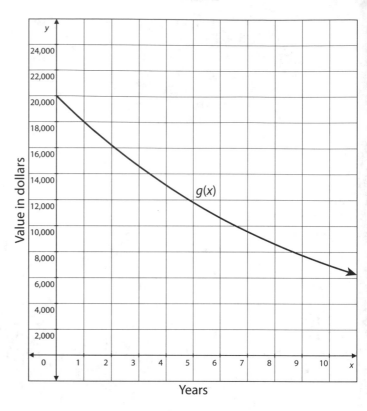

6. Compare the properties of each exponential function over the interval [0, 5].

Function A

Mr. Annear received a job offer with a starting salary of $40,000 and a 2.5% increase each year.

Function B

Mr. Annear received a second job offer that can be described by the function $g(x) = 42,500(1 + 0.02)^x$.

continued

UNIT 2 • LINEAR AND EXPONENTIAL RELATIONSHIPS
Lesson 6: Comparing Functions

7. Compare the properties of each exponential function over the interval [0, 20].

Function A

The enrollment of Oceanside High School, $f(x)$, after x years is modeled by the function $f(x) = 930(1 + 0.013)^x$.

Function B

The enrollment of Oceanside's rival is shown in the table below.

x	$g(x)$
0	875
4	985
8	1109
12	1249
16	1406
20	1583

8. Compare the properties of each exponential function over the interval [0,15].

Function A

The table shows the value in dollars of a rare coin, $f(x)$, x years from the date purchased.

x	$f(x)$
0	17.50
5	40.00
10	175.00
15	200.00

Function B

The graph models the value in dollars of another rare coin, $g(x)$, x years from the date purchased.

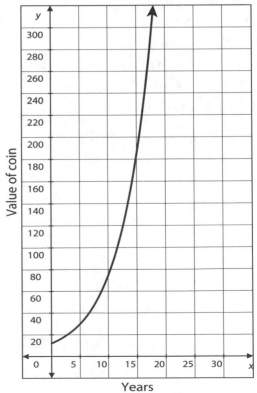

continued

9. Compare the properties of each exponential function over the interval [0, 4].

Function A

The value in dollars of a car $f(x)$ depreciates after each year x. The table below shows the value of a car for each of the first 4 years after it was purchased.

x	$f(x)$
0	32,000
1	25,600
2	20,480
3	16,384
4	13,107

Function B

The value in dollars of a second car is modeled by the equation $g(x) = 27,500(1 - 0.15)^x$, where $g(x)$ represents the value of the car x years from the date purchased.

10. Compare the properties of each exponential function over the interval [0, 10].

Function A

Your parents have $2,500 to invest for your college education fund. They find an account where the investment can earn 3.655%, compounded monthly.

Function B

The value of a second investment is modeled in the graph below.

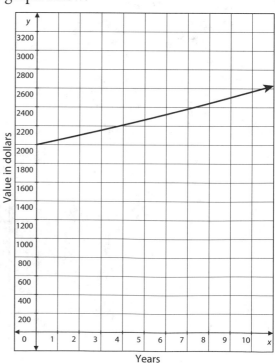

Lesson 2.6.3: Comparing Linear to Exponential Functions

Introduction

In previous lessons, linear functions were compared to linear functions and exponential functions to exponential. In this lesson, the properties of linear functions will be compared to properties of exponential functions.

Key Concepts

- Linear functions are written in the form $f(x) = mx + b$.

- A **factor** is one of two or more numbers or expressions that when multiplied produce a given product.

- The variable of a linear function is a factor of the function.

- As the value of x increases, the value of $f(x)$ will increase at a constant rate.

- The rate of change of linear functions remains constant.

- Exponential functions are written in the form $g(x) = ab^x$.

- The variable of an exponential function is part of the exponent.

- As the value of x increases, the value of $g(x)$ will increase by a multiple of b.

- As discussed previously, the rate of change of an exponential function varies depending on the interval observed.

- Graphs of exponential functions of the form $g(x) = ab^x$, where b is greater than 1, will increase faster than graphs of linear functions of the form $f(x) = mx + b$.

- A quantity that increases exponentially will always eventually exceed a quantity that increases linearly.

Guided Practice 2.6.3

Example 1

Which function increases faster, $f(x) = 4x - 5$ or $g(x) = 4^x - 5$? Justify your answer with a graph.

1. Make a general observation.

   $f(x) = 4x - 5$ is a linear function of the form $f(x) = mx + b$.

   The variable x is multiplied by the coefficient 4.

   $g(x) = 4^x - 5$ is an exponential function of the form $g(x) = ab^x$.

   The variable x is the exponent.

2. Create a table of values.

   Substitute values for x into each function.

$f(x) = 4x - 5$		$g(x) = 4^x - 5$	
x	$f(x)$	x	$g(x)$
−2	−13	−2	−4.9375
−1	−9	−1	−4.75
0	−5	0	−4
1	−1	1	−1
2	3	2	11

3. Graph both functions on the same coordinate plane.

   Use the tables of values created in order to plot both functions.

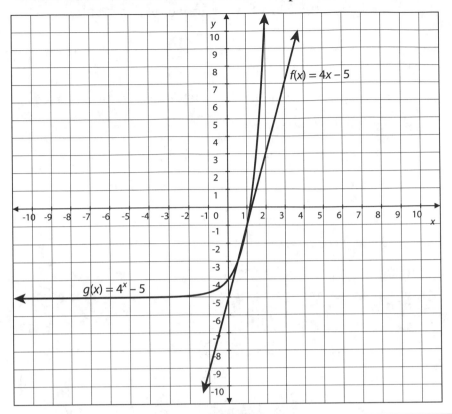

4. Compare the rate of change of each function.

   The graph of $f(x) = 4x - 5$ appears to be steeper than the graph of $g(x) = 4^x - 5$ until the point $(1, -2)$. At this point, the graphs of both functions appear to be equal. Once x is greater than 1, the graph of $g(x) = 4^x - 5$ becomes steeper. From there, $g(x) = 4^x - 5$ increases faster than $f(x) = 4x - 5$.

Example 2

At approximately what point does the value of $f(x)$ exceed the value of $g(x)$ if $f(x)=2(4)^{\frac{x}{20}}$ and $g(x) = 0.5x$? Justify your answer with a graph.

1. Make a general observation.

   $f(x)=2(4)^{\frac{x}{20}}$ is an exponential function of the form $g(x) = ab^x$.

   The variable x is the exponent.

   $g(x) = 0.5x$ is a linear function of the form $f(x) = mx + b$.

   The variable x is multiplied by the coefficient 0.5.

2. Create a table of values.

   Substitute values for x into each function.

$f(x)=2(4)^{\frac{x}{20}}$		$g(x) = 0.5x$	
x	$f(x)$	x	$g(x)$
0	2	0	0
2	2.30	2	1
4	2.64	4	2
6	3.03	6	3

3. Graph both functions on the same coordinate plane.

Use the tables of values created in order to plot both functions.

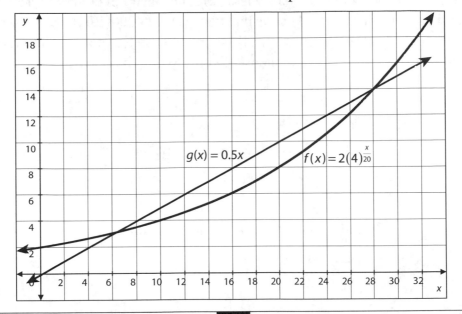

4. Identify the approximate point where $f(x)$ is greater than $g(x)$.

It can be seen from the graph that both functions are equal where x is approximately equal to 28. When x is greater than 28, $f(x)$ is greater than $g(x)$.

Example 3

Lena has been offered a job with two salary options. The first option is modeled by the function $f(x) = 500x + 31{,}000$, where $f(x)$ is her salary in dollars after x years. The second option is represented by the function $g(x) = 29{,}000(1.04)^x$, where $g(x)$ is her salary in dollars after x years. If Lena is hoping to keep this position for at least 5 years, which salary option should she choose? Support your answer with a graph.

1. Make a general observation.

   $f(x) = 500x + 31{,}000$ is a linear function of the form $f(x) = mx + b$.

   The variable x is multiplied by the coefficient 500 and added to the constant 31,000.

   $g(x) = 29{,}000(1.04)^x$ is an exponential function of the form $g(x) = ab^x$.

   The variable x is the exponent.

   Create a table of values.

   Substitute values for x into each function.

$f(x) = 500x + 31{,}000$		$g(x) = 29{,}000(1.04)^x$	
x	$f(x)$	x	$g(x)$
0	31,000	0	29,000
2	32,000	2	31,366.40
4	33,000	4	33,925.90
6	34,000	6	36,694.25

2. Graph both functions on the same coordinate plane.

   Use the tables of values created in order to plot both functions.

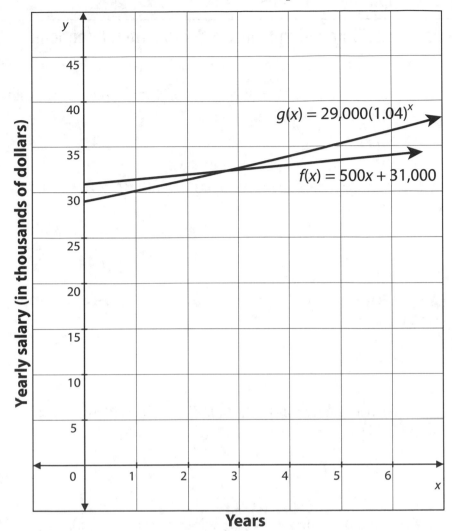

3. Identify the approximate point where $g(x)$ is greater than $f(x)$.

   It can be seen from the graph that after 3 years, $g(x)$ is greater than $f(x)$. If Lena is hoping to keep this position for at least 5 years, it is in her best interest to choose the salary option modeled by $g(x) = 29{,}000(1.04)^x$.

UNIT 2 • LINEAR AND EXPONENTIAL RELATIONSHIPS
Lesson 6: Comparing Functions

Practice 2.6.3: Comparing Linear to Exponential Functions

Use what you know about linear and exponential functions to complete problems 1–6.

1. Which increases faster, $f(x) = 4x$ or $g(x) = 3^x$? Justify your answer using a graph.

2. Which increases faster, $f(x) = 4x + 3$ or $g(x) = 4^x + 3$? Justify your answer using a table of values.

3. Which decreases faster, $f(x) = 200(0.82)^x$ or $g(x) = 200 - 8.2x$? Justify your answer using a graph.

4. Which decreases faster, $f(x) = 2000(0.75)^x$ or $g(x) = 2000 - 0.25x$? Justify your answer using a table of values.

5. At what point does the value of $f(x)$ exceed the value of $g(x)$ if $f(x) = 3(2)^{\frac{x}{2}}$ and $g(x) = 3x + 2$? Justify your answer with a graph.

6. At what point does the value of $f(x)$ exceed the value of $g(x)$ if $f(x) = 200(1.194)^{\frac{x}{8}}$ and $g(x) = 8x + 225$? Justify your answer with a graph.

continued

UNIT 2 • LINEAR AND EXPONENTIAL RELATIONSHIPS
Lesson 6: Comparing Functions

Use the following information to answer questions 7–10.

You are looking to invest $1,200. One savings option follows the

function $f(x) = 1200 + 1200(0.055)x$, where $f(x)$ is the amount of money

in savings after x years. The second option is represented by the function

$g(x) = 1200\left(1 + \dfrac{0.035}{12}\right)^{12x}$, where $g(x)$ is the amount of money after

x years.

7. Which increases faster, $f(x)$ or $g(x)$? Use a graph to explain your answer.

8. After what point does the value of $g(x)$ exceed the value of $f(x)$?

9. If you were looking to invest your money for less than 10 years, which option would you choose? Explain your reasoning.

10. If you were looking to invest your money for more than 25 years, which option would you choose? Explain your reasoning.

Lesson 7: Building Functions

Common Core State Standards

F–BF.1   Write a function that describes a relationship between two quantities. ★

a. Determine an explicit expression, a recursive process, or steps for calculation from a context.

F–LE.2   Construct linear and exponential functions, including arithmetic and geometric sequences, given a graph, a description of a relationship, or two input-output pairs (include reading these from a table). ★

Essential Questions

1. How can an unknown quantity be represented in an expression or an equation?

2. What is the difference between the slope of a linear function and the slope of an exponential function?

3. What is the difference between the shape of the graph of a linear function and the shape of the graph of an exponential function?

WORDS TO KNOW

equation	a mathematical sentence that uses an equal sign (=) to show that two quantities are equal
explicit equation	an equation describing the nth term of a pattern
exponential equation	an equation that has a variable in the exponent; the general form is $y = a \cdot b^x$, where a is the initial value, b is the base, x is the time, and y is the final output value
expression	a combination of variables, quantities, and mathematical operations; 4, $8x$, and $b + 10^2$ are all expressions.
function	a relation in which each element in the domain is mapped to exactly one element in the range; that is, for every value of x, there is exactly one value of y

linear equation	an equation that can be written in the form $ax + by = c$, where a, b, and c are rational numbers; can also be written as $y = mx + b$, in which m is the slope, b is the y-intercept, and the graph is a straight line
slope	the measure of the rate of change of one variable with respect to another variable; $\text{slope} = \dfrac{y_2 - y_1}{x_2 - x_1} = \dfrac{\Delta y}{\Delta x} = \dfrac{\text{rise}}{\text{run}}$
variable	a letter used to represent a value or unknown quantity that can change or vary in an expression or equation
y-intercept	the point at which the line intersects the y-axis at $(0, y)$

Recommended Resources

- Discovery Education. "Find the Equation of a Line Given that You Know Two Points It Passes Through."

  http://walch.com/rr/CAU3L6LinearEquationGenerator

  Input two coordinate pairs to have the computer generate a linear equation. The user is then walked through a step-by-step process for the input coordinate pairs that also explains how to find the equation in slope-intercept form.

- Kennesaw State University. "The Role of a and b in $y = ab^x$."

  http://walch.com/rr/CAU3L6ExponentialFunctionApplet

  Users can manipulate this applet by using sliders to change the values of a and b in the equation $y = ab^x$. The graph is instantly modified as the sliders are moved.

Lesson 2.7.1: Building Functions from Context

Introduction

Verbal descriptions of mathematical patterns and situations can be represented using equations and expressions. A **variable** is a letter used to represent a value or unknown quantity that can change or vary in an expression or equation. An **expression** is a combination of variables, quantities, and mathematical operations; 4, $8x$, and $b + 10^2$ are all expressions. An **equation** is an expression set equal to another expression; $a = 4$, $1 + 2^3 = x + 9$, and $(2 + 3)^1 = 2c$ are all equations.

Drawing a model can help clarify a situation. When examining a pattern, look for changes in quantities. A **function** is a relation between two variables, where one is independent and the other is dependent. For each independent variable there is only one dependent variable. One way to generalize a functional relationship is to write an equation. A linear function can be represented using a linear equation. A **linear equation** relates two variables, and both variables are raised to the 1st power; the equation $s = 2r - 7$ is a linear equation. The slope-intercept form of a linear equation is $y = mx + b$. The form of a linear function is similar, $f(x) = mx + b$, where x is the independent quantity, m is the slope, b is the y-intercept, and $f(x)$ is the function evaluated at x or the dependent quantity. The **slope**, or the measure of the rate of change of one variable with respect to another variable, between any two pairs of independent and dependent quantities is constant if the relationship between the quantities is linear. Consecutive terms in a pattern have a common difference if the pattern is linear.

An exponential function can be represented using an exponential equation. An **exponential equation** relates two variables, and a constant in the equation is raised to a variable; the equation $w = 3^v$ is an exponential equation. The general form of an exponential equation is $y = ab^x$. The form of an exponential function is similar, $f(x) = ab^x$, where a and b are real numbers. Terms have a common ratio if the pattern is exponential. An **explicit equation** describes the nth term of a pattern, and is the algebraic representation of a relationship between two quantities. An equation that represents a function, such as $f(x) = 2x$, is one type of explicit equation. Evaluating an equation for known term numbers is a good way to determine if an explicit equation correctly describes a pattern.

Key Concepts

- A situation that has a mathematical pattern can be represented using an equation.

- A variable is a letter used to represent an unknown quantity.

- An expression is a combination of variables, quantities, and mathematical operations.

- An equation is an expression set equal to another expression.

- An explicit equation describes the nth term in a pattern.

- A linear equation relates two variables, and each variable is raised to the 1st power.

- The general equation to represent a linear function is $f(x) = mx + b$, where m is the slope and b is the y-intercept.

- An exponential equation relates two variables, and a constant in the equation is raised to a variable.

- The general equation to represent an exponential function is $f(x) = ab^x$, where a and b are real numbers.

- Consecutive dependent terms in a linear function have a common difference.

- If consecutive terms in a linear pattern have an independent quantity that increases by 1, the common difference is the slope of the relationship between the two quantities.

- Use the slope of a linear relationship and a single pair of independent and dependent values to find the linear equation that represents the relationship. Use the general equation $f(x) = mx + b$, and replace m with the slope, $f(x)$ with the dependent quantity, and x with the independent quantity. Solve for b.

- Consecutive dependent terms in an exponential function have a common ratio.

- Use the common ratio to find the exponential equation that describes the relationship between two quantities. In the general equation $f(x) = ab^x$, b is the common ratio. Let a_0 be the value of the dependent quantity when the independent quantity is 0. The general equation to represent the relationship would be: $f(x) = a_0 b^x$. Let a_1 be the value of the dependent quantity when the independent quantity is 1. The general equation to represent the relationship would be: $f(x) = a_1 b^{x-1}$.

- A model can be used to analyze a situation.

Guided Practice 2.7.1

Example 1

The starting balance of Anna's account is $1,250. She takes $30 out of her account each month. How much money is in her account after 1, 2, and 3 months? Find an equation to represent the balance in her account at any month.

1. Use the description of the account balance to find the balance after each month.

    Anna's account has $1,250. After 1 month, she takes out $30, so her account balance decreases by $30: $1250 – $30 = $1220.

    The new starting balance of Anna's account is $1,220. After 2 months, she takes out another $30. Subtract this $30 from the new balance of her account: $1220 – $30 = $1190.

    The new starting balance of Anna's account is $1,190. After 3 months, she takes out another $30. Subtract this $30 from the new balance of her account: $1190 – $30 = $1160.

2. Determine the independent and dependent quantities.

    The month number is the independent quantity, since the account balance depends on the month. The account balance is the dependent quantity.

3. Determine if there is a common difference or common ratio that describes the change in the dependent quantity.

   Organize your results in a table. Enter the independent quantity in the first column, and the dependent quantity in the second column. The balance at zero months is the starting balance of the account, before any money has been taken out. Because the independent quantity is changing by one unit, analyzing the differences between the dependent quantities will determine if there is a common difference between the dependent quantities.

Month	Account balance in dollars ($)	Difference
0	1250	
1	1220	$1250 - 1220 = -30$
2	1190	$1220 - 1190 = -30$
3	1160	$1190 - 1160 = -30$

   The account balance has a common difference; it decreases by $30 for every 1 month. The relationship between the month and the account balance can be represented using a linear function.

4. Use the common difference to write an explicit equation.

   The general form of a linear function is: $f(x) = mx + b$, where m is the slope and b is the y-intercept. The common difference between the dependent terms in the pattern is the slope of the relationship between the independent and dependent quantities. Replace m with the slope, and replace x and $f(x)$ with an independent and dependent quantity pair in the relationship, such as (1, 1220). Solve for b.

   $1220 = (-30) \cdot (1) + b$

   $1250 = b$

   $f(x) = -30x + 1250$

5. Evaluate the equation to verify that it is correct.

Organize your results in a table. Use the explicit equation to find each term. The terms that are calculated should match the terms in the original list.

Month, x	Account balance, $f(x)$, in dollars ($)
0	$(-30) \cdot (0) + 1250 = 1250$
1	$(-30) \cdot (1) + 1250 = 1220$
2	$(-30) \cdot (2) + 1250 = 1190$
3	$(-30) \cdot (3) + 1250 = 1160$

The pairs of dependent and independent quantities match the ones in the original pattern, so the explicit equation is correct.

The balance in Anna's account can be represented using the equation $f(x) = -30x + 1250$.

Example 2

Consider that the first figure below has two 180° angles, one on each side of the line segment. Each of these angles is then bisected or cut in half. This pattern continues, and the first 4 figures in the pattern are shown.

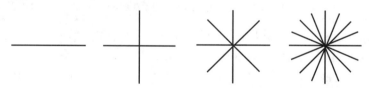

Write an equation to represent the relationship between the figure number and the number of angles in the figure.

1. Use the figures to determine the number of angles in figure numbers 1, 2, 3, and 4.

Count the angles in each figure, taking into consideration the note that the first figure has 2 angles.

Figure 1: 2 angles

Figure 2: 4 angles

Figure 3: 8 angles

Figure 4: 16 angles

2. Define the independent and dependent quantity.

The figure number is the independent quantity, and the number of angles in the figure is the dependent quantity.

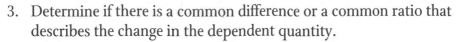

3. Determine if there is a common difference or a common ratio that describes the change in the dependent quantity.

Organize your results in a table. Enter the independent quantity in the first column, and the dependent quantity in the second column. The pattern appears to have a common ratio. Use a table to find the ratio between the terms. Divide the current term by the previous term.

Figure	Number of angles	Ratio
1	2	
2	4	$\dfrac{4}{2} = 2$
3	8	$\dfrac{8}{4} = 2$
4	16	$\dfrac{16}{8} = 2$

The common ratio between the dependent terms is 2.

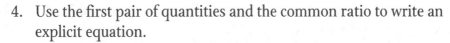

4. Use the first pair of quantities and the common ratio to write an explicit equation.

If b is the common ratio and a_1 is the value of the dependent quantity when the independent quantity is 1, then the general equation to represent the relationship is $f(x) = a_1 b^{x-1}$. In this case, $a_1 = 2$ and $b = 2$, so the equation to represent the relationship is $f(x) = 2 \cdot 2^{x-1}$.

5. Evaluate the equation to verify that it is correct.

Organize your results in a table. Use the explicit equation to find each dependent term. The terms that are calculated should match the terms in the original list.

Figure	Number of angles
1	$2 \cdot 2^{1-1} = 2$
2	$2 \cdot 2^{2-1} = 4$
3	$2 \cdot 2^{3-1} = 8$
4	$2 \cdot 2^{4-1} = 16$

The dependent terms match the ones in the original pattern, so the explicit equation is correct.

The relationship between the number of angles and the figure number can be described using the equation $f(x) = 2 \cdot 2^{x-1}$.

Example 3

A video arcade charges an entrance fee, then charges a fee per game played. The entrance fee is $5, and each game costs an additional $1. Find the total cost for playing 0, 1, 2, or 3 games. Describe the total cost with an explicit equation.

1. Use the description of the costs to find the total costs.

If no games are played, then only the entrance fee is paid. The total cost for playing 0 games is $5.

If 1 game is played, then the entrance fee is paid, plus the cost of one game. If each game is $1, the cost of one game is $1. The total cost is $5 + $1 = $6.

If 2 games are played, then the entrance fee is paid, plus the cost of two games. If each game is $1, the cost of two games is $1 \cdot 2 = $2. The total cost is $5 + $2 = $7.

If 3 games are played, then the entrance fee is paid, plus the cost of three games. If each game is $1, the cost of three games is $1 \cdot 3 = $3. The total cost is: $5 + $3 = $8.

2. Identify the independent and dependent quantities.

The total cost is dependent on the number of games played, so the number of games is the independent quantity and the total cost is the dependent quantity.

3. Determine if there is a common difference or a common ratio between the dependent terms.

There appears to be a common difference between the dependent terms. Use a table to find the difference between the dependent quantities. Subtract the current term from the previous term.

Games	Cost in dollars ($)	Difference
0	5	
1	6	$6 - 5 = 1$
2	7	$7 - 6 = 1$
3	8	$8 - 7 = 1$

The common difference between the dependent terms is $1.

4. Use the common difference to write an explicit equation.

The general form of a linear function is: $f(x) = mx + b$, where m is the slope and b is the y-intercept. The common difference between the dependent terms in the pattern is the slope of the relationship between the independent and dependent quantities. Replace m with the slope, and replace x and $f(x)$ with an independent and dependent quantity pair in the relationship, such as (1, 6). Solve for b.

$6 = (1) \bullet (1) + b$

$5 = b$

5. Evaluate the equation to verify that it is correct.

   Organize your results in a table. Use the explicit equation to find each term. The terms that are calculated should match the terms in the original list.

Games	Cost in dollars ($)
0	$1 \cdot (0) + 5 = 5$
1	$1 \cdot (1) + 5 = 6$
2	$1 \cdot (2) + 5 = 7$
3	$1 \cdot (3) + 5 = 8$

   The pairs of independent and dependent quantities match the ones in the original pattern, so the explicit equation is correct.

   The total cost of any number of games, x, can be represented using the equation: $f(x) = x + 5$.

UNIT 2 • LINEAR AND EXPONENTIAL RELATIONSHIPS
Lesson 7: Building Functions

Practice 2.7.1: Building Functions from Context

Write an explicit equation to represent each pattern.

1. Pedro is holding a fund-raiser. He is taking donations from his friends to support a charity. Each friend donates the same amount. The total amounts donated after 1, 2, 3, and 4 friends give money are $15, $30, $45, and $60, respectively.

2. Diana goes on vacation with $260. Each day, she spends the same amount of money. After 1, 2, 3, and 4 days on vacation, she has $242, $224, $206, and $188, respectively.

3. Gemma is picking blueberries. When she starts picking them, she has 7 berries in her bucket. After 1, 2, 3, and 4 minutes of picking berries, she has 16, 25, 34, and 43 total berries, respectively.

4. Housepainters work together to complete a painting project. One painter can paint 6 square feet in a minute. Two painters can paint 24 square feet in a minute. Three painters can paint 96 square feet in a minute, and four painters can paint 384 square feet in a minute.

5. Isaac records the temperature of a cup of water each minute. At 0 minutes, the water starts at 60°F. After 1, 2, and 3 minutes, the temperature is 54°F, 48.6°F, and 43.74°F, respectively.

6. Given the diagram that follows, describe the number of triangles in Figure x.

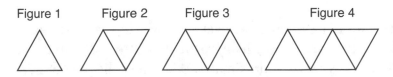

Figure 1   Figure 2   Figure 3   Figure 4

continued

UNIT 2 • LINEAR AND EXPONENTIAL RELATIONSHIPS
Lesson 7: Building Functions

7. Given the diagram that follows, describe the number of squares in Figure x.

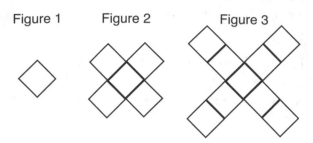

Figure 1   Figure 2   Figure 3

8. The number of end points is increasing from figure to figure in the diagram below. Write an explicit equation to find the total number of end points in any figure.

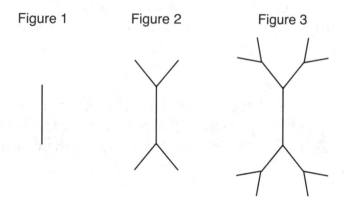

Figure 1   Figure 2   Figure 3

9. An overnight shipping service charges a fixed fee of $10.00, plus an additional fee based on the weight of the item being shipped. The service charges an additional $0.25 for each pound. Find an explicit equation to represent the shipping charge for a package of any weight.

10. The value of a car decreases over time. Mario's car was originally worth $15,000. Each year, his car is worth approximately 20% less than the year before; in other words, it decreases approximately 0.20 times the previous year's worth. Find an explicit equation to represent the value of the car in any year.

Lesson 2.7.2: Constructing Functions from Graphs and Tables

Introduction

Tables and graphs can be represented by equations. Data represented in a table can either be analyzed as a pattern, like the data presented in the previous lesson, or it can be graphed first. The shape of a graph helps identify which type of equation can be used to represent the data. Data that is represented using a linear equation has a constant slope and the graph is a straight line. The general form of a linear equation is $y = mx + b$, where m is the slope and b is the y-intercept. The y-intercept is the point at which the graph intersects the y-axis. To find the equation of a line, first find the slope, then replace x and y in the general equation with x and y from an ordered pair on the graph. Then, solve the equation for b.

The slope of a line is the change in the independent variable divided by the change in the dependent variable, and describes the rate of change of the variables. Using the points (x_1, y_1) and (x_2, y_2), the slope can be calculated by finding $\dfrac{\left(y_2 - y_1\right)}{\left(x_2 - x_1\right)}$. The slope is similar to the common difference between terms, except the slope can be found between points that have x-values that are more than one unit apart. The slope allows us to compare the change between any two points on a graph or in a table. An exponential equation has a slope that is constantly changing, either increasing or decreasing. Graphically, exponential equations are a curve. The general form of an exponential equation is $y = ab^x$, where a and b are real numbers, and b is the common ratio. The values of a and b change the shape of the graph of an exponential function. On the following pages, you'll find four examples of functions with different a and b values.

$a > 0$ and $b > 1$

$f(x) = 2^x$

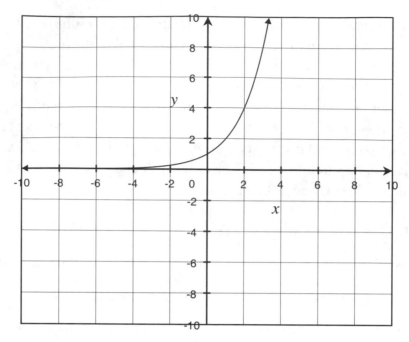

$a > 0$ and $0 < b < 1$

$f(x) = (0.5)^x$

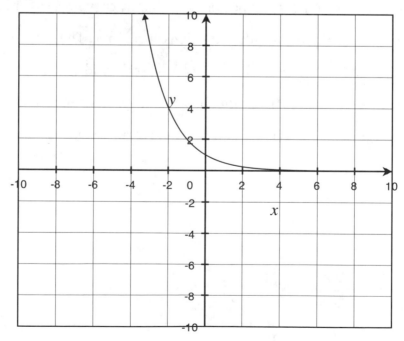

$a < 0$ and $b > 1$

$f(x) = (-1) \cdot 2^x$

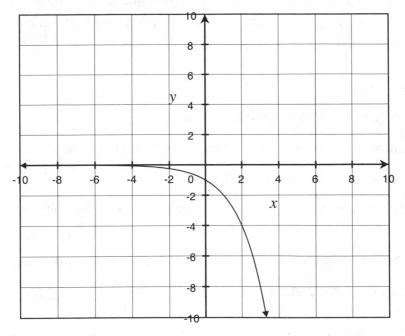

$a < 0$ and $0 < b < 1$

$f(x) = -1\left(\dfrac{1}{2}\right)^x$

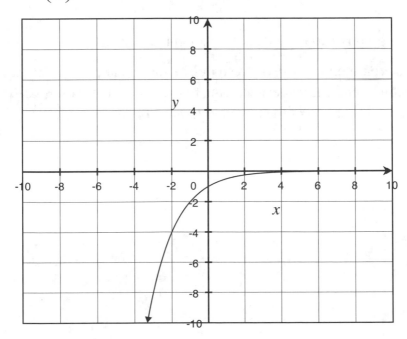

Data that follows an exponential pattern has a common ratio between the dependent quantities. When looking for the common ratio, be sure to verify that the x-values, or independent quantities, are each one unit apart. The common ratio, b, can be used to write an equation to represent the exponential pattern. Find the value of the equation at $x = 0$, $f(0)$. The general equation of the function is $f(x) = f(0) \cdot b^x$.

Key Concepts

- The graph of a linear equation is a straight line.

- Linear equations have a constant slope, or rate of change.

- Linear equations can be written as functions.

- The general form of a linear function is $f(x) = mx + b$, where m is the slope and b is the y-intercept.

- The slope of a linear function can be calculated using any two points, (x_1, y_1) and (x_2, y_2): the formula is $\dfrac{(y_2 - y_1)}{(x_2 - x_1)}$.

- The y-intercept is the point at which the graph of the equation crosses the y-axis.

- Exponential equations have a slope that is constantly changing.

- Exponential equations can be written as functions.

- The general form of an exponential function is $f(x) = ab^x$, where a and b are real numbers.

- The graph of an exponential equation is a curve.

- The common ratio, b, between independent quantities in an exponential pattern, and the value of the equation at $x = 0$, $f(0)$, can be used to write the general equation of the function: $f(x) = f(0) \cdot b^x$.

Guided Practice 2.7.2

Example 1

Determine the equation that represents the relationship between x and y in the graph below.

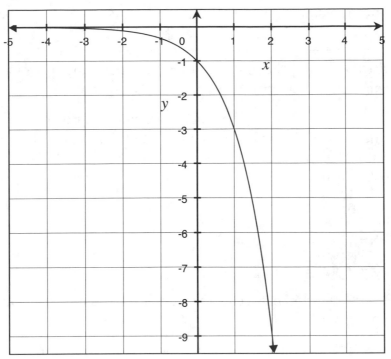

1. Determine which type of equation, linear or exponential, will fit the graph.

   The graph of a linear equation is a straight line, and a graph of an exponential equation is a curve. An exponential equation can be used to represent the graph.

2. Identify at least three points from the graph, with one of the points at $x = 0$.

   From the graph, three points are: $(0, -1)$, $(1, -3)$, and $(2, -9)$.

3. Find the common ratio between the terms, ensuring that the x-values are one unit apart.

   The three points are at the x-values 0, 1, and 2, so the x-values are each one unit apart. Look at the pattern of the y-values: -1, -3, and -9. Each value is multiplied by 3 to find the next value, so the common ratio is 3.

4. Use the value of the equation at $x = 0$ and the common ratio to write an equation to represent the graph.

   When $x = 0$, $f(0) = -1$. The exponential equation is: $f(x) = f(0) \cdot b^x$, where $f(0)$ is the value of the equation at $x = 0$ and b is the common ratio. The equation of the graph is: $f(x) = (-1) \cdot 3^x$. Check the equation by evaluating it at the values of x from previously identified points.

   $x = 0, f(0) = (-1) \cdot 3^0 = -1$

   $x = 1, f(1) = (-1) \cdot 3^1 = -3$

   $x = 2, f(2) = (-1) \cdot 3^2 = -9$

   The relationship between x and y can be represented using the equation $f(x) = (-1) \cdot 3^x$.

Example 2

Determine the equation that represents the relationship between x and y in the graph below.

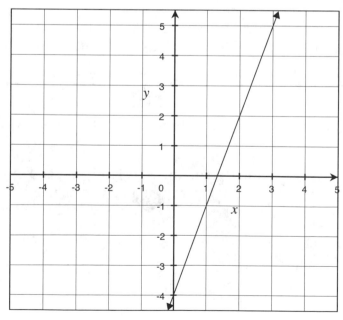

1. Determine which type of equation, linear or exponential, will fit the graph.

   The graph of a linear equation is a straight line, and a graph of an exponential equation is a curve. A linear equation can be used to represent the graph.

2. Identify at least three points from the graph.

   From the graph, three points are: (0, –4), (1, –1), and (2, 2).

3. Find the slope of the line, using any two of the points.

   The slope of the line is $\dfrac{(y_2 - y_1)}{(x_2 - x_1)}$ for any two points (x_1, y_1) and (x_2, y_2).
   Using the points (0, –4) and (1, –1), the slope is $\dfrac{(-1-(-4))}{(1-0)} = 3$.

4. Find the y-intercept of the line.

   The y-intercept can either be found by solving the equation $f(x) = mx + b$ for b, or by finding the value of y when $x = 0$. On the graph, we can see the point (0, –4). The y-intercept is –4.

5. Use the slope and y-intercept to find an equation of the line.

   The general form of the linear function is $f(x) = mx + b$, where m is the slope and b is the y-intercept. The equation to represent the line is $f(x) = 3x - 4$. Check the equation by evaluating it at the values of x from previously identified points.

   $x = 0, f(0) = 3(0) - 4 = -4$

   $x = 1, f(1) = 3(1) - 4 = -1$

   $x = 2, f(2) = 3(2) - 4 = 2$

   The relationship can be represented using the equation $f(x) = 3x - 4$.

Example 3

A clothing store discounts items on a regular schedule. Each week, the price of an item is reduced. The prices for one item are in the table below. Week 0 is the starting price of the item.

Week	Price in dollars ($)
0	100.00
1	60.00
2	36.00
3	21.60

Determine a linear or exponential equation that represents the relationship between the week and the price of the item.

1. Create a graph of the data.

   Let the x-axis represent the week, and the y-axis represent the price in dollars.

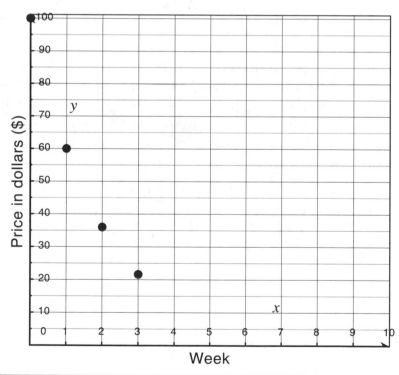

2. Determine if a linear or exponential equation could represent the data.

The x-values of the points vary by 1. Look at the vertical distance between each pair of points. It appears to be decreasing, and is not remaining constant. An exponential equation could represent the data.

3. Find the common ratio between the terms.

The four points are at the x-values 0, 1, 2, and 3, so the x-values are each one unit apart. Look at the pattern of the y-values: 100, 60, 36, and 21.60. Divide each y-value by the previous y-value to identify the common ratio.

y	Ratio
100	
60	$\dfrac{60}{100} = 0.60$
36	$\dfrac{36}{60} = 0.60$
21.6	$\dfrac{21.6}{36} = 0.60$

The common ratio is 0.60.

4. Use the value of the equation at $x = 0$ and the common ratio to write an equation to represent the relationship.

At week 0, the price is $100. The common ratio is 0.60. An equation to represent the relationship is $f(x) = 100 \cdot (0.60)^x$. Evaluate the equation at the given values of x to check the equation.

$x = 0, f(0) = 100 \cdot (0.60)^0 = 100$

$x = 1, f(1) = 100 \cdot (0.60)^1 = 60$

$x = 2, f(2) = 100 \cdot (0.60)^2 = 36$

$x = 3, f(3) = 100 \cdot (0.60)^3 = 21.6$

The price of the clothing item, y, at any week, x, can be represented by the equation $f(x) = 100 \cdot (0.60)^x$.

UNIT 2 • LINEAR AND EXPONENTIAL RELATIONSHIPS
Lesson 7: Building Functions

Practice 2.7.2: Constructing Functions from Graphs and Tables

Determine a linear or exponential equation that represents the relationship between x and y in each graph or table that follows.

1.

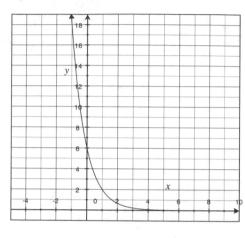

3.

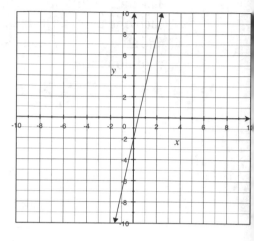

2.

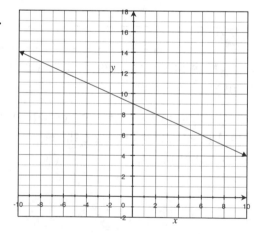

4.

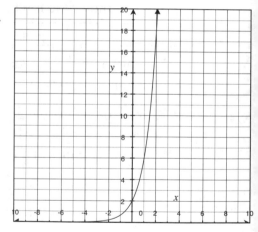

continued

UNIT 2 • LINEAR AND EXPONENTIAL RELATIONSHIPS
Lesson 7: Building Functions

5.

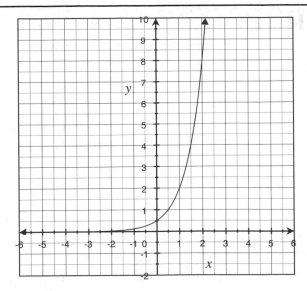

6.

x	y
0	82
3	37
4	22
5	7

9.

x	y
0	−0.5
1	−3
2	−18
3	−108
4	−648

7.

x	y
1	4
2	26
3	48
5	92

10.

x	y
0	0.2
1	1
2	5
3	25
4	125

8.

x	y
0	3
1	30
2	300
3	3000
4	30,000

Lesson 8: Operating on Functions and Transformations

Common Core State Standards

F–BF.1   Write a function that describes a relationship between two quantities. ★

        b. Combine standard function types using arithmetic operations. *For example, build a function that models the temperature of a cooling body by adding a constant function to a decaying exponential, and relate these functions to the model.*

F–BF.3   Identify the effect on the graph of replacing $f(x)$ by $f(x) + k$, $k\,f(x)$, $f(kx)$, and $f(x + k)$ for specific values of k (both positive and negative); find the value of k given the graphs. Experiment with cases and illustrate an explanation of the effects on the graph using technology. *Include recognizing even and odd functions from their graphs and algebraic expressions for them.*

Essential Questions

1. How can functions be combined by adding, subtracting, multiplying, or dividing?

2. How are the graph of a function and the equation of a function related?

3. How do transformations of the graph of a function relate to the function's equation?

WORDS TO KNOW

function	a relation in which each element in the domain is mapped to exactly one element in the range; that is, for every value of x, there is exactly one value of y
transformation	moving a graph, including reflections, rotations, and translations
translation	moving a graph either vertically, horizontally, or both, without changing its shape; a slide
vertical shift	number of units the graph of the function is moved up or down; a translation

Recommended Resources

- Interactivate. "Function Flyer."

  http://walch.com/rr/CAU3L7FunctionFlyer

  Users can manipulate the constants and coefficients in any function in order to explore the effects of those manipulations on the graph of the function.

- NCTM Illuminations. "Function Matching."

  http://walch.com/rr/CAU3L7FunctionMatching

  In this activity, users try to guess a function rule to match given graphs.

- Purplemath.com. "Operations on Functions."

  http://walch.com/rr/CAU3L7OperationsOnFunctions

  This site demonstrates how to add, subtract, multiply, or divide functions.

Lesson 2.8.1: Operating on Functions

Introduction

Functions are relations in which each element in the domain is mapped to exactly one element in the range; that is, for every value of x, there is exactly one value of y. In order to understand how functions are related, we need to understand how to perform different arithmetic operations on functions. In this lesson, we will add, subtract, multiply, and divide exponential and linear functions.

Key Concepts

- Combine linear and exponential expressions using addition: $(f + g)(x) = f(x) + g(x)$. In other words, add the two functions together by combining like terms.

- Combine linear and exponential expressions using subtraction: $(f - g)(x) = f(x) - g(x)$. In other words, subtract the second function from the first while making sure to distribute the negative across all terms of the second function.

- Combine linear and exponential expressions using multiplication: $(f \cdot g)(x) = f(x) \cdot g(x)$. In other words, multiply the two functions together.

- Combine linear and exponential expressions using division: $(f \div g)(x) = f(x) \div g(x)$. In other words, divide the first function by the second function. Use a fraction bar to display the final function.

Guided Practice 2.8.1

Example 1

If $f(x) = 3x + 2$ and $g(x) = 2x - 7$, what is the result of adding the two functions? What is $(f + g)(x)$? How do you represent this algebraically?

1. Add the two function rules.

   $(f + g)(x) = f(x) + g(x)$

   Since $f(x) = 3x + 2$ and $g(x) = 2x - 7$, $(f + g)(x) = (3x + 2) + (2x - 7)$.

2. Combine like terms.

   Clear the parentheses and reorder the terms on the right side of the equation.

   $(f + g)(x) = (3x + 2) + (2x - 7)$ Equation

   $(f + g)(x) = 3x + 2 + 2x - 7$ Remove the parentheses.

   $(f + g)(x) = 3x + 2x + 2 - 7$ Reorder the terms: variables with coefficients first, followed by constants.

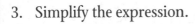

3. Simplify the expression.

   $(f + g)(x) = 3x + 2x + 2 - 7$ Equation

   $(f + g)(x) = 5x - 5$

   The result of adding $f(x) = 3x + 2$ and $g(x) = 2x - 7$ is $(f + g)(x) = 5x - 5$.

Example 2

If $f(x) = 3^x$ and $g(x) = 5$, what is the result of multiplying the two functions? What is $(f \cdot g)(x)$? How do you represent this algebraically?

1. Multiply the two function rules.

    $(f \cdot g)(x) = f(x) \cdot g(x)$

    Since $f(x) = 3^x$ and $g(x) = 5$, $(f \cdot g)(x) = (3^x) \cdot (5)$.

2. Simplify the equation.

    $(f \cdot g)(x) = (3^x) \cdot (5)$ Equation

    $(f \cdot g)(x) = 5(3^x)$

    $(f \cdot g)(x) = 5(3^x)$ is the result of multiplying $f(x) = 3^x$ and $g(x) = 5$.

Example 3

If $f(x) = 2x - 3$ and $g(x) = 4x - 11$, what is the result of subtracting the two functions? What is $(f - g)(x)$? How do you represent this algebraically?

1. Subtract the two function rules.

    $(f - g)(x) = f(x) - g(x)$

    Since $f(x) = 2x - 3$ and $g(x) = 4x - 11$, $(f - g)(x) = (2x - 3) - (4x - 11)$.

2. Combine like terms.

    Clear the parentheses and reorder the terms on the right side of the equation. Be careful to correctly distribute the negative sign.

    $(f - g)(x) = (2x - 3) - (4x - 11)$ Equation

    $(f - g)(x) = 2x - 3 - 4x + 11$ Distribute the negative.

    $(f - g)(x) = 2x - 4x - 3 + 11$ Reorder the terms: variables with coefficients first, followed by constants.

3. Simplify the equation.

$(f - g)(x) = 2x - 4x - 3 + 11$ Equation

$(f - g)(x) = -2x + 8$

$(f - g)(x) = -2x + 8$ is the result of subtracting $f(x) = 2x - 3$ and $g(x) = 4x - 11$.

Example 4

If $f(x) = 2^x$ and $g(x) = 2$, what is the result of dividing the two functions? What is $(f \div g)(x)$? How do you represent this algebraically?

1. Divide the two function rules.

$(f \div g)(x) = f(x) \div g(x)$

Since $f(x) = 2^x$ and $g(x) = 2$, $(f \div g)(x) = (2^x) \div 2$.

2. Simplify the equation.

$(f \div g)(x) = (2^x) \div 2$ Equation

$(f \div g)(x) = \dfrac{2^x}{2}$ Simplify as needed.

$(f \div g)(x) = \dfrac{1}{2}(2^x)$

$(f \div g)(x) = \dfrac{1}{2}(2^x)$ is the result of dividing $f(x) = 2^x$ by $g(x) = 2$.

UNIT 2 • LINEAR AND EXPONENTIAL RELATIONSHIPS
Lesson 8: Operating on Functions and Transformations

Practice 2.8.1: Operating on Functions

Find the value of each operation using the given functions.

For problems 1 and 2, $f(x) = 3x + 7$ and $g(x) = 5x - 8$.

1. Find $(f + g)(x)$.

2. Find $(f - g)(x)$.

For problems 3 and 4, $f(x) = 2^x$ and $g(x) = 3$.

3. Find $(f \cdot g)(x)$.

4. Find $(f \div g)(x)$.

For problems 5–8, $f(x) = 7$ and $g(x) = -4x + 12$.

5. Find $(f + g)(x)$.

6. Find $(f - g)(x)$.

7. Find $(f \cdot g)(x)$.

8. Find $(f \div g)(x)$.

Use what you know about functions to complete problems 9 and 10.

9. Raquel invests $100 in an account that pays 2% interest per year. Write a function that represents this scenario. Devon also invests $100 in an account that pays 2% interest per year, and then hides $200 in his mattress. Write a function that represents Devon's scenario. How are the two function rules different?

10. Nick joins a movie club. He pays $3.50 per month plus $2.50 per movie rental. Write a function that represents the amount of money that Nick pays per month. The club increases the rental fee per movie by $1.25. Write a function that represents Nick's new monthly costs. How are the two functions different?

Lesson 2.8.2: Transformations of Linear and Exponential Functions

Introduction

It is important to understand the relationship between a function and the graph of a function. In this lesson, we will explore how a function and its graph change when a constant value is added to the function. When a constant value is added to a function, the graph undergoes a vertical shift. A **vertical shift** is a type of translation that moves the graph up or down depending on the value added to the function. A **translation** of a graph moves the graph either vertically, horizontally, or both, without changing its shape. A translation is sometimes called a slide. A translation is a specific type of transformation. A **transformation** moves a graph. Transformations can include reflections and rotations in addition to translations. We will also examine translations of graphs and determine how they are similar or different.

Key Concepts

- Vertical translations can be performed on linear and exponential graphs using $f(x) + k$, where k is the value of the vertical shift.

- A vertical shift moves the graph up or down k units.

- If k is positive, the graph is translated up k units.

- If k is negative, the graph is translated down k units.

- Translations are one type of transformation.

- Given the graphs of two functions that are vertical translations of each other, the value of the vertical shift, k, can be found by finding the distance between the y-intercepts.

Guided Practice 2.8.2

Example 1

Graph the following functions on the same set of axes:

$$f(x) = 3x$$

$$g(x) = 3x + 1$$

$$h(x) = 3x + 2$$

$$q(x) = 3x - 1$$

1. Graph the functions.

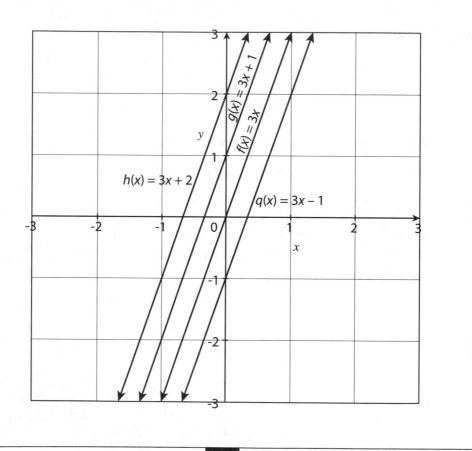

2. What is the y-intercept of $f(x)$? $g(x)$? $h(x)$? $q(x)$?

    The y-intercept of $f(x)$ is 0.

    The y-intercept of $g(x)$ is 1.

    The y-intercept of $h(x)$ is 2.

    The y-intercept of $q(x)$ is –1.

3. How could you describe the translation of $h(x)$ from $f(x)$?

    The graph of $h(x)$ is shifted up 2 units from the graph of $f(x)$.

4. How could you describe the translation of $q(x)$ from $f(x)$?

    The graph of $q(x)$ is shifted down 1 unit from the graph of $f(x)$.

5. How could you describe the translation of $q(x)$ from $g(x)$?

    The graph of $q(x)$ is shifted down 2 units from the graph of $g(x)$.

Example 2

Given $f(x) = 2^x + 1$ and the graph of $f(x)$ below, graph $g(x) = f(x) - 5$.

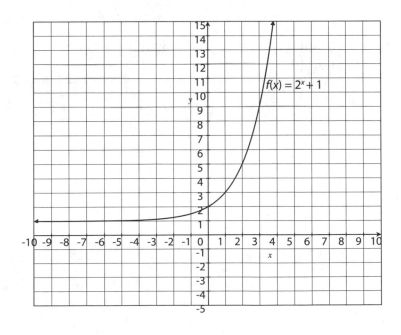

1. Graph $g(x)$.

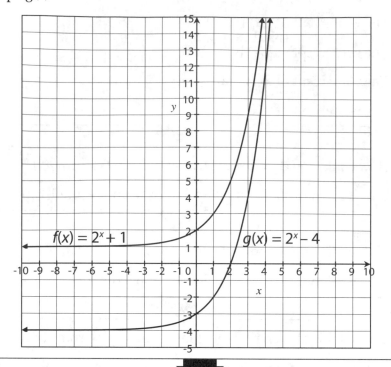

$f(x) = 2^x + 1$

$g(x) = 2^x - 4$

2. How are $f(x)$ and $g(x)$ related?

   $g(x)$ is a vertical shift down 5 units of $f(x)$.

3. What are the steps you need to follow to graph $g(x)$?

   For each point on $f(x)$, plot a point 5 units lower on the graph and connect the points.

Example 3

The graphs of two functions $f(x)$ and $g(x)$ are shown below. Write a rule for $g(x)$ in terms of $f(x)$.

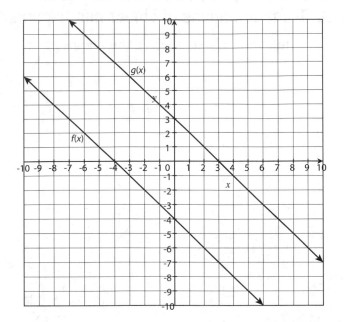

1. Write a function rule for the graph of $f(x)$.

    $f(x) = -x - 4$

2. Write a function rule for the graph of $g(x)$.

    $g(x) = -x + 3$

3. How are $f(x)$ and $g(x)$ related?

    $g(x)$ is a vertical shift up 7 units from $f(x)$, since the vertical distance is the distance between the y-intercepts (–4 and 3), and $3 - (-4) = 7$. You could also count the units on the graph.

4. Write a function rule for $g(x)$ in terms of $f(x)$.

    $g(x) = f(x) + 7$

UNIT 2 • LINEAR AND EXPONENTIAL RELATIONSHIPS
Lesson 8: Operating on Functions and Transformations

Practice 2.8.2: Transformations of Linear and Exponential Functions

Graph the following functions of $f(x) + k$ given the graphs of $f(x)$.

1. $f(x) - 15$

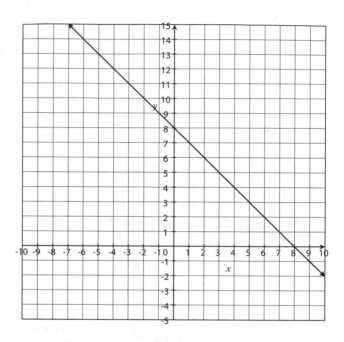

2. $f(x) + 2$

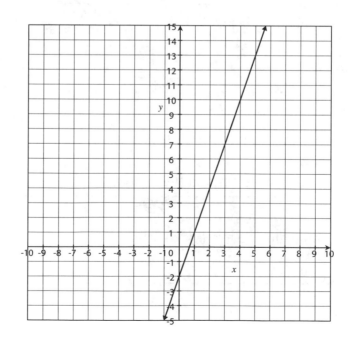

continued

3. $f(x) - 6$

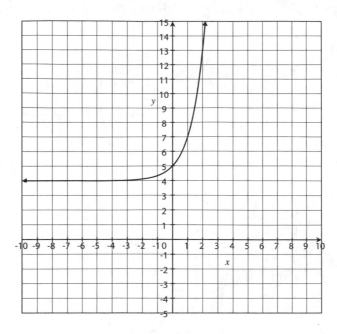

4. $f(x) + 7$

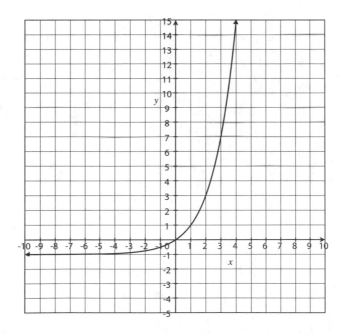

continued

5. Given the graphs of $f(x)$ and $g(x)$ below, write a function rule for $g(x)$ in terms of $f(x)$.

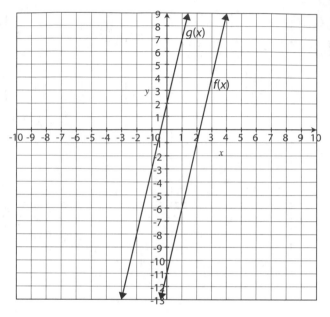

6. Given the graphs of $f(x)$ and $g(x)$ below, write a function rule for $g(x)$ in terms of $f(x)$.

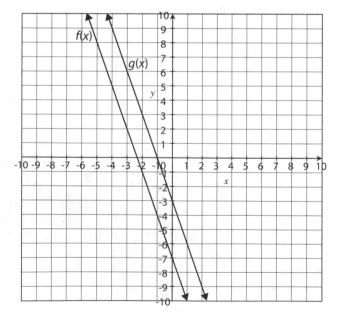

continued

7. Given the graphs of $f(x)$ and $g(x)$ below, write a function rule for $g(x)$ in terms of $f(x)$.

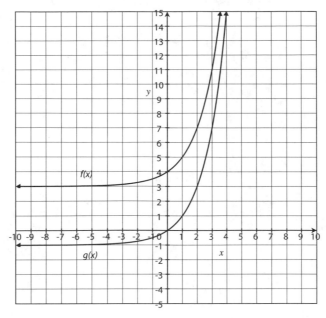

8. Given the graphs of $f(x)$ and $g(x)$ below, write a function rule for $g(x)$ in terms of $f(x)$.

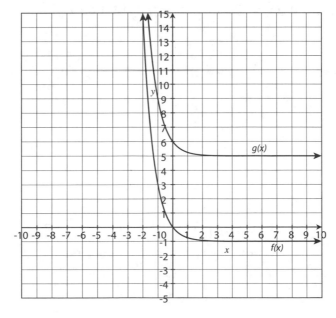

continued

9. $f(x) = 3x - 5$ and $g(x) = 3x + 8$. If $g(x)$ can be written as $f(x) + k$, what is the value of k?

10. $f(x) = 3^x + 2$ and $g(x) = 3^x - 1$. If $g(x)$ can be written as $f(x) + k$, what is the value of k?

Lesson 9: Arithmetic and Geometric Sequences

Common Core State Standard

F–BF.2 Write arithmetic and geometric sequences both recursively and with an explicit formula, use them to model situations, and translate between the two forms. ★

Essential Questions

1. How are arithmetic sequences and linear functions connected in theory?

2. What are the different ways that an arithmetic sequence can be defined?

3. How are geometric sequences and exponential functions connected in theory?

4. What are the different ways that a geometric sequence can be defined?

5. How can arithmetic and geometric sequences be used to model real-world problems?

WORDS TO KNOW

arithmetic sequence	a linear function with a domain of positive consecutive integers in which the difference between any two consecutive terms is equal
common difference	the number added to each consecutive term in an arithmetic sequence
constant ratio	the number each consecutive term is multiplied by in a geometric sequence
explicit formula	a formula used to find the nth term of a sequence; the explicit formula for an arithmetic sequence is $a_n = a_1 + (n-1)d$; the explicit formula for a geometric sequence is $a_n = a_1 \cdot r^{n-1}$
geometric sequence	an exponential function that results in a sequence of numbers separated by a constant ratio

recursive formula a formula used to find the next term of a sequence when the previous term is known; the recursive formula for an arithmetic sequence is $a_n = a_{n-1} + d$; the recursive formula for a geometric sequence is $a_n = a_{n-1} \cdot r$

Recommended Resources

- Education.TI.com. "*Numb3rs* Activity: Growing Geometrically."

  http://walch.com/rr/CAU3L8GrowingGeometrically

  This site features an activity based on the television show *Numb3rs* in which users explore geometric sequences.

- Lake Tahoe Community College. "Arithmetic and Geometric Sequences."

  http://walch.com/rr/CAU3L8SequenceFormulas

  This site walks users through the process of finding the formulas for arithmetic and geometric sequences, beginning with deciding whether a given sequence is arithmetic or geometric. Feedback is provided at each step and hints are available.

- MSTE.Illinois.edu. "Teaching Arithmetic Sequences and Series."

  http://walch.com/rr/CAU3L8TeachingSequences

  This website has links to a detailed lesson plan including the use of manipulatives to derive the formula for arithmetic sequences.

- Oswego City School District Regents Exam Prep Center. "Practice with Arithmetic and Geometric Sequences and Series."

  http://walch.com/rr/CAU3L8SequencesPractice

  This interactive page provides problems that users answer; users can check their answers against the correct answer.

- Purplemath.com. "Arithmetic and Geometric Sequences."

  http://walch.com/rr/CAU3L8SequencesTutorial

  This tutorial introduces both arithmetic and geometric sequences.

- YouTube. "Arithmetic Sequences: A Formula for the '*n*-th' Term."

  http://walch.com/rr/CAU3L8SequencesVideo

  This video gives an excellent breakdown of how arithmetic sequences work.

Lesson 2.9.1: Arithmetic Sequences

Introduction

Arithmetic sequences are linear functions that have a domain of positive consecutive integers in which the difference between any two consecutive terms is equal. Arithmetic sequences can be represented by formulas, either explicit or recursive, and those formulas can be used to find a certain term of the sequence or the number of a certain value in the sequence. An explicit formula is a formula used to find the nth term of a sequence and a recursive formula is a formula used to find the next term of a sequence when the previous term is known.

Key Concepts

- An arithmetic sequence is a list of terms separated by a **common difference**, the number added to each consecutive term in an arithmetic sequence.

- An arithmetic sequence is a linear function with a domain of positive consecutive integers in which the difference between any two consecutive terms is equal.

- The rule for an arithmetic sequence can be expressed either explicitly or recursively.

- The explicit rule for an arithmetic sequence is $a_n = a_1 + (n - 1)d$, where a_1 is the first term in the sequence, n is the term, d is the common difference, and a_n is the nth term in the sequence.

- The recursive rule for an arithmetic sequence is $a_n = a_{n-1} + d$, where a_n is the nth term in the sequence, a_{n-1} is the previous term, and d is the common difference.

Guided Practice 2.9.1

Example 1

Find the common difference, write the explicit formula, and find the tenth term for the following arithmetic sequence.

$$3, 9, 15, 21, \dots$$

1. Find the common difference by subtracting two successive terms.

   $9 - 3 = 6$

2. Confirm that the difference is the same between all of the terms.

   $15 - 9 = 6$ and $21 - 15 = 6$

3. Identify the first term (a_1).

   $a_1 = 3$

4. Write the explicit formula.

   $a_n = a_1 + (n - 1)d$ Explicit formula for any given arithmetic sequence

   $a_n = 3 + (n - 1)6$ Substitute values for a_1 and d.

5. Simplify the explicit formula.

   $a_n = 3 + 6n - 6$ Distribute 6 over $(n - 1)$.

   $a_n = 6n - 3$ Combine like terms.

6. To find the tenth term, substitute 10 for n.

   $a_{10} = 6(10) - 3$

   $a_{10} = 60 - 3$

   $a_{10} = 57$

   The tenth term in the sequence is 57.

Example 2

Write a linear function that corresponds to the following arithmetic sequence.

$8, 1, -6, -13, \ldots$

1. Find the common difference by subtracting two successive terms.

   $1 - 8 = -7$

2. Confirm that the difference is the same between all of the terms.

   $-6 - 1 = -7$ and $-13 - (-6) = -7$

3. Identify the first term (a_1).

   $a_1 = 8$

4. Write the explicit formula.

   $a_n = a_1 + (n-1)d$ Explicit formula for any given arithmetic sequence

   $a_n = 8 + (n-1)(-7)$ Substitute values for a_1 and d.

5. Simplify the explicit formula.

   $a_n = 8 - 7n + 7$ Distribute -7 over $(n-1)$.

   $a_n = -7n + 15$ Combine like terms.

6. Write the formula in function notation.

   $f(x) = -7x + 15$

   Note that the domain of an arithmetic sequence is positive consecutive integers.

Example 3

An arithmetic sequence is defined recursively by $a_n = a_{n-1} + 5$, with $a_1 = 29$. Find the first 5 terms of the sequence, write an explicit formula to represent the sequence, and find the 15th term.

1. Using the recursive formula:

   $a_1 = 29$

   $a_2 = a_1 + 5$

   $a_2 = 29 + 5 = 34$

   $a_3 = 34 + 5 = 39$

   $a_4 = 39 + 5 = 44$

   $a_5 = 44 + 5 = 49$

   The first five terms of the sequence are 29, 34, 39, 44, and 49.

2. The first term is $a_1 = 29$ and the common difference is $d = 5$, so the explicit formula is $a_n = 29 + (n-1)5$.

3. Simplify.

   $a_n = 29 + 5n - 5$

   $a_n = 5n + 24$ Combine like terms.

4. Substitute 15 in for n to find the 15th term in the sequence.

   $a_{15} = 5(15) + 24$

   $a_{15} = 75 + 24$

   $a_{15} = 99$

   The 15th term in the sequence is 99.

UNIT 2 • LINEAR AND EXPONENTIAL RELATIONSHIPS
Lesson 9: Arithmetic and Geometric Sequences

Practice 2.9.1: Arithmetic Sequences

Find the common difference and write the explicit formula for the nth term of each arithmetic sequence.

1. 4.2, 6, 7.8, 9.6, ...

2. 11, 3, –5, –13, ...

3. –237, –194, –151, –108, ...

4. $\dfrac{5}{3}, \dfrac{8}{3}, \dfrac{11}{3}, \dfrac{14}{3}, \dots$

5. Find the first five terms of the arithmetic sequence defined as follows:

    $$a_{n-1} = a_1 + 0.6; a_1 = 12.3$$

6. Find the first five terms of the arithmetic sequence defined as follows:

    $$a_{n-1} = a_1 - 31; a_1 = 52$$

7. You have read 15 pages of a book. You plan to read an additional 12 pages each night. Write the explicit formula to represent the number of pages you will read after n nights.

8. You have $53 in your lunch account. You spend $3 each day for lunch. You need to have $5 remaining at the end the month to keep your account open. Write an explicit formula to represent this scenario. For how many days can you buy lunch?

9. Jaden is starting a wellness plan. Walking each day is part of her plan. She begins by walking for $\dfrac{1}{2}$ hour on the first day. She plans to increase by $\dfrac{1}{4}$ hour each day. Write an explicit formula to represent this scenario. After how many days will Jaden be walking for $1\dfrac{3}{4}$ hours?

10. Augie is saving to buy a new scooter. He has $78 in his account. He delivers newspapers and plans to save $14 each week. Write an explicit formula to represent this scenario. How much money will Augie have at the end of 11 weeks?

Lesson 2.9.2: Geometric Sequences

Introduction

Geometric sequences are exponential functions that have a domain of consecutive positive integers. Geometric sequences can be represented by formulas, either explicit or recursive, and those formulas can be used to find a certain term of the sequence or the number of a certain value in the sequence.

Key Concepts

- A geometric sequence is a list of terms separated by a **constant ratio**, the number multiplied by each consecutive term in a geometric sequence.

- A geometric sequence is an exponential function with a domain of positive consecutive integers in which the ratio between any two consecutive terms is equal.

- The rule for a geometric sequence can be expressed either explicitly or recursively.

- The explicit rule for a geometric sequence is $a_n = a_1 \cdot r^{n-1}$, where a_1 is the first term in the sequence, n is the term, r is the constant ratio, and a_n is the nth term in the sequence.

- The recursive rule for a geometric sequence is $a_n = a_{n-1} \cdot r$, where a_n is the nth term in the sequence, a_{n-1} is the previous term, and r is the constant ratio.

Guided Practice 2.9.2

Example 1

Find the constant ratio, write the explicit formula, and find the seventh term for the following geometric sequence.

3, 1.5, 0.75, 0.375, ...

1. Find the constant ratio by dividing two successive terms.

   $1.5 \div 3 = 0.5$

2. Confirm that the ratio is the same between all of the terms.

   $0.75 \div 1.5 = 0.5$ and $0.375 \div 0.75 = 0.5$

3. Identify the first term (a_1).

   $a_1 = 3$

4. Write the explicit formula.

   $a_n = a_1 \cdot r^{n-1}$　　　　Explicit formula for any given geometric sequence

   $a_n = (3)(0.5)^{n-1}$　　　Substitute values for a_1 and n.

5. To find the seventh term, substitute 7 for n.

   $a_7 = (3)(0.5)^{7-1}$

   $a_7 = (3)(0.5)^6$　　　Simplify.

   $a_7 = 0.046875$　　　Multiply.

   The seventh term in the sequence is 0.046875.

Example 2

The fifth term of a geometric sequence is 1,792. The constant ratio is 4. Write an explicit formula for the sequence, and then write the corresponding exponential function.

---

1. The fifth term is 1,792; therefore $n = 5$ and $a_n = 1792$.

---

2. The constant ratio is 4; therefore, $r = 4$.

---

3. Substitute the known values into the explicit form of the formula and solve for a.

$1792 = a(4)^{5-1}$ Substitute values.

$1792 = 256a$ Simplify.

$a = 7$

---

4. Write the explicit formula.

$a_n = a_1 \bullet r^{n-1}$ Explicit formula for any given geometric sequence

$a_n = 7(4)^{n-1}$ Substitute values.

---

5. Write the formula in function notation.

$f(x) = 7(4)^{x-1}$

Note that the domain of a geometric sequence is consecutive positive integers.

Example 3

A geometric sequence is defined recursively by $a_n = (a_{n-1})\left(-\dfrac{1}{3}\right)$, with $a_1 = 729$. Find the first five terms of the sequence, write an explicit formula to represent the sequence, and find the eighth term.

1. Using the recursive formula:

   $a_1 = 729$

   $a_2 = (a_1)\left(-\dfrac{1}{3}\right)$

   $a_2 = (729)\left(-\dfrac{1}{3}\right) = -243$

   $a_3 = (-243)\left(-\dfrac{1}{3}\right) = 81$

   $a_4 = (81)\left(-\dfrac{1}{3}\right) = -27$

   $a_5 = (-27)\left(-\dfrac{1}{3}\right) = 9$

   The first five terms of the sequence are 729, –243, 81, –27, and 9.

2. The first term is $a_1 = 729$ and the constant ratio is $r = -\dfrac{1}{3}$, so the explicit formula is $a_n = (729)\left(-\dfrac{1}{3}\right)^{n-1}$.

3. Substitute 8 in for n and evaluate.

   $a_8 = (729)\left(-\dfrac{1}{3}\right)^{8-1}$

   $a_8 = (729)\left(-\dfrac{1}{3}\right)^{7}$

   $a_8 = -\dfrac{1}{3}$

   The eighth term of the sequence is $-\dfrac{1}{3}$.

UNIT 2 • LINEAR AND EXPONENTIAL RELATIONSHIPS
Lesson 9: Arithmetic and Geometric Sequences

Practice 2.9.2: Geometric Sequences

Find the constant ratio and write the explicit formula for the nth term of each geometric sequence.

1. $1, 3, 9, 27, 81, \ldots$

2. $\dfrac{5}{16}, \dfrac{25}{16}, \dfrac{125}{16}, \dfrac{625}{16}, \ldots$

3. $16, -8, 4, -2, \ldots$

4. $18, 9, 4.5, 2.25, \ldots$

5. Find the first five terms of the geometric sequence defined as follows:

$$a_{n-1} = a_1 \left(-\frac{1}{3} \right); \ a_1 = 48$$

6. Find the first five terms of the geometric sequence defined as follows:

$$a_{n-1} = a_1 (1.5); \ a_1 = 36$$

7. You open a savings account with \$350 that you have saved. The bank offers 2.8% simple interest each year. How much money will you have in your account after 10 years?

8. A bicyclist is training for a race. During her first week of training she rides 12 miles. She increases the length of each ride by 20% each week. Write the explicit formula to represent the length of her bike ride after n weeks.

9. Your grandmother owns a rare antique lamp that is valued at \$5,000. An antique dealer estimates that the lamp will gain value at a rate of 10% each year. In how many years will the lamp be worth \$6,655?

10. The number of dandelions in your yard spread following a geometric sequence each day. On the third day, there are 156 dandelions. On the sixth day, there are 1,248 dandelions. How many dandelions will there be after 9 days?

Lesson 10: Interpreting Parameters

Common Core State Standard

F–LE.5   Interpret the parameters in a linear or exponential function in terms of a context. ★

Essential Questions

1. What are the parameters in a linear function?

2. What are the parameters in an exponential function?

3. How do you determine the parameters in the context of a word problem?

4. How does changing the parameter in a function change the graph of a function?

WORDS TO KNOW

exponential function	a function that has a variable in the exponent:

- the general form is $f(x) = ab^x$, where a is the initial value, b is the growth or decay factor, x is the time, and $f(x)$ is the final output value

- can also be written in the form $f(x) = b^x + k$, where b is a positive integer not equal to 1 and k can equal 0; the parameters are b and k. b is the growth factor and k is the vertical shift.

linear function	a function that can be written in the form $f(x) = mx + b$, in which m is the slope, b is the y-intercept, and the graph is a straight line
parameter	a term in a function that determines a specific form of a function but not the nature of the function
vertical shift	number of units the graph of the function is moved up or down; a translation

Recommended Resources

- NCTM Illuminations. "Function Matching."

  http://walch.com/rr/CAU3L9FunctionMatching

  At this site, users can match graphs to function rules on an interactive graph.

- NCTM Illuminations. "Movie Lines."

  http://walch.com/rr/CAU3L9MovieLines

  In this activity, users identify the y-intercept and slope and state their significance in the context of a real-world problem.

- RonBlond.com. "Linear Relation Graph Applet."

  http://walch.com/rr/CAU3L9LinearRelation

  This interactive applet allows users to choose the form of the linear equation, $y = mx + b$, $ax + by = c$, or $y - y_1 = m(x - x_1)$, and change the parameters by using sliders. The graph of the linear function changes as the sliders are manipulated.

- Texas Instruments. "Characteristics of Exponential Functions."

  http://walch.com/rr/CAU3L9FunctionCharacteristics

  Users can investigate how the graph of an exponential function changes as the base changes.

Lesson 2.10.1: Interpreting Parameters

Introduction

In order to fully understand how various functions model real-world contexts, we need to understand how changing parameters will affect the functions. This lesson will explore the effect of changing parameters on linear and exponential functions. We will also interpret the effects of changing these parameters in a context.

Key Concepts

- An exponential function is a function that may be written in the form $f(x) = b^x + k$.

- A linear function is a function in the form $f(x) = mx + b$.

- The **parameter** of a function is a term that determines a specific form of a function but not the nature of the function.

- For a linear function written in slope-intercept form, $f(x) = mx + b$, the parameters are m and b. m represents the slope and b represents the y-intercept. Changing either of these parameters will change the function and the graph of the function.

- For an **exponential function** in the form $f(x) = b^x + k$, where b is a positive integer not equal to 1 and k can equal 0, the parameters are b and k. b is the growth factor and k is the vertical shift, or number of units the graph of the function is moved up or down. Changing either of these parameters will change the function and the graph of the function.

  ### Graphing Equations Using a TI-83/84:

  > Step 1: Press [Y=].
  >
  > Step 2: Key in the equation using [X, T, θ, n] for x.
  >
  > Step 3: Press [WINDOW] to change the viewing window, if necessary.
  >
  > Step 4: Enter in appropriate values for Xmin, Xmax, Xscl, Ymin, Ymax, and Yscl, using the arrow keys to navigate.
  >
  > Step 5: Press [GRAPH].

Graphing Equations Using a TI-Nspire:

Step 1: Press the home key.

Step 2: Arrow over to the graphing icon (the picture of the parabola or the U-shaped curve) and press [enter].

Step 3: Enter in the equation and press [enter].

Step 4: To change the viewing window: press [menu], arrow down to number 4: Window/Zoom, and click the center button of the navigation pad.

Step 5: Choose 1: Window settings by pressing the center button.

Step 6: Enter in the appropriate XMin, XMax, YMin, and YMax fields.

Step 7: Leave the XScale and YScale set to auto.

Step 8: Use [tab] to navigate among the fields.

Step 9: Press [tab] to "OK" when done and press [enter].

Guided Practice 2.10.1

Example 1

You visit a pick-your-own apple orchard. There is an entrance fee of $5.00, plus you pay $0.50 for each apple you pick. Write a function to represent this scenario. Complete a table of values to show your total cost if you pick 10, 20, 30, 40, and 50 apples. Graph the line and identify the parameters in this problem. What do the parameters represent in the context of the problem?

1. Write a function.

   This scenario is represented by a linear function.

   Identify the slope and the y-intercept.

   - The slope is the $0.50 charged for each apple picked.

   - The y-intercept is the entrance fee of $5.00.

   Substitute the slope and the y-intercept into the linear function $f(x) = mx + b$, where m is the slope and b is the y-intercept.

   The function for this scenario is $f(x) = 0.5x + 5$.

2. Create a table.

   Let $x =$ the number of apples picked and $f(x) =$ the total cost.

   Use the values 0, 10, 20, 30, 40, and 50 for x.

x	$0.5x + 5$	$f(x)$
0	$0.5(0) + 5$	0
10	$0.5(10) + 5$	10
20	$0.5(20) + 5$	15
30	$0.5(30) + 5$	20
40	$0.5(40) + 5$	25
50	$0.5(50) + 5$	30

3. Graph the function.

   Use the table of values to plot the equation of the line.

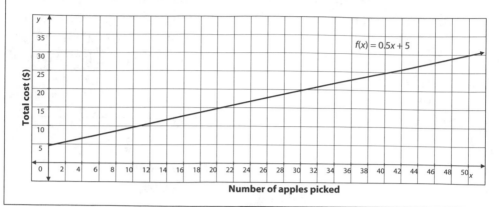

4. Identify the parameters.

   The parameters in this problem are the slope and the y-intercept. In this problem, the y-intercept is the entrance fee, $5.00, and the slope is the cost per apple, $0.50.

Example 2

You deposit $100 into a long-term certificate of deposit (CD) in which your money will double every 7 years. Write a function to show how much money you will have in total in 7, 14, 21, 28, and 35 years. Use the function to create a table, and then graph the function. What do the parameters represent in the context of this problem?

1. Write a function.

   This scenario is represented by an exponential function.

   • The initial deposit is $100.

   • Your money doubles every 7 years, so the growth factor is 2.

   • The time period is 7 years.

   Substitute these values into the exponential function.

   The function for this scenario is $f(x)=100(2)^{\frac{x}{7}}$.

2. Create a table.

Let x = the number of years and $f(x)$ = the amount of money in dollars.

Use the values 7, 14, 21, 28, and 35 for x.

x	$100(2)^{\frac{x}{7}}$	$f(x)$
7	$100(2)^{\frac{7}{7}}$	200
14	$100(2)^{\frac{14}{7}}$	400
21	$100(2)^{\frac{21}{7}}$	800
28	$100(2)^{\frac{28}{7}}$	1600
35	$100(2)^{\frac{35}{7}}$	3200

3. Graph the function.

Use the table of values to plot the function.

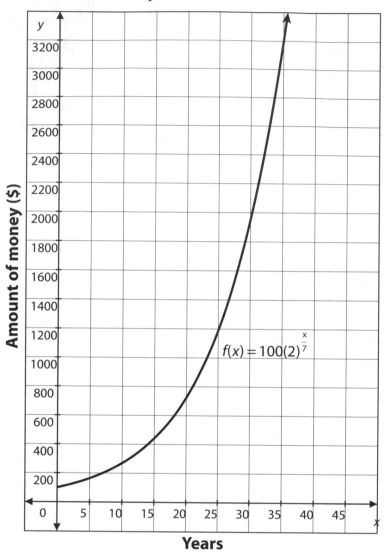

$$f(x) = 100(2)^{\frac{x}{7}}$$

4. Identify the parameters.

The parameters in this problem are the starting amount of $100 and the base of 2.

Example 3

You are growing bacteria in science class. You start with 1 bacterium, which doubles every 12 hours. Write a function to show how many bacteria you have after 12 hours, 24 hours, 36 hours, 48 hours, and 60 hours. Use the function to create a table, then graph the function. What are the parameters in this problem?

1. Write a function.

   This scenario is represented by an exponential function.

   - The initial number of bacteria is 1.

   - The bacteria double every 12 hours, so the growth factor is 2.

   - The time period is 12 hours.

   Substitute these values into the exponential function.

   The function for this scenario is $f(x) = 2^{\frac{x}{12}}$.

2. Create a table.

   Let x = the number of hours and $f(x)$ = the number of bacteria.

   Use the values 0, 12, 24, 36, 48, and 60 for x.

x	$1(2)^{\frac{x}{12}}$	$f(x)$
0	$1(2)^{\frac{0}{12}}$	1
12	$1(2)^{\frac{12}{12}}$	2
24	$1(2)^{\frac{24}{12}}$	4
36	$1(2)^{\frac{36}{12}}$	8
48	$1(2)^{\frac{48}{12}}$	16
60	$1(2)^{\frac{60}{12}}$	32

3. Graph the function.

   Use the table of values to plot the function.

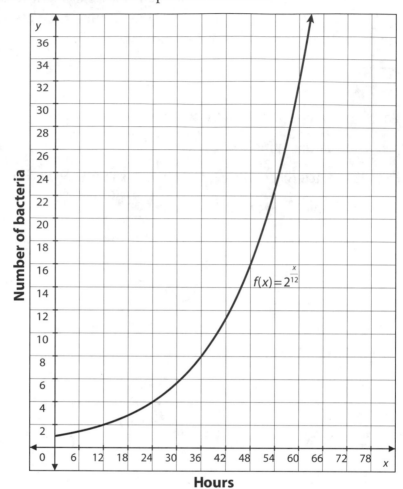

4. Identify the parameters.

   The parameters are the starting amount of 1 bacterium and the base of 2.

UNIT 2 • LINEAR AND EXPONENTIAL RELATIONSHIPS
Lesson 10: Interpreting Parameters

Practice 2.10.1: Interpreting Parameters

Identify the parameters in the following equations.

1. $f(x) = 3x + 12$

2. $f(x) = 4^x - 8$

3. $f(x) = -6x + 13$

4. $f(x) = 5(2^x)$

5. $f(x) = 2(4^x) + 9$

Use what you know about functions to complete problems 6–10.

6. Your aunt hides $100 in her mattress and deposits $300 into an account that triples every 15 years. What is the function that represents this scenario? What are the parameters?

7. Lily subscribes to a game rental program. She pays a monthly fee of $7.00 plus $2.50 for each game rented. What are the parameters in this scenario?

8. You join a gym. The monthly membership fee is $12.00 and the rate per hour of gym use is $3.75. What are the parameters in this scenario?

9. Kendall is picking strawberries with his sister. The number of strawberries in his basket is described by $f(x) = 35x + 20$, where x is the number of minutes Kendall spends picking strawberries. What do the numbers 35 and 20 tell you about Kendall's strawberry picking?

10. You have an ant farm. The number of ants in your colony is described by $f(x) = 25(3)^{\frac{x}{4}}$, where x is in days. What do the numbers 25 and 3 tell you about the number of ants in your colony?

Unit 3
Reasoning with Equations

Lesson 1: Solving Equations and Inequalities

Common Core State Standards

A–REI.1   Explain each step in solving a simple equation as following from the equality of numbers asserted at the previous step, starting from the assumption that the original equation has a solution. Construct a viable argument to justify a solution method.

A–REI.3   Solve linear equations and inequalities in one variable, including equations with coefficients represented by letters.

Essential Questions

1. How are the properties of equality used to solve equations?

2. How is solving a literal equation different from solving a linear equation?

3. How is finding the solution to an inequality similar to finding the solution to an equation?

4. What effect does multiplying or dividing an inequality by a negative number have?

5. How is solving an exponential equation different from solving a linear equation?

WORDS TO KNOW

laws of exponents	rules that must be followed when working with exponents
properties of equality	rules that allow you to balance, manipulate, and solve equations
properties of inequality	rules that allow you to balance, manipulate, and solve inequalities

Recommended Resources

- IXL. "Solve Linear Equations: Mixed Review."

  http://walch.com/rr/CAU2L1EquationsReview

  This site includes various types of linear equations to solve. Explanations are provided for wrong answers given.

- Math Interactives. "Exploring Laws of Exponents—Use It."

  http://walch.com/rr/CAU2L1ExponentDig

  This interactive resource allows users to explore the laws of exponents while completing a virtual paleontological dig.

- NCTM Illuminations. "Pan Balance—Expressions."

  http://walch.com/rr/CAU2L1PanBalance

  Create numeric or algebraic expressions and observe how operations affect equality with this interactive tool.

Lesson 3.1.1: Properties of Equality

Introduction

Equations are mathematical sentences that state two expressions are equal. In order to solve equations in algebra, you must perform operations that maintain equality on both sides of the equation using the **properties of equality**. These properties are rules that allow you to balance, manipulate, and solve equations.

Key Concepts

- In mathematics, it is important to follow the rules when solving equations, but it is also necessary to justify, or prove that the steps we are following to solve problems are correct and allowed.

- The following table summarizes some of these rules.

Properties of Equality

Property	In symbols	In words
Reflexive property of equality	$a = a$	A number is equal to itself.
Symmetric property of equality	If $a = b$, then $b = a$.	If numbers are equal, they will still be equal if the order is changed.
Transitive property of equality	If $a = b$ and $b = c$, then $a = c$.	If numbers are equal to the same number, then they are equal to each other.
Addition property of equality	If $a = b$, then $a + c = b + c$.	Adding the same number to both sides of an equation does not change the equality of the equation.
Subtraction property of equality	If $a = b$, then $a - c = b - c$.	Subtracting the same number from both sides of an equation does not change the equality of the equation.
Multiplication property of equality	If $a = b$ and $c \neq 0$, then $a \bullet c = b \bullet c$.	Multiplying both sides of the equation by the same number, other than 0, does not change the equality of the equation.
Division property of equality	If $a = b$ and $c \neq 0$, then $a \div c = b \div c$.	Dividing both sides of the equation by the same number, other than 0, does not change the equality of the equation.
Substitution property of equality	If $a = b$, then b may be substituted for a in any expression containing a.	If two numbers are equal, then substituting one in for another does not change the equality of the equation.

- You may remember from other classes the properties of operations that explain the effect that the operations of addition, subtraction, multiplication, and division have on equations. The following table describes some of those properties.

Properties of Operations

Property	General rule	Specific example
Commutative property of addition	$a + b = b + a$	$3 + 8 = 8 + 3$
Associative property of addition	$(a + b) + c = a + (b + c)$	$(3 + 8) + 2 = 3 + (8 + 2)$
Commutative property of multiplication	$a \bullet b = b \bullet a$	$3 \bullet 8 = 8 \bullet 3$
Associative property of multiplication	$(a \bullet b) \bullet c = a \bullet (b \bullet c)$	$(3 \bullet 8) \bullet 2 = 3 \bullet (8 \bullet 2)$
Distributive property of multiplication over addition	$a \bullet (b + c) = a \bullet b + a \bullet c$	$3 \bullet (8 + 2) = 3 \bullet 8 + 3 \bullet 2$

- When we solve an equation, we are rewriting it into a simpler, equivalent equation that helps us find the unknown value.

- When you are solving an equation that contains parentheses, apply the properties of operations and perform the operation that's in the parentheses first.

- The properties of equality, as well as the properties of operations, not only justify our reasoning, but also help us to understand our own thinking.

- When identifying which step is being used, it helps to review each step in the sequence and make note of what operation was performed, and whether it was done to one side of the equation or both. (What changed and where?)

- When operations are performed on one side of the equation, the properties of operations are generally followed.

- When an operation is performed on both sides of the equation, the properties of equality are generally followed.

- Once you have noted which steps were taken, match them to the properties listed in the tables.

- If a step being taken can't be justified, then the step shouldn't be done.

Guided Practice 3.1.1

Example 1

Which property of equality is missing in the steps to solve the equation $-7x + 22 = 50$?

Equation	Steps
$-7x + 22 = 50$	Original equation
$-7x = 28$	
$x = -4$	Division property of equality

> 1. Observe the differences between the original equation and the next equation in the sequence. What has changed?
>
>   Notice that 22 has been taken away from both expressions, $-7x + 22$ and 50.

> 2. Refer to the table of Properties of Equality.
>
>   The subtraction property of equality tells us that when we subtract a number from both sides of the equation, the expressions remain equal.
>
>   The missing step is "Subtraction property of equality."

Example 2

Which property of equality is missing in the steps to solve the equation $-3 - \dfrac{x}{6} = 4$?

Equation	Steps
$-3 - \dfrac{x}{6} = 4$	Original equation
$-\dfrac{x}{6} = 7$	Addition property of equality
$-x = 42$	
$x = -42$	Division property of equality

1. Observe the differences between the original equation and the next equation in the sequence. What has changed?

   Notice that 3 has been added to both expressions, $-3-\dfrac{x}{6}$ and 4. The result of this step is $-\dfrac{x}{6}=7$.

   In order to move to the next step, the division of 6 has been undone. The inverse operation of the division of 6 is the multiplication of 6. The result of multiplying $-\dfrac{x}{6}$ by 6 is $-x$ and the result of multiplying 7 by 6 is 42. This matches the next step in the sequence.

2. Refer to the table of Properties of Equality.

   The multiplication property of equality tells us that when we multiply both sides of the equation by a number, the expressions remain equal.

   The missing step is "Multiplication property of equality."

Example 3

Which property of equality is missing in the steps to solve the equation $76 = 5x - 15 + 2x$?

Equation	Steps
$76 = 5x - 15 + 2x$	Original equation
$76 = 5x + 2x - 15$	Commutative property of addition
$76 = 7x - 15$	Distributive property to combine like terms
$91 = 7x$	Addition property of equality
$13 = x$	Division property of equality
$x = 13$	

1. Observe the differences between the original equation and the next equation in the sequence. What has changed?

   Notice that the expression $5x - 15 + 2x$ was rearranged using the commutative property of addition. The new expression, $5x + 2x - 15$, although in a different order, has the same meaning.

   The distributive property allows us to combine like terms by thinking of $5x + 2x$ as $x(5 + 2)$. Simplifying this expression to $7x - 15$ has the same meaning as the prior step.

   The addition property of equality allows us to add 15 to both sides of the equation, bringing us one step closer to finding out the value of x.

   To isolate x in the equation $91 = 7x$, we use the division property of equality to divide both sides of the equation by the coefficient 7.

2. Notice that the equation now reads $13 = x$. Compare this to the final line, $x = 13$. The symmetric property of equality allows us to write $x = 13$. This more standard way of writing the solution means the same as the previous step.

   The missing step is "Symmetric property of equality."

Example 4

What equation is missing in the steps to solve the equation $5x + 3(x + 4) = 28$?

Equation	Steps
$5x + 3(x + 4) = 28$	Original equation
$5x + 3x + 12 = 28$	Distributive property
$8x + 12 = 28$	Distributive property to combine like terms
	Subtraction property of equality
$x = 2$	Division property of equality

1. Look at the differences between the original equation and the next equation in the sequence. What has changed?

   Notice that the expression $5x + 3(x + 4)$ was rewritten using the distributive property. The new expression, $5x + 3x + 12$, looks different but has the same meaning.

   The distributive property also allows us to combine like terms by thinking of $5x + 3x$ as $x(5 + 3)$. Simplifying this expression to $8x + 12$ has the same meaning as the prior step.

2. We are told that the subtraction property of equality justifies the next step. This property states that we can subtract the same number from both sides of the equation and not change the equality of the equation. In order to solve for x, we have learned to isolate the variable. We do this by subtracting the constant from both sides. The constant is 12, so subtract 12 from both sides.

   $$\begin{aligned} 8x + 12 &= 28 \\ -12 \quad &-12 \\ \hline 8x &= 16 \end{aligned}$$

   Now we have an equation, $8x = 16$, which may be our missing equation. Let's look at what happens to get to the final statement in the table to see if this equation makes sense.

3. The table lists the division property of equality as the property that leads to $x = 2$. Look at the equation we found: $8x = 16$. In this equation, the coefficient of x is 8. If we divide both sides of the equation by 8, we get the final statement, $x = 2$.

   $$\begin{aligned} 8x &= 16 \\ \div 8 \quad &\div 8 \\ \hline x &= 2 \end{aligned}$$

   The division property of equality justifies the division of the equation $8x = 16$ by the coefficient, 8.

   The missing equation is $8x = 16$.

UNIT 3 • REASONING WITH EQUATIONS
Lesson 1: Solving Equations and Inequalities

Practice 3.1.1: Properties of Equality

Identify the property of equality that justifies each missing step or equation.

1.

Equation	Steps
$6 + x = 72$	Original equation
$x = 66$	

2.

Equation	Steps
$\dfrac{x}{9} = 2.4$	Original equation
$x = 21.6$	

3.

Equation	Steps
$-7x - 12 = 16$	Original equation
$-7x = 28$	Addition property of equality
$x = -4$	

4.

Equation	Steps
$8 = 0.4x - 2$	Original equation
$10 = 0.4x$	
$25 = x$	Division property of equality
$x = 25$	Symmetric property of equality

5.

Equation	Steps
$5(6x - 2) = 50$	Original equation
$30x - 10 = 50$	Distributive property of multiplication over addition
$30x = 60$	
	Division property of equality

continued

6.

Equation	Steps
$\dfrac{x}{4} - 5 = 6$	Original equation
	Addition property of equality
$x = 44$	

7.

Equation	Steps
$\dfrac{3x}{2} - 5 = 16$	Original equation
$\dfrac{3x}{2} = 21$	
$3x = 42$	
$x = 14$	

8.

Equation	Steps
$8(2x - 1) = 56$	Original equation
$2x - 1 = 7$	
$2x = 8$	
$x = 4$	

Solve each equation that follows. Justify each step in your process using the properties of equality. Be sure to include the properties of operations, if used.

9. $\dfrac{4x}{9} = 20$

10. $13 = \dfrac{1}{3}x - 5$

Lesson 3.1.2: Solving Linear Equations

Introduction

While it may not be efficient to write out the justification for each step when solving equations, it is important to remember that the properties of equality must always apply in order for an equation to remain balanced.

As equations become more complex, it may be helpful to refer to the properties of equality used in the previous lesson.

Key Concepts

- When solving equations, first take a look at the expressions on either side of the equal sign.

- You may need to simplify one or both expressions before you can solve for the unknown. Sometimes you may need to combine like terms by using the associative, commutative, or distributive properties.

- Pay special attention if the same variable appears on either side of the equal sign.

- Just like with numbers, variables may be added or subtracted from both sides of the equation without changing the equality of the statement or the solution to the problem.

Solving Equations with the Variable in Both Expressions of the Equation
1. Choose which side of the equation you would like the variable to appear on.
2. Add or subtract the other variable from both sides of the equation using either the addition or subtraction property of equality.
3. Simplify both expressions.
4. Continue to solve the equation.
5. As with any equation, check that your answer is correct by substituting the value into the original equation to ensure both expressions are equal.

- Some equations may have no solution. This is the case when, after you've completed all of the appropriate steps to solve an equation, the result is something impossible, like $2 = 6$. The resulting equation is never true for any value of the variable.

- Some equations will be true for any value the variable is replaced with. This is the case when following all of the appropriate steps for solving an equation results in the same value on each side of the equal sign, such as $2x = 2x$. The resulting equation is always true for any value of the variable.

- Other equations will only have one solution, where the final step in solving results in the variable equal to a number, such as $x = 5$.

Guided Practice 3.1.2

Example 1

Solve the equation $5x + 9 = 2x - 36$.

1. Move the variable to one side of the equation.

   Notice that the same variable, x, is on both sides of the equation: $5x$ is on the left of the equation and $2x$ is on the right. It makes no difference whether you choose to have the variables on the left or on the right; your solution will remain the same. It's common to have the variable on the left, but not necessary.

   It's often easier to move the variable with the smallest coefficient to the opposite side of the equation. Here, $2x$ is smaller than $5x$, so let's move $2x$.

   $2x$ is positive, so to get it to the other side of the equal sign you will need to subtract it from both expressions in the equation.

   It helps to line up what you are subtracting with the terms that are similar in order to stay organized. In this case, we are subtracting variables from variables.

$$
\begin{array}{r}
5x+9=2x-36 \\
\underline{-2x \quad -2x} \\
3x+9= \quad -36
\end{array}
$$

   When $2x$ is subtracted, it's important not to forget the remaining terms of each expression. Look out for subtraction signs that now act as negative signs. Here, since 36 was originally being subtracted from $2x$, the subtraction sign left behind makes 36 negative.

$$3x + 9 = -36$$

2. Continue to solve the equation $3x + 9 = -36$.

   To isolate x, subtract 9 from both expressions in the equation.

$$3x + 9 = -36$$
$$\underline{ -9 \quad -9}$$
$$3x \quad\quad = -45$$

   Divide both expressions by the coefficient of x, 3.

$$\frac{3x}{3} = \frac{-45}{3}$$
$$x = -15$$

3. The solution to the equation $5x + 9 = 2x - 36$ is $x = -15$.

   A quick check will verify this. Substitute –15 for all instances of x in the original equation, and then evaluate each expression.

$$5x + 9 = 2x - 36$$

$$5(-15) + 9 = 2(-15) - 36$$

$$-75 + 9 = -30 - 36$$

$$-66 = -66$$

   Our check verified that both sides of the equation are still equal; therefore, $x = -15$ is correct.

Example 2

Solve the equation $7x + 4 = -9x$.

1. Move the variable to one side of the equation.

   Notice that the variable x is on both sides of the equation. Again, it makes no difference mathematically which term, $7x$ or $-9x$, you choose to eliminate.

   $-9x$ is the only term in the expression on the right side of the equation, so it may be easier to eliminate $7x$ from the left side.

   Subtract $7x$ from both expressions of the equation.

   $$7x + 4 = -9x$$
   $$\underline{-7x \qquad -7x}$$
   $$4 = -16x$$

2. Continue to solve the equation $4 = -16x$.

   To isolate x, divide both expressions by the coefficient of x, -16.

   $$\frac{4}{-16} = \frac{-16x}{-16}$$

   $$-\frac{1}{4} = x$$

   $$x = -\frac{1}{4}$$

3. The solution to the equation $7x + 4 = -9x$ is $x = -\dfrac{1}{4}$.

A quick check will verify this. Substitute $-\dfrac{1}{4}$ for all instances of x in the original equation, and then evaluate each expression.

$7x + 4 = -9x$	Original equation
$7\left(-\dfrac{1}{4}\right) + 4 = -9\left(-\dfrac{1}{4}\right)$	Substitute $-\dfrac{1}{4}$ for x.
$\left(-\dfrac{7}{4}\right) + 4 = \dfrac{9}{4}$	Multiply.
$\left(-\dfrac{7}{4}\right) + \left(\dfrac{16}{4}\right) = \dfrac{9}{4}$	Convert the whole number 4 to a fraction with a common denominator.
$\dfrac{9}{4} = \dfrac{9}{4}$	Add and review the result.

Our check verified that both sides of the equation are still equal; therefore, $x = -\dfrac{1}{4}$ is correct.

Example 3

Solve the equation $2(3x + 1) = 6x + 14$.

1. Simplify each side of the equation.

   Notice that the variable x is on both sides of the equation. Also notice the set of parentheses in the expression on the left side of the equation.

   Eliminate the parentheses by first distributing the 2 over $3x + 1$.

   $2(3x + 1) = 6x + 14$ Multiply 2 and $3x + 1$.

   $6x + 2 = 6x + 14$

2. Move the variable to one side of the equation. Again, you need to eliminate one of the terms with the variable x. Subtract $6x$ from both expressions of the equation.

$$6x + 2 = 6x + 14$$
$$\underline{-6x \quad\quad -6x}$$
$$2 = 14$$

3. This equation has no solution.

Subtracting the variables gives us an impossible result: $2 = 14$. This is not a true statement; therefore, there are no solutions to this equation.

Example 4

Solve the equation $3(4x + 2) = 12x + 6$.

1. Simplify each side of the equation.

Notice that the variable x is on both sides of the equation. Also notice the set of parentheses in the expression on the left side of the equation.

Eliminate the parentheses by first distributing the 3 over $4x + 2$.

$3(4x + 2) = 12x + 6$ Multiply 3 and $4x + 2$.

$12x + 6 = 12x + 6$

2. This equation has an infinite number of solutions.

The expressions on either side of the equation are the same. This means that any value substituted for x will result in a true statement.

Example 5

Solve the literal equation $A = \dfrac{1}{2}(b_1 + b_2)h$ for b_1.

1. Isolate b_1.

    As we saw in Unit 1, to solve literal equations for a specific variable, we follow the same steps as solving equations.

    In this equation, we could distribute $\dfrac{1}{2}$ over $b_1 + b_2$, but this may cause more work for us. Instead, let's get rid of the fraction. Multiply both sides of the equation by the inverse of $\dfrac{1}{2}$, or 2.

    $$A = \frac{1}{2}(b_1 + b_2)h$$

    $$2 \bullet A = 2 \bullet \frac{1}{2}(b_1 + b_2)h$$

    $$2A = (b_1 + b_2)h$$

2. Again, you could distribute h over $b_1 + b_2$, but it's more efficient to divide both sides of the equation by h.

    $$2A = (b_1 + b_2)h$$

    $$\frac{2A}{h} = \frac{(b_1 + b_2)h}{h}$$

    $$\frac{2A}{h} = b_1 + b_2$$

3. Finally, to solve the equation for b_1, subtract b_2 from both expressions of the equation.

$$\frac{2A}{h} = b_1 + b_2$$

$$\underline{\quad -b_2 \qquad -b_2 \quad}$$

$$\frac{2A}{h} - b_2 = b_1$$

4. The equation 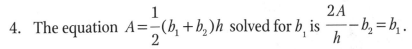 $A = \frac{1}{2}(b_1 + b_2)h$ solved for b_1 is $\frac{2A}{h} - b_2 = b_1$.

The equation can be rewritten as $b_1 = \frac{2A}{h} - b_2$ using the symmetric property of equality.

UNIT 3 • REASONING WITH EQUATIONS
Lesson 1: Solving Equations and Inequalities

Practice 3.1.2: Solving Linear Equations

Solve each equation that follows.

1. $4x - 15 = 17 - 4x$

2. $3x - 2x = -4x + 4$

3. $4t - 5t + 9 = 5t - 9$

4. $53a - 55 = 42a$

5. $3(2x - 4) = 6(x - 2)$

6. $8(3x + 2) = 2(12x - 5)$

7. $8a - 15 - 6a = 85 - 3a$

8. $3m - 5m - 12 = 7m - 88 - 50$

9. Solve the formula $n = \dfrac{a - K}{5K}$ for a.

10. Solve the formula $A = \dfrac{1}{2}h(b + c)$ for c.

Lesson 3.1.3: Solving Linear Inequalities

Introduction

Solving inequalities is similar to solving equations. To find the solution to an inequality, use methods similar to those used in solving equations. In addition to using properties of equality, we will also use properties of inequalities, to change inequalities into simpler equivalent inequalities.

Key Concepts

- The **properties of inequality** are the rules that allow you to balance, manipulate, and solve inequalities. The properties are summarized below.

Properties of Inequality

Property	Example
If $a > b$ and $b > c$, then $a > c$.	If $10 > 6$ and $6 > 2$, then $10 > 2$.
If $a > b$, then $b < a$.	If $10 > 6$, then $6 < 10$.
If $a > b$, then $-a < -b$.	If $10 > 6$, then $-10 < -6$.
If $a > b$, then $a \pm c > b \pm c$.	If $10 > 6$, then $10 \pm 2 > 6 \pm 2$.
If $a > b$ and $c > 0$, then $a \bullet c > b \bullet c$.	If $10 > 6$ and $2 > 0$, then $8 \bullet 2 > b \bullet 2$.
If $a > b$ and $c < 0$, then $a \bullet c < b \bullet c$.	If $10 > 6$ and $-1 < 0$, then $10 \bullet -1 < 6 \bullet -1$.
If $a > b$ and $c > 0$, then $a \div c > b \div c$.	If $10 > 6$ and $2 > 0$, then $8 \div 2 > 6 \div 2$.
If $a > b$ and $c < 0$, then $a \div c < b \div c$.	If $10 > 6$ and $-1 < 0$, then $10 \div -1 < 6 \div -1$.

- When solving more complicated inequalities, first simplify the inequality by clearing any parentheses. Do this by either distributing by the leading number or dividing both sides of the inequality by the leading number. Then solve the inequality by following the steps learned earlier, as outlined in the table that follows.

Solving Inequalities

1. If a variable appears on both sides of the inequality, choose which side of the inequality you would like the variable to appear on.

2. Add or subtract the other variable from both sides of the inequality using either the addition or subtraction property of equality.

3. Simplify both expressions.

4. Continue to solve the inequality by working to isolate the variable.

5. Check that your answer is correct by substituting a value included in your solution statement into the original inequality to ensure a true statement.

- It is important to remember that when solving inequalities, the direction of the inequality symbol (<, >, ≤, or ≥) changes when you divide or multiply by a negative number. Here's an example.

  - If we had the simple statement that $4 < 8$, we know that we can multiply both sides of the inequality by a number, such as 3, and the statement will still be true.

$4 < 8$	Original inequality
$4 \cdot 3 < 8 \cdot 3$	Multiply both expressions of the inequality by 3.
$12 < 24$	This is a true statement.

  - We can also divide both sides of the inequality by a number, such as 2.

$4 < 8$	Original inequality
$4 \div 2 < 8 \div 2$	Divide both expressions of the equation by 2.
$2 < 4$	This is a true statement.

  - Notice what happens when we multiply the inequality by -3.

$4 < 8$	Original inequality
$4 \cdot -3 < 8 \cdot -3$	Multiply both expressions of the inequality by -3.
$-12 < -24$	This is NOT a true statement.

  - To make this a true statement, change the direction of the inequality symbol.

$-12 > -24$	This is a true statement.

  - The same is true when dividing by a negative number; you must change the direction of the inequality symbol.

$4 < 8$	Original inequality
$4 \div -2 < 8 \div -2$	Divide both expressions of the equation by -2.
$-2 < -4$	This is NOT a true statement. Change the direction of the inequality symbol.
$-2 > -4$	This is a true statement.

Guided Practice 3.1.3

Example 1

Solve the inequality $\dfrac{-3x-4}{7} > 5$.

1. Isolate the variable by eliminating the denominator.

   In this inequality, the denominator means "divide by 7." Eliminate it by performing the inverse operation, multiplication. Multiply both expressions of the inequality by 7.

   $$7 \bullet \dfrac{-3x-4}{7} > 7 \bullet 5$$

   $$-3x - 4 > 35$$

2. Isolate the variable.

   Perform the inverse operation of adding 4 to both expressions of the inequality.

   $$-3x - 4 > 35$$
   $$\underline{+4\ \ +4}$$
   $$-3x\ \ \ \ > 39$$

   Now solve.

3. Divide both sides of the inequality by the coefficient, –3.

   $$\dfrac{-3x}{-3} > \dfrac{39}{-3}$$

   $$x < -13$$

   Notice that the direction of the inequality symbol changed because we divided by –3.

4. The solution to the original inequality $\dfrac{-3x-4}{7} > 5$ is all numbers less than -13. To check this, choose any number less than -13 to show a true statement. Let's try -20. Be sure to substitute the value into the original inequality.

$$\dfrac{-3x-4}{7} > 5 \qquad\qquad \text{Original inequality}$$

$$\dfrac{-3(-20)-4}{7} > 5 \qquad\qquad \text{Substitute } -20 \text{ for } x.$$

$$\dfrac{60-4}{7} > 5 \qquad\qquad \text{Multiply, then subtract.}$$

$$\dfrac{56}{7} > 5 \qquad\qquad \text{Simplify the fraction.}$$

$$8 > 5$$

$8 > 5$ is a true statement; therefore, all numbers less than -13 will result in a true statement.

Example 2

Solve the inequality $5x + 4 \geq 11 - 2x$.

1. Move the variable to one side of the inequality.

   Notice the variable x is in both expressions of the inequality. Begin by choosing which side you want your variable to appear on. Just like with equations, this is a choice, but most people choose to have all variables on the left side of the inequality. Continue by adding $2x$ to both expressions of the inequality.

   $$5x+4 \geq 11-2x$$
   $$\underline{+2x \qquad\qquad +2x}$$
   $$7x+4 \geq 11$$

2. Isolate the variable.

   Subtract 4 from both expressions.

   $$7x + 4 \geq 11$$
   $$\underline{-4\ -4}$$
   $$7x \quad\ \geq 7$$

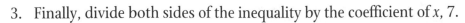

3. Finally, divide both sides of the inequality by the coefficient of x, 7.

   $$\frac{7x}{7} \geq \frac{7}{7}$$
   $$x \geq 1$$

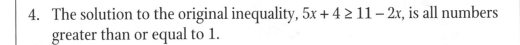

4. The solution to the original inequality, $5x + 4 \geq 11 - 2x$, is all numbers greater than or equal to 1.

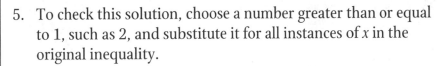

5. To check this solution, choose a number greater than or equal to 1, such as 2, and substitute it for all instances of x in the original inequality.

$5x + 4 \geq 11 - 2x$	Original inequality
$5(2) + 4 \geq 11 - 2(2)$	Substitute 2 for each instance of x.
$10 + 4 \geq 11 - 4$	Simplify each expression.
$14 \geq 7$	This is a true statement.

   Our check proved true, so we can be sure that our solution of $x \geq 1$ is accurate.

UNIT 3 • REASONING WITH EQUATIONS
Lesson 1: Solving Equations and Inequalities

Practice 3.1.3: Solving Linear Inequalities

Find the solution to each inequality.

1. $3x + 7 > 4x + 9$

2. $13x - 11 \leq 7x + 37$

3. $2(x - 3) < 3(2x + 2)$

4. $7y - 4 < 6 + 2y$

5. $2x - 1 > 4 - \dfrac{1}{2}x$

6. $\dfrac{2x}{3} - 2 < x + 6$

7. $\dfrac{5x + 3}{8} < 3x$

8. $3x - 6 \leq 3(7 + 2x)$

9. $-3(4x - 8) > 2(3 + 2x)$

10. $2x + 3x < 4x + 1$

Lesson 3.1.4: Solving Exponential Equations

Introduction

As we have already seen, exponential equations are equations that have the variable in the exponent. Some exponential equations are complex and some are quite simple. In this lesson, we will focus on solving exponential equations of the form $b^x = c$, where b is the base and x is the exponent.

Key Concepts

- It may help to look at the **laws of exponents**. These laws, sometimes referred to as properties, are the rules that must be followed when working with exponents. The following table summarizes these laws.

Laws of Exponents

Law	General rule	Specific example
Multiplication of exponents	$b^m \bullet b^n = b^{m+n}$	$4^6 \bullet 4^3 = 4^9$
Power of exponents	$(b^m)^n = b^{mn}$ $(bc)^n = b^n c^n$	$(4^6)^3 = 4^{18}$ $(4 \bullet 2)^3 = 4^3 2^3$
Division of exponents	$\dfrac{b^m}{b^n} = b^{m-n}$	$\dfrac{4^6}{4^3} = 4^{6-3} = 4^3$
Exponents of zero	$b^0 = 1$	$4^0 = 1$
Negative exponents	$b^{-n} = \dfrac{1}{b^n}$ and $\dfrac{1}{b^{-n}} = b^n$	$4^{-3} = \dfrac{1}{4^3}$ and $\dfrac{1}{4^{-3}} = 4^3$

- Keep these laws in mind when solving exponential equations.

- There are two forms of exponential equations. One form is used when each side of the equation can be written using the same base, such as $a^b = a^c$. In this case, b and c must be equal as long as $a > 0$ and $a \neq 1$.

- The second form of exponential equations is used when it isn't possible to write each side of the equation using the same base. How to solve this type of exponential equation will be covered in a later lesson.

- Follow the guidelines on the next page to solve an exponential equation where the bases of both sides of the equation can be written so that they are equal.

Solving Exponential Equations

1. Rewrite the bases as powers of a common base.

2. Substitute the rewritten bases into the original equation.

3. Simplify exponents.

4. Solve for the variable.

Guided Practice 3.1.4

Example 1

Solve $4^x = 1024$.

---

1. Rewrite the base as powers of a common base.

   You may not recognize right away if it is possible to write 1,024 as an exponential expression with a base of 4. Begin by finding values of powers of 4 to see if it is possible.

   $4^1 = 4$

   $4^2 = 16$

   $4^3 = 64$

   $4^4 = 256$

   $4^5 = 1024$

   We now know that it is possible to write 1,024 as a power of 4.

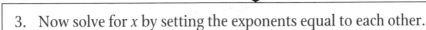

2. Rewrite the equation so both sides have a base of 4.

   $4^x = 4^5$

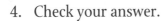

3. Now solve for x by setting the exponents equal to each other.

   $x = 5$

   The solution to the equation $4^x = 1024$ is $x = 5$.

4. Check your answer.

   Substitute 5 for the variable x in the original equation.

   $4^x = 1024$

   $4^5 = 1024$

   $1024 = 1024$ This is a true statement.

Example 2

Solve the equation $\left(\dfrac{1}{2}\right)^x = 16$.

1. Rewrite the base as powers of a common base.

   Both $\dfrac{1}{2}$ and 16 are powers of base 2.

   Referring back to the Laws of Exponents table, we know that $\dfrac{1}{2}$ is equal to 2 to the power of –1.

   16 is equal to 2 to the power of 4.

2. Rewrite the equation so both sides have a base of 2.

   $$\left(\dfrac{1}{2}\right)^x = 16$$

   $$(2^{-1})^x = 2^4$$

   Following the laws of exponents, we know that we can rewrite $(2^{-1})^x$ as 2^{-x}.

   $$(2^{-1})^x = 2^4$$

   $$2^{-x} = 2^4$$

3. Now solve for x by setting the exponents equal to each other.

   $$-x = 4$$

   Divide by –1 to isolate the variable.

   $$x = -4$$

   The solution to the equation $\left(\dfrac{1}{2}\right)^x = 16$ is $x = -4$.

4. Check your answer.

   Substitute –4 for the variable x in the original equation.

   $$\left(\frac{1}{2}\right)^x = 16$$

   $$\left(\frac{1}{2}\right)^{-4} = 16$$

   $$2^4 = 16$$

   $$16 = 16 \qquad \text{This is a true statement.}$$

Example 3

Solve the equation $\dfrac{1}{49} = 7^x$.

1. Rewrite the base as powers of a common base.

   $\dfrac{1}{49}$ can be rewritten as $\dfrac{1}{7^2}$.

   Referring back to the Laws of Exponents table, we know that $\dfrac{1}{7^2}$ is equal to 7 to the power of –2.

2. Rewrite the equation so both sides have a base of 7.

   $$\frac{1}{49} = 7^x$$

   $$\frac{1}{7^2} = 7^x$$

   $$7^{-2} = 7^x$$

3. Now solve for x by setting the exponents equal to each other.

$x = -2$

The solution to the equation $\dfrac{1}{49} = 7^x$ is $x = -2$.

4. Check your answer.

Substitute -2 for the variable x in the original equation.

$$\dfrac{1}{49} = 7^x$$

$$\dfrac{1}{49} = 7^{-2}$$

$$\dfrac{1}{49} = \dfrac{1}{7^2}$$

$$\dfrac{1}{49} = \dfrac{1}{49} \qquad \text{This is a true statement.}$$

Example 4

Solve the equation $117 = 5^x - 8$.

1. Begin by eliminating the subtraction of 8 from the right side of the equal sign. Do so by adding 8 to each side of the equation.

$$117 = 5^x - 8$$
$$\underline{+8 \qquad\quad +8}$$
$$125 = 5^x$$

2. Rewrite the base as powers of a common base.

125 can be rewritten as 5 to the power of 3.

3. Rewrite the equation so both sides have a base of 5.

$125 = 5^x$

$5^3 = 5^x$

4. Now solve for x by setting the exponents equal to each other.

$x = 3$

The solution to the equation $117 = 5^x - 8$ is $x = 3$.

5. Check your answer.

Substitute 3 in for the variable x of the original equation.

$117 = 5^x - 8$

$117 = 5^3 - 8$

$117 = 125 - 8$

$117 = 117$ This is a true statement.

UNIT 3 • REASONING WITH EQUATIONS
Lesson 1: Solving Equations and Inequalities

Practice 3.1.4: Solving Exponential Equations

Solve for x.

1. $16 = 2^x$

2. $5^x = 15,625$

3. $\dfrac{1}{16} = 4^x$

4. $6^x = \dfrac{1}{1296}$

5. $27 = \left(\dfrac{1}{3}\right)^x$

6. $\left(\dfrac{1}{7}\right)^x = 49$

7. $81 = 3^x$

8. $0.008 = 0.2^x$

9. $131 = 5^x + 6$

10. $12 = 512^x + 4$

Lesson 2: Solving Systems of Equations

Common Core State Standards

A–REI.5 Prove that, given a system of two equations in two variables, replacing one equation by the sum of that equation and a multiple of the other produces a system with the same solutions.

A–REI.6 Solve systems of linear equations exactly and approximately (e.g., with graphs), focusing on pairs of linear equations in two variables.

Essential Questions

1. What does it mean for two systems of linear equations to be equivalent to each other?

2. How many solutions can a system of equations have?

3. Why is knowing the solution to a system of equations helpful in the real world?

4. What are the benefits of having different types of strategies to solve systems of equations related to real-world situations?

WORDS TO KNOW

consistent	a system of equations with at least one ordered pair that satisfies both equations
dependent	a system of equations that has an infinite number of solutions; lines coincide when graphed
elimination method	adding or subtracting the equations in the system together so that one of the variables is eliminated; multiplication might be necessary before adding the equations together
graphing method	solving a system by graphing equations on the same coordinate plane and finding the point of intersection
inconsistent	a system of equations with no solutions; lines are parallel when graphed

independent	a system of equations with exactly one solution
point of intersection	the point at which two lines cross or meet
substitution method	solving one of a pair of equations for one of the variables and substituting that into the other equation
system of equations	a set of equations with the same unknowns

Recommended Resources

- Math Warehouse. "Interactive System of Linear Equations."

  http://walch.com/rr/CAU2L2InteractiveGraph

  This site features an interactive graph of a system of equations. Users can move the various points around to observe how the solution changes.

- Purplemath. "Systems of Linear Equations."

  http://walch.com/rr/CAU2L2LinearEquations

  This resource provides a summary of systems of linear equations and methods to solve them.

- Tutorials for *Finite Math.* "Systems of Two Linear Equations in Two Unknowns."

  http://walch.com/rr/CAU2L2EquationTutorial

  This tutorial summarizes systems of linear equations and methods to solve them.

Lesson 3.2.1: Proving Equivalencies

Introduction

Two equations that are solved together are called **systems of equations**. The solution to a system of equations is the point or points that make both equations true. Systems of equations can have one solution, no solutions, or an infinite number of solutions. Finding the solution to a system of equations is important to many real-world applications.

Key Concepts

- There are various methods to solving a system of equations. Two methods include the **substitution method** and the **elimination method**.

Solving Systems of Equations by Substitution

- This method involves solving one of the equations for one of the variables and substituting that into the other equation.

Substitution Method
1. Solve one of the equations for one of the variables in terms of the other variable.
2. Substitute, or replace the resulting expression into the other equation.
3. Solve the equation for the second variable.
4. Substitute the found value into either of the original equations to find the value of the other variable.

- Solutions to systems are written as an ordered pair, (x, y). This is where the lines would cross if graphed.

- If the resulting solution is a true statement, such as $9 = 9$, then the system has an infinite number of solutions. This is where lines would coincide if graphed.

- If the result is an untrue statement, such as $4 = 9$, then the system has no solutions. This is where lines would be parallel if graphed.

- Check your answer by substituting the x and y values back into the original equations. If the answer is correct, the equations will result in true statements.

Solving Systems of Equations by Elimination Using Addition or Subtraction

- This method involves adding or subtracting the equations in the system so that one of the variables is eliminated.

- Properties of equality allow us to combine the equations by adding or subtracting the equations to eliminate one of the variables.

Elimination Method Using Addition or Subtraction
1. Add the two equations if the coefficients of one of the variables are opposites of each other.
2. Subtract the two equations if the coefficients of one of the variables are the same.
3. Solve the equation for the second variable.
4. Substitute the found value into either of the original equations to find the value of the other variable.

Solving Systems of Equations by Elimination Using Multiplication

- This method is used when one set of the variables are neither opposites nor the same. Applying the multiplication property of equality changes one or both equations.

Elimination Method Using Multiplication
1. Multiply each term of the equation by the same number. It may be necessary to multiply the second equation by a different number in order to have one set of variables that are opposites or the same.
2. Add or subtract the two equations to eliminate one of the variables.
3. Solve the equation for the second variable.
4. Substitute the found value into either of the original equations to find the value of the other variable.

- Solving a system of equations algebraically will always result in an exact answer.

Guided Practice 3.2.1

Example 1

Solve the following system by substitution.

$$\begin{cases} x+y=2 \\ x-y=0 \end{cases}$$

1. Solve one of the equations for one of the variables in terms of the other variable.

   It doesn't matter which equation you choose, nor does it matter which variable you solve for.

   Let's solve $x + y = 2$ for the variable y.

   Isolate y by subtracting x from both sides.

   $$\begin{array}{r} x+y= 2 \\ \underline{-x \qquad\quad -x} \\ y= 2 -x \end{array}$$

   Now we know that y is equal to $2 - x$.

2. Substitute, or replace $2 - x$ into the other equation, $x - y = 0$.

   It helps to place parentheses around the expression you are substituting.

$x - y = 0$	Second equation of the system
$x - (2 - x) = 0$	Substitute $(2 - x)$ for y.

3. Solve the equation for the second variable.

$$x - (2 - x) = 0$$

$x - 2 + x = 0$ Distribute the negative over $(2 - x)$.

$2x - 2 = 0$ Simplify.

$2x = 2$ Add 2 to both sides.

$x = 1$ Divide both sides by 2.

4. Substitute the found value, $(x = 1)$, into either of the original equations to find the value of the other variable.

$x + y = 2$ First equation of the system

$(1) + y = 2$ Substitute 1 for x.

$1 + y = 2$ Simplify.

$y = 1$ Subtract 1 from both sides.

The solution to the system of equations is (1, 1).
If graphed, the lines would cross at (1, 1).

Example 2

Solve the following system by elimination.

$$\begin{cases} 2x-3y=-11 \\ x+3y=11 \end{cases}$$

---

1. Add the two equations if the coefficients of one of the variables are opposites of each other.

   $3y$ and $-3y$ are opposites, so the equations can be added.

   Add downward, combining like terms only.

   $2x-3y=-11$

   $\underline{x\ +3y=\ \ \ 11}$

   $3x+0\ =\ \ \ 0$

   Simplify.

   $3x = 0$

---

2. Solve the equation for the second variable.

   $3x = 0$

   $x = 0$ Divide both sides by 3.

---

3. Substitute the found value, $x = 0$, into either of the original equations to find the value of the other variable.

   $2x - 3y = -11$ First equation of the system

   $2(0) - 3y = -11$ Substitute 0 for x.

   $-3y = -11$ Simplify.

   $y = \dfrac{11}{3}$ Divide both sides by –3.

4. The solution to the system of equations is $\left(0, \dfrac{11}{3}\right)$.

If graphed, the lines would cross at $\left(0, \dfrac{11}{3}\right)$.

Example 3

Solve the following system by multiplication.

$$\begin{cases} x - 3y = 5 \\ -2x + 6y = 4 \end{cases}$$

1. Multiply each term of the equation by the same number.

   The variable x has a coefficient of 1 in the first equation and a coefficient of −2 in the second equation. Multiply the first equation by 2.

$x - 3y = 5$	Original equation
$2(x - 3y = 5)$	Multiply the equation by 2.
$2x - 6y = 10$	

2. Add or subtract the two equations to eliminate one of the variables.

   $$\begin{aligned} 2x - 6y &= 10 \\ +(-2x + 6y &= 4) \\ \hline 0 + 0 &= 14 \end{aligned}$$

3. Simplify.

   $0 + 0 = 14$

   $0 = 14$ This is NOT a true statement.

4. The system $\begin{cases} x - 3y = 5 \\ -2x + 6y = 4 \end{cases}$ does not have a solution. There are no points that will make both equations true.

UNIT 3 • REASONING WITH EQUATIONS
Lesson 2: Solving Systems of Equations

Practice 3.2.1: Proving Equivalencies

Find the solution to each of the following systems by using the substitution method.

1. $\begin{cases} y+3x=28 \\ 4x+y=10 \end{cases}$

2. A-Plus Cellphone Service charges $0.08 for each minute used. Better Brand Cellphone Service charges $0.06 per minute, but also charges a fee of $8 per month. Write and solve a system of equations that you could use to determine the number of minutes when the cost of the two cell phone plans is the same.

Find the solution to each of the following systems by using the elimination method.

3. $\begin{cases} x-2y=3 \\ 3x-6y=9 \end{cases}$

4. At a pizzeria, the cost of 3 pizzas and 5 beverages is $36.10. The cost for 2 pizzas and 3 beverages is $23.65. Write and solve a system of equations to find the cost of 1 pizza and 1 beverage.

Choose an appropriate method to solve each system of equations, then find the solution.

5. $\begin{cases} 5x+15y=5 \\ 3x+2y=-11 \end{cases}$

6. $\begin{cases} 2x=3y \\ 4x-3y=12 \end{cases}$

UNIT 3 • REASONING WITH EQUATIONS
Lesson 2: Solving Systems of Equations

For problems 7–10, write a system of equations, choose an appropriate method to solve each system, and then solve it.

7. You spent $12 at the store for milk and muffins for your friends. One bottle of milk costs $1.35, and each muffin costs $1.10. You bought 10 items. How many bottles of milk and muffins did you buy?

8. Tickets to the movies cost $8 for adults and $5 for children. A group of 20 adults and children are attending the movies. If the total cost was $118, how many adult tickets and how many child tickets were purchased?

9. Nina invests $1,750 into two savings accounts. One account earns 3.5% annual interest and the other earns 4.7% annual interest. At the end of 1 year, Nina earned $73.85 in interest. How much did she invest at each rate?

10. Mikhail bought 7 shirts and 4 pairs of shoes for $490. His friend, who paid the same prices, bought 5 shirts and 2 pairs of shoes for $290. How much does each shirt and each pair of shoes cost?

Lesson 3.2.2: Solving Systems of Linear Equations

Introduction

The solution to a system of equations is the point or points that make both equations true. Systems of equations can have one solution, no solutions, or an infinite number of solutions. On a graph, the solution to a system of equations can be easily seen. The solution to the system is the **point of intersection**, the point at which two lines cross or meet.

Key Concepts

- There are various methods to solving a system of equations. One is the **graphing method**.

Solving Systems of Equations by Graphing

- Graphing a system of equations on the same coordinate plane allows you to visualize the solution to the system.

- Use a table of values, the slope-intercept form ($y = mx + b$) of the equations, or a graphing calculator.

- Creating a table of values can be time consuming depending on the equations, but will work for all equations.

- Equations not written in slope-intercept form will need to be rewritten in order to determine the slope and y-intercept.

- Once graphed, you can determine the number of solutions the system has.

- Graphs of systems with one solution have two intersecting lines. The point of intersection is the solution to the system. These systems are considered **consistent**, or having at least one solution, and are also **independent**, meaning there is exactly one solution.

- Graphs of systems with no solution have parallel lines. There are no points that satisfy both of the equations. These systems are referred to as **inconsistent**.

- Systems with an infinite number of solutions are equations of the same line— the lines for the equations in the system overlap. These are referred to as **dependent** and also consistent, having at least one solution.

Intersecting Lines	Parallel Lines	Same Line
One solution	No solutions	Infinitely many solutions
Consistent Independent	Inconsistent	Consistent Dependent

- Graphing the system of equations can sometimes be inaccurate, but solving the system algebraically will always give an exact answer.

Graphing Equations Using a TI-83/84:

Step 1: Press [Y=] and key in the first equation using [X, T, θ, n] for x.

Step 2: Press [ENTER] and key in the second equation.

Step 3: Press [WINDOW] to change the viewing window, if necessary.

Step 4: Enter in appropriate values for Xmin, Xmax, Xscl, Ymin, Ymax, and Yscl, using the arrow keys to navigate.

Step 5: Press [GRAPH].

Step 6: Press [2ND] and [TRACE] to access the Calculate Menu.

Step 7: Choose 5: intersect.

Step 8: Press [ENTER] 3 times for the point of intersection.

Graphing Equations Using a TI-Nspire:

Step 1: Press the home key.

Step 2: Arrow over to the graphing icon (the picture of the parabola or the U-shaped curve) and press [enter].

Step 3: At the blinking cursor at the bottom of the screen, enter in the equation and press [enter].

Step 4: To change the viewing window: press [menu], arrow down to number 4: Window/Zoom, and click the center button of the navigation pad.

Step 5: Choose 1: Window settings by pressing the center button.

Step 6: Enter in the appropriate XMin, XMax, YMin, and YMax fields.

Step 7: Leave the XScale and YScale set to auto.

Step 8: Use [tab] to navigate among the fields.

Step 9: Press [tab] to "OK" when done and press [enter].

Step 10: Press [tab] to enter the second equation, then press [enter].

Step 11: Enter the second equation and press [enter].

Step 12: Press [menu] and choose 6: Analyze Graph.

Step 13: Choose 4: Intersection.

Step 14: Select the lower bound.

Step 15: Select the upper bound.

Guided Practice 3.2.2

Example 1

Graph the system of equations. Then determine whether the system has one solution, no solution, or infinitely many solutions. If the system has a solution, name it.

$$\begin{cases} 4x - 6y = 12 \\ y = -x + 3 \end{cases}$$

1. Solve each equation for y.

   The first equation needs to be solved for y.

$4x - 6y = 12$	Original equation
$-6y = 12 - 4x$	Subtract $4x$ from both sides.
$y = -2 + \dfrac{2}{3}x$	Divide both sides by -6.
$y = \dfrac{2}{3}x - 2$	Write the equation in slope-intercept form $(y = mx + b)$.

   The second equation $(y = -x + 3)$ is already in slope-intercept form.

2. Graph both equations using the slope-intercept method.

The y-intercept of $y = \dfrac{2}{3}x - 2$ is –2. The slope is $\dfrac{2}{3}$.

The y-intercept of $y = -x + 3$ is 3. The slope is –1.

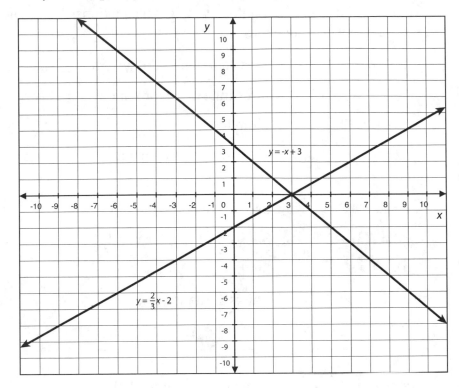

3. Observe the graph.

The lines intersect at the point (3, 0).

This appears to be the solution to this system of equations.

To check, substitute (3, 0) into both original equations. The result should be a true statement.

$4x - 6y = 12$	First equation in the system
$4(3) - 6(0) = 12$	Substitute (3, 0) for x and y.
$12 - 0 = 12$	Simplify.
$12 = 12$	This is a true statement.

$y = -x + 3$	Second equation in the system
$(0) = -(3) + 3$	Substitute (3, 0) for x and y.
$0 = -3 + 3$	Simplify.
$0 = 0$	This is a true statement.

4. The system $\begin{cases} 4x - 6y = 12 \\ y = -x + 3 \end{cases}$ has one solution, (3, 0).

Example 2

Graph the system of equations. Then determine whether the system has one solution, no solution, or infinitely many solutions. If the system has a solution, name it.

$$\begin{cases} -8x + 4y = 4 \\ y = 2x + 1 \end{cases}$$

1. Solve each equation for y.

   The first equation needs to be solved for y.

$-8x + 4y = 4$	Original equation
$4y = 4 + 8x$	Add $8x$ to both sides.
$y = 1 + 2x$	Divide both sides by 4.
$y = 2x + 1$	Write the equation in slope-intercept form ($y = mx + b$).

   The second equation ($y = 2x + 1$) is already in slope-intercept form.

2. Graph both equations using the slope-intercept method.

   The y-intercept of both equations is 1.

   The slope of both equations is 2.

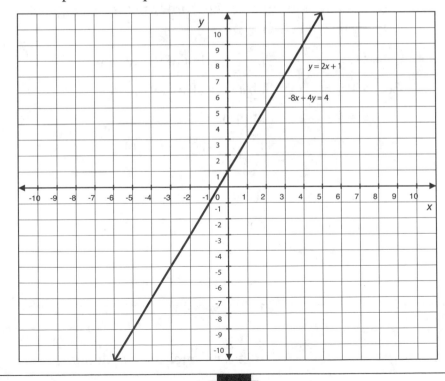

3. Observe the graph.

The graphs of $y = 2x + 1$ and $-8x + 4y = 4$ are the same line.

There are infinitely many solutions to this system of equations.

To check, choose any point on the graph of $-8x + 4y = 4$ and substitute it into both original equations. The result should be a true statement. Let's use (2, 5).

$-8x + 4y = 4$	First equation of the system
$-8(2) + 4(5) = 4$	Substitute (2, 5) for x and y.
$-16 + 20 = 4$	Simplify.
$4 = 4$	This is a true statement.

$y = 2x + 1$	Second equation of the system
$(5) = 2(2) + 1$	Substitute (2, 5) for x and y.
$5 = 4 + 1$	Simplify.
$5 = 5$	This is a true statement.

You could choose any other point on the line of $-8x + 4y = 4$ to show it is true for any point, and not just for the point you originally chose. Let's try again with (1, 3).

$-8x + 4y = 4$	First equation of the system
$-8(1) + 4(3) = 4$	Substitute (1, 3) for x and y.
$-8 + 12 = 4$	Simplify.
$4 = 4$	This is a true statement.

$y = 2x + 1$	Second equation of the system
$(3) = 2(1) + 1$	Substitute (1, 3) for x and y.
$3 = 2 + 1$	Simplify.
$3 = 3$	This is a true statement.

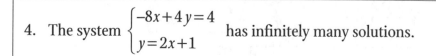

4. The system $\begin{cases} -8x + 4y = 4 \\ y = 2x + 1 \end{cases}$ has infinitely many solutions.

Example 3

Graph the system of equations. Then determine whether the system has one solution, no solution, or infinitely many solutions. If the system has a solution, name it.

$$\begin{cases} -6x + 2y = 8 \\ y = 3x - 5 \end{cases}$$

1. Solve each equation for y.

   The first equation needs to be solved for y.

$-6x + 2y = 8$	Original equation
$2y = 8 + 6x$	Add $6x$ to both sides.
$y = 4 + 3x$	Divide both sides by 2.
$y = 3x + 4$	Write in slope-intercept form ($y = mx + b$).

   The second equation ($y = 3x - 5$) is already in slope-intercept form.

2. Graph both equations using the slope-intercept method.

   The y-intercept of $y = 3x + 4$ is 4. The slope is 3.

   The y-intercept of $y = 3x - 5$ is –5. The slope is 3.

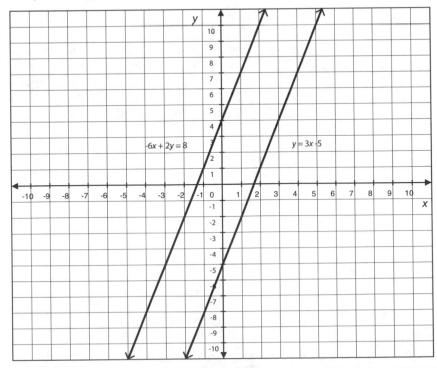

3. Observe the graph.

    The graphs of $-6x + 2y = 8$ and $y = 3x - 5$ are parallel lines and never cross.

    There are no values for x and y that will make both equations true.

4. The system $\begin{cases} -6x+2y=8 \\ y=3x-5 \end{cases}$ has no solutions.

Practice 3.2.2: Solving Systems of Linear Equations

Graph each system of equations. Determine whether the system has one solution, no solution, or infinitely many solutions. If the system has a solution, name it.

1. $\begin{cases} 2x-3y=-6 \\ 4x+12y=60 \end{cases}$

3. $\begin{cases} 4x-y=3 \\ 8y=32x-24 \end{cases}$

2. $\begin{cases} x+y=4 \\ x-y=6 \end{cases}$

4. $\begin{cases} 3x-y=10 \\ 2y=6x-4 \end{cases}$

For problems 5–10, write a system of equations, and then use the graphing method to solve each system.

5. Luis spent $9.50 on snacks at the basketball game. Candy costs $1.25 per package and chips cost $0.50. Luis bought 10 snacks. Graph a system of equations that you could use to determine how many of each type of snack he bought.

6. Movie tickets are $9.00 for adults and $5.50 for children. One evening, the theater sold 45 tickets worth $273. How many adult tickets were sold? How many children's tickets were sold?

7. A test worth 100 points has 14 questions. Short-answer questions are worth 5 points and essay questions are worth 15 points. How many short-answer questions are on the test? How many essay questions are on the test?

8. The basketball team scored a total of 109 points last game. They made a total of 47 shots, including 2-point shots and 3-point shots. How many 2-point shots did they make? How many 3-point shots did they make?

9. Abe is selling lollipops and chocolate bars for a fund-raiser. Lollipops sell for $0.50 and chocolate bars sell for $1.25. Abe sold 37 pieces of candy for a total of $29. How many lollipops did Abe sell? How many chocolate bars did Abe sell?

10. Esther has a total of 23 dimes and pennies. The value of her coins is $1.85. How many dimes does Esther have? How many pennies does Esther have?

Unit 4
Descriptive Statistics

Lesson 1: Working with a Single Measurement Variable

Common Core State Standards

S–ID.1   Represent data with plots on the real number line (dot plots, histograms, and box plots).★

S–ID.2   Use statistics appropriate to the shape of the data distribution to compare center (median, mean) and spread (interquartile range, standard deviation) of two or more different data sets.★

S–ID.3   Interpret differences in shape, center, and spread in the context of the data sets, accounting for possible effects of extreme data points (outliers).★

Essential Questions

1. What do measures of spread describe about a data set?

2. What can be learned about a data set by looking at a frequency plot?

3. How can two data sets be compared quantitatively?

4. How do outliers influence measures of center?

WORDS TO KNOW

box plot

a plot showing the minimum, maximum, first quartile, median, and third quartile of a data set; the middle 50% of the data is indicated by a box. Example:

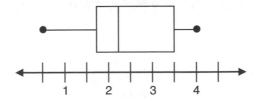

dot plot	a frequency plot that shows the number of times a response occurred in a data set, where each data value is represented by a dot. Example:

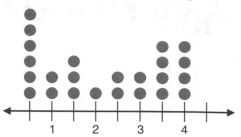

first quartile	the value that identifies the lower 25% of the data; the median of the lower half of the data set; written as Q_1
histogram	a frequency plot that shows the number of times a response or range of responses occurred in a data set. Example:

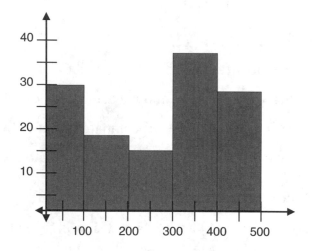

interquartile range	the difference between the third and first quartiles; 50% of the data is contained within this range
mean	the average value of a data set, found by summing all values, and dividing by the number of data points
mean absolute deviation	the average absolute value of the difference between each data point and the mean; found by summing the absolute value of the difference between each data point and the mean, then dividing this sum by the total number of data points
measures of center	values that describe expected and repeated data values in a data set; the mean and median are two measures of center

measures of spread	a measure that describes the variance of data values, and identifies the diversity of values in a data set
median	the middle-most value of a data set; 50% of the data is less than this value, and 50% is greater than it
outlier	a data value that is much greater than or much less than the rest of the data in a data set; mathematically, any data less than $Q_1 - 1.5(IQR)$ or greater than $Q_3 + 1.5(IQR)$ is an outlier
skewed to the left	data concentrated on the higher values in the data set, which has a tail to the left. Example:

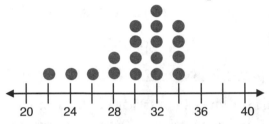

skewed to the right	data concentrated on the lower values in the data set, which has a tail to the right. Example:

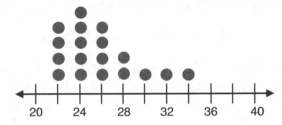

symmetric	situation in which data is concentrated toward the middle of the range of data; data values are distributed in the same way above and below the middle of the sample. Example:

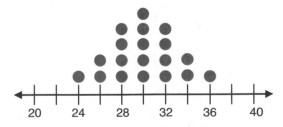

third quartile	value that identifies the upper 25% of the data; the median of the upper half of the data set; 75% of all data is less than this value; written as Q_3

Recommended Resources

- Braining Camp. "Box Plots—Questions."

  http://walch.com/rr/CAU4L1BoxPlotQuestions

  This site provides an interactive quiz with 10 multiple-choice questions about box plots. The computer scores the results.

- Khan Academy. "Box-and-whisker Plot."

  http://walch.com/rr/CAU4L1BoxPlotVideo

  This video demonstrates how to create a box plot (also known as a box-and-whisker plot) given a data set. Available for free.

- Math Is Fun! "Histograms."

  http://walch.com/rr/CAU4L1Histograms

  This site gives an overview of what histograms are and aren't. Users can answer questions about histograms, and the computer scores the results.

- Onlinestatbook.com. "Dot Plots."

  http://walch.com/rr/CAU4L1DotPlots

  This site describes four different types of dot plots and then asks questions about interpreting the dot plots.

Lesson 4.1.1: Representing Data Sets

Introduction

Measures of center and variability can be used to describe a data set. The mean and median are two measures of center. The **mean** is the average value of the data. The **median** is the middle-most value in a data set. These measures are used to generalize data sets and identify common or expected values. Interquartile range and mean absolute deviation describe variability of the data set. **Interquartile range** is the difference between the third and first quartiles. The **first quartile** is the median of the lower half of the data set. The **third quartile** is the median of the upper half of the data set. The **mean absolute deviation** is the average absolute value of the difference between each data point and the mean. **Measures of spread** describe the variance of data values (how spread out they are), and identify the diversity of values in a data set. Measures of spread are used to help explain whether data values are very similar or very different.

Data can be represented graphically using a number line. Graphs provide a visual representation of data; just by looking at a graph, you can quickly understand the spread and center of a data set. Dot plots and histograms show the frequency of a data value. In a **dot plot,** each data value is represented by a dot. The number of times a value is repeated corresponds to the number of dots above that value. In a **histogram,** the height of a rectangle above a value corresponds to the number of data values with that value. When looking at either a dot plot or histogram, it is easy to see both the most repeated data values and the spread of the data. If a data set is large, a histogram is easier to use because a single dot does not need to be drawn for each data value.

A **box plot** shows the minimum, maximum, first quartile, median, and third quartile of numerical data. The middle 50% of the data is represented with a box. Lines on either side of the box extend to the minimum and maximum data values. A box plot shows the range of data in a data set, and measures of center can be easily seen on a box plot. Box plots can be used to compare expected values of multiple data sets.

Key Concepts

- Numerical data can be represented graphically on the real number line.

- Dot plots and histograms show the frequency of each data value in a data set.

- Each data value in a data set is represented by a dot over that value in a dot plot.

- In a histogram, a rectangle is drawn above each value in a data set. The height of each rectangle corresponds to the number of data points with that value.

- A histogram can show the frequency of a range of values.

- The minimum, maximum, first quartile, median, and third quartile of a data set must be calculated before creating a box plot.

- In a box plot, a rectangle is drawn starting at the first quartile and ending at the third quartile. The rectangle shows the middle 50% of the data set. The median is represented in the rectangle by a line. Whiskers are drawn from the rectangle to the minimum and maximum data values.

- A box plot shows more information about the expected value of a data set than a dot plot or histogram.

- A dot plot or histogram provides information about the size of a data set, which cannot be seen in a box plot.

Guided Practice 4.1.1

Example 1

A pharmacy records the number of customers each hour that the pharmacy is open. The staff is using the information to determine how many people need to be working at the pharmacy at each time of day. The number of customers is in the table below. Use the table to create a histogram to help the pharmacy staff understand how many customers are in the pharmacy at each time of day.

Time frame	Number of customers
8:00 A.M.–9:00 A.M.	2
9:00 A.M.–10:00 A.M.	0
10:00 A.M.–11:00 A.M.	8
11:00 A.M.–12:00 P.M.	14
12:00 P.M.–1:00 P.M.	23
1:00 P.M.–2:00 P.M.	12
2:00 P.M.–3:00 P.M.	7
3:00 P.M.–4:00 P.M.	3
4:00 P.M.–5:00 P.M.	5

1. Draw a number line on an *x*-axis that corresponds to the range of the data.

   The *x*-axis for this data will show the times the customers were counted. The number line for the pharmacy must include the times from 8:00 A.M. until 5:00 P.M. If using a number line that counts by twos, extend the number line to 6:00 P.M.

   8:00 A.M.   10:00 A.M.   12:00 P.M.   2:00 P.M.   4:00 P.M.   6:00 P.M.

2. Draw a *y*-axis that corresponds to the least and greatest number of times a data value is repeated. The *y*-axis should be to the left of the labeled *x*-axis.

   The number of customers arriving in each time frame ranges from 0 customers to 23 customers. The *y*-axis needs to show values from 0 to 23. If using a number line that counts by twos, extend the number line to 24.

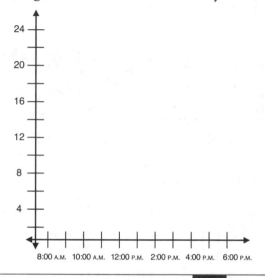

3. Create a rectangle at each value showing the number of data points at each data value.

   The rectangles will each span an hour, and will show the number of customers in that hour. There will be no rectangle from 9:00 A.M. to 10:00 A.M., because there were no customers at that hour.

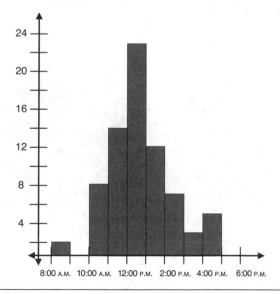

Example 2

Anna and Ethan watch 20 thirty-minute shows during the month of June. They record the number of commercials that air during each show in the table below. Create a dot plot to display the number of commercials that aired during the 20 shows.

Television show	Number of commercials
A	17
B	17
C	15
D	17
E	14
F	17
G	15
H	19
I	15
J	16
K	12
L	14
M	15
N	17
O	18
P	18
Q	18
R	18
S	13
T	14

1. Arrange the data from least to greatest.

Television show	Number of commercials
K	12
S	13
E	14
L	14
T	14
C	15
G	15
I	15
M	15
J	16
A	17
B	17
D	17
F	17
N	17
O	18
P	18
Q	18
R	18
H	19

2. Draw a number line on an *x*-axis that corresponds to the range of the data values.

   The *x*-axis for this data will show the number of commercials during a 30-minute television show. The number line must include values from 12 to 19. If counting by twos, extend the number line to 20.

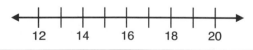

3. Draw each data value as a dot above the number line. The number of dots above each data value should show the number of times that value occurs in the data set.

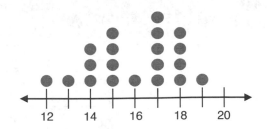

Example 3

The website Rate My Phone conducts reviews of smartphones. One aspect of the phones that is tested is battery life. The minutes of battery life for the newest 25 phones is recorded in the table below. Draw a box plot to represent the data.

Smartphone	Minutes of battery life	Smartphone	Minutes of battery life
A	380	N	470
B	530	O	280
C	350	P	300
D	390	Q	440
E	520	R	490
F	520	S	530
G	430	T	340
H	330	U	250
I	550	V	260
J	290	W	730
K	360	X	520
L	550	Y	320
M	370		

1. Order the data from least to greatest. Note the minimum and maximum data values.

Smartphone	Minutes of battery life	Smartphone	Minutes of battery life
U	250	G	430
V	260	Q	440
O	280	N	470
J	290	R	490
P	300	X	510
Y	320	E	520
H	330	F	520
T	340	B	530
C	350	S	530
K	360	I	550
M	370	L	550
A	380	W	730
D	390		

The minimum data value is 250, and the maximum data value is 730.

2. Find the median of the data.

The median is the middle-most data value. There are an odd number of data values, so the median is the 13th data value, 390.

3. Find the first quartile of the data.

The first quartile is the middle-most value of the lower half of the data. There are 12 data values in the lower half of the data, so the first quartile is the average of the sixth and seventh data values (320 and 330).

$$\frac{320+330}{2} = 325$$

4. Find the third quartile of the data.

   The third quartile is the middle-most value of the upper half of the data. There are 12 data values in the upper half of the data, so the third quartile is the average of the 19th and 20th data values (520 and 520).

   $$\frac{520+520}{2}=520$$

5. Draw a number line that includes the minimum and maximum data values.

   The minimum data value is 250, and the maximum data value is 730. If counting by 50s, extend the number line to 750.

6. Draw a box, beginning at the first quartile (325) and ending at the third quartile (520).

   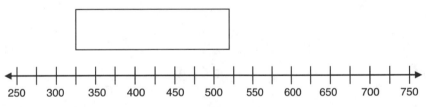

7. Draw a line in the box at the median (390).

   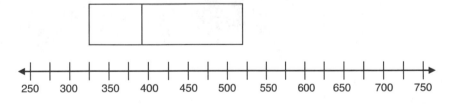

8. Draw a point at the minimum and maximum data values (250 and 730).

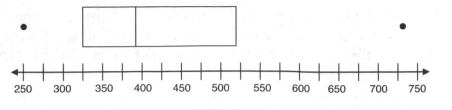

9. Connect the minimum and maximum data values to the box.

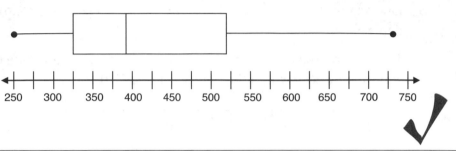

UNIT 4 • DESCRIPTIVE STATISTICS
Lesson 1: Working with a Single Measurement Variable

Practice 4.1.1: Representing Data Sets

The following table lists Knoxville's average temperature for 15 days of May, in degrees Fahrenheit. Use the table to complete problems 1–3.

Day	Temperature in °F	Day	Temperature in °F
1	61	9	64
2	63	10	58
3	68	11	61
4	73	12	69
5	65	13	72
6	69	14	74
7	77	15	73
8	74		

1. What are the minimum, maximum, and median temperatures for these 15 days of May?

2. What are the first and third quartiles of the data?

3. Create a box plot to show the distribution of the temperatures over these 15 days.

UNIT 4 • DESCRIPTIVE STATISTICS
Lesson 1: Working with a Single Measurement Variable

The following table shows Birmingham's average rainfall each month, rounded to the nearest half-inch. Use the table to complete problems 4 and 5.

Month	Rainfall in inches
January	5
February	4.5
March	5.5
April	4
May	4
June	4
July	5
August	3.5
September	4
October	3.5
November	4
December	4

4. A farmer is considering buying land near Birmingham. He only wants to buy the land if he can expect more than 3.5 inches of rainfall per month for at least 6 months out of the year. Which type of graph would show this information? Explain.

5. Create the graph you identified in problem 4.

continued

UNIT 4 • DESCRIPTIVE STATISTICS
Lesson 1: Working with a Single Measurement Variable

A toy shop manager tracks sales of store gift cards. Gift cards are only sold in $5, $10, $15, $20, $25, or $30 denominations. The denominations of the 15 most recent gift cards sold are in the table below. Use the data in it to complete problems 6–10.

Customer	Gift card value	Customer	Gift card value
1	$20	9	$20
2	$10	10	$25
3	$25	11	$15
4	$5	12	$5
5	$5	13	$20
6	$15	14	$10
7	$10	15	$10
8	$15		

6. The toy shop manager wants to understand how many of each type of gift card are being sold. Which type of graph would show this information? Explain.

7. Create the graph identified in problem 6.

8. The toy shop manager also wants to understand the center and spread of the gift card values. Which type of graph would show this information? Explain.

9. Create the graph identified in problem 8.

10. The shop's customers buy 15 more gift cards. The median gift card value of this set of 15 gift cards is $20. How does this compare to the gift card values in the table?

Lesson 4.1.2: Comparing Data Sets

Introduction

Data sets can be compared by examining the differences and similarities between measures of center and spread. The mean and median of a data set are measures of center. These measures describe the expected value of a data set. The mean absolute deviation is a measure of spread that describes the range of data values, with respect to the mean. The mean absolute deviation is the average of the absolute values of the differences between each data value and the mean. The interquartile range is a measure of spread that describes the range of the middle 50% of a data set. The interquartile range is the difference between the third and first quartiles.

The center and spread of a data set can also be seen in the shape of a graphical representation of the data. The range of data values can be seen in the x-axis of a graphical representation. Clusters of data values can be seen in graphs that show frequency, such as dot plots and histograms. The interquartile range and median are shown in box plots.

Key Concepts

- Measures of center, such as the mean and median, describe the expected value of a data set. The mean is influenced by very small or large data values, whereas the median is not.

- Measures of spread describe the range of data in a set. Interquartile range and mean absolute deviation are measures of spread.

- The interquartile range shows the range of the middle 50% of a data set. It is the difference between the third and first quartiles.

- The mean absolute deviation compares data values to the mean of a data set. If the mean absolute deviation is large, this is a sign that the data points are distributed farther from the mean.

- Two or more data sets can be compared using measures of center and spread. When choosing a measure of center or spread, identify whether there are very large or very small data values that may influence the mean.

- Data can be compared graphically. The shape of a data set can be seen in a frequency plot, such as a dot plot or histogram.

- Data that is **symmetric** is concentrated toward the middle of the range of data. The data is arranged the same way on both sides, as seen in the diagram on the following page.

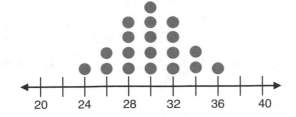

- Data that is **skewed to the right** is concentrated toward the lower range of the data; it has a tail to the right.

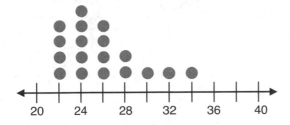

- Data that is **skewed to the left** is concentrated toward the upper range of the data; it has a tail to the left.

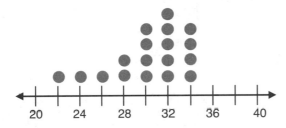

- Data that is widely or evenly distributed has greater variation, and data that clusters around a set of values has less variation.

- Data can also be compared using a box plot. The width of the box displays the range of the middle 50% of the data; the width increases as variation increases.

Guided Practice 4.1.2

Example 1

Two hockey teams recorded the number of goals scored in each game in the tables below. Use the tables to compare the expected number of goals scored per game for the two teams using both measures of center and spread.

Team 1: Ice Kings		Team 2: Gliders	
Game	Number of goals scored	Game	Number of goals scored
1	0	1	3
2	0	2	6
3	0	3	0
4	2	4	6
5	1	5	0
6	2	6	1
7	2	7	1
8	1	8	2
9	2	9	0
10	6	10	3
11	5	11	3
12	2	12	2
13	5	13	4
14	2	14	2

1. Determine which measure of center to use. Order the goals scored for each team from least to greatest.

Team 1: Ice Kings		Team 2: Gliders	
Game	**Number of goals scored**	**Game**	**Number of goals scored**
1	0	3	0
2	0	5	0
3	0	9	0
5	1	6	1
8	1	7	1
4	2	8	2
6	2	12	2
7	2	14	2
9	2	1	3
12	2	10	3
14	2	11	3
11	5	13	4
13	5	2	6
10	6	4	6

2. Look at the range of values. Determine if there are any data values in either table that are much larger or much smaller than the rest of the data set. If there are, use the median. If there are not, use either the mean or the median.

The largest and smallest data values in each data set are not much smaller or much larger than the rest of the data. There aren't any values in the tables that will greatly influence the mean, so either the median or mean would be valid measures of center.

3. Calculate the chosen measure of center.

    Since it was determined that either measure of center was acceptable, select one. Let's use the mean. To calculate the mean, find the sum of goals scored for each team, and then divide the total goals by the number of games played.

    Ice Kings:

    $$\frac{0+0+0+1+1+2+2+2+2+2+2+5+5+6}{14} \approx 2.14$$

    Gliders:

    $$\frac{0+0+0+1+1+2+2+2+3+3+3+4+6+6}{14} \approx 2.36$$

4. Compare the measures of center for the two teams.

    The two teams have performed similarly over the 14 games. In any given game, you could expect either team to score at least 2 goals.

5. Calculate a measure of spread.

    Since we chose to calculate the mean, now we will use the mean absolute deviation to compare the goals per team. Mean absolute deviation compares the range of values to the mean value. To calculate the mean absolute deviation, first find the absolute value of the difference between each data point and the mean:

    |data point – mean|

    The mean for the Ice Kings is 2.14. The mean for the Gliders is 2.36.

    (continued)

Team 1: Ice Kings		
Game	**Number of goals scored**	**Absolute difference**
1	0	$|0 - 2.14| = 2.14$
2	0	$|0 - 2.14| = 2.14$
3	0	$|0 - 2.14| = 2.14$
5	1	$|1 - 2.14| = 1.14$
8	1	$|1 - 2.14| = 1.14$
4	2	$|2 - 2.14| = 0.14$
6	2	$|2 - 2.14| = 0.14$
7	2	$|2 - 2.14| = 0.14$
9	2	$|2 - 2.14| = 0.14$
12	2	$|2 - 2.14| = 0.14$
14	2	$|2 - 2.14| = 0.14$
11	5	$|5 - 2.14| = 2.86$
13	5	$|5 - 2.14| = 2.86$
10	6	$|6 - 2.14| = 3.86$

Next, sum the absolute differences.

$2.14 + 2.14 + 2.14 + 1.14 + 1.14 + 0.14 + 0.14 + 0.14 + 0.14 + 0.14 + 0.14 + 2.86 + 2.86 + 3.86 = 19.12$

Lastly, divide the sum of the absolute differences by the number of data points (14).

$$\frac{19.12}{14} \approx 1.37$$

The mean absolute deviation for the Ice Kings is 1.37.

(continued)

Team 2: Gliders		
Game	**Number of goals scored**	**Absolute difference**
3	0	$|0 - 2.36| = 2.36$
5	0	$|0 - 2.36| = 2.36$
9	0	$|0 - 2.36| = 2.36$
6	1	$|1 - 2.36| = 1.36$
7	1	$|1 - 2.36| = 1.36$
8	2	$|2 - 2.36| = 0.36$
12	2	$|2 - 2.36| = 0.36$
14	2	$|2 - 2.36| = 0.36$
1	3	$|3 - 2.36| = 0.64$
10	3	$|3 - 2.36| = 0.64$
11	3	$|3 - 2.36| = 0.64$
13	4	$|4 - 2.36| = 1.64$
2	6	$|6 - 2.36| = 3.64$
4	6	$|6 - 2.36| = 3.64$

Next, sum the absolute differences.

$2.36 + 2.36 + 2.36 + 1.36 + 1.36 + 0.36 + 0.36 + 0.36 + 0.64 +$
$0.64 + 0.64 + 1.64 + 3.64 + 3.64 = 21.72$

Lastly, divide the sum of the absolute differences by the number of data points (14).

$$\frac{21.72}{14} \approx 1.55$$

The mean absolute deviation for the Gliders is 1.55.

6. Compare the measures of spread and center for the two teams.

The Ice Kings have a slightly lower mean, but the number of goals scored per game also varies less than the Gliders. The Gliders have a higher mean, but with higher variation.

Example 2

Each girl in Mr. Sanson's class and in Mrs. Kwei's class measured her own height. The heights were plotted on the dot plots below. Use the dot plots to compare the heights of the girls in the two classes.

Mr. Sanson's class

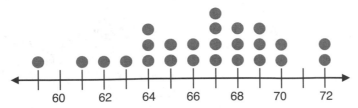

Mrs. Kwei's class

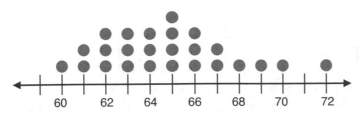

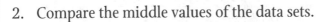

1. Compare the range of recorded values.

   The overall range of heights of girls in the two classes is similar. The heights in the two classes range from 59 inches to 72 inches, and 60 inches to 72 inches.

2. Compare the middle values of the data sets.

   The girls in Mr. Sanson's class appear to be taller than the girls in Mrs. Kwei's class. By looking at where the dots are clustered, we can estimate that the middle height in Mr. Sanson's class is around 67 inches. The middle height in Mrs. Kwei's class is 65 inches.

3. Compare the variation in the data sets.

   The variation in the two sets of heights appears to be similar, except Mr. Sanson's data is skewed to the left and Mrs. Kwei's data is skewed to the right. The majority of the heights are within approximately 6 inches in both classes. The majority of the girls in Mr. Sanson's class are between 64 and 70 inches, and the majority of the girls in Mrs. Kwei's class are between 61 and 67 inches.

Example 3

Sam wants to buy a lottery ticket. There are two different tickets that he can buy, and each costs $10. He found a website with information about how much money others have won with their lottery tickets. The information is presented in two box plots, shown below. Use the two box plots to compare the amounts others have won with Ticket 1 and with Ticket 2.

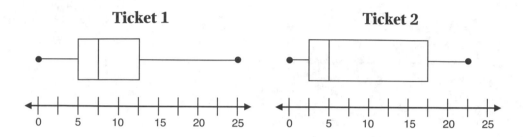

1. Compare the range of data.

    The range of amounts won is similar. With Ticket 1, winnings ranged from $0 to $25, and with Ticket 2, winnings ranged from $0 to $22.50.

2. Compare the center of the data sets.

    The median of the data sets is shown by the vertical line inside the box. The median winnings from Ticket 1 are higher than the median winnings from Ticket 2.

3. Compare the variation of the data.

    The interquartile range, or middle 50% of each data set, is contained within the box in each box plot. The IQR of winnings with Ticket 1 is smaller than the IQR of winnings with Ticket 2. Also, consider where the median is in the interquartile range. The median winnings with Ticket 1 are slightly to the left in the interquartile range, indicating that half of the winnings were less than $7.50 and half were greater. The median winnings with Ticket 2 are to the left in the interquartile range, indicating that half the winnings were less than $5 and half were more. Given the wide range of winnings with Ticket 2, but the lower median, it is more likely that Sam will win a greater amount with Ticket 1.

UNIT 4 • DESCRIPTIVE STATISTICS
Lesson 1: Working with a Single Measurement Variable

Practice 4.1.2: Comparing Data Sets

Mr. Roy asks his students in his two science classes how old they were the first time they rode on a plane. The responses are in the tables below. Use the tables to solve problems 1–4.

Class 1	
Student	Age in years
1	10
2	9
3	2
4	10
5	11
6	3
7	9
8	9
9	11
10	8
11	9
12	12
13	8
14	15
15	15

Class 2	
Student	Age in years
1	4
2	9
3	1
4	13
5	3
6	11
7	13
8	12
9	14
10	2
11	6
12	7
13	10
14	14
15	11

1. Determine which measure of center to use to compare the data.

2. Calculate the measure of center for both data sets.

3. Calculate the mean absolute deviation for both data sets.

4. Use the measures of center and spread to describe any similarities and differences between the data sets.

continued

UNIT 4 • DESCRIPTIVE STATISTICS
Lesson 1: Working with a Single Measurement Variable

Chloe works at a clothing store. She earns commission each time she makes a sale. She records how much she earns on a Tuesday and a Wednesday in the tables below. Use the tables to solve problems 5–8.

Tuesday's commissions in dollars	Wednesday's commissions in dollars
19.50	24.10
12.40	33.70
15.60	27.70
12.70	29.90
17.10	33.40
10.60	6.00
21.40	8.60
14.40	10.50
17.00	5.60
5.00	22.90

5. Determine the minimum, maximum, first quartile, median, and third quartile of each data set.

6. Create a box plot of each data set.

7. Compare the center and spread of the data from each day.

8. Next week, Chloe has the option of working on either Tuesday or Wednesday. Which day should she work?

continued

UNIT 4 • DESCRIPTIVE STATISTICS
Lesson 1: Working with a Single Measurement Variable

Schools in Florida and South Carolina were surveyed about the current price of a school lunch. The responses to the surveys are in the dot plots below. Use the dot plots to complete problems 9 and 10.

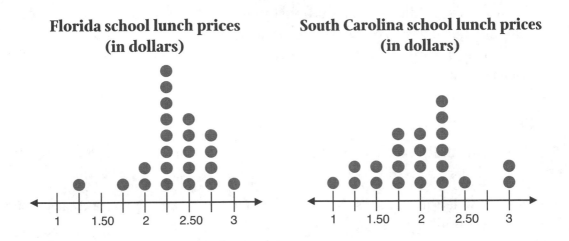

9. Which state appears to have the higher mean cost for school lunch? Explain.

10. Which state appears to have the higher variation in school lunch cost? Explain.

Lesson 4.1.3: Interpreting Data Sets

Introduction

Data sets can be compared and interpreted in the context of the problem. Data values that are much greater than or much less than the rest of the data are called **outliers**. Outliers can impact the mean and any calculations that depend on the mean, such as the mean absolute deviation. An outlier that is less than the rest of the data will decrease the mean, and an outlier that is greater than the rest of the data will increase the mean. The median is not influenced by outliers, because it is the middle-most value and not an average. Outliers can be interpreted in the context of the data; an outlier may be the result of poor data collection, or a value that is not typical in the given context.

Key Concepts

- An outlier is a data value that is much greater than or less than the rest of a data set.

- Outliers influence calculations related to center and spread, and can cause misleading conclusions.

Calculating Outliers

1. Determine the first quartile (Q_1) and third quartile (Q_3).

2. Calculate IQR, the interquartile range, which is $Q_3 - Q_1$.

3. Multiply 1.5 by the IQR.

4. Take Q_1 and subtract 1.5(IQR). Any data values less than $Q_1 - 1.5(IQR)$ are outliers.

5. Take Q_3 and add 1.5(IQR). Any data values greater than $Q_3 + 1.5(IQR)$ are outliers.

If outliers are present in the data set, use the median for the measure of center since the outlier will influence the mean and pull it toward the outlier.

Guided Practice 4.1.3

Example 1

Each student in Mr. Lamb's class measured a pencil. The data set below shows the pencil lengths in centimeters (cm). What is the expected length of any given pencil? Describe the shape, center, and spread of the data.

Student	Pencil length in cm	Student	Pencil length in cm
1	17.8	11	14.0
2	19.0	12	14.3
3	16.7	13	15.1
4	16.5	14	17.3
5	16.1	15	15.6
6	15.6	16	16.1
7	10.2	17	16.2
8	15.7	18	16.2
9	17.9	19	18.6
10	15.7	20	16.0

1. Order the data from least to greatest.

Student	Pencil length in cm	Student	Pencil length in cm
7	10.2	16	16.1
11	14.0	17	16.2
12	14.3	18	16.2
13	15.1	4	16.5
6	15.6	3	16.7
15	15.6	14	17.3
8	15.7	1	17.8
10	15.7	9	17.9
20	16.0	19	18.6
5	16.1	2	19.0

2. Calculate the interquartile range (IQR).

To find the IQR, first find the median, first quartile (Q_1), and third quartile (Q_3).

There are 20 data points in the set. First, find the median.

The median is the average of the 10th and 11th data points.

$$\frac{16.1+16.1}{2}=16.1$$

Next find Q_1, the median of the lower half of the data set.

Q_1 is the average of the fifth and sixth data values.

$$\frac{15.6+15.6}{2}=15.6$$

Next find Q_3, the median of the upper half of the data.

Q_3 is the average of the 15th and 16th data values.

$$\frac{16.7+17.3}{2}=17$$

Now find the IQR, which is the difference between Q_3 and Q_1 ($Q_3 - Q_1$).

17 − 15.6 = 1.4

IQR = 1.4

3. Multiply 1.5 times IQR.

1.5(IQR) = 1.5(1.4) = 2.1

4. Determine if there are any outliers at the lower end of the data.

Subtract 1.5(IQR) from Q_1.

Q_1 − 1.5(IQR) = 15.6 − 2.1 = 13.5

Any data values less than 13.5 are outliers. Examine the data. There is one value in the data set that is less than 13.5. Therefore, there is one outlier: 10.2.

5. Determine if there are any outliers at the upper end of the data.

Add 1.5(IQR) to Q_3.

$$Q_3 + 1.5(IQR) = 17 + 2.1 = 19.1$$

Any data values greater than 19.1 are outliers. Examine the data. There are no values in the data set that are greater than 19.1. Therefore, there are no more outliers.

6. List all the outliers.

All of the outliers are those values that are less than $Q_1 - 1.5(IQR)$ and those values that are greater than $Q_3 + 1.5(IQR)$.

The only outlier for this data set is 10.2.

7. Calculate a measure of center. This will give us an approximate expected length of any given pencil, based on Mr. Lamb's data.

Because there is an outlier, the mean would be influenced by this value. Instead of using the mean, use the median as a measure of center, because it is not influenced by outliers.

We already determined that the median is 16.1.

The approximate expected length of any given pencil is 16.1 cm.

8. Describe the shape, center, and spread in the context of the problem.

To describe the shape, plot the data using a box plot.

Create the box plot using the five values found earlier: minimum = 10.2; Q_1 = 15.6; median = 16.1; Q_3 = 17; maximum = 19.0.

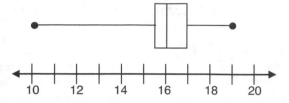

The data is skewed left because the box plot has a long tail on the left side. This is due to the low value of the outlier, 10.2. The spread of the data is large. Notice the width of the box compared to the width of the minimum and maximum values. The center is better described by the median, which is not influenced by outliers. Therefore, the approximate length of a pencil based on Mr. Lamb's data is 16.1 cm, with a large variation in the data.

Example 2

Kayla is trying to estimate the cost of a house painter. She receives the following estimates, in dollars.

1288 1640 1547 1842 1553 1604 2858 1150 1844 1045 1347

She takes the mean of the data and states that the estimated cost of a house painter is $1,610.73. Is her estimate accurate?

1. Order the data from least to greatest.

1045 1150 1288 1347 1547 1553 1604 1640 1842 1844 2858

2. Calculate the interquartile range (IQR).

To find the IQR, first find the median, first quartile (Q_1), and third quartile (Q_3).

There are 11 data points in the set. First, find the median.

The median is the sixth data point: 1,553.

Next find Q_1, the median of the lower half of the data set.

Q_1 is the third data value: 1,288.

Next find Q_3, the median of the upper half of the data.

Q_3 is the ninth data value: 1,842.

Now find the IQR, which is the difference between Q_3 and Q_1 ($Q_3 - Q_1$).

$$1842 - 1288 = 554$$

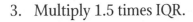

3. Multiply 1.5 times IQR.

$$1.5(\text{IQR}) = 1.5(554) = 831$$

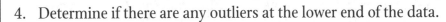

4. Determine if there are any outliers at the lower end of the data.

Subtract 1.5(IQR) from Q_1.

$$Q_1 - 1.5(\text{IQR}) = 1288 - 831 = 457$$

Any data values less than 457 are outliers. Examine the data. There are no values in the data set that are less than 457.

5. Determine if there are any outliers at the upper end of the data.

Add 1.5(IQR) to Q_3.

$$Q_3 + 1.5(\text{IQR}) = 1842 + 831 = 2673$$

Any data values greater than 2,673 are outliers. Examine the data. There is one value in the data set that is greater than 2,673. Therefore, there is one outlier: 2,858.

6. List all the outliers.

    All of the outliers are those values that are less than $Q_1 - 1.5(IQR)$ and those values that are greater than $Q_3 + 1.5(IQR)$.

    The only outlier for this data set is 2,858.

7. Create a box plot of the data set.

    Use the values we found for minimum, maximum, Q_1, median, and Q_3 to create a box plot.

    The minimum is the lowest value, 1,045; the maximum is the greatest value, 2,858; Q_1 is 1,288; the median is 1,553; and Q_3 is 1,842.

    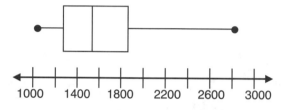

8. Describe how the outlier has influenced the center of the data.

    Compare the calculated mean to the median.

    The outlier is larger than the rest of the data set, and increased the mean. This can also be seen when comparing the mean and median; Kayla's mean is greater than the median.

9. Describe how the outlier has influenced the shape of the data.

    Identify if the data is skewed to the left or right.

    Data represented in the box plot that is skewed to the left has a longer tail on the left side of the box plot.

    Similarly, data that is skewed to the right has a longer tail on the right side of the box plot.

    The data is skewed to the right because of the influence of the large outlier.

10. Describe how the outlier has influenced the spread of the data.

The overall range of the data has been increased by the outlier. Without the outlier, the maximum would be 1,844, making the range (the difference between the maximum and minimum) 799:

$$1844 - 1045 = 799$$

With the outlier, the range is 1,813:

$$2858 - 1045 = 1813$$

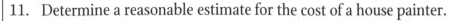

11. Determine a reasonable estimate for the cost of a house painter.

Either the median or the mean without the outlier could be used as an estimate. The mean without the outlier is the mean of the remaining 10 data points:

$$\frac{1045+1150+1288+1347+1547+1553+1604+1640+1842+1844}{10} = 1486$$

Kayla's estimate is not correct. One of the values is an outlier, which increased her estimate. A more accurate estimate is the mean without the outlier ($1,486) or the median ($1,553).

Example 3

The National Basketball Association has strict regulations about the dimensions of basketballs used during games. The circumference of the basketball must be between 749 mm and 780 mm. A basketball manufacturer is sending a shipment of various brands of basketballs to the NBA. Brandon notices that the mean circumference of the balls is in this range, so he decides to send all the balls to the NBA. The NBA gets the shipment, and is not happy. Many of the balls in the shipment do not have the right circumference. What could have happened? How could the mean circumference be in this range, but many of the individual balls have the wrong circumference?

1. Consider how the mean is calculated. Is there any way the mean could not accurately represent the rest of the data?

   The mean is an average of all the data. If there are very large or very small data values, the mean could be greater than or less than many of the data points. One or more outliers could influence the mean.

2. Describe how the mean could misrepresent the data, and what Brandon could do to ensure he doesn't send the wrong size basketballs.

   Brandon should use more measures of center and spread to understand the circumferences of the balls being delivered. Even if there are many basketballs being delivered, he could use a computer to help create a box plot. This would show information about the middle 50% of the circumferences. This would also show outliers.

UNIT 4 • DESCRIPTIVE STATISTICS
Lesson 1: Working with a Single Measurement Variable

Practice 4.1.3: Interpreting Data Sets

Mr. Wilde surveys his students. He asks each student the number of states he or she has visited, and records the results in the table below. Use the table to answer questions 1–3.

Student	States visited	Student	States visited
A	11	K	4
B	10	L	7
C	9	M	2
D	4	N	2
E	1	O	9
F	6	P	3
G	1	Q	3
H	10	R	10
I	18	S	2
J	4	T	5

1. Are there any outliers in the data set? Explain.

2. Mr. Wilde wants to estimate the number of states any given student has visited. How should he calculate his estimation? Why?

3. What is the estimated number of states visited by any given student?

UNIT 4 • DESCRIPTIVE STATISTICS
Lesson 1: Working with a Single Measurement Variable

Rosa surveys 12 nearby gyms. She records each gym's monthly membership cost in the table below. Use the table to solve problems 4–7.

Gym	Monthly cost in dollars	Gym	Monthly cost in dollars
1	35	7	25
2	15	8	25
3	15	9	35
4	40	10	65
5	30	11	10
6	20	12	30

4. Create a dot plot showing the cost of nearby gyms.

5. Are there any outliers in the data set? Explain.

6. Rosa wants to estimate the monthly membership cost of nearby gyms. How should she estimate the cost? Calculate the estimated monthly membership cost.

7. Describe the shape and spread of the data.

continued

UNIT 4 • DESCRIPTIVE STATISTICS
Lesson 1: Working with a Single Measurement Variable

A game on Jackson's phone keeps track of his scores, in points, in a histogram. The scores are all multiples of 100. The current histogram shown on his phone is below. Use the histogram to answer questions 8–10.

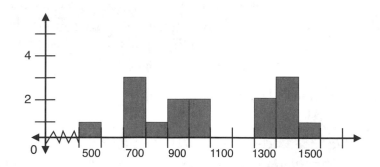

8. Are there any outliers in the data set? Explain.

9. How should Jackson estimate his score per game? Calculate the estimated score.

10. Jackson is playing one more game. With the score of this game, Jackson wants to increase his mean score by 100 points. What is the minimum score Jackson needs to increase his mean by 100 points? Recall that the scores are all multiples of 100.

Lesson 2: Working with Two Categorical and Quantitative Variables

Common Core State Standards

S–ID.5 Summarize categorical data for two categories in two-way frequency tables. Interpret relative frequencies in the context of the data (including joint, marginal, and conditional relative frequencies). Recognize possible associations and trends in the data.★

S–ID.6 Represent data on two quantitative variables on a scatter plot, and describe how the variables are related.★

  a. Fit a function to the data; use functions fitted to data to solve problems in the context of the data. Use given functions or choose a function suggested by the context. Emphasize linear, quadratic, and exponential models.

  b. Informally assess the fit of a function by plotting and analyzing residuals.

  c. Fit a linear function for a scatter plot that suggests a linear association.

Essential Questions

1. When is a two-way frequency table a good way to present data?

2. Why is data represented in a scatter plot?

3. What does a residual plot display?

4. How can it be determined graphically that a line is a good estimate for a data set?

WORDS TO KNOW

conditional relative frequency	the percentage of a joint frequency as compared to the total number of respondents, total number of people with a given characteristic, or the total number of times a specific response was given
function	a relation of two variables where each input is assigned to one and only one output
joint frequency	the number of times a specific response is given by people with a given characteristic; the cell values in a two-way frequency table

marginal frequency	the total number of times a specific response is given, or the total number of people with a given characteristic
residual	the vertical distance between an observed data value and an estimated data value on a line of best fit
residual plot	provides a visual representation of the residuals for a set of data; contains the points (x, residual for x)
scatter plot	a graph of data in two variables on a coordinate plane, where each data pair is represented by a point
trend	a pattern of behavior, usually observed over time or over multiple iterations
two-way frequency table	a table that divides responses into categories, showing both a characteristic in the table rows and a characteristic in the table columns; values in cells are a count of the number of times each response was given by a respondent with a certain characteristic

Recommended Resources

- Interactivate. "Finding Residuals."

  http://walch.com/rr/CAU4L2FindingResiduals

  This site provides a discussion about residuals—what they are and how they are calculated—and gives an example.

- Interactivate. "Regression."

  http://walch.com/rr/CAU4L2Regression

  This site allows users to plot points in a scatter plot and then have the computer generate a line of best fit. Users can also fit a line to the data using their own equation.

- MathIsFun.com. "Scatter Plots."

  http://walch.com/rr/CAU4L2ScatterPlots

  This site explains how to create a scatter plot, draw a line of best fit, and analyze correlation. The site ends with a short, interactive quiz.

- VCE Further Maths. "Tutorial 15—Two-way Frequency Tables."

  http://walch.com/rr/CAU4L2TwoWayFrequencies

  This site offers a ten-minute video tutorial of how to create two-way frequency tables.

Lesson 4.2.1: Summarizing Data Using Two-Way Frequency Tables

Introduction

Information about people who are surveyed can be captured in two-way frequency tables. A **two-way frequency table** is a table of data that separates responses by a characteristic of the respondents.

Type of characteristic	Type of response	
	Response 1	**Response 2**
Characteristic 1	a	b
Characteristic 2	c	d

Each cell in the table contains a count of the people with a given characteristic who gave each response. For example, in the table above a, b, c, and d would each be counts for the responses given by people with each characteristic. The sum of all the cells, $a + b + c + d$, is the total number of respondents. Two-way frequency tables help organize information and provide greater insight into features of a population being surveyed. A **trend**, or pattern in the data, can be examined using a two-way frequency table.

A **joint frequency** is the number of responses for a given characteristic. The entries in the cells of a two-way frequency table are joint frequencies. In the sample table, a, b, c, and d are each joint frequencies. A **marginal frequency** is the total number of times a response was given, or the total number of respondents with a given characteristic. This is the sum of either a row or a column in a two-way frequency table. In the sample table, $a + b$ would be the marginal frequency of people with Characteristic 1.

A **conditional relative frequency** allows a comparison to be made for multiple responses in a single row, single column, or table. Relative frequencies are expressed as a percentage, usually written as a decimal, and are found by dividing the number of responses by either the total number of people who gave that response, the total number of people with a given characteristic, or the total number of respondents. In the sample table, $\dfrac{a}{a+b}$ is the relative frequency of Response 1 for people with Characteristic 1.

Key Concepts

- A two-way frequency table divides survey responses by characteristics of respondents.

- The number of times a response was given by people with a certain characteristic is called a joint frequency.

- A marginal frequency is the total number of times a response is given, or the total number of people with a certain characteristic.

- A conditional relative frequency expresses a number of responses as a percentage of the total number of respondents, the total number of people with a given characteristic, or the total number of times a specific response was given.

- Trends, or patterns of responses, can be identified by looking at the frequency of responses.

Guided Practice 4.2.1

Example 1

Cameron surveys students in his school who play sports, and asks them which sport they prefer. He records the responses in the table below.

Gender	Preferred sport		
	Baseball	Soccer	Basketball
Male	49	52	16
Female	23	64	33

What is the joint frequency of male students who prefer soccer?

---

1. Look for the row of male students.

   The characteristic "male" is in the first row of responses.

---

2. Look for the column with the response "soccer."

   The response "soccer" is in the second column of responses.

---

3. The frequency for the given characteristic and the given response is the joint frequency.

   The cell in the first characteristic row and the second response column is 52.

   The joint frequency of male students who prefer soccer is 52.

Example 2

Abigail surveys students in different grades, and asks each student which pet they prefer. The responses are in the table below.

Grade	Preferred pet			
	Bird	**Cat**	**Dog**	**Fish**
9	3	49	53	22
10	7	36	64	10

What is the marginal frequency of each type of pet?

---

1. Sum the responses of people with each characteristic for the first pet type, "bird."

   3 people in grade 9 preferred birds, and 7 people in grade 10 preferred birds.

   $3 + 7 = 10$ people who preferred birds

---

2. Sum the responses of people with each characteristic for the second pet type, "cat."

   49 people in grade 9 preferred cats, and 36 people in grade 10 preferred cats.

   $49 + 36 = 85$ people who preferred cats

---

3. Sum the responses of people with each characteristic for the third pet type, "dog."

   53 people in grade 9 preferred dogs, and 64 people in grade 10 preferred dogs.

   $53 + 64 = 117$ people who preferred dogs

4. Sum the responses of people with each characteristic for the fourth pet type, "fish."

22 people in grade 9 preferred fish, and 10 people in grade 10 preferred fish.

22 + 10 = 32 people who preferred fish

5. Organize the marginal frequencies in a two-way frequency table.

Create a row and include the marginal frequencies of each response under the name of each response.

Grade	Preferred pet			
	Bird	Cat	Dog	Fish
9	3	49	53	22
10	7	36	64	10
Total	10	85	117	32

Example 3

Ms. Scanlon surveys her students about the time they spend studying. She creates a table showing the amount of time students studied and the score each student earned on a recent test.

Time spent studying in hours	Test score			
	0–25	26–50	51–75	76–100
0–2	2	8	12	2
2–4	0	10	8	24
4–6	1	0	2	9
6+	0	0	1	4

Ms. Scanlon wants to understand the distribution of scores among all the students, and to get a sense of how students are performing and how much students are studying. Find the conditional relative frequencies as a percentage of the total number of students.

1. Find the total number of students represented in the table by summing the joint frequencies.

    $$2 + 8 + 12 + 2 + 0 + 10 + 8 + 24 + 1 + 0 + 2 + 9 + 0 + 0 + 1 + 4 = 83$$

2. Divide each joint frequency by the total number of students.

    $$\frac{2}{83} \approx 0.024 \qquad \frac{8}{83} \approx 0.096 \qquad \frac{12}{83} \approx 0.145 \qquad \frac{2}{83} \approx 0.024$$

    $$\frac{0}{83} \approx 0 \qquad \frac{10}{83} \approx 0.120 \qquad \frac{8}{83} \approx 0.096 \qquad \frac{24}{83} \approx 0.289$$

    $$\frac{1}{83} \approx 0.012 \qquad \frac{0}{83} \approx 0 \qquad \frac{2}{83} \approx 0.024 \qquad \frac{9}{83} \approx 0.108$$

    $$\frac{0}{83} \approx 0 \qquad \frac{0}{83} \approx 0 \qquad \frac{1}{83} \approx 0.012 \qquad \frac{4}{83} \approx 0.048$$

3. Represent the conditional joint frequencies in a new table.

    Insert each conditional joint frequency in a table set up the same way as the two-way frequency table.

Time spent studying in hours	Test score			
	0–25	26–50	51–75	76–100
0–2	0.024	0.096	0.145	0.024
2–4	0	0.120	0.096	0.289
4–6	0.012	0	0.024	0.108
6+	0	0	0.012	0.048

UNIT 4 • DESCRIPTIVE STATISTICS
Lesson 2: Working with Two Categorical and Quantitative Variables

Practice 4.2.1: Summarizing Data Using Two-Way Frequency Tables

A town surveys 50 of its residents to help decide where to place some new buildings. Each resident was asked to identify the building he or she would use most frequently: a library, a recreation center, or a playground. Each resident also noted if they lived in the north or south side of town. The results of the survey are recorded below and on the next page. Use the data to answer the questions that follow.

Resident	Location	Building preference	Resident	Location	Building preference
1	North	Library	18	North	Playground
2	South	Playground	19	North	Playground
3	North	Playground	20	South	Library
4	South	Playground	21	North	Library
5	North	Library	22	North	Recreation center
6	South	Recreation center	23	South	Library
7	North	Library	24	South	Library
8	South	Library	25	South	Recreation center
9	North	Playground	26	North	Library
10	South	Playground	27	South	Playground
11	North	Library	28	North	Playground
12	South	Recreation center	29	South	Playground
13	North	Library	30	South	Recreation center
14	South	Library	31	South	Recreation center
15	North	Library	32	North	Playground
16	South	Library	33	South	Recreation center
17	North	Recreation center	34	North	Recreation center

continued

UNIT 4 • DESCRIPTIVE STATISTICS
Lesson 2: Working with Two Categorical and Quantitative Variables

Resident	Location	Building preference	Resident	Location	Building preference
35	North	Library	43	South	Library
36	North	Playground	44	South	Recreation center
37	South	Recreation center	45	South	Recreation center
38	South	Recreation center	46	North	Library
39	North	Recreation center	47	South	Library
40	South	Recreation center	48	South	Recreation center
41	North	Playground	49	South	Library
42	South	Recreation center	50	North	Recreation center

1. Create a two-way frequency table showing the buildings preferred by residents of each location.

2. Find the marginal frequencies for each location and for each building. Include the marginal frequencies in the table.

3. What are the conditional frequencies relative to the total number of people surveyed? Include the values in a table.

4. What are the conditional frequencies relative to the total number of people from each location?

5. Describe any trends in the buildings preferred by all residents and the buildings preferred by residents in the north of town versus residents in the south of town.

6. How could this information be used to decide where to build each of the three buildings?

continued

UNIT 4 • DESCRIPTIVE STATISTICS
Lesson 2: Working with Two Categorical and Quantitative Variables

Favorite meals of Mrs. Gale's students are listed in the two-way frequency table below. Use the table to answer the questions that follow.

Gender	Favorite meal			
	Pizza	Hamburger	Hot dog	Spaghetti
Male	18	17	9	12
Female	14	7	13	19

7. Find the marginal frequencies for each food and for each gender. Include the marginal frequencies in a table.

8. What are the conditional frequencies relative to the total number of males and females? Include the values in a table.

9. What are the conditional frequencies relative to the total number of people surveyed?

10. Describe any trends in the foods preferred by all students and the foods preferred by males and females.

Lesson 4.2.2: Solving Problems Given Functions Fitted to Data

Introduction

Data with two quantitative variables can be represented using a scatter plot. A **scatter plot** is a graph of data on a coordinate plane, where each data pair is represented by a point. Relationships between the two quantitative variables can be observed on the graph. A **function** is a relation of two variables where each input is assigned to one and only one output. Functions in two variables can be represented algebraically with an equation, or graphically on the coordinate plane. Graphing a function on the same coordinate plane as a scatter plot for a data set allows us to see if the function is a good estimation of the relationship between the two variables in the data set. The graph and the equation of the function can be used to estimate coordinate pairs that are not included in the data set.

Key Concepts

- Data with two quantitative variables can be represented graphically on a scatter plot.

- To create a scatter plot, plot each pair of data as a point on a coordinate plane.

- To compare a data set and a function, plot the function on the same coordinate plane as the scatter plot of a data set. The graph of the function should approximate the shape of the scatter plot.

- Evaluating or solving a function that has a similar shape as a data set can provide an estimate for data not included in the plotted data set.

- Solve a function algebraically by substituting a value for y and solving for x.

- Solve a function graphically by finding the point on the graph of the function with the known y-value, then finding the corresponding x-value of that point.

- Evaluate a function algebraically by replacing x with a known value and simplifying the expression to determine y.

- Evaluate a function graphically by finding the point on the graph of the function with the known x-value, then finding the corresponding y-value of that point.

- Graph a linear function by plotting two points and drawing a line through those two points.

- Graph an exponential function by plotting at least five points. Connect the points with a curve.

Guided Practice 4.2.2

Example 1

Andrew wants to estimate his gas mileage, or miles traveled per gallon of gas used. He records the number of gallons of gas he purchased and the total miles he traveled with that gas.

Gallons	Miles
15	313
17	340
18	401
19	423
18	392
17	379
20	408
19	437
16	366
20	416

Create a scatter plot showing the relationship between gallons of gas and miles driven. Which function is a better estimate for the function that relates gallons to miles: $y = 10x$ or $y = 22x$? How is the equation of the function related to his gas mileage?

1. Plot each point on the coordinate plane.

   Let the x-axis represent gallons and the y-axis represent miles.

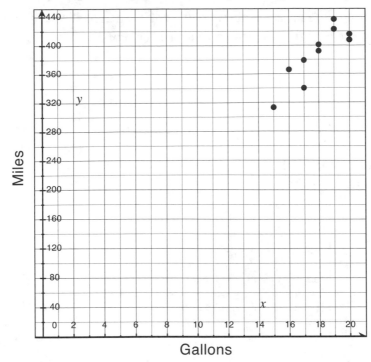

2. Graph the function $y = 10x$ on the coordinate plane.

It is a linear function, so only two points are needed to draw the line.

Evaluate the function at two values of x, such as 0 and 10, and draw a line through these points on the scatter plot.

$y = 10x$

$y = 10(0) = 0$ Substitute 0 for x.

$y = 10(10) = 100$ Substitute 10 for x.

Two points on the line are $(0, 0)$ and $(10, 100)$.

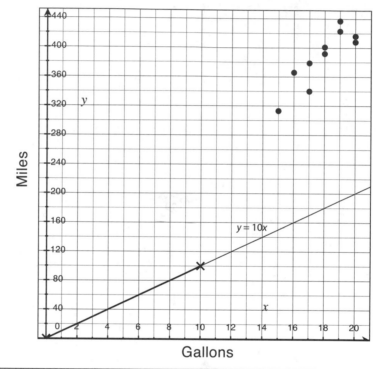

3. Graph the function $y = 22x$ on the same coordinate plane.

This is also a linear function, so only two points are needed to draw the line.

Evaluate the function at two values of x, such as 0 and 10, and draw a line through these points on the scatter plot.

$y = 22(0) = 0$ Substitute 0 for x.

$y = 22(10) = 220$ Substitute 10 for x.

Two points on the line are (0, 0) and (0, 220).

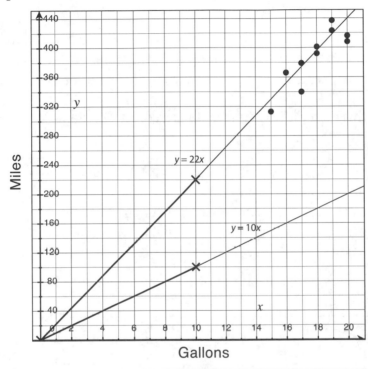

4. Look at the graph of the data and the functions.

Identify which function comes closer to the data values. This function is the better estimate for the data.

The graph of the function $y = 22x$ goes through approximately the center of the points in the scatter plot. The function $y = 10x$ is not steep enough to match the data values. The function $y = 22x$ is a better estimate of the data.

5. Interpret the equation in the context of the problem, using the units of the x- and y-axes.

For a linear equation in the form $y = mx + b$, the slope (m) of the equation is the rate of change of the function, or the change in y over the change in x. The y-intercept (b) of the equation is the initial value.

In this example, y is miles and x is gallons. The slope is $\dfrac{\text{change in miles}}{\text{change in gallons}}$.

For the equation $y = 22x$, the slope of 22 is equal to $\dfrac{22 \text{ miles}}{1 \text{ gallon}}$.

The gas mileage of Andrew's car is the miles driven per gallon of gas used. The gas mileage is equal to the slope of the line that fits the data.

Andrew's car has a gas mileage of approximately 22 miles per gallon.

Example 2

The principal at Park High School records the total number of students each year. The table below shows the number of students for each of the last 8 years.

Year	Number of students
1	630
2	655
3	690
4	731
5	752
6	800
7	844
8	930

Create a scatter plot showing the relationship between the year and the total number of students. Show that the function $y = 600(1.05)^x$ is a good estimate for the relationship between the year and the population. Approximately how many students will attend the high school in year 9?

1. Plot each point on the coordinate plane.

   Let the x-axis represent years and the y-axis represent the number of students.

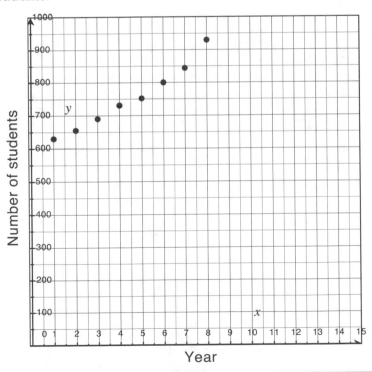

2. Graph $y = 600(1.05)^x$ on the coordinate plane.

Calculate the value of y for a few different values of x. Start with $x = 0$. Calculate the value of the function for at least four more x-values that are in the table of data.

x	y
0	$600(1.05)^0 = 600$
1	$600(1.05)^1 = 630$
3	$600(1.05)^3 = 694.575$
5	$600(1.05)^5 = 765.769$
7	$600(1.05)^7 = 855.260$

Plot these points on the same coordinate plane. Connect the points with a curve.

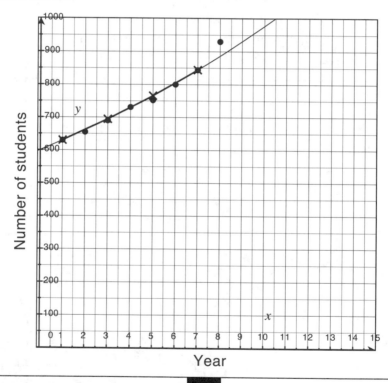

3. Compare the graph of the function to the scatter plot of the data.

   The graph of the function appears to be very close to the points in the scatter plot. The function $y = 600(1.05)^x$ is a good estimate of the data.

4. Use the function to estimate the population in year 9.

   Evaluate the function $y = 600(1.05)^x$ for year 9, when $x = 9$.

   $y = 600(1.05)^9 = 930.797$

   The function $y = 600(1.05)^x$ is a good estimate of the population. There will be approximately 931 students in the school in year 9.

Example 3

The weights of oranges vary. Maria wants to come up with a way to estimate the number of oranges given a weight. She weighs oranges and records the weights in the table below.

Number of oranges	Weight in pounds
1	0.47
3	1.29
5	2.54
6	2.65
8	4.12
10	5.57
12	7.18
13	8.48
14	7.07

Create a scatter plot showing the relationship between the number of oranges and the weight in pounds. Is the function $y = 0.6x - 0.5$ a good fit for the data? Maria has a bag of oranges that weighs 2 pounds. Approximately how many oranges are in the bag?

1. Plot each point on the coordinate plane.

   Let the *x*-axis represent the number of oranges and the *y*-axis represent the weight in pounds.

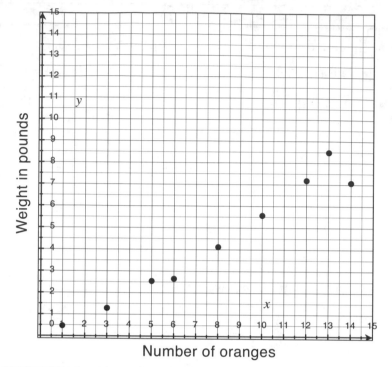

2. Graph the function $y = 0.6x - 0.5$ to determine if it is a good estimate for the data set.

Find two points on the line by evaluating the function at two values of x.

Two easy values to use are 0 and 1.

$y = 0.6(0) - 0.5 = -0.5$ Substitute 0 for x.

$y = 0.6(1) - 0.5 = 0.1$ Substitute 1 for x.

Two points on the line are $(0, -0.5)$ and $(1, 0.1)$.

Graph the two points on the same graph as the scatter plot, and then draw a line through the two points.

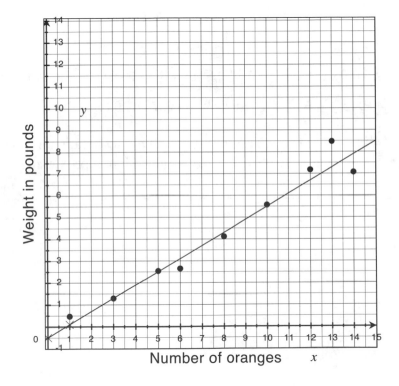

3. Look at the relationship between the graph of the function and the graph of the function. Determine if the function closely resembles the graph of the data.

    If a linear function is a good estimate for a data set, some of the data values will be above the line and some will be below the line. It appears that this equation is a good fit for the data.

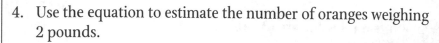

4. Use the equation to estimate the number of oranges weighing 2 pounds.

    In the equation $y = 0.6x - 0.5$, x is the number of oranges and y is the weight of the oranges. Solve the equation for $y = 2$ to estimate the number of oranges that weigh 2 pounds.

$2 = 0.6x - 0.5$	Set y equal to 2.
$2.5 = 0.6x$	Add 0.5 to both sides of the equation.
$4.2 \approx x$	Divide both sides by 0.6.

    Maria can use the equation $y = 0.6x - 0.5$ to estimate how many oranges have a given weight. 4 oranges weigh approximately 2 pounds.

UNIT 4 • DESCRIPTIVE STATISTICS
Lesson 2: Working with Two Categorical and Quantitative Variables

Practice 4.2.2: Solving Problems Given Functions Fitted to Data

Derrick started a new website. He tracks the number of new visitors to the site each day. The number of new visitors each day is listed in the table below. Use the data to answer the questions that follow.

Day	Number of new visitors
1	3
2	10
3	26
4	79
5	244

1. Create a scatter plot of the data set.

2. Would a linear or exponential function be a better estimate for the data? Explain.

3. Which function is a better fit for the data: $y = 4^x$ or $y = 3^x$? Use a graph to explain your answer.

4. On which day will Derrick's site have approximately 750 visitors? Use the graph to find your answer.

5. Approximately how many new visitors will Derrick's site have on day 7?

UNIT 4 • DESCRIPTIVE STATISTICS
Lesson 2: Working with Two Categorical and Quantitative Variables

A sandwich shop makes 100 sandwiches each morning to prepare for the day's orders. Each half hour, they record the number of sandwiches remaining. Use the data to answer the questions that follow.

Hours open	Sandwiches remaining
0	100
0.5	95
1	94
1.5	92
2	85
2.5	85
3	82
3.5	81
4	73
4.5	68

6. Create a scatter plot of the data set.

7. Would a linear or exponential function be a better estimate for the data?

8. Which function is a better fit for the data: $y = -3.8x + 92$ or $y = -5.8x + 99$? Use a graph to explain your answer.

9. Fifteen minutes after the shop opened, approximately how many sandwiches were remaining?

10. Approximately how long will it take for all the sandwiches to be sold?

Lesson 4.2.3: Analyzing Residuals

Introduction

The fit of a linear function to a set of data can be assessed by analyzing **residuals**. A residual is the vertical distance between an observed data value and an estimated data value on a line of best fit. Representing residuals on a **residual plot** provides a visual representation of the residuals for a set of data. A residual plot contains the points: (x, residual for x). A random residual plot, with both positive and negative residual values, indicates that the line is a good fit for the data. If the residual plot follows a pattern, such as a U-shape, the line is likely not a good fit for the data.

Key Concepts

- A residual is the distance between an observed data point and an estimated data value on a line of best fit. For the observed data point (x, y) and the estimated data value on a line of best fit (x, y_0), the residual is $y - y_0$.

- A residual plot is a plot of each x-value and its corresponding residual. For the observed data point (x, y) and the estimated data value on a line of best fit (x, y_0), the point on a residual plot is (x, $y - y_0$).

- A residual plot with a random pattern indicates that the line of best fit is a good approximation for the data.

- A residual plot with a U-shape indicates that the line of best fit is not a good approximation for the data.

Guided Practice 4.2.3

Example 1

Pablo's science class is growing plants. He recorded the height of his plant each day for 10 days. The plant's height, in centimeters, over that time is listed in the table below.

Day	Height in centimeters
1	3
2	5.1
3	7.2
4	8.8
5	10.5
6	12.5
7	14
8	15.9
9	17.3
10	18.9

Pablo determines that the function $y = 1.73x + 1.87$ is a good fit for the data. How close is his estimate to the actual data? Approximately how much does the plant grow each day?

1. Create a scatter plot of the data.

   Let the *x*-axis represent days and the *y*-axis represent height, in centimeters.

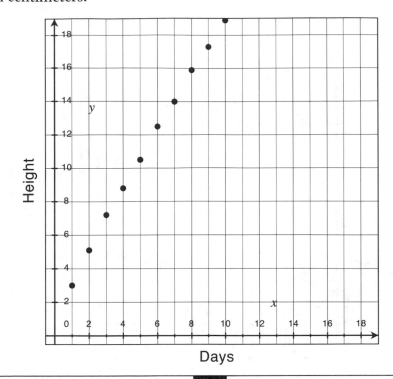

2. Draw the line of best fit through two of the data points.

A good line of best fit will have some points below the line and some above the line. Use the graph to initially determine if the function is a good fit for the data.

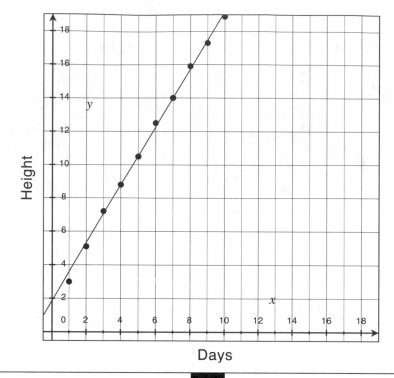

3. Find the residuals for each data point.

The residual for each data point is the difference between the observed value and the estimated value using a line of best fit. Evaluate the equation of the line at each value of x.

x	$y = 1.73x + 1.87$
1	$y = 1.73(1) + 1.87 = 3.6$
2	$y = 1.73(2) + 1.87 = 5.33$
3	$y = 1.73(3) + 1.87 = 7.06$
4	$y = 1.73(4) + 1.87 = 8.79$
5	$y = 1.73(5) + 1.87 = 10.52$
6	$y = 1.73(6) + 1.87 = 12.25$
7	$y = 1.73(7) + 1.87 = 13.98$
8	$y = 1.73(8) + 1.87 = 15.71$
9	$y = 1.73(9) + 1.87 = 17.44$
10	$y = 1.73(10) + 1.87 = 19.17$

Next, find the difference between each observed value and each calculated value for each value of x.

x	Residual
1	$3 - 3.6 = -0.6$
2	$5.1 - 5.33 = -0.23$
3	$7.2 - 7.06 = 0.14$
4	$8.8 - 8.79 = 0.01$
5	$10.5 - 10.52 = -0.02$
6	$12.5 - 12.25 = 0.25$
7	$14 - 13.98 = 0.02$
8	$15.9 - 15.71 = 0.19$
9	$17.3 - 17.44 = -0.14$
10	$18.9 - 19.17 = -0.27$

4. Plot the residuals on a residual plot.

Plot the points (x, residual for x).

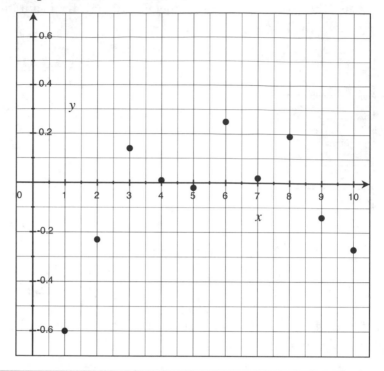

5. Describe the fit of the line based on the shape of the residual plot.

The plot of the residuals appears to be random, with some negative and some positive values. This indicates that the line is a good line of fit.

6. Use the equation to estimate the centimeters grown each day.

The change in the height per day is the centimeters grown each day. In the equation of the line, the slope is the change in height per day. The plant is growing approximately 1.73 centimeters each day.

Example 2

Lindsay created the table below showing the population of fruit flies over the last 10 weeks.

Week	Number of flies
1	50
2	78
3	98
4	122
5	153
6	191
7	238
8	298
9	373
10	466

She estimates that the population of fruit flies can be represented by the equation $y = 46x - 40$. Using residuals, determine if her representation is a good estimate.

1. Find the estimated population at each x-value.

   Evaluate the equation at each value of x.

x	$y = 46x - 40$
1	$46(1) - 40 = 6$
2	$46(2) - 40 = 52$
3	$46(3) - 40 = 98$
4	$46(4) - 40 = 144$
5	$46(5) - 40 = 190$
6	$46(6) - 40 = 236$
7	$46(7) - 40 = 282$
8	$46(8) - 40 = 328$
9	$46(9) - 40 = 374$
10	$46(10) - 40 = 420$

2. Find the residuals by finding each difference between the observed
   population and estimated population.

x	Residual
1	$50 - 6 = 44$
2	$78 - 52 = 26$
3	$98 - 98 = 0$
4	$122 - 144 = -22$
5	$153 - 190 = -37$
6	$191 - 236 = -45$
7	$238 - 282 = -44$
8	$298 - 328 = -30$
9	$373 - 374 = -1$
10	$466 - 420 = 46$

3. Create a residual plot.

   Plot the points (x, residual for x).

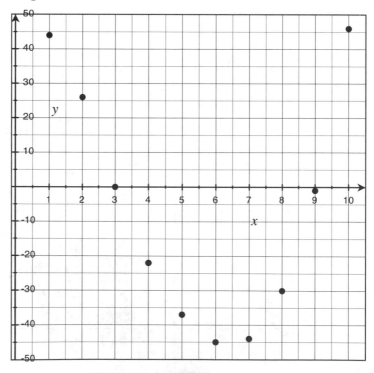

4. Analyze the residual plot to determine if the equation is a good estimate for the population.

   The residual plot has a U-shape. This indicates that a non-linear estimation would be a better fit for this data set.

   The shape of the residual plot indicates that the equation $y = 46x - 40$ is not a good estimate for this data set.

Example 3

Anthony is traveling across the country by car. He keeps track of the hours he has driven and total miles he has traveled in the table below.

Hours	Miles
1	38
3	170
4	234
8	390
11	495
12	528
15	699
17	767
20	857

Anthony uses the equation $y = 42.64x + 42.12$ to estimate his total miles driven after any number of hours. Use a residual plot to determine how well the line fits the data. Approximately how many miles had Anthony driven after 13 hours?

1. Create a scatter plot of the data set.

   Let the *x*-axis represent hours and the *y*-axis represent miles.

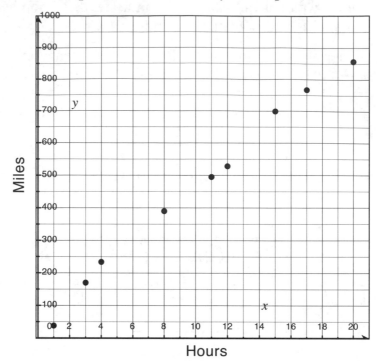

2. Plot the line of the equation Anthony used to estimate the total miles driven.

   To graph a linear equation, find two points on the line. Then draw a straight line through the two points. Two easy values of x to use are 0 and 1.

   $y = 42.64(0) + 42.12 = 42.12$ Substitute 0 for x.

   $y = 42.64(1) + 42.12 = 84.76$ Substitute 1 for x.

   Two points on the line are (0, 42.12) and (1, 84.76).

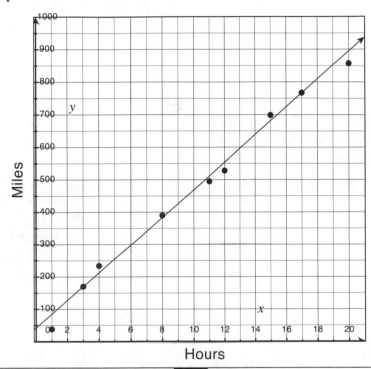

3. Find the residuals.

Evaluate the line of best fit for each value of x.

x	$y = 42.64x + 42.12$
1	$42.64(1) + 42.12 = 84.76$
3	$42.64(3) + 42.12 = 170.04$
4	$42.64(4) + 42.12 = 212.68$
8	$42.64(8) + 42.12 = 383.24$
11	$42.64(11) + 42.12 = 511.16$
12	$42.64(12) + 42.12 = 553.8$
15	$42.64(15) + 42.12 = 681.72$
17	$42.64(17) + 42.12 = 767$
20	$42.64(20) + 42.12 = 894.92$

4. Find the difference between each observed distance and estimated distance.

x	Residual
1	$38 - 84.76 = -46.76$
3	$170 - 170.04 = -0.04$
4	$234 - 212.68 = 21.32$
8	$390 - 383.24 = 6.76$
11	$495 - 511.16 = -16.16$
12	$528 - 553.8 = -25.8$
15	$699 - 681.72 = 17.28$
17	$767 - 767 = 0$
20	$857 - 894.92 = -37.92$

5. Create a residual plot.

Plot the points (x, residual for x).

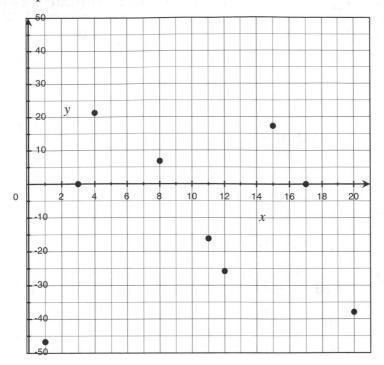

6. Determine if the linear function is a good estimate for the data.

The residual plot has a random shape, indicating that the linear function is a good estimate for the data.

7. Use the equation to estimate the total miles driven when the time equals 13 hours.

In the line of best fit, x = hours driven and y = total miles driven. Evaluate the function at $x = 13$ to estimate the total miles driven after 13 hours.

$y = 42.64(13) + 42.12 = 596.44$ Substitute 13 for x.

After 13 hours, Anthony had driven approximately 596 miles.

UNIT 4 • DESCRIPTIVE STATISTICS
Lesson 2: Working with Two Categorical and Quantitative Variables

Practice 4.2.3: Analyzing Residuals

A ball is dropped from a height of 600 meters. The height of the ball is recorded as it falls. The data is shown in the table below. Use the data for problems 1–4.

Time in seconds	Height in meters
2	581
3	550
5	506
6	446
7	387
8	312
9	224
10	122
12	10

1. Create a scatter plot showing the time and height of the ball.

2. Ian determines that the height of the ball can be estimated using the equation $y = -61x + 732.5$. Draw the line of the equation on the scatter plot.

3. Does it appear that this line is a good fit for the data?

4. Use a residual plot to determine if a linear function is a good fit for the data.

continued

UNIT 4 • DESCRIPTIVE STATISTICS
Lesson 2: Working with Two Categorical and Quantitative Variables

Dr. Sanchez is a pediatrician. She tracks the age and height of each patient. The height data for one male child is in the table below. Use the data for problems 5–8.

Age in months	Height in inches
1	20
3	23
6	27
8	29
9	31
12	32
15	34

5. Create a scatter plot showing the age and height of the child.

6. Dr. Sanchez determines that the height can be estimated using the equation $y = x + 20$. Draw the line of the equation on the scatter plot.

7. Does it appear that this line is a good fit for the data? Explain.

8. Use a residual plot to determine if a linear function is a good fit for the data.

UNIT 4 • DESCRIPTIVE STATISTICS
Lesson 2: Working with Two Categorical and Quantitative Variables

Each student in Mrs. Goldman's class records his or her height and his or her arm span in the table below. Use the data for problems 9 and 10.

Height in inches	Arm span in inches
66	65.3
58	61.5
47	47.0
71	66.7
68	66.6
65	63.7
64	60.8
74	71.0
50	49.0
57	59.9
56	56.6
52	56.2
55	58.9

9. Create a scatter plot of the heights versus arm spans.

10. Mrs. Goldman determines that arm spans can be estimated using the equation $y = 0.78x + 13$. Use a residual plot to determine if a linear function is a good fit for the data.

Lesson 4.2.4: Fitting Linear Functions to Data

Introduction

The relationship between two variables can be estimated using a function. The equation can be used to estimate values that are not in the observed data set. To determine which type of equation should be used for a data set, first create a scatter plot of the data. Data that has a linear shape, or can be approximated by a straight line, can be fitted to a linear equation. Points in the data set can be used to find a linear equation that is a good approximation for the data. Only two points are needed to draw a line.

Drawing a line through two data points on the same coordinate plane as the scatter plot helps display how well the line matches the data set. If the line is a good fit for the data, some data points will be above the line and some data points will be below the line. After creating a graphical representation of a line that fits the data, find the equation of this line using the two known points on the line. Use the two known points on the line to calculate the slope and y-intercept of the line.

Key Concepts

- A scatter plot that can be estimated with a linear function will look approximately like a line.

- A line through two points in the scatter plot can be used to find a linear function that fits the data.

- If a line is a good fit for a data set, some of the data points will be above the line and some will be below the line.

- The general equation of a line in point-slope form is $y = mx + b$, where m is the slope and b is the y-intercept.

- To find the equation of a line with two known points, calculate the slope and y-intercept of a line through the two points.

- Slope is the change in y divided by the change in x; a line through the points (x_1, y_1) and (x_2, y_2) has a slope of $\dfrac{y_2 - y_1}{x_2 - x_1}$.

- To find the y-intercept, or b in the equation $y = mx + b$, replace m with the calculated slope, and replace x and y with values of x and y from a point on the line. Then solve the equation for b.

- For example, for a line with a slope of 2 containing the point $(1, -3)$, $m = 2$, $y = -3$, and $x = 1$; $-3 = (2)(1) + b$, and $-5 = b$.

Guided Practice 4.2.4

Example 1

A weather team records the weather each hour after sunrise one morning in May. The hours after sunrise and the temperature in degrees Fahrenheit are in the table below.

Hours after sunrise	Temperature in °F
0	52
1	53
2	56
3	57
4	60
5	63
6	64
7	67

Can the temperature 0–7 hours after sunrise be represented by a linear function? If yes, find the equation of the function.

1. Create a scatter plot of the data.

   Let the x-axis represent the hours after sunrise and the y-axis represent the temperature in degrees Fahrenheit.

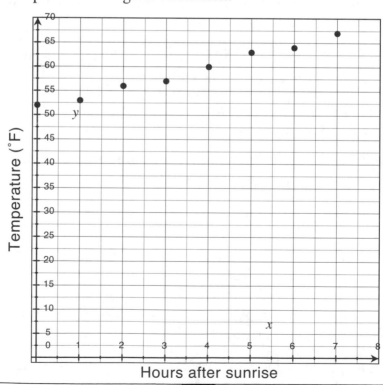

2. Determine if the data can be represented by a linear function.

    The graph of a linear equation is a line. If the data looks like it could fit a line, then a linear equation could be used to represent the data.

    The temperatures appear to increase in a line, and a linear equation could be used to represent the data set.

3. Draw a line to estimate the data set.

    Two points in the data set can be used to draw a line that estimates that data. When the line is drawn, some of the data values should be above the line, and some should be below the line.

    A line through (2, 56) and (6, 64) looks like a good fit for the data.

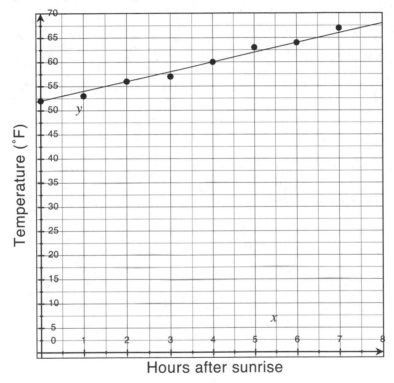

4. Find the equation of the line.

The general equation of a line in point-slope form is $y = mx + b$, where m is the slope, and b is the y-intercept.

Find the slope, m, of the line through the two chosen points. The slope is $\dfrac{\text{change in } y}{\text{change in } x}$. For any two points (x_1, y_1) and (x_2, y_2), the slope is $\dfrac{y_2 - y_1}{x_2 - x_1}$.

For the two points $(2, 56)$ and $(6, 64)$, the slope is $\dfrac{64 - 56}{6 - 2} = 2$.

Next, find the y-intercept, b. Use the general equation of a line to solve for b. Substitute x and y from a known point on the line, and replace m with the calculated slope.

$y = mx + b$

For the point $(2, 56)$: $56 = 2(2) + b$; $b = 52$

Replace m and b with the calculated values in the general equation of a line.

$y = 2x + 52$

The temperature between 0 and 7 hours after sunrise can be approximated with the equation $y = 2x + 52$.

Example 2

To learn more about the performance of an engine, engineers conduct tests and record the time it takes the car to reach certain speeds. A car starts from a stop and accelerates to 75 miles per hour. The table below shows the time, in seconds, after the car starts to accelerate and the speed it reaches at each time.

Time in seconds	Speed in miles per hour
0	0
1	2.3
2	6.6
3	13.5
4	22.4
5	32.2
6	44.2
7	57.8
8	74.6

Can the speed between 0 and 8 seconds be represented by a linear function? If yes, find the equation of the function.

1. Create a scatter plot of the data set.

   Let the *x*-axis represent the time, in seconds, and the *y*-axis represent the speed.

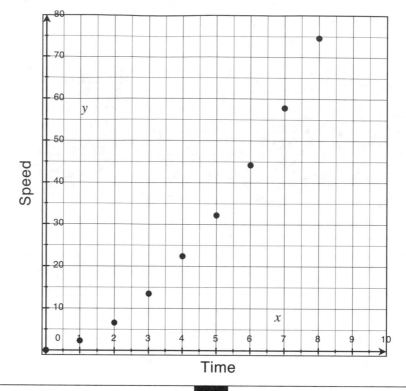

2. Determine if the data can be represented by a linear function.

   The *x*-values of each point are increasing by 1 unit. The *y*-values of each point are increasing by greater amounts as *x* gets larger. The first two points are close together, but the last two points show a large change in the speed. A curved graph has been created.

   This data should not be approximated using a line, and therefore should not be represented by a linear equation.

   No, the speed should not be represented by a linear equation.

Example 3

Automated tractors can mow lawns without being driven by a person. A company runs trials using fields of different sizes, and records the amount of time it takes the tractor to mow each field. The field sizes are measured in acres.

Acres	Time in hours
5	15
7	10
10	22
17	32.3
18	46.8
20	34
22	39.6
25	75
30	70
40	112

Can the time to mow acres of a field be represented by a linear function? If yes, find the equation of the function.

1. Create a scatter plot of the data.

   Let the x-axis represent the acres, and the y-axis represent the time in hours.

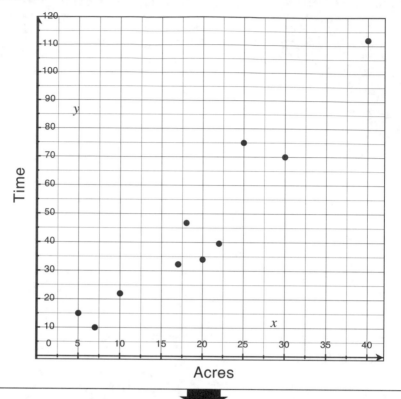

Time

Acres

2. Determine if the data can be represented by a linear function.

   The graph of a linear equation is a line. If the data looks like it could fit a line, then a linear equation could be used to represent the data.

   The temperatures appear to increase in a line, and a linear equation could be used to represent the data set.

3. Draw a line to estimate the data set.

Two points in the data set can be used to draw a line that estimates the data. When the line is drawn, some of the data values should be above the line, and some should be below the line.

A line through (7, 10) and (40, 112) looks like a good fit for the data.

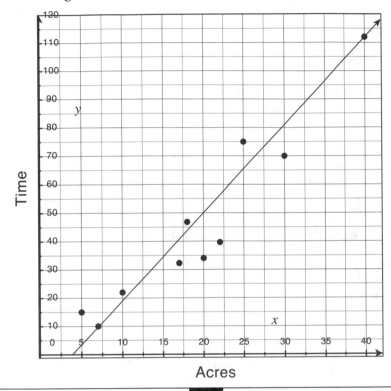

Acres

4. Find the equation of the line.

   The general equation of a line in point-slope form is $y = mx + b$, where m is the slope, and b is the y-intercept.

   Find the slope, m, of the line through the two chosen points. The slope is $\dfrac{\text{change in } y}{\text{change in } x}$. For any two points (x_1, y_1) and (x_2, y_2), the slope is $\dfrac{y_2 - y_1}{x_2 - x_1}$.

   For the two points (7, 10) and (40, 112), the slope is $\dfrac{112 - 10}{40 - 7} = 3.1$.

   Next, find the y-intercept, b. Use the general equation of a line to solve for b. Substitute x and y from a known point on the line, and replace m with the calculated slope.

   $y = mx + b$

   For the point (7, 10): $10 = 3.1(7) + b$; $b = -12$

   Replace m and b with the calculated values in the general equation of a line.

   $y = 3.1x - 12$

   The amount of time to mow the acres of a field can be represented using the equation $y = 3.1x - 12$.

UNIT 4 • DESCRIPTIVE STATISTICS
Lesson 2: Working with Two Categorical and Quantitative Variables

Practice 4.2.4: Fitting Linear Functions to Data

Max starts working out and eating healthy foods to reach a healthy weight. Each week, he records his weight in the table below. Use the data for problems 1–4.

Week	Weight in pounds
0	194
1	193.2
2	190.4
3	190.1
4	188
5	187.5
6	186.4
7	184.8
8	182
9	180.2

1. Create a scatter plot of the data set.

2. Describe the shape of the data.

3. Draw a line to estimate the data set.

4. Find the equation of the line that estimates the relationship between Max's weight and the number of weeks since Max started working out and eating healthy foods.

continued

UNIT 4 • DESCRIPTIVE STATISTICS
Lesson 2: Working with Two Categorical and Quantitative Variables

Daria is playing a word game. In the game, the score for a word is the sum of the points shown on each letter of the word plus any increase given by special spaces on the game board. Letters have different point values, and using special tiles can dramatically increase a word score. Daria records the length of each of her words and the score earned for the word. Use the data for problems 5 and 6.

Word length in letters	Word score in points
7	16
10	13
4	18
3	16
3	5
4	13
7	18
7	16
8	17

5. Create a scatter plot of the data set. Describe the shape of the data.

6. Can the data be represented using a linear equation? If yes, find the equation. If no, explain why not.

continued

UNIT 4 • DESCRIPTIVE STATISTICS
Lesson 2: Working with Two Categorical and Quantitative Variables

Penelope planted a new flower. Each week, she recorded the height of the flower in centimeters in the table below. Use the data for problems 7 and 8.

Week	Height in cm
1	3.5
2	4.8
3	6.7
4	7.2
5	7.9
6	8.9
7	9.8
8	10.3

7. Create a scatter plot of the data set, and draw a line to fit the data.

8. Find the equation to estimate the relationship between the number of weeks and the height of the flower in centimeters.

UNIT 4 • DESCRIPTIVE STATISTICS
Lesson 2: Working with Two Categorical and Quantitative Variables

A grocery store manager surveys 15 customers. Each customer indicates the number of people in his or her family and the amount the family spends each week on groceries. The results are in the table below. Use the data for problems 9 and 10.

Family size	Weekly grocery spending, in dollars ($)
5	295
3	222
1	64
1	37
6	390
6	348
7	343
4	192
4	136
4	144
7	448
2	142
6	330
1	33
7	336

9. Create a scatter plot of the data set, and draw a line to fit the data.

10. Find the equation to estimate the relationship between the size of a family and the amount spent on groceries.

Lesson 3: Interpreting Linear Models

Common Core State Standards

S–ID.7   Interpret the slope (rate of change) and the intercept (constant term) of a linear model in the context of the data.★

S–ID.8   Compute (using technology) and interpret the correlation coefficient of a linear fit.★

S–ID.9   Distinguish between correlation and causation.★

Essential Questions

1. How can you use units to help interpret the slope and *y*-intercept of a line fitted to data?

2. What is the relationship between the correlation coefficient and the correlation of two events?

3. What is the difference between correlation and causation?

WORDS TO KNOW

causation	a relationship between two events where a change in one event is responsible for a change in the second event
correlation	a relationship between two events, where a change in one event is related to a change in the second event. A correlation between two events does not imply that the first event is responsible for the change in the second event; the correlation only shows how likely it is that a change also took place in the second event.

correlation coefficient	a quantity that assesses the strength of a linear relationship between two variables, ranging from –1 to 1; a correlation coefficient of –1 indicates a strong negative correlation, a correlation coefficient of 1 indicates a strong positive correlation, and a correlation coefficient of 0 indicates a very weak or no linear correlation
linear fit (or linear model)	an approximation of data using a linear function
slope	a measure of the rate of change of one variable with respect to another variable; slope $= \dfrac{y_2 - y_1}{x_2 - x_1} = \dfrac{\Delta y}{\Delta x} = \dfrac{\text{rise}}{\text{run}}$; the slope in the equation $y = mx + b$ is m.
y-intercept	the point at which the graph crosses the y-axis; written as $(0, y)$; the y-intercept in the equation $y = mx + b$ is b.

Recommended Resources

- NCTM Illuminations. "Linear Regression I."

  http://walch.com/rr/CAU4L3CorrelationCoefficient

  This site allows users to plot points on a coordinate plane. Then the applet generates the line of best fit and displays the correlation coefficient.

- Office for Mathematics, Science, and Technology Education, University of Illinois. "Linear Regression Applet."

  http://walch.com/rr/CAU4L3LinearRegression

  This applet generates a theoretical line of best fit for points entered by the user. Users then manipulate a slider to change the slope of another line to try to match the theoretical line of best fit. A thermometer shows if the user's line is a good fit.

- WiseGeek.com. "What is the Difference Between Cause and Correlation?"

  http://walch.com/rr/CAU4L3CauseVsCorrelation

  This site offers an explanation of the difference between causation and correlation.

Lesson 4.3.1: Interpreting Slope and *y*-intercept

Introduction

When linear functions are used to model real-world relationships, the slope and *y*-intercept of the linear function can be interpreted in context. Recall that data in a scatter plot can be approximated using a linear fit, or linear function that models real-world relationships. A **linear fit** is the approximation of data using a linear function.

The **slope** of a linear function is the change in the dependent variable divided by the change in the independent variable, or $\frac{\text{change in } y}{\text{change in } x}$, sometimes written as $\frac{\Delta y}{\Delta x}$. The slope between two points (x_1, y_1) and (x_2, y_2) is $\frac{y_2 - y_1}{x_2 - x_1}$, and the slope in the equation $y = mx + b$ is m. The slope describes how much y changes when x changes by 1.

When analyzing the slope in the context of a real-world situation, remember to use the units of x and y in the calculation of the slope. For example, if the *x*-axis of a graph represents hours and the *y*-axis represents miles traveled, the slope of a linear function graphed on these axes would be $\frac{\text{change in miles}}{\text{change in hours}}$, or the miles traveled each hour.

The ***y*-intercept** of a function is the value of *y* at which the graph of the function crosses the *y*-axis, or the value of *y* when *x* equals 0. When analyzing the *y*-intercept in a real-world context, this is the starting value of whatever is represented by the *y*-axis. For example, if the *x*-axis represents hours and the *y*-axis represents miles traveled, the *y*-intercept would be the miles traveled when the number of hours equals 0. The *y*-intercept in the equation $y = mx + b$ is b. In some cases, the *y*-intercept doesn't make sense in context, such as when the quantity of *x* equals 0 and the *y*-intercept is something other than 0 (see Example 2).

Key Concepts

- The slope of a line with the equation $y = mx + b$ is m.

- The slope of a line is $\dfrac{\text{change in } y}{\text{change in } x}$; the slope between two points (x_1, y_1) and (x_2, y_2) is $\dfrac{y_2 - y_1}{x_2 - x_1}$.

- In context, the slope describes how much the dependent variable changes each time the independent variable changes by 1 unit.

- The y-intercept of a line with the equation $y = mx + b$ is b.

- The y-intercept is the value of y at which a graph crosses the y-axis.

- In context, the y-intercept is the initial value of the quantity represented by the y-axis, or the quantity of y when the quantity represented by the x-axis equals 0.

Guided Practice 4.3.1

Example 1

The graph below contains a linear model that approximates the relationship between the size of a home and how much it costs. The x-axis represents size in square feet, and the y-axis represents cost in dollars. Describe what the slope and the y-intercept of the linear model mean in terms of housing prices.

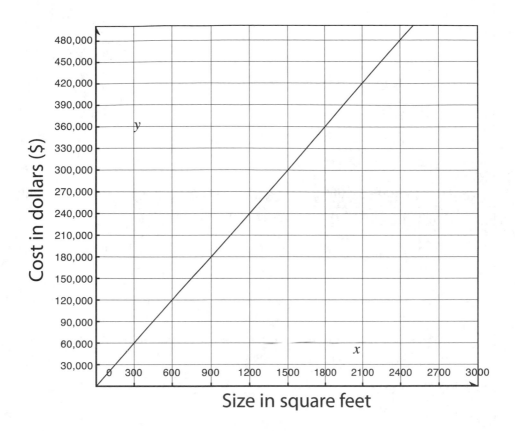

1. Find the equation of the linear fit.

   The general equation of a line in slope-intercept form is $y = mx + b$, where m is the slope and b is the y-intercept.

   Find two points on the line using the graph.

   The graph contains the points (300, 60,000) and (600, 120,000).

   The formula to find the slope between two points (x_1, y_1) and (x_2, y_2) is $\dfrac{y_2 - y_1}{x_2 - x_1}$.

   Substitute (300, 60,000) and (600, 120,000) into the formula to find the slope.

   $\dfrac{y_2 - y_1}{x_2 - x_1}$ Slope formula

   $= \dfrac{120,000 - 60,000}{600 - 300}$ Substitute (300, 60,000) and (600, 120,000) for (x_1, y_1) and (x_2, y_2).

   $\dfrac{60,000}{300} = 200$ Simplify as needed.

   The slope between the two points (300, 60,000) and (600, 120,000) is 200.

   Find the y-intercept. Use the equation for slope-intercept form, $y = mx + b$, where b is the y-intercept.

   Replace x and y with values from a single point on the line. Let's use (300, 60,000).

   Replace m with the slope, 200. Solve for b.

   $y = mx + b$ Equation for slope-intercept form

   $60,000 = 200(300) + b$ Substitute values for x, y, and m.

   $60,000 = 60,000 + b$ Multiply.

   $0 = b$ Subtract 60,000 from both sides.

   The y-intercept of the linear model is 0.

   The equation of the line is $y = 200x$.

2. Determine the units of the slope.

Divide the units on the *y*-axis by the units on the *x*-axis: $\dfrac{\text{dollars}}{\text{square feet}}$.

The units of the slope are dollars per square foot.

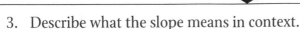

3. Describe what the slope means in context.

The slope is the change in cost of the home for each square foot of the home. The slope describes how price is affected by the size of the home purchased. A positive slope means the quantity represented by the *y*-axis increases when the quantity represented by the *x*-axis also increases.

The cost of the home increases by \$200 for each square foot.

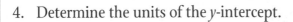

4. Determine the units of the *y*-intercept.

The units of the *y*-intercept are the units of the *y*-axis: dollars.

5. Describe what the *y*-intercept means in context.

The *y*-intercept is the value of the equation when *x* = 0, or when the size of the home is 0 square feet. For a home with no area, or for no home, the cost is \$0.

Example 2

A teller at a bank records the amount of time a customer waits in line and the number of people in line ahead of that customer when he or she entered the line. Describe the relationship between waiting time and the people ahead of a customer when the customer enters a line.

People ahead of customer	Minutes waiting
1	10
2	21
3	32
5	35
8	42
9	45
10	61

1. Create a scatter plot of the data.

   Let the *x*-axis represent the number of people ahead of the customer and the *y*-axis represent the minutes spent waiting.

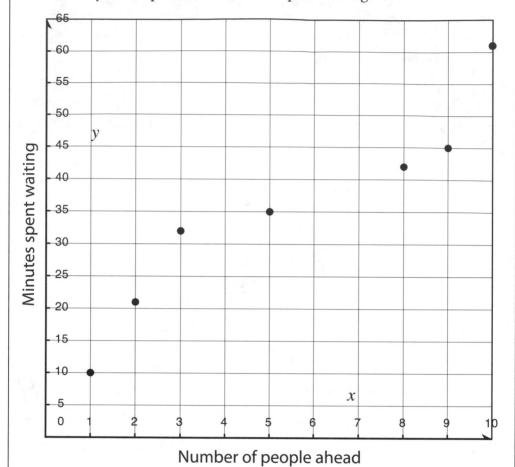

2. Find the equation of a linear model to represent the data.

Use two points to estimate a linear model. A line through the two points should have approximately the same number of data values both above and below the line. A line through the first and last data points, (1, 10) and (10, 61), appears to be a good approximation of the data. Find the slope.

The slope between two points (x_1, y_1) and (x_2, y_2) is $\dfrac{y_2 - y_1}{x_2 - x_1}$. Substitute the points into the formula to find the slope.

$\dfrac{y_2 - y_1}{x_2 - x_1}$	Slope formula
$\dfrac{61 - 10}{10 - 1}$	Substitute (1, 10) and (10, 61) for (x_1, y_1) and (x_2, y_2).
$\dfrac{51}{9} \approx 5.67$	Simplify as needed.

The slope between the two points (1, 10) and (10, 61) is ≈ 5.67.

Find the y-intercept. Use the equation for slope-intercept form, $y = mx + b$, where b is the y-intercept.

Replace x and y with values from a single point on the line. Let's use (1, 10).

Replace m with the slope, 5.67. Solve for b.

$y = mx + b$	Equation for slope-intercept form
$10 = 1(5.67) + b$	Substitute values for x, y, and m.
$10 = 5.67 + b$	Simplify.
$4.33 = b$	Subtract 5.67 from both sides.

The y-intercept of the linear model is 4.33.

The equation of the line is $y = 5.67x + 4.33$.

3. Determine the units of the slope.

   Divide the units on the *y*-axis by the units on the *x*-axis:

   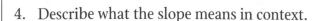

   $$\frac{\text{minutes spent waiting}}{\text{number of people ahead}} = \frac{\text{minutes}}{\text{person}}$$

   The units of the slope are minutes per person.

4. Describe what the slope means in context.

   The slope describes how the waiting time increases for each person in line ahead of the customer. A customer waits approximately 5.67 minutes for each person who is in line ahead of the customer.

5. Determine the units of the *y*-intercept.

   The units of the *y*-intercept are the units of the *y*-axis: minutes.

6. Describe what the *y*-intercept means in context.

   The *y*-intercept is the value of the equation when $x = 0$, or when the number of people ahead of the customer is 0. The *y*-intercept is 4.33. In this context, the *y*-intercept isn't relevant, because if no one was in line ahead of a customer, the wait time would be 0 minutes. Creating a linear model that matched the data resulted in a *y*-intercept that wasn't 0, but this value isn't related to the context of the situation.

Example 3

For hair that is 12 inches or longer, a hair salon charges for haircuts based on hair length according to the equation $y = 5x + 35$, where x is the number of inches longer than 12 inches (hair length − 12) and y is the cost in dollars. Describe what the slope and y-intercept mean in context.

1. Determine the units of the slope.

   Divide the units of the dependent variable, y, by the units of the independent variable, x:

   $$\frac{\text{cost in dollars}}{\text{hair length greater than 12 inches}} = \frac{\text{dollars}}{\text{inch}}$$

2. Describe what the slope means in context.

   The units of the slope are dollars per inch. The slope describes how the cost of the haircut increases for each inch of hair length greater than 12 inches.

3. Determine the units of the y-intercept.

   The units of the y-intercept are the units of the dependent variable, y: dollars.

4. Describe what the y-intercept means in context.

   The y-intercept is the value of the equation when $x = 0$, or when hair length is not greater than 12 inches. The y-intercept is the cost of a haircut when a customer's hair is no longer than 12 inches.
   A haircut is $35 if a customer's hair isn't longer than 12 inches.

UNIT 4 • DESCRIPTIVE STATISTICS
Lesson 3: Interpreting Linear Models

Practice 4.3.1: Interpreting Slope and *y*-intercept

A ring toss game at a fair is set up so that only a small percentage of players win. Each day, the fair records the number of players and the number of winners. The data is in the table below. Use the table for problems 1–3.

Number of players	Number of winners
11	2
36	6
36	5
39	8
35	7
18	3
10	1
24	3
38	6
36	7
25	5

1. Create a scatter plot of the data set.

2. Find the equation of a line that fits the data.

3. Interpret the slope and *y*-intercept of the equation in context.

continued

UNIT 4 • DESCRIPTIVE STATISTICS
Lesson 3: Interpreting Linear Models

A delivery service ships packages from a central warehouse by truck. Twelve trucks make deliveries in one day. Each truck records the number of packages delivered and the total time spent delivering packages, in minutes. The results are in the table below. Use the table for problems 4–6.

Number of packages	Minutes to deliver
107	139
120	120
104	117
56	66
123	164
70	92
126	120
66	79
73	114
51	78
109	110
116	140

4. Create a scatter plot of the data set.

5. Find the equation of a line that fits the data.

6. Interpret the slope and y-intercept of the equation in context.

continued

UNIT 4 • DESCRIPTIVE STATISTICS
Lesson 3: Interpreting Linear Models

A small dairy farm records the number of cows producing milk each day and the total liters of milk produced. The data is in the scatter plot below. Use the scatter plot for problems 7 and 8.

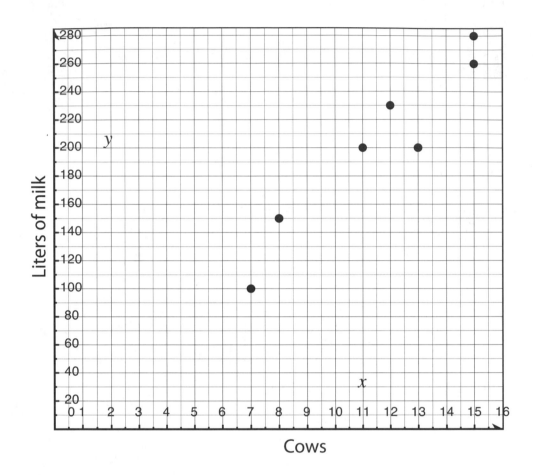

7. Find the equation of a line that fits the data.

8. Interpret the slope and y-intercept of the equation in context.

continued

UNIT 4 • DESCRIPTIVE STATISTICS
Lesson 3: Interpreting Linear Models

Mrs. Lopez recorded the shoe size and height in inches of each girl in her class. Her results are in the scatter plot below. Use the scatter plot for problems 9 and 10.

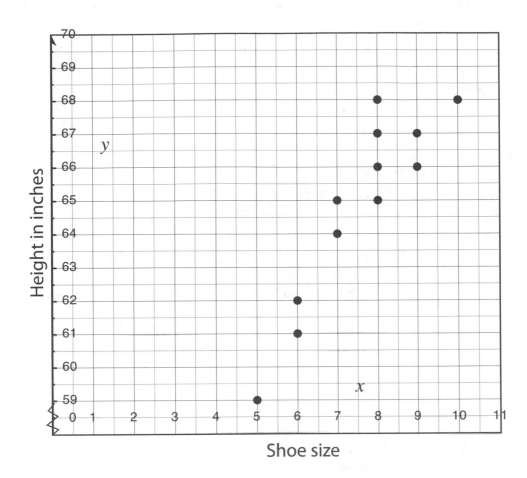

9. Find the equation of a line that fits the data.

10. Interpret the slope and y-intercept of the equation in context.

Lesson 4.3.2: Calculating and Interpreting the Correlation Coefficient

Introduction

In previous lessons, we have plotted and analyzed data that appears to have a linear relationship. The data points in some data sets were very close to a linear model, while other data sets had points that were farther from the linear model. The strength of the relationship between data that has a linear trend can be analyzed using the correlation coefficient. A **correlation** is a relationship between two events, such as x and y, where a change in one event implies a change in another event. The **correlation coefficient**, r, is a quantity that allows us to determine how strong this relationship is between two events. It is a value that ranges from -1 to 1; a correlation coefficient of -1 indicates a strong negative correlation, a correlation coefficient of 1 indicates a strong positive correlation, and a correlation coefficient of 0 indicates a very weak or no linear correlation. You will use a calculator to calculate the correlation coefficient. Note that a correlation between two events does not imply that changing one event *causes* a change in the other event—only that a change might have taken place in the other event. This will be explored more later.

Key Concepts

- A correlation is a relationship between two events, where a change in one event implies a change in another event.

- Correlation doesn't mean that a change in the first event *caused* a change in the other event.

- The strength of a linear correlation can be measured using a correlation coefficient.

- Before determining the correlation coefficient, look at the scatter plot of the data and make an initial assessment of the strength of a linear relationship between the two events.

- To calculate the correlation coefficient on a graphing calculator, follow the steps on the next page.

On a TI-83/84:

Step 1: Set up the calculator to find correlations. Press [2nd], then [CATALOG] (the "0" key). Scroll down and select DiagnosticOn, then press [ENTER]. (This step only needs to be completed once. The calculator will stay in this mode until changed in this menu.)

Step 2: To calculate the correlation coefficient, first enter the data into a list. Press [2nd], then L1 (the "1" key). Scroll to enter data sets. Press [2nd], then L2 (the "2" key). Enter the second event in L2.

Step 3: Calculate the correlation coefficient. Press [STAT], then select CALC at the top of the screen. Scroll down to 8:LinReg(a+bx), and press [ENTER].

The r value (the correlation coefficient) is displayed along with the equation.

On a TI-Nspire:

Step 1: Go to the lists and spreadsheet page. The icon looks like a table.

Step 2: Enter the data into the first column underneath the shaded row, pressing [enter] after each data value.

Step 3: Use the nav pad to arrow up to the first row below the shaded row and then arrow over to the right so that you are in the second column. Enter the data values, pressing [enter] after each data value.

Step 4: Press the [menu] key.

Step 5: Arrow down to 4: Statistics, and press the center click key.

Step 6: Press the center click key again to select 1: Stat Calculations.

Step 7: Choose 3: Linear Regression (mx+b).

Step 8: At the X List field, press [clear] and then type in "a[]". To type "[]", press the [ctrl] key and then the [(] key.

Step 9: Press [tab] to go the Y List field and type in "b[]".

Step 10: Press [tab] to go the Results field and check that results are listed in "c[]". If not, change them.

Step 11: Press [tab] to "OK" and press the center click key.

Step 12: Arrow down until you see the "r" and look to the right. The number to the right is the correlation coefficient, r.

- A correlation coefficient of –1 indicates a strong negative correlation.

- A correlation coefficient of 1 indicates a strong positive correlation.

- A correlation coefficient of 0 indicates a very weak or no linear correlation.

- The correlation coefficient only assesses the strength of a linear relationship between two variables.

- The correlation coefficient does not assess causation—that one event causes the other.

Guided Practice 4.3.2

Example 1

An education research team is interested in determining if there is a relationship between a student's vocabulary and how frequently the student reads books. The team gives 20 students a 100-question vocabulary test, and asks students to record how many books they read in the past year. The results are in the table below. Is there a linear relationship between the number of books read and test scores? Use the correlation coefficient, r, to explain your answer.

Books read	Test score
12	23
8	3
19	14
9	8
14	56
19	19
15	25
6	30
2	6
14	42
5	12
15	30
8	36
5	19
1	0
13	63
4	9
16	78
16	16
7	9

1. Create a scatter plot of the data.

   Let the *x*-axis represent books read and the *y*-axis represent test score.

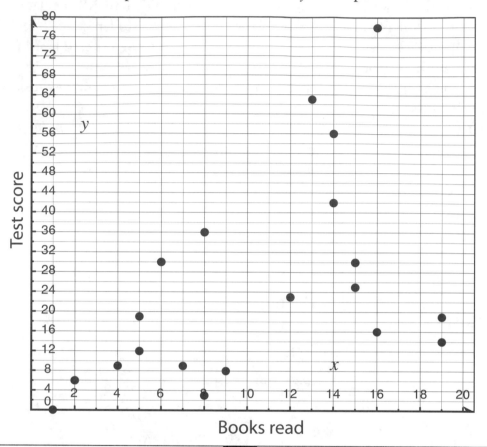

Books read

2. Describe the relationship between the data using the graphical representation.

   It appears that the higher scores were from students who read more books, but the data does not appear to lie on a line. There is not a strong linear relationship between the two events.

3. Calculate the correlation coefficient on your graphing calculator. Refer to the steps in the Key Concepts section.

   The correlation coefficient, *r*, is approximately 0.48.

4. Use the correlation coefficient to describe the strength of the relationship between the data.

A correlation coefficient of 1 indicates a strong positive correlation, and a correlation of 0 indicates no correlation. A correlation coefficient of 0.48 is about halfway between 1 and 0, and indicates that there is a weak positive linear relationship between the number of books a student read in the past year and his or her score on the vocabulary test. ✓

Example 2

A hockey coach wants to determine if players who take many practice shots during practice have a higher shooting percentage. The shooting percentage is calculated by dividing the number of goals scored by the number of shots taken. The coach records the number of practice shots 20 players take each practice, and compares the number with each player's shooting percentage over the season. Is there a linear relationship between the practice shots and shooting percentage? Use the correlation coefficient, r, to explain your answer.

Practice shots	Shooting percentage	Practice shots	Shooting percentage
228	9	223	10
164	9	133	7
64	3	238	10
213	12	228	11
166	9	138	8
60	3	139	7
109	6	118	6
83	4	210	10
229	13	103	5
160	8	114	6

1. Create a scatter plot of the data.

   Let the *x*-axis represent the number of practice shots and the *y*-axis represent the shooting percentage.

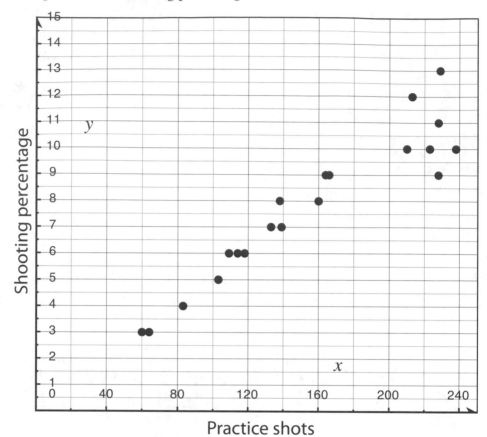

Practice shots

2. Describe the relationship between the data using the graphical representation.

   It appears that there is a linear relationship between shots taken per practice and shooting percentage. As the number of practice shots increases, shooting percentage also increases, and the graph appears to have a linear shape.

3. Calculate the correlation coefficient on your graphing calculator. Follow the steps in the Key Concepts section.

   The correlation coefficient, *r*, is 0.94.

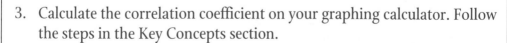

4. Use the correlation coefficient to describe the strength of the relationship between the data.

A correlation coefficient of 1 indicates a strong positive correlation, and a correlation of 0 indicates no correlation. A correlation coefficient of 0.94 is close to 1, and indicates that there is a strong positive linear relationship between the number of shots taken and the shooting percentage.

Example 3

Caitlyn thinks that there may be a relationship between class size and student performance on standardized tests. She tracks the average test performance of students from 20 different classes, and notes the number of students in each class in the table below. Is there a linear relationship between class size and average test score? Use the correlation coefficient, r, to explain your answer.

Class size	Average student test score	Class size	Average student test score
26	28	32	33
36	25	27	30
29	27	21	33
26	32	28	27
19	38	23	41
34	32	29	28
17	43	37	23
14	42	14	39
23	37	25	31
17	41	33	30

1. Create a scatter plot of the data.

    Let the *x*-axis represent the number of students in each class and the *y*-axis represent the average test score.

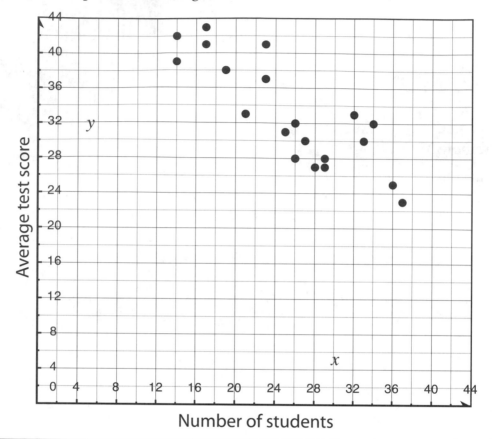

2. Describe the relationship between the data using the graphical representation.

    As the class size increases, the average test score decreases. It appears that there is a linear relationship with a negative slope between the two variables.

3. Calculate the correlation coefficient on your graphing calculator. Follow the steps in the Key Concepts section.

    The correlation coefficient, *r*, is approximately –0.84.

4. Use the correlation coefficient to describe the strength of the relationship between the data.

    A correlation coefficient of −1 indicates a strong negative correlation, and a correlation of 0 indicates no correlation. A correlation coefficient of −0.84 is close to −1, and indicates that there is a strong negative linear relationship between class size and average test score.

UNIT 4 • DESCRIPTIVE STATISTICS
Lesson 3: Interpreting Linear Models

Practice 4.3.2: Calculating and Interpreting the Correlation Coefficient

For each of the following scatter plots, describe the type of linear correlation between the two variables: positive, negative, or no correlation, and identify whether it is strong or weak.

1.

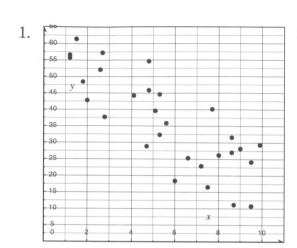

3.

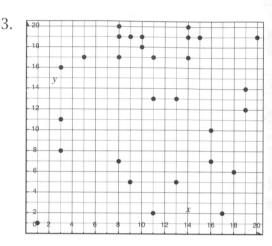

2.

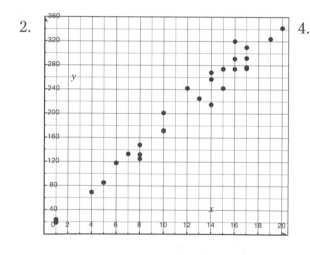

4.

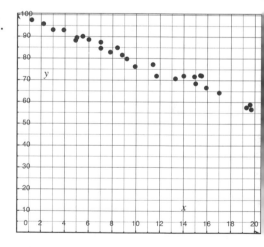

continued

UNIT 4 • DESCRIPTIVE STATISTICS
Lesson 3: Interpreting Linear Models

An airline wants to examine the relationship between the number of passengers on each flight and the pounds of luggage stored on the plane. The data is in the table below. Use the table for problems 5–7.

Number of passengers	Pounds of luggage	Number of passengers	Pounds of luggage
427	17,100	416	17,500
359	15,800	371	17,100
465	21,900	323	12,900
481	23,600	362	16,700
330	13,900	517	22,200
357	15,400	436	18,800
402	20,100	436	18,700
420	18,100	503	21,100
312	15,000	510	23,000
304	15,200	361	17,000

5. Create a scatter plot of the data.

6. Use your graph to describe the relationship between the number of passengers on a flight and the pounds of luggage on the plane.

7. Find the correlation coefficient, r, of the data. Describe what the correlation coefficient indicates about the relationship between the data.

UNIT 4 • DESCRIPTIVE STATISTICS
Lesson 3: Interpreting Linear Models

A magazine publisher wants to understand if there is a relationship between the number of print magazines sold and the number of unique visitors to the magazine's website. The publisher records the number of magazines sold and number of unique website visitors for 20 different days in the table below.

Magazines sold	Unique website visitors	Magazines sold	Unique website visitors
2,900	5,100	1,400	9,800
2,700	6,900	2,400	9,500
1,200	7,800	1,100	5,800
2,200	7,600	1,700	5,900
2,200	5,000	2,000	8,800
1,700	9,100	1,000	7,100
1,600	9,500	2,400	8,600
2,700	7,800	1,700	9,100
2,400	7,400	2,100	7,800
2,700	7,000	2,500	8,300

8. Create a scatter plot of the data.

9. Use your graph to describe the relationship between the number of print magazines sold and the number of website visitors.

10. Find the correlation coefficient, r, of the data. Describe what the correlation coefficient indicates about the relationship between the data.

Lesson 4.3.3: Distinguishing Between Correlation and Causation

Introduction

A correlation between two events simply means that there is a consistent relationship between two events, and that a change in one event implies that the other event will change according to the linear relationship. A correlation does not imply **causation**, or that a change in one event causes the change in the second event. Because many factors influence changes in events, it is very difficult to prove causation, sometimes referred to as a causal relationship. For example, researchers gathered the data below comparing the hours of television watched per day by viewers and each viewer's weight in pounds.

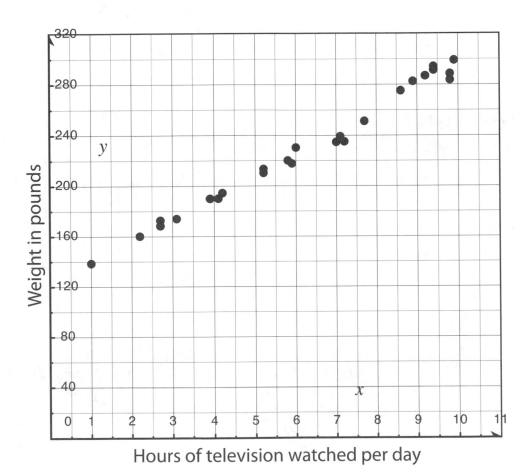

Hours of television watched per day

The correlation coefficient, *r*, between the two events is 0.994. According to this data, a person's weight could be estimated based on the hours of television he or she watches each day. This is due to the strong correlation between the two events. Can the researchers conclude that watching television is responsible for increased weight, or that watching television causes a person to gain weight?

The correlation does not give any information about *why* weight increases when a person watches more television. If the data is accurate, it is likely that there is a factor not included in the data set that is associated with both events. For example, a person who watches more television may spend less time exercising and more time sitting. Or, a person who watches more television may eat less healthy foods than someone who spends less time watching television.

There may be many contributing factors that explain how this relationship works. The important note is that watching television by itself cannot cause weight gain. It is also possible that a correlation appears to exist because of a small sample size or a poorly selected sample. Knowing the difference between correlation and causation is particularly important when reading advertisements or other persuasive materials. Think closely about outside factors that may have influenced both events and led to a strong correlation before believing that one event is responsible for the change in another event.

Key Concepts

- Correlation does not imply causation.

- If a change in one event is responsible for a change in another event, the two events have a causal relationship.

- Outside factors may influence and explain a strong correlation between two events.

- Use a calculator to find the correlation coefficient.

  On a TI-83/84:

  > Step 1: Set up the calculator to find correlations. Press [2nd], then [CATALOG] (the "0" key). Scroll down and select DiagnosticOn, then press [ENTER]. (This step only needs to be completed once. The calculator will stay in this mode until changed in this menu.)
  >
  > Step 2: To calculate the correlation coefficient, first enter the data into a list. Press [2nd], then L1 (the "1" key). Scroll to enter data sets. Press [2nd], then L2 (the "2" key). Enter the second event in L2.
  >
  > Step 3: Calculate the correlation coefficient. Press [STAT], then select CALC at the top of the screen. Scroll down to 8:LinReg(a+bx), and press [ENTER].
  >
  > The *r* value (the correlation coefficient) is displayed along with the equation.

On a TI-Nspire:

Step 1: Go to the lists and spreadsheet page. The icon looks like a table.

Step 2: Enter the data into the first column underneath the shaded row, pressing [enter] after each data value.

Step 3: Use the nav pad to arrow up to the first row below the shaded row and then arrow over to the right so that you are in the second column. Enter the data values, pressing [enter] after each data value.

Step 4: Press the [menu] key.

Step 5: Arrow down to 4: Statistics, and press the center click key.

Step 6: Press the center click key again to select 1: Stat Calculations.

Step 7: Choose 3: Linear Regression (mx+b).

Step 8: At the X List field, press [clear] and then type in "a[]". To type "[]", press the [ctrl] key and then the [(] key.

Step 9: Press [tab] to go the Y List field and type in "b[]".

Step 10: Press [tab] to go the Results field and check that results are listed in "c[]". If not, change them.

Step 11: Press [tab] to "OK" and press the center click key.

Step 12: Arrow down until you see the "r" and look to the right. The number to the right is the correlation coefficient, r.

Guided Practice 4.3.3

Example 1

Alex coaches basketball, and wants to know if there is a relationship between height and free throw shooting percentage. Free throw shooting percentage is the number of free throw shots completed divided by the number of free throw shots attempted:

$$\frac{\text{free throw shots completed}}{\text{free throw shots attempted}}$$

He takes some notes on the players in his team, and records his results in the table below. What is the correlation between height and free throw shooting percentage? Alex looks at his data and decides that increased height causes a reduced free throw shooting percentage. Is he correct?

Height in inches	Free throw percentage	Height in inches	Free throw percentage
75	28	72	28
75	22	76	33
67	30	76	25
80	6	67	54
71	43	79	5
67	40	67	55
76	10	78	25
76	25	75	13
70	42	71	30
72	47	68	29
79	24	79	14
69	23	78	25
76	27		

1. Create a scatter plot of the data.

    Let the *x*-axis represent height, in inches, and the *y*-axis represent free throw shooting percentage.

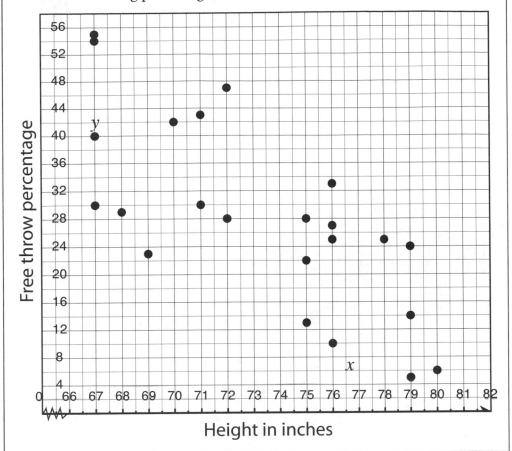

2. Analyze the scatter plot, and describe any relationship between the two events.

    As height increases, free throw shooting percentage decreases. It appears that there is a weak negative linear correlation between the two events.

3. Find the correlation coefficient using a graphing calculator. Follow the steps in the Key Concepts section.

    $r = -0.727$

4. Describe the correlation between the two events.

   −0.727 is close to −1. There is a negative linear correlation between the events.

5. Consider the causal relationship between the two events. Determine if it is likely that height is responsible for the decrease in free throw shooting percentage.

   Even if there is a correlation between height and free throw percentage, it is not likely that height causes a basketball player to have more difficulty making free throw shots. If two equally skilled players were of different heights, would you expect one of them to make fewer free throws based only on his or her height? What about a very tall player who spends more time practicing free throws than a very short player? What if the sample size is too small to gather data that's true for the larger population? There is most likely not a causal relationship between height and free throw percentage.

Example 2

Mr. Gray's students are interested in learning how studying can improve test performance. Mr. Gray provides students with practice problems related to particular tests. The class records the number of practice problems completed and the score on that related test in the table below. What is the correlation between the number of practice problems completed and the test score? Is there a causal relationship between the number of practice problems completed and the test score?

Problems completed	Test score, out of 100 points	Problems completed	Test score, out of 100 points
10	56	100	75
40	70	110	72
100	83	100	74
40	54	120	90
0	45	130	99
50	58	160	100
90	72	0	49
150	97	60	59
30	50	0	55
60	58	180	96
90	74	150	100
110	89	30	67
30	59	30	56
130	95	20	50
10	46		

1. Create a scatter plot of the data.

   Let the *x*-axis represent the number of completed practice problems and the *y*-axis represent the test score.

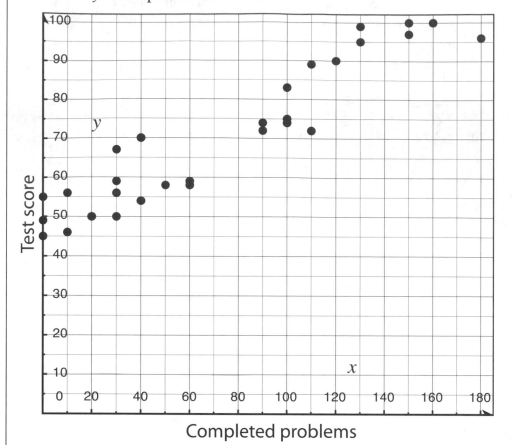

2. Analyze the scatter plot, and describe any relationship between the two events.

   As the number of completed practice problems increases, the test score also increases. The shape of the graph is approximately a line, and it appears there is a positive linear correlation between the number of practice problems completed and the test score.

3. Find the correlation coefficient using a graphing calculator. Follow the steps in the Key Concepts section.

   $r = 0.942$

4. Describe the correlation between the two events.

   0.942 is close to 1. There is a strong positive linear correlation between the number of practice problems completed and the test score.

5. Consider the causal relationship between the two events. Determine if it is likely that the number of practice problems completed is responsible for increased test scores. Note any other factors that could influence test scores.

   There is a strong correlation between the two events. A score on a test is related to a student's knowledge of the test content, and a student's ability to use content to solve problems. Completing practice problems allows students to develop skills directly related to test performance, and although there are other factors that are related to test performance, it is likely that there is a causal relationship between the number of practice problems completed and the test score.

Example 3

Nadia is a salesperson at a car dealership. She earns money each time she sells a car. To determine if there is a relationship between the number of hours she works and her income, she records the number of hours worked and the amount of money she earns each day. Her data is in the scatter plot that follows. Is there a causal relationship between the hours Nadia works and her daily income?

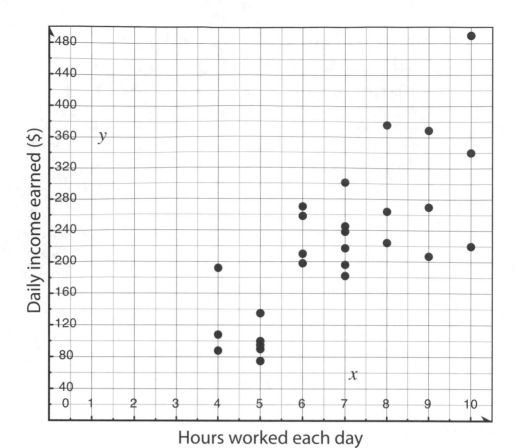

Hours worked each day

1. Analyze the scatter plot, and describe any relationship between the two events.

As the number of hours increase, the daily income also increases, but there is much variation in the increase of income as hours increase. There appears to be a weak linear correlation between hours and income.

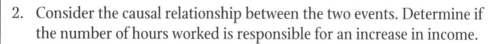

2. Consider the causal relationship between the two events. Determine if the number of hours worked is responsible for an increase in income.

Nadia earns money when she sells a car. The more hours she works, the greater the opportunity she has to sell more cars. However, the only way to earn more money is to either sell more cars or to sell cars that are more expensive. She could work for 10 hours, but if she doesn't sell any cars, or make no effort to sell any cars, then her income will reflect this lack of sales or effort. Working more hours does not cause the increase in income. Selling more cars causes the increase in income. There is likely not a causal relationship between hours worked and income earned.

Practice 4.3.3: Distinguishing Between Correlation and Causation

A movie production company is interested in learning about the connection between dollars invested to make a film and dollars earned by the film in U.S. theaters. Data for recent movie investments and earnings are in the table below. Use this table for problems 1–4.

Millions of dollars invested	Millions of dollars earned in U.S. theaters	Millions of dollars invested	Millions of dollars earned in U.S. theaters
144	22	124	181
64	45	101	203
79	36	3	74
176	57	167	129
132	97	25	15
46	101	74	48
154	110	72	116
113	202	121	73
24	78	150	190
188	207	77	202
59	31	85	116
68	159	170	132
35	13	108	39
67	197	125	202
6	103		

1. Create a scatter plot of the data.

2. Describe the shape of the graph.

3. Find the correlation coefficient, r, and describe what this indicates about the relationship between dollars invested and dollars earned for films.

4. Is it likely that there is a causal relationship between money spent making a movie and money earned by the movie in theaters?

continued

UNIT 4 • DESCRIPTIVE STATISTICS
Lesson 3: Interpreting Linear Models

When shopping at one shoe store, customers must work with a salesperson to get a pair of shoes in the correct size. The store manager wants to know if having a larger sales staff increases shoe sales. The manager records the number of salespeople working and the number of pairs of shoes sold in the table below. Note that if 4 people are working, this indicates that 4 people were working simultaneously at the store throughout the day. Use this table for problems 5–8.

Salespeople	Pairs of shoes sold	Salespeople	Pairs of shoes sold
1	5	3	31
5	22	2	20
5	30	8	48
6	54	2	14
7	57	2	8
7	71	6	28
3	20	7	51
2	15	7	60
2	18	7	39
1	9	2	14
4	35	7	73
6	46	3	16
8	49	8	76
7	47	7	58
4	33		

5. Create a scatter plot of the data.

6. Describe the shape of the graph.

7. Find the correlation coefficient, r, and describe what this indicates about the relationship between the number of salespeople and the number of shoes sold.

8. Is it likely that there is a causal relationship between the number of salespeople and the number of shoes sold?

continued

UNIT 4 • DESCRIPTIVE STATISTICS
Lesson 3: Interpreting Linear Models

A cell phone app developer conducts research about cell phone usage. The developer randomly surveys cell phone users, and asks each user to record his or her age and the number of apps the user has on his or her cell phone. The results are in the scatter plot below. Use this scatter plot for problems 9 and 10.

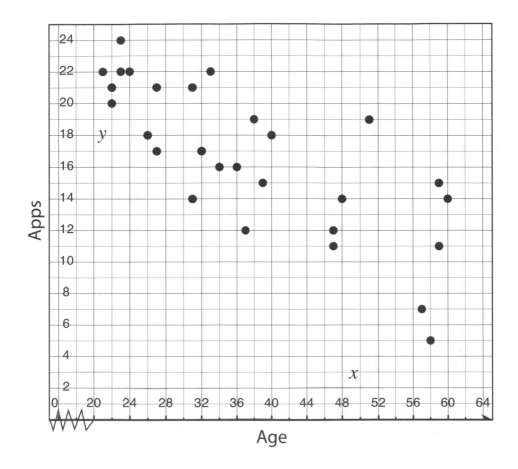

9. Describe the shape of the graph, and describe any possible correlation between age and the number of cell phone apps.

10. Is it likely that there is a causal relationship between the age of cell phone users and the number of cell phone apps used?

Unit 5
Congruence, Proof, and Constructions

Lesson 1: Introducing Transformations

Common Core State Standards

G–CO.1 Know precise definitions of angle, circle, perpendicular line, parallel line, and line segment, based on the undefined notions of point, line, distance along a line, and distance around a circular arc.

G–CO.2 Represent transformations in the plane using, e.g., transparencies and geometry software; describe transformations as functions that take points in the plane as inputs and give other points as outputs. Compare transformations that preserve distance and angle to those that do not (e.g., translation versus horizontal stretch).

G–CO.3 Given a rectangle, parallelogram, trapezoid, or regular polygon, describe the rotations and reflections that carry it onto itself.

Essential Questions

1. What does it mean to be parallel? What does it mean to be perpendicular?

2. What is a function? Are transformations functions?

3. What does it mean to be symmetrical?

4. Are there different types of transformations?

5. How do we define transformations?

WORDS TO KNOW

acute angle	an angle measuring less than 90° but greater than 0°
angle	two rays or line segments sharing a common endpoint. The difference in direction of the two parts is called the angle. Angles can be measured in degrees or radians; written as $\angle A$.
arc length	the distance between the endpoints of an arc; written as $d\left(\overset{\frown}{ABC}\right)$
circle	the set of points on a plane at a certain distance, or radius, from a single point, the center

circular arc	on a circle, the unshared set of points between the endpoints of two radii
congruent	having the same shape, size, or angle
distance along a line	the linear distance between two points on a given line; written as $d(PQ)$
image	the new, resulting figure after a transformation
isometry	a transformation in which the preimage and image are congruent
line	the set of points between two points P and Q in a plane and the infinite number of points that continue beyond those points; written as $\overleftrightarrow{PQ}$
line of symmetry	a line separating a figure into two halves that are mirror images; written as ℓ
line segment	a line with two endpoints; written as $\overline{PQ}$
line symmetry	exists for a figure if for every point on one side of the line of symmetry, there is a corresponding point the same distance from the line
obtuse angle	an angle measuring greater than 90° but less than 180°
one-to-one	a relationship wherein each point in a set of points is mapped to exactly one other point
parallel lines	lines in a plane that either do not share any points and never intersect, or share all points; written as $\overleftrightarrow{AB} \parallel \overleftrightarrow{PQ}$
perpendicular lines	two lines that intersect at a right angle (90°); written as $\overleftrightarrow{AB} \perp \overleftrightarrow{PQ}$
point	an exact position or location in a given plane
preimage	the original figure before undergoing a transformation
ray	a line with only one endpoint; written as $\overrightarrow{PQ}$
reflection	a transformation where a mirror image is created; also called a flip
regular polygon	a two-dimensional figure with all sides and all angles congruent

right angle	an angle measuring 90°
rotation	a transformation that turns a figure around a point; also called a turn
transformation	a change in a geometric figure's position, shape, or size
translation	a transformation that moves each point of a figure the same distance in the same direction; also called a slide

Recommended Resources

- MathIsFun.com. "What is a Function?"

  http://walch.com/rr/CAU5L1Functions

  This site gives a general overview of functions.

- NLVM Geometry Manipulatives. "Transformations—Reflection."

  http://walch.com/rr/CAU5L1Reflections

  This site allows for exploration of reflecting figures on a coordinate plane.

- NLVM Geometry Manipulatives. "Transformations—Rotation."

  http://walch.com/rr/CAU5L1Rotations

  This site allows for exploration of rotating figures on a coordinate plane.

- Purplemath. "Function Transformations/Translations."

  http://walch.com/rr/CAU5L1FunctionTrans

  The graphs and explanations at this site provide a thorough look at various function transformations.

Lesson 5.1.1: Defining Terms

Introduction

Geometric figures can be graphed in the coordinate plane, as well as manipulated. However, before sliding and reflecting figures, the definitions of some important concepts must be discussed.

Each of the manipulations that will be discussed will move points along a parallel line, a perpendicular line, or a circular arc. In this lesson, each of these paths and their components will be introduced.

Key Concepts

- A **point** is not something with dimension; a point is a "somewhere." A point is an exact position or location in a given plane. In the coordinate plane, these locations are referred to with an ordered pair (x, y), which tells us where the point is horizontally and vertically. The symbol $A\ (x, y)$ is used to represent point A at the location (x, y).

- A **line** requires two points to be defined. A line is the set of points between two reference points and the infinite number of points that continue beyond those two points in either direction. A line is infinite, without beginning or end. This is shown in the diagram below with the use of arrows. The symbol $\overleftrightarrow{AB}$ is used to represent line AB.

- You can find the linear distance between two points on a given line. **Distance along a line** is written as $d(PQ)$ where P and Q are points on a line.

- Like a line, a **ray** is defined by two points; however, a ray has only one endpoint. The symbol $\overrightarrow{AB}$ is used to represent ray AB.

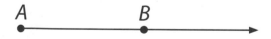

- Similarly, a **line segment** is also defined by two points, but both of those points are endpoints. A line segment can be measured because it has two endpoints and finite length. Line segments are used to form geometric figures. The symbol $\overline{AB}$ is used to represent line segment *AB*.

- An **angle** is formed where two line segments or rays share an endpoint, or where a line intersects with another line, ray, or line segment. The difference in direction of the parts is called the angle. Angles can be measured in degrees or radians. The symbol $\angle A$ is used to represent angle *A*. *A* represents the vertex of the angle. Sometimes it is necessary to use three letters to avoid confusion. In the diagram below, $\angle BAC$ can be used to represent the same angle, $\angle A$. Notice that *A* is the vertex of the angle and it will always be listed in between the points on the rays of the angle.

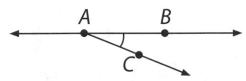

- An **acute angle** measures less than 90° but greater than 0°. An **obtuse angle** measures greater than 90° but less than 180°. A **right angle** measures exactly 90°.

- Two relationships between lines that will help us define transformations are parallel and perpendicular. **Parallel lines** are two lines that have unique points and never cross. If parallel lines share one point, then they will share every point; in other words, a line is parallel to itself.

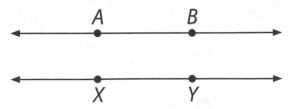

- **Perpendicular lines** meet at a right angle (90°), creating four right angles.

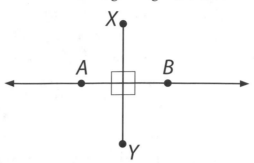

- A **circle** is the set of points on a plane at a certain distance, or radius, from a single point, the center. Notice that a radius is a line segment. Therefore, if we draw any two radii of a circle, we create an angle where the two radii share a common endpoint, the center of the circle.

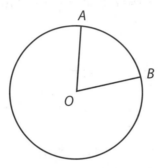

- Creating an angle inside a circle allows us to define a **circular arc**, the set of points along the circle between the endpoints of the radii that are not shared. The **arc length**, or distance along a circular arc, is dependent on the length of the radius and the angle that creates the arc—the greater the radius or angle, the longer the arc.

$$\angle AOC > \angle AOB \rightarrow \overarc{AC} > \overarc{AB} \qquad \overline{OA} > \overline{OX} \rightarrow \overarc{AB} > \overarc{XY}$$

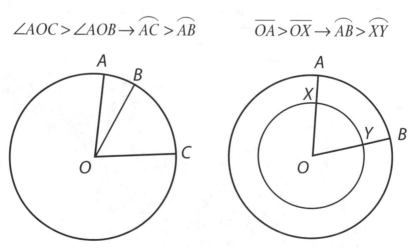

Guided Practice 5.1.1

Example 1

Refer to the figures below. Can a line segment be defined using the points *A* and *B*? Can a line segment be defined using the point *C*? Justify your response to each question.

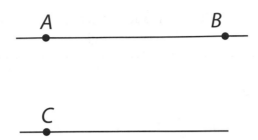

1. The points *A* and *B* can be used to define a line segment because *A* and *B* are on the same line and are unique points.

2. The point *C* cannot be used to define a line segment because there is not a second point defined on the line.

Example 2

Refer to the figures below. In the first, do the line segments $\overline{AB}$ and $\overline{BC}$ form an angle? In the second figure, do the line segments $\overline{AB}$ and $\overline{CD}$ form an angle? Justify your response to each question.

I.

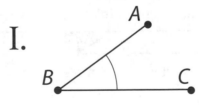

II.

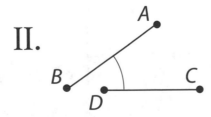

1. In the first figure, the line segments $\overline{AB}$ and $\overline{BC}$ meet the angle definition of two lines, rays, or line segments intersecting; the two segments form an angle.

2. In the second figure, the line segments $\overline{AB}$ and $\overline{CD}$ do not intersect, so they do not form an angle.

Example 3

By definition, $\overline{AB}$ is perpendicular to $\overline{CD}$ because $m\angle CXI$ is 90°. What are the measures of $\angle AXC$, $\angle AXD$, and $\angle DXB$?

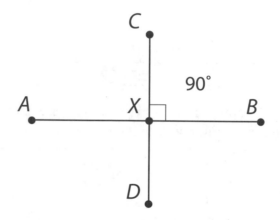

1. The measures of $\angle AXC$, $\angle AXL$, and $\angle DXB$ are all 90°. The importance of the perpendicular relationship is that all four angles created by the intersection are equal.

2. In the figure that follows, we can see the result when the lines are not perpendicular: the angles of intersection are not equal.

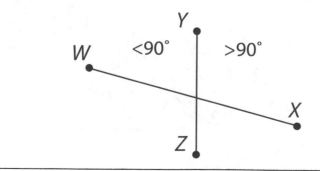

Example 4

Given the following:

$$\overline{AC} \cong \overline{BD} \qquad\qquad \overline{WY} < \overline{XZ}$$

$$\overline{AB} \perp \overline{AC} \qquad\qquad \overline{WX} \perp \overline{WY}$$

$$\overline{AB} \perp \overline{BD} \qquad\qquad \overline{WX} \perp \overline{XZ}$$

Are $\overline{AB}$ and $\overline{CD}$ parallel? Are $\overline{WX}$ and $\overline{YZ}$ parallel? Explain.

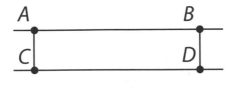

1. $\overline{AC}$ and $\overline{BD}$ intersect $\overline{AB}$ at the same angle and $\overline{AC} \cong \overline{BD}$. $\overleftrightarrow{AB}$ will never cross $\overleftrightarrow{CD}$. Therefore, $\overline{AB}$ is parallel to $\overline{CD}$.

2. $\overline{WY}$ and $\overline{XZ}$ intersect $\overline{WX}$ at the same angle, but $\overline{WY} < \overline{XZ}$. As you move from Z to Y on $\overleftrightarrow{YZ}$, you move closer to, and will eventually intersect, $\overleftrightarrow{WX}$. Therefore, $\overline{WX}$ is not parallel to $\overline{YZ}$.

Example 5

Refer to the figures below. Given $\overline{AB} \cong \overline{BC}$, is the set of points with center B a circle? Given $\overline{XY} > \overline{YZ}$, is the set of points with center Y a circle?

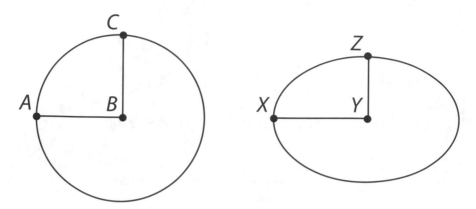

1. The set of points with center B is a circle because all points are equidistant from the center, B.	

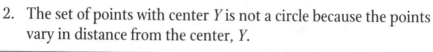

2. The set of points with center Y is not a circle because the points vary in distance from the center, Y.	✓

UNIT 5 • CONGRUENCE, PROOF, AND CONSTRUCTIONS
Lesson 1: Introducing Transformations

Practice 5.1.1: Defining Terms

Use what you've learned to answer the questions that follow.

1. What geometric figure consists of all points in a plane that are a given distance from a given point in the plane?

2. What type of angle has a measure that is greater than 90° but less than 180°?

3. What does $\overline{AB}$ represent?

4. What type of angle has a measure that is greater than 0° but less than 90°?

5. What term is used to describe the exact position on a plane?

6. Two circular arcs, $\overset{\frown}{CD}$ and $\overset{\frown}{FG}$, share the same center, O. The point C is on $\overline{OF}$ and D is on $\overline{OG}$. What can be said about the relation of the lengths of arc $\overset{\frown}{CD}$ and arc $\overset{\frown}{FG}$?

7. If two lines are perpendicular, at what angle do they intersect?

8. What is the definition of an angle?

9. What is the definition of a line?

10. Two circular arcs, $\overset{\frown}{MN}$ and $\overset{\frown}{MP}$, share the same center, O. The point N lies on the circle between points M and P. What can be said about the relation of the lengths of arc $\overset{\frown}{MN}$ and arc $\overset{\frown}{MNP}$?

Lesson 5.1.2: Transformations As Functions

Introduction

The word *transform* means "to change." In geometry, a **transformation** changes the position, shape, or size of a figure on a coordinate plane. The original figure, called a **preimage**, is changed or moved, and the resulting figure is called an **image**. We will be focusing on three different transformations: translations, reflections, and rotations. These transformations are all examples of **isometry**, meaning the new image is congruent to the preimage. Figures are **congruent** if they have the same shape, size, or angle. The new image is simply moving to a new location. In this lesson, we will learn to describe transformations as functions on points in the coordinate plane. Let's first review functions and how they are written.

A function is a relationship between two sets of data, inputs and outputs, where the function of each input has exactly one output. Because of this relationship, functions are defined in terms of their potential inputs and outputs. For example, we can say that a function f takes real numbers as inputs and its outputs are also real numbers. Once we have determined what the potential inputs and outputs are for a given function, the next step is to define the exact relationship between the individual inputs and outputs. To do this, we need to have a name for each output in terms of the input. So, for a function f with input x, the output is called "f of x," written $f(x)$. For example, if we say f takes x as input and the output is $x + 2$, then we write $f(x) = x + 2$.

Now that we understand the idea of a function, we can discuss transformations in the coordinate plane as functions. First we need to determine our potential inputs and outputs. In the coordinate plane we define each coordinate, or point, in the form (x, y) where x and y are real numbers. This means we can describe the coordinate plane as the set of points of all real numbers x by all real numbers y. Therefore, the potential inputs for a transformation function f in the coordinate plane will be a real number coordinate pair, (x, y), and each output will be a real number coordinate pair, $f(x, y)$. For example, f is a function in the coordinate plane such that f of $f(x, y)$ is $(x + 1, y + 2)$, which can be written as: $f(x, y) = (x + 1, y + 2)$.

Finally, transformations are generally applied to a set of points such as a line, triangle, square, or other figure. In geometry, these figures are described by points, P, rather than coordinates (x, y), and transformation functions are often given the letters R, S, or T. Also, we will see $T(x, y)$ written $T(P)$ or P', known as "P prime." Putting it all together, a transformation T on a point P is a function where $T(P)$ is P'.

When a transformation is applied to a set of points, such as a triangle, then all points in the set are moved according to the transformation. For example, if $T(x, y) = (x + h, y + k)$, then $T(\triangle ABC)$ would be:

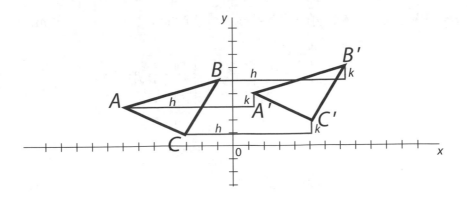

Key Concepts

- Transformations are **one-to-one**, which means each point in the set of points will be mapped to exactly one other point and no other point will be mapped to that point.

- If a function is one-to-one, no elements are lost during the function.

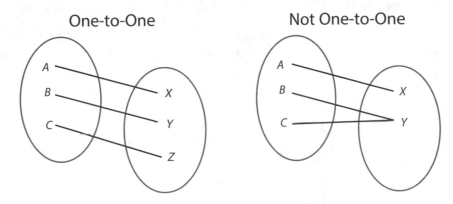

- The simplest transformation is the identity function I where I: $(x', y') = (x, y)$.

- Transformations can be combined to form a new transformation that will be a new function.

- For example, if $S(x, y) = (x + 3, y + 1)$ and $T(x, y) = (x - 1, y + 2)$, then $S(T(x, y)) = S((x - 1, y + 2)) = ((x - 1) + 3, (y + 2) + 1) = (x + 2, y + 3)$.

- It is important to understand that the order in which functions are taken will affect the output. In the function above, we see $S(T(x, y)) = (x + 2, y + 3)$. Does $T(S(x, y)) = (x + 2, y + 3)$?

- In this case, $T(S(x, y)) = S(T(x, y))$, and in the graph below we can see why.

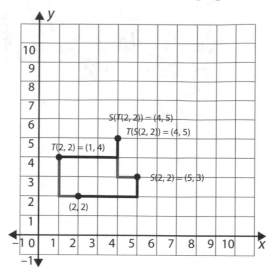

- However, here are two functions where the order in which they are taken changes the outcome: $T_{2,3}(x, y)$ and a reflection through the line $y = x$, $r_{y=x}(x, y)$ on $\triangle ABC$. In the first two graphs we see $r_{y=x}\left(T_{2,3}(\triangle ABC)\right)$, and in the second two graphs we see $T_{2,3}\left(r_{y=x}(\triangle ABC)\right)$. Notice the outcome is different depending on the order of the functions.

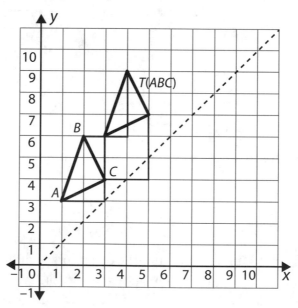

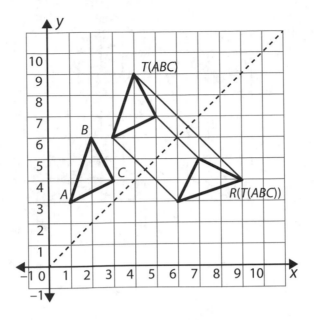

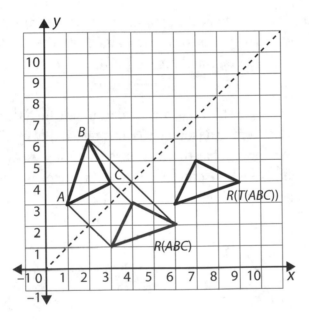

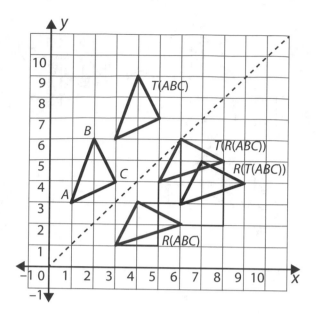

- Because the order in which functions are taken can affect the output, we always take functions in a specific order, working from the inside out. For example, if we are given the set of functions $h(g(f(x)))$, we would take $f(x)$ first and then g and finally h.

- Remember, an isometry is a transformation in which the preimage and the image are congruent. An isometry is also referred to as a "rigid transformation" because the shape still has the same size, area, angles, and line lengths. The previous example is an isometry because the image is congruent to the preimage.

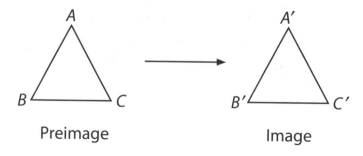

Preimage   Image

- In this lesson, we will be focusing on three isometric transformations: translations, reflections, and rotations. A **translation**, or slide, is a transformation that moves each point of a figure the same distance in the same direction. A **reflection**, or flip, is a transformation where a mirror image is created. A **rotation**, or turn, is a transformation that turns a figure around a point.

- Some transformations are not isometric. Examples of non-isometric transformations are horizontal stretch and dilation.

- For example, a horizontal stretch transformation, $T(x, y) = (3x - 4, y)$, applied to $\square ABCD$ is one-to-one—every point in $\square ABCD$ is mapped to just one point in $\square A'B'C'D'$. However, horizontal distance is not preserved.

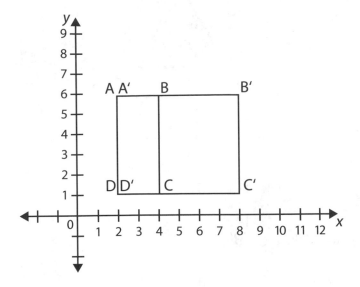

- Note that $\overline{AB} \neq \overline{A'B'}$ and $\overline{CD} \neq \overline{C'D'}$. From the graph, we can see that $\square ABCD$ and $\square A'B'C'D'$ are not congruent; therefore T is not isometric.

- Another transformation that is not isometric is a dilation. A dilation stretches or contracts both coordinates.

- If we have the dilation $D(x, y) = (2x - 5, y - 4)$, we can graph $D(\triangle ABC) = \triangle A'B'C'$, as seen below.

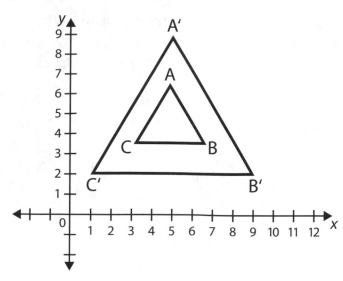

Note that $\triangle ABC \not\cong \triangle A'B'C'$.

Guided Practice 5.1.2

Example 1

Given the point $P(5, 3)$ and $T(x, y) = (x + 2, y + 2)$, what are the coordinates of $T(P)$?

1. Identify the point given.

   We are given $P(5, 3)$.

2. Identify the transformation.

   We are given $T(P) = (x + 2, y + 2)$.

3. Calculate the new coordinates.

   $T(P) = (x + 2, y + 2)$

   $(5 + 2, 3 + 2)$

   $(7, 5)$

   $T(P) = (7, 5)$

Example 2

Given $\triangle ABC: A(5,2), B(3,5),$ and $C(2,2)$, and the transformation $T(x, y) = (x, -y)$, what are the coordinates of the vertices of $T(\triangle ABC)$? What kind of transformation is T?

1. Identify the vertices of the triangle.

   We are given the coordinates of the vertices $A(5, 2), B(3, 5),$ and $C(2, 2)$.

2. Identify the transformation.

   We are given $T(x, y) = (x, -y)$.

3. Calculate the new coordinates of the triangle.

$$T(A)=T(5,2)=(5,-2)=A'$$
$$T(B)=T(3,5)=(3,-5)=B'$$
$$T(C)=T(2,2)=(2,-2)=C'$$

When $\triangle ABC$ and $\triangle A'B'C'$ are drawn, we can see that the transformation is a reflection transformation through the x-axis.

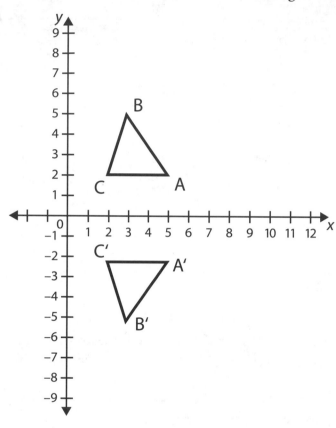

Example 3

Given the transformation of a translation $T_{5,-3}$, and the points $P(-2, 1)$ and $Q(4, 1)$, show that the transformation of a translation is isometric by calculating the distances, or lengths, of $\overline{PQ}$ and $\overline{P'Q'}$.

1. Plot the points of the preimage.

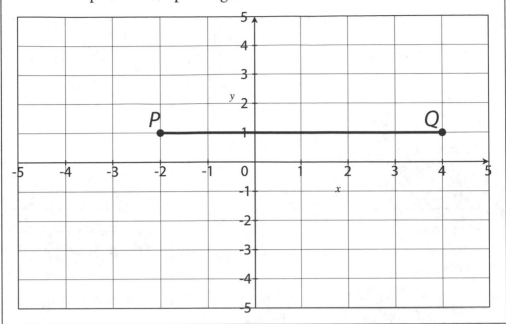

2. Transform the points.

$$T_{5,-3}(x, y) = (x + 5, y - 3)$$

$$T_{5,-3}(P) = (-2 + 5, 1 - 3) \implies P'(3, -2)$$

$$T_{5,-3}(Q) = (4 + 5, 1 - 3) \implies P'(9, -2)$$

3. Plot the image points.

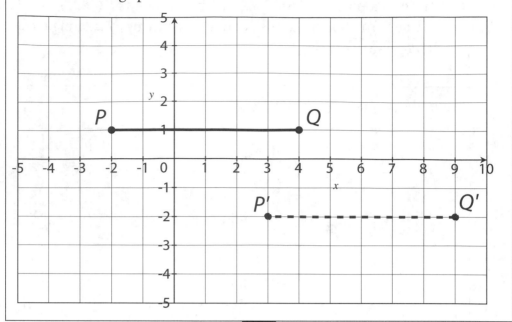

4. Calculate the distance, *d*, of each segment from the preimage and the image and compare them.

Since the line segments are horizontal, count the number of units the segment spans to determine the distance.

$d(PQ) = 5$

$d(P'Q') = 5$

The distances of the segments are the same. The translation of the segment is isometric.

Example 4

Given $T_{-6,2}(x, y) = (x - 6, y + 2)$, state the translation that would yield the identity transformation, $I = T_{h,k}(T_{-6,2}(x, y))$.

---

1. Recall that the identity function brings a preimage back onto itself. Note what changes are made to the coordinates.

   The x-coordinate is being translated 6 units to the left.

   The y-coordinate is being translated 2 units up.

▼

2. Determine what transformation needs to happen to bring the point (x, y) back to its original position.

   The x-coordinate needs to be brought back to the right 6 units.

   The y-coordinate needs to be brought back down 2 units.

▼

3. Write symbolically the translation that will bring the point back to its original position.

   $T_{6,-2}$

▼

4. Put all the pieces together to write the identity transformation.

   $T_{6,-2}(T_{-6,2}(x, y)) = I$

Practice 5.1.2: Transformations As Functions

Use what you know about transformations to answer the questions.

1. What three transformations have isometry?

2. When combining functions such as $f(g(h(x)))$, which operation should be performed first?

3. When a transformation is described as isometric, what does this tell you?

4. If you were to translate a point up 2 units and down 3 units, and then move the point down 2 units and up 3 units, what happens? Write this symbolically.

5. If the transformation T is isometric and $d(AB) = 4$, what is $d(T(AB))$?

6. Given $T_{h,k}(x, y) = (x + h, y + k)$ and $P(-6, 7)$, what is $T_{1,-9}(P)$?

7. Using the form $T_{h,k}(x, y) = (x + h, y + k)$, how can we describe a translation S that moves a point right 8 units and down 3 units in the coordinate plane?

8. Given $R_{180}(x, y) = (-x, -y)$ and $Q(2, -5)$, what is $R_{180}(Q)$?

9. Find $T(S(x, y))$ if $T(x, y) = (x + 1, y - 1)$ and $S(x, y) = (x - 4, y + 3)$. Label your answer P. What values of h and k would prove the equation $T_{h,k}(P) = (x, y)$ true?

10. Given $T_{1,-3}(x, y) = (x + 1, y - 3)$, state the translation that would yield the identity transformation, $I = T_{h,k}(T_{1,-3}(x, y))$.

Lesson 5.1.3: Applying Lines of Symmetry

Introduction

A **line of symmetry**, ℓ, is a line separating a figure into two halves that are mirror images. **Line symmetry** exists for a figure if for every point P on one side of the line, there is a corresponding point Q where ℓ is the perpendicular bisector of $\overline{PQ}$.

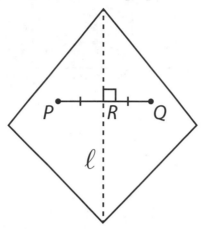

From the diagram, we see that ℓ is perpendicular to $\overline{PQ}$. The tick marks on the segment from P to R and from R to Q show us that the lengths are equal; therefore, R is the point that is halfway between $\overline{PQ}$.

Depending on the characteristics of a figure, a figure may contain many lines of symmetry or none at all. In this lesson, we will discuss the rotations and reflections that can be applied to squares, rectangles, parallelograms, trapezoids, and other regular polygons that carry the figure onto itself. **Regular polygons** are two-dimensional figures with all sides and all angles congruent.

Squares

Because squares have four equal sides and four equal angles, squares have four lines of symmetry. If we rotate a square about its center 90°, we find that though the points have moved, the square is still covering the same space.

Similarly, we can rotate a square 180°, 270°, or any other multiple of 90° with the same result.

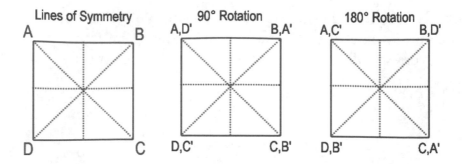

We can also reflect the square through any of the four lines of symmetry and the image will project onto its preimage.

Rectangles

A rectangle has two lines of symmetry: one vertical and one horizontal. Unlike a square, a rectangle does not have diagonal lines of symmetry. If a rectangle is rotated 90°, will the image be projected onto its preimage? What if it is rotated 180°?

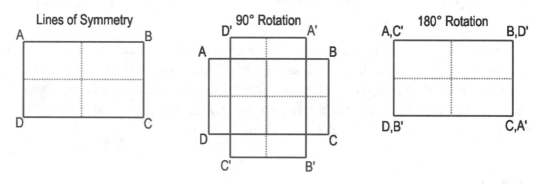

If a rectangle is reflected through its horizontal or vertical lines of symmetry, the image is projected onto its preimage.

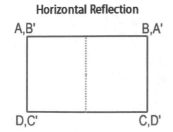

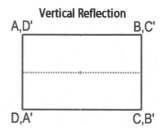

Trapezoids

A trapezoid has one line of symmetry bisecting, or cutting, the parallel sides in half if and only if the non-parallel sides are of equal length (called an isosceles trapezoid). We can reflect the isosceles trapezoid shown below through the line of symmetry; doing so projects the image onto its preimage. However, notice that in the last trapezoid shown below $\overline{AD}$ is longer than $\overline{BC}$, so there is no symmetry. The only rotation that will carry a trapezoid that is not isosceles onto itself is 360°.

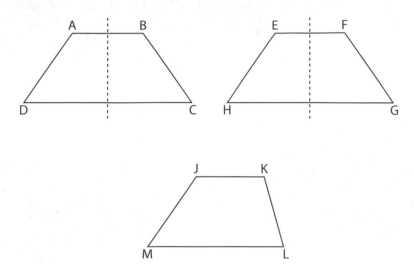

Parallelograms

There are no lines of symmetry in a parallelogram if a 90° angle is not present in the figure. Therefore, there is no reflection that will carry a parallelogram onto itself. However, what if it is rotated 180°?

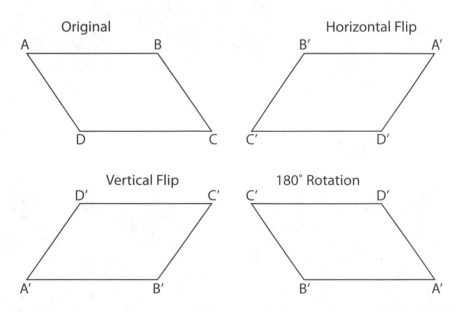

Key Concepts

- Figures can be reflected through lines of symmetry onto themselves.

- Lines of symmetry determine the amount of rotation required to carry them onto themselves.

- Not all figures are symmetrical.

- Regular polygons have sides of equal length and angles of equal measure. There are *n* number of lines of symmetry for a number of sides, *n*, in a regular polygon.

Guided Practice 5.1.3

Example 1

Given a regular pentagon *ABCDE*, draw the lines of symmetry.

1. First, draw the pentagon and label the vertices. Note the line of symmetry from *A* to $\overline{DC}$.

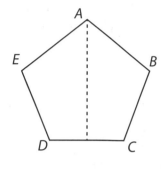

2. Now move to the next vertex, *B*, and extend a line to the midpoint of $\overline{DE}$.

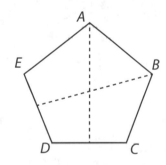

3. Continue around to each vertex, extending a line from the vertex to the midpoint of the opposing line segment.

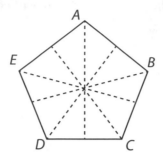

Note that a regular pentagon has five sides, five vertices, and five lines of reflection.

Example 2

A piece of rectangular paper is folded in the following way:

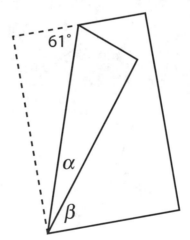

Find the angles alpha, α, and beta, β.

1. First, label the vertices.

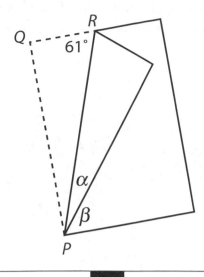

2. Find the measure of $\angle QPR$.

    We know the sum of the interior angles of a triangle is 180°. We also know $m\angle Q$ is 90° because we are told the paper is rectangular. Therefore, subtract $61 + 90$ from 180 to find the measure of $\angle QPR$.

    $180 - (61 + 90) = 180 - (151) = 29$

3. Now we know $m\angle QPR$ is 29°. Because of the symmetry of the folded paper, we know $m\angle\alpha$ must also be 29°.

4. Finally, we know the measures of $\angle QPR$, $\angle\alpha$, and $\angle\beta$ total 90° because the paper is rectangular, so
    $m\angle\beta = 90 - 2(29) = 90 - 58 = 32$.

Example 3

Given the quadrilateral *ABCE*, the square *ABCD*, and the information that *F* is the same distance from *A* and *C*, show that *ABCE* is symmetrical along $\overline{BE}$.

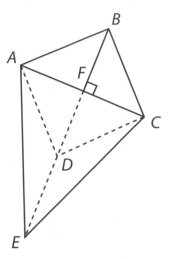

1. Recall the definition of line symmetry.

   Line symmetry exists for a figure if for every point on one side of the line of symmetry, there is a corresponding point the same distance from the line.

   We are given that *ABCD* is square, so we know $\overline{AB} \cong \overline{BC}$.

   We also know that $\square ABCD$ is symmetrical along $\overline{BD}$.

   We know $\overline{AF} \cong \overline{FC}$.

2. Since $\overline{AB} \cong \overline{BC}$ and $\overline{AF} \cong \overline{FC}$, $\overline{BF}$ is a line of symmetry for $\triangle ABC$ where $\triangle ABF \cong \triangle CBF$.

3. $\triangle AFE$ has the same area as $\triangle CFE$ because they share a base and have equal height. $\overline{AF} \cong \overline{FC}$, so $\triangle AFE \cong \triangle CFE$.

4. We now know $\overline{FE}$ is a line of symmetry for $\triangle ACE$ and $\overline{BF}$ is a line of symmetry for $\triangle ABC$, so $\triangle ABE \cong \triangle CBE$ and quadrilateral *ABCE* is symmetrical along $\overline{BE}$.

UNIT 5 • CONGRUENCE, PROOF, AND CONSTRUCTIONS
Lesson 1: Introducing Transformations

Practice 5.1.3: Applying Lines of Symmetry

Use what you've learned about symmetry to answer the questions.

1. How many lines of symmetry does a circle have?

2. How many lines of symmetry does a regular octagon have?

3. When does a parallelogram have fewer than 4 lines of symmetry?

4. What type of triangle has one line of symmetry?

5. How many lines of symmetry does an equilateral triangle have?

6. What is the smallest number of degrees needed to rotate a regular hexagon around its center onto itself?

7. What is the smallest number of degrees needed to rotate a regular pentagon around its center onto itself?

8. How many lines of symmetry are there in one red rectangle on the American flag?

9. The face of a dog is symmetrical along the bridge of its nose, which falls on the line of symmetry that extends directly between the eyes. If a dog's left eye is 4 inches from the bridge of its nose, how far is the dog's right eye from its left eye?

10. How many different ways can a regular pentagon be sliced into 2 equal halves?

Lesson 2: Defining and Applying Rotations, Reflections, and Translations

Common Core State Standards

G–CO.4 Develop definitions of rotations, reflections, and translations in terms of angles, circles, perpendicular lines, parallel lines, and line segments.

G–CO.5 Given a geometric figure and a rotation, reflection, or translation, draw the transformed figure using, e.g., graph paper, tracing paper, or geometry software. Specify a sequence of transformations that will carry a given figure onto another.

Essential Questions

1. What linear relation defines the movement of a translation?

2. What linear relation defines the movement of a reflection?

3. Why do circular arcs define the movement of a rotation rather than a linear point-to-point relationship?

WORDS TO KNOW

clockwise rotating a figure in the direction that the hands on a clock move

counterclockwise rotating a figure in the opposite direction that the hands on a clock move

quadrant the coordinate plane is separated into four sections:

- In Quadrant I, x and y are positive.
- In Quadrant II, x is negative and y is positive.
- In Quadrant III, x and y are negative.
- In Quadrant IV, x is positive and y is negative.

reflection an isometry in which a figure is moved along a line perpendicular to a given line called the line of reflection

rotation	an isometry where all points in the preimage are moved along circular arcs determined by the center of rotation and the angle of rotation
translation	an isometry where all points in the preimage are moved parallel to a given line

Recommended Resources

- Interactivate. "3D Transmographer."

  http://walch.com/rr/CAU5L2PolygonsIn3-D

  Create a three-dimensional polygon on the coordinate plane and animate it using options to translate, reflect, or revolve the figure. Drag on the plane itself for a side view. Users may specify angles of rotation, units reflected, and more.

- MathIsFun.com. "Transformations."

  http://walch.com/rr/CAU5L2Transformations

  This site offers an overview of the three main transformations. Click each term to open a page with interactive manipulatives to see the transformations animated. Rotations, translations, and reflections are all covered.

- NCTM Illuminations. "Shape Cutter."

  http://walch.com/rr/CAU5L2TransformShapes

  This interactive tool allows users to cut, slide, turn, and flip shapes on a virtual geoboard.

Lesson 5.2.1: Defining Rotations, Reflections, and Translations

Introduction

Now that we have built our understanding of parallel and perpendicular lines, circular arcs, functions, and symmetry, we can define three fundamental transformations: translations, reflections, and rotations. We will be able to define the movement of each transformation in the coordinate plane with functions that have preimage coordinates for input and image coordinates as output.

Key Concepts

- The coordinate plane is separated into four **quadrants**, or sections:

  - In Quadrant I, x and y are positive.

  - In Quadrant II, x is negative and y is positive.

  - In Quadrant III, x and y are negative.

  - In Quadrant IV, x is positive and y is negative.

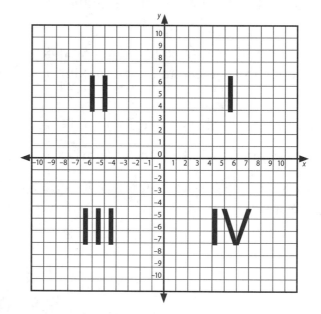

- A **translation** is an isometry where all points in the preimage are moved parallel to a given line. No matter which direction or distance the translation moves the preimage, the image will have the same orientation as the preimage. Because the orientation does not change, a translation is also called a slide.

- In the translation below, we can see the points A, B, and C are translated along parallel lines to the points A', B', and C'. Each point is carried the same distance and direction, so not only is $\triangle A'B'C'$ congruent to $\triangle ABC$, it also maintains the same orientation.

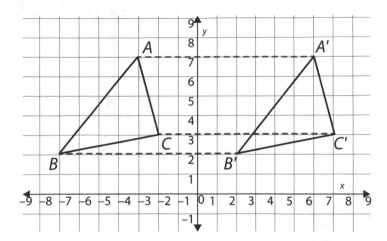

- Translations are described in the coordinate plane by the distance each point is moved with respect to the x-axis and y-axis. If we assign h to be the change in x and k to be the change in y, we can define the translation function T such that $T_{h, k}(x, y) = (x + h, y + k)$.

- A **reflection** is an isometry in which a figure is moved along a line perpendicular to a given line called the line of reflection. Unlike a translation, each point in the figure will move a distance determined by its distance to the line of reflection. In fact, each point in the preimage will move twice the distance from the line of reflection along a line that is perpendicular to the line of reflection. The result of a reflection is the mirror image of the original figure; therefore, a reflection is also called a flip.

Reflection through line ℓ

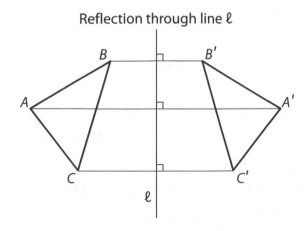

- As seen in the image on the previous page, A, B, and C are reflected along lines that are perpendicular to the line of reflection, ℓ. Also note that the line segments $\overline{AA'}$, $\overline{BB'}$, and $\overline{CC'}$ are all of different lengths. Depending on the line of reflection in the coordinate plane, reflections can be complicated to describe as a function. Therefore, in this lesson we will consider the following three reflections.

  - through the x-axis: $r_{x\text{-axis}}(x, y) = (x, -y)$
  - through the y-axis: $r_{y\text{-axis}}(x, y) = (-x, y)$
  - through the line $y = x$: $r_{y=x}(x, y) = (y, x)$

- A **rotation** is an isometry where all points in the preimage are moved along circular arcs determined by the center of rotation and the angle of rotation. A rotation may also be called a turn. This transformation can be more complex than a translation or reflection because the image is determined by circular arcs instead of parallel or perpendicular lines. Similar to a reflection, a rotation will not move a set of points a uniform distance. When a rotation is applied to a figure, each point in the figure will move a distance determined by its distance from the point of rotation. A figure may be rotated **clockwise**, in the direction that the hands on a clock move, or **counterclockwise**, in the opposite direction that the hands on a clock move. The figure below shows a 90° counterclockwise rotation around the point R.

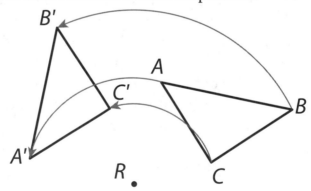

- Comparing the arc lengths in the figure, we see that point B moves farther than points A and C. This is because point B is farther from the center of rotation, R.

- Depending on the point and angle of rotation, the function describing a rotation can be complex. Thus, we will consider the following counterclockwise rotations, which can be easily defined.

  - 90° rotation about the origin: $R_{90}(x, y) = (-y, x)$
  - 180° rotation about the origin: $R_{180}(x, y) = (-x, -y)$
  - 270° rotation about the origin: $R_{270}(x, y) = (y, -x)$

Guided Practice 5.2.1

Example 1

How far and in what direction does the point $P(x, y)$ move when translated by the function $T_{24, 10}$?

---

1. Each point translated by $T_{24, 10}$ will be moved right 24 units, parallel to the x-axis.

2. The point will then be moved up 10 units, parallel to the y-axis.

3. Therefore, $T_{24, 10}(P) = P' = (x + 24, y + 10)$.

Example 2

Using the definitions described earlier, write the translation $T_{5, 3}$ of the rotation R_{180} in terms of a function F on (x, y).

---

1. Write the problem symbolically.

   $F = T_{5, 3}(R_{180}(x, y))$

2. Start from the inside and work outward.

   $R_{180}(x, y) = (-x, -y)$

   Therefore, $T_{5, 3}(R_{180}(x, y)) = T_{5, 3}(-x, -y)$.

3. Now translate the point.

   $T_{5, 3}(-x, -y) = (-x + 5, -y + 3)$

4. Write the result of both translations.

   $F = T_{5, 3}(R_{180}(x, y)) = (-x + 5, -y + 3)$

Example 3

Using the definitions described earlier, write the reflection $r_{y=x}$ of the translation $T_{2,3}$ of the reflection $r_{x\text{-axis}}(x, y)$ in terms of a function S on (x, y).

1. Write the problem symbolically.

   $$S = r_{y=x}(T_{2,3}(r_{x\text{-axis}}(x, y)))$$

2. Start from the inside and work outward. First address the reflection through the x-axis. Solve $r_{x\text{-axis}}(x, y)$ for $(x, -y)$.

   $$S = r_{y=x}(T_{2,3}(r_{x\text{-axis}}(x, y))) = r_{y=x}(T_{2,3}(x, -y))$$

3. Next, solve for the translation function, $T_{2,3}$, using the input from above, $T_{2,3}(x, -y) = (x + 2, -y + 3)$.

   $$S = r_{y=x}(T_{2,3}(x, -y)) = r_{y=x}(x + 2, -y + 3)$$

4. Finally, solve the reflection $r_{y=x}$ using the input from above.

   $$S = r_{y=x}(x + 2, -y + 3) = (-y + 3, x + 2)$$

UNIT 5 • CONGRUENCE, PROOF, AND CONSTRUCTIONS
Lesson 2: Defining and Applying Rotations, Reflections, and Translations

Practice 5.2.1: Defining Rotations, Reflections, and Translations

Complete the following problems about transformations.

1. State the transformation for which all points in the preimage are moved along a circular arc.

2. State the transformation for which all points in the preimage are moved parallel to a given line.

3. State the transformation for which all points in the preimage are moved perpendicular to a given line.

4. In a rotation, why does one point on the preimage move farther than the other points?

5. State the image point of A (1, 1) if it is reflected over the vertical line $x = 1$.

6. How far and in what direction would a point move under $T_{4, -3}$?

7. State the point B'' after the point B (–2, 5) is transformed first under r_y then under R_{180}.

8. Find the image coordinates of $\triangle ABC$ given A (2, 1), B (7, 6), and C (10, 3) under the transformation $R_{90}(T_{-1, 2}(\triangle ABC))$.

9. Given P (8, –12) and $T(x – 5, y + 3)$, state P'' after a reflection over the line $y = x$ of the point $T(P)$.

10. How far does the point V (7, 5) move in the transformation $T_{7, -2}(R_{90}(V))$?

Lesson 5.2.2: Applying Rotations, Reflections, and Translations

Introduction

First we learned that transformations can be functions in the coordinate plane. Then we learned the definitions and properties of three isometric transformations: rotations, reflections, and translations. Now we are able to apply what we have learned to graph geometric figures and images created through transformations.

Key Concepts

- Transformations can be precisely and accurately graphed using the definitions learned.

- Given a set of points and a target we can determine the transformation(s) necessary to move the given set of points to the target.

- Observing the orientations of the preimage and image is the first tool in determining the transformations required.

- Graphs can be interpreted differently, allowing for many transformation solution sets. While there are many different solution sets of transformations that will satisfy a particular graph, we will look for the more concise possibilities.

- Formulas can be used to determine translations, reflections, and rotations.

- Translation: $T_{h,k}(x, y) = (x + h, y + k)$

- Reflection:

  - through the x-axis: $r_{x\text{-axis}}(x, y) = (x, -y)$

  - through the y-axis: $r_{y\text{-axis}}(x, y) = (-x, y)$

  - through the line $y = x$: $r_{y=x}(x, y) = (y, x)$

- Rotation:

  - 90° rotation about the origin: $R_{90}(x, y) = (-y, x)$

  - 180° rotation about the origin: $R_{180}(x, y) = (-x, -y)$

  - 270° rotation about the origin: $R_{270}(x, y) = (y, -x)$

Guided Practice 5.2.2

Example 1

Use the definitions you have learned to graph the translation $T_{2,3}(\triangle ABC)$ for which $\triangle ABC$ has the points $A\ (1, 1)$, $B\ (3, 5)$, and $C\ (5, 1)$.

1. On graph paper, draw the x- and y-axes and graph $\triangle ABC$ with the points $A\ (1, 1)$, $B\ (3, 5)$, and $C\ (5, 1)$.

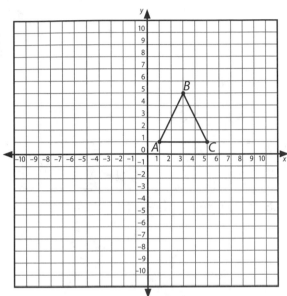

2. Determine the new points.

$$T_{2,3}(\triangle ABC) = \triangle A'B'C' \text{ where }$$

$$A' = T_{2,3}(A) = (1+2, 1+3) = (3, 4)$$

$$B' = T_{2,3}(B) = (3+2, 5+3) = (5, 8)$$

$$C' = T_{2,3}(C) = (5+2, 1+3) = (7, 4)$$

3. Plot the new points A', B', and C'.

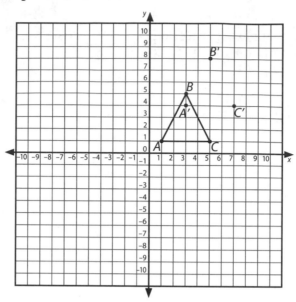

4. Connect the vertices to graph the translation $T_{2,3}$ of $\triangle ABC$.

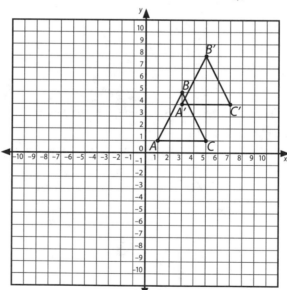

Example 2

Use the definitions you have learned to graph the reflection of parallelogram $ABCD$, or $\square ABCD$, through the y-axis given $\square ABCD$ with the points A (–5, 5), B (–3, 4), C (–4, 1), and D (–6, 2).

1. Using graph paper, draw the x- and y-axes and graph $\square ABCD$ with A (–5, 5), B (–3, 4), C (–4, 1), and D (–6, 2).

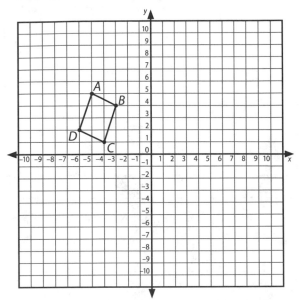

2. Write the new points.

$$r_{y\text{-axis}}\left(\square ABCD\right)=\square A'B'C'D' \text{ where}$$

$$A'=r_{y\text{-axis}}\left(A\right)=r_{y\text{-axis}}\left(-5,5\right)=\left(-(-5),5\right)=\left(5,5\right)$$

$$B'=r_{y\text{-axis}}\left(B\right)=r_{y\text{-axis}}\left(-3,4\right)=\left(-(-3),4\right)=\left(3,4\right)$$

$$C'=r_{y\text{-axis}}\left(C\right)=r_{y\text{-axis}}\left(-4,1\right)=\left(-(-4),1\right)=\left(4,1\right)$$

$$D'=r_{y\text{-axis}}\left(D\right)=r_{y\text{-axis}}\left(-6,2\right)=\left(-(-6),2\right)=\left(6,2\right)$$

3. Plot the new points A', B', C', and D'.

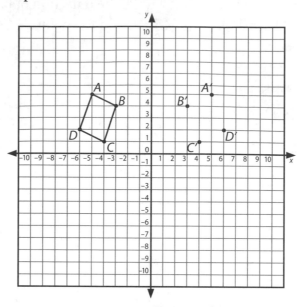

4. Connect the corners of the points to graph the reflection $r_{y\text{-axis}}$ of $\square A'B'C'D'$.

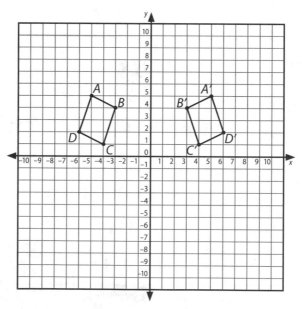

Example 3

Using the definitions you have learned, graph a 90° rotation of $\triangle ABC$ with the points $A\,(1, 4)$, $B\,(6, 3)$, and $C\,(3, 1)$.

1. Using graph paper, draw the x- and y-axes and graph $\triangle ABC$ with the points $A\,(1, 4)$, $B\,(6, 3)$, and $C\,(3, 1)$.

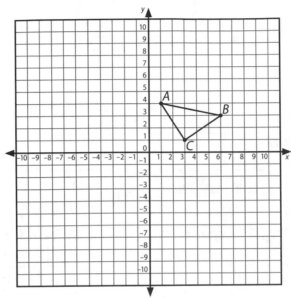

2. Write the new points.

$$R_{90}\left(\triangle ABC\right)=\triangle A'B'C' \text{ where } \begin{aligned} A' &= R_{90}(A)= R_{90}\left(1,4\right)=\left(-4,1\right)\\ B' &= R_{90}(B)= R_{90}\left(6,3\right)=\left(-3,6\right)\\ C' &= R_{90}(C)= R_{90}\left(3,1\right)=\left(-1,3\right) \end{aligned}$$

3. Plot the new points A', B', and C'.

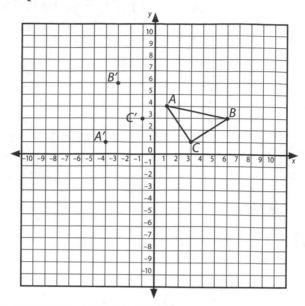

4. Connect the vertices to graph a 90° rotation of $\triangle ABC$.

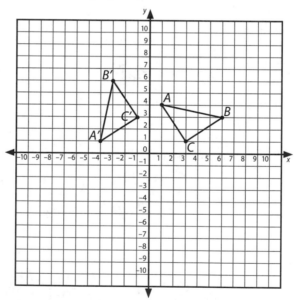

UNIT 5 • CONGRUENCE, PROOF, AND CONSTRUCTIONS
Lesson 2: Defining and Applying Rotations, Reflections, and Translations

Practice 5.2.2: Applying Rotations, Reflections, and Translations

Use what you know about transformations to complete each problem.

1. Graph the transformation $T_{3,-1}(T_{4,2}(\triangle ABC))$ where A (2, 1), B (7, 2), and C (1, 4).

2. Graph the transformation $R_{180}(T_{8,3}(\triangle DEF))$ where D (–4, 0), E (–3, 4), and F (–1, 1).

3. In what quadrant is $T_{9,5}(T_{2,2}(P))$ when P (–6, 3)?

4. Given $R_{90}(x, y) = (-y, x)$ and P (8, –2), what is $R_{90}(T_{3,3}(P))$?

5. Given $\square ABCD$ where A (2, 2), B (5, 2), C (5, –1), and D (2, –1), what is $R_{180}(\square ABCD)$?

6. Find R_m such that $R_m(\square ABCD)$ is equivalent to $r_x(r_{y=x}(\square ABCD))$.

7. A reflection through what line will move P (–4, 5) to P' (4, 5)?

8. Graph the transformation $r_y(r_x(\triangle ABC))$ where A (2, 2), B (4, 4), and C (3, –3).

9. Graph the transformation $R_{180}(T_{1,-6}(\triangle DEF))$ where D (–3, 2), E (–2, –2), and F (1, 4).

10. Determine the transformation given the preimage $\triangle ABC$ where A (1, 0), B (6, –7), and C (0, –4) and the image $\triangle A'B'C'$ where A' (0, –1), B' (–7, –6), and C' (–4, 0).

Lesson 3: Constructing Lines, Segments, and Angles

Common Core State Standard

G–CO.12   Make formal geometric constructions with a variety of tools and methods (compass and straightedge, string, reflective devices, paper folding, dynamic geometric software, etc.). *Copying a segment; copying an angle; bisecting a segment; bisecting an angle; constructing perpendicular lines, including the perpendicular bisector of a line segment; and constructing a line parallel to a given line through a point not on the line.*

Essential Questions

1. What is the difference between sketching geometric figures, drawing geometric figures, and constructing geometric figures?

2. What tools are used with geometric constructions and why?

3. How can you justify a construction was done correctly?

WORDS TO KNOW

altitude	the perpendicular line from a vertex of a figure to its opposite side; height
angle	two rays or line segments sharing a common endpoint; the symbol used is $\angle$
bisect	to cut in half
compass	an instrument for creating circles or transferring measurements that consists of two pointed branches joined at the top by a pivot
congruent	having the same shape, size, or angle
construct	to create a precise geometric representation using a straightedge along with either patty paper (tracing paper), a compass, or a reflecting device

construction	a precise representation of a figure using a straightedge and a compass, patty paper and a straightedge, or a reflecting device and a straightedge
drawing	a precise representation of a figure, created with measurement tools such as a protractor and a ruler
endpoint	either of two points that mark the ends of a line segment; a point that marks the end of a ray
equidistant	the same distance from a reference point
line	the set of points between two points P and Q and the infinite number of points that continue beyond those points
median	the segment joining the vertex to the midpoint of the opposite side
midpoint	a point on a line segment that divides the segment into two equal parts
midsegment	a line segment joining the midpoints of two sides of a figure
parallel lines	lines that either do not share any points and never intersect, or share all points
perpendicular bisector	a line constructed through the midpoint of a segment
perpendicular lines	two lines that intersect at a right angle (90°)
ray	a line with only one endpoint
segment	a part of a line that is noted by two endpoints
sketch	a quickly done representation of a figure; a rough approximation of a figure
straightedge	a bar or strip of wood, plastic, or metal having at least one long edge of reliable straightness

Recommended Resources

- Math Open Reference. "Bisecting an angle."

  http://www.walch.com/rr/00001

  This site provides step-by-step instructions for bisecting an angle with a compass and straightedge.

- Math Open Reference. "Copying a line segment."

  http://www.walch.com/rr/00002

  This site provides step-by-step instructions for copying a line segment with a compass and straightedge.

- Math Open Reference. "Copying an angle."

  http://www.walch.com/rr/00003

  This site provides step-by-step instructions for copying an angle with a compass and straightedge.

- Math Open Reference. "Perpendicular at a point on a line."

  http://www.walch.com/rr/00004

  This site provides step-by-step instructions for constructing a perpendicular line at a point on the given line.

- Math Open Reference. "Perpendicular bisector of a line segment."

  http://www.walch.com/rr/00005

  This site provides step-by-step instructions for constructing a perpendicular bisector of a line segment using a compass and straightedge.

- Math Open Reference. "Perpendicular to a line from an external point."

  http://www.walch.com/rr/00006

  This site provides step-by-step instructions for constructing a perpendicular line from a point not on the given line.

Lesson 5.3.1: Copying Segments and Angles

Introduction

Two basic instruments used in geometry are the straightedge and the compass. A **straightedge** is a bar or strip of wood, plastic, or metal that has at least one long edge of reliable straightness, similar to a ruler, but without any measurement markings. A **compass** is an instrument for creating circles or transferring measurements. It consists of two pointed branches joined at the top by a pivot. It is believed that during early geometry, all geometric figures were created using just a straightedge and a compass. Though technology and computers abound today to help us make sense of geometry problems, the straightedge and compass are still widely used to **construct** figures, or create precise geometric representations. Constructions allow you to draw accurate segments and angles, segment and angle bisectors, and parallel and perpendicular lines.

Key Concepts

- A geometric figure precisely created using only a straightedge and compass is called a **construction**.

- A straightedge can be used with patty paper (tracing paper) or a reflecting device to create precise representations.

- Constructions are different from drawings or sketches.

- A **drawing** is a precise representation of a figure, created with measurement tools such as a protractor and a ruler.

- A **sketch** is a quickly done representation of a figure or a rough approximation of a figure.

- When constructing figures, it is very important not to erase your markings.

- Markings show that your figure was constructed and not measured and drawn.

- An **endpoint** is either of two points that mark the ends of a line, or the point that marks the end of a ray.

- A line **segment** is a part of a line that is noted by two endpoints.

- An **angle** is formed when two rays or line segments share a common endpoint.

- A constructed figure and the original figure are **congruent**; they have the same shape, size, or angle.

- Follow the steps outlined on the following pages to copy a segment and an angle.

Copying a Segment Using a Compass

1. To copy $\overline{AB}$, first make an endpoint on your paper. Label the endpoint C.

2. Put the sharp point of your compass on endpoint A. Open the compass until the pencil end touches endpoint B.

3. Without changing your compass setting, put the sharp point of your compass on endpoint C. Make a large arc.

4. Use your straightedge to connect endpoint C to any point on your arc.

5. Label the point of intersection of the arc and your segment D.

Do not erase any of your markings.

$\overline{AB}$ is congruent to $\overline{CD}$.

Copying a Segment Using Patty Paper

1. To copy $\overline{AB}$, place your sheet of patty paper over the segment.

2. Mark the endpoints of the segment on the patty paper. Label the endpoints C and D.

3. Use your straightedge to connect points C and D.

$\overline{AB}$ is congruent to $\overline{CD}$.

Copying an Angle Using a Compass

1. To copy $\angle A$, first make a point to represent the vertex A on your paper. Label the vertex E.

2. From point E, draw a ray of any length. This will be one side of the constructed angle.

3. Put the sharp point of the compass on vertex A of the original angle. Set the compass to any width that will cross both sides of the original angle.

4. Draw an arc across both sides of $\angle A$. Label where the arc intersects the angle as points B and C.

5. Without changing the compass setting, put the sharp point of the compass on point E. Draw a large arc that intersects the ray. Label the point of intersection as F.

6. Put the sharp point of the compass on point B of the original angle and set the width of the compass so it touches point C.

7. Without changing the compass setting, put the sharp point of the compass on point F and make an arc that intersects the arc in step 5. Label the point of intersection as D.

8. Draw a ray from point E to point D.

Do not erase any of your markings.

$\angle A$ is congruent to $\angle E$.

Copying an Angle Using Patty Paper

1. To copy $\angle A$, place your sheet of patty paper over the angle.

2. Mark the vertex of the angle. Label the vertex E.

3. Use your straightedge to trace each side of $\angle A$.

$\angle A$ is congruent to $\angle E$.

Guided Practice 5.3.1

Example 1

Copy the following segment using only a compass and a straightedge.

1. Make an endpoint on your paper. Label the endpoint *P*.

   Original segment   **Construction**

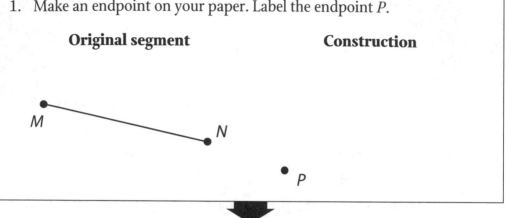

2. Put the sharp point of your compass on endpoint *M*. Open the compass until the pencil end touches endpoint *N*.

   Original segment   **Construction**

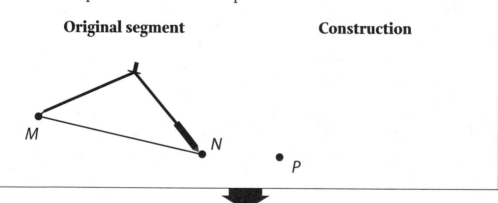

3. Without changing your compass setting, put the sharp point of your compass on endpoint *P*. Make a large arc.

Original segment   **Construction**

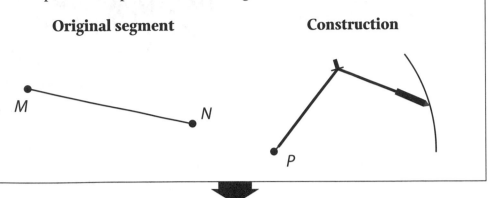

4. Use your straightedge to connect endpoint *P* to any point on your arc.

Original segment   **Construction**

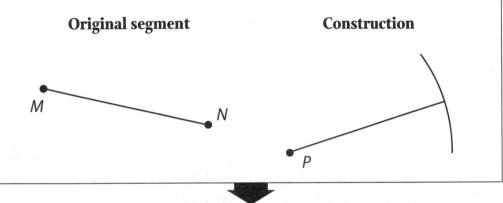

5. Label the point of intersection of the arc and your segment *Q*.

Original segment   **Construction**

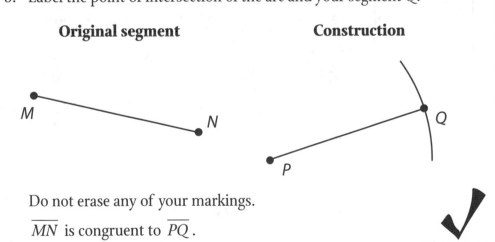

Do not erase any of your markings.

$\overline{MN}$ is congruent to $\overline{PQ}$.

Example 2

Copy the following angle using only a compass and a straightedge.

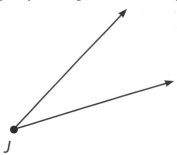

1. Make a point to represent vertex *J*. Label the vertex *R*.

Original angle   **Construction**

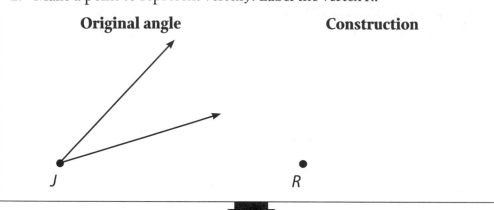

2. From point *R*, draw a ray of any length. This will be one side of the constructed angle.

Original angle   **Construction**

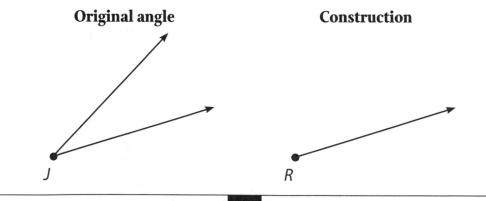

3. Put the sharp point of the compass on vertex *J* of the original angle. Set the compass to any width that will cross both sides of the original angle.

Original angle   **Construction**

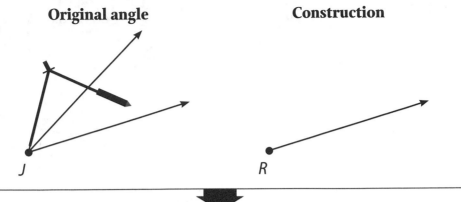

4. Draw an arc across both sides of ∠*J*. Label where the arc intersects the angle as points *K* and *L*.

Original angle   **Construction**

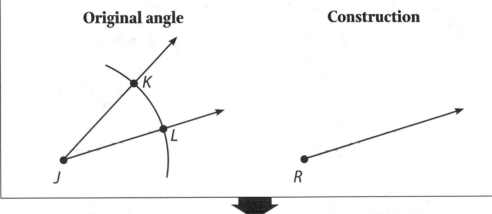

5. Without changing the compass setting, put the sharp point of the compass on point *R*. Draw a large arc that intersects the ray. Label the point of intersection as *S*.

Original angle   **Construction**

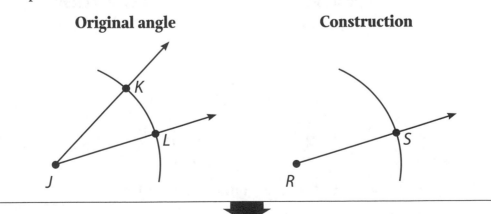

6. Put the sharp point of the compass on point L of the original angle and set the width of the compass so it touches point K.

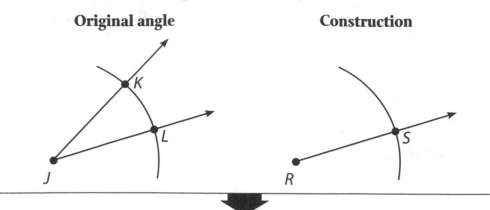

Original angle

Construction

7. Without changing the compass setting, put the sharp point of the compass on point S and make an arc that intersects the arc you drew in step 5. Label the point of intersection as T.

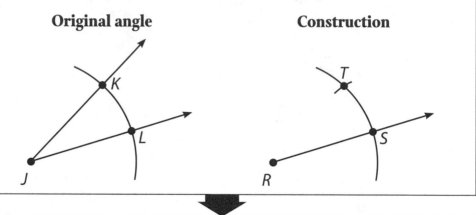

Original angle

Construction

8. Draw a ray from point R to point T.

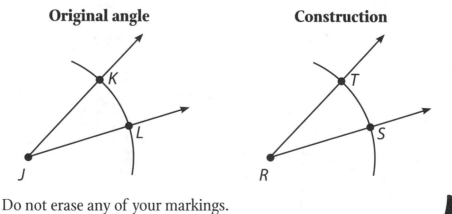

Original angle

Construction

Do not erase any of your markings.

$\angle J$ is congruent to $\angle R$.

Example 3

Use the given line segment to construct a new line segment with length $2AB$.

1. Use your straightedge to draw a long ray. Label the endpoint C.

2. Put the sharp point of your compass on endpoint A of the original segment. Open the compass until the pencil end touches B.

3. Without changing your compass setting, put the sharp point of your compass on C and make a large arc that intersects your ray.

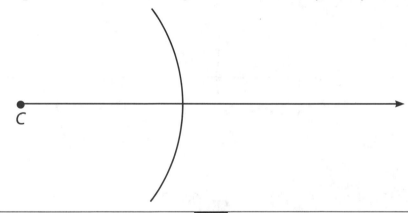

4. Mark the point of intersection as point D.

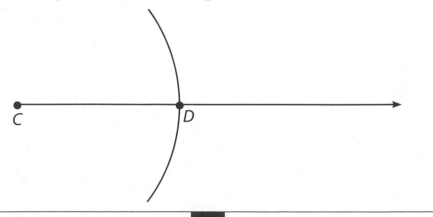

5. Without changing your compass setting, put the sharp point of your compass on D and make a large arc that intersects your ray.

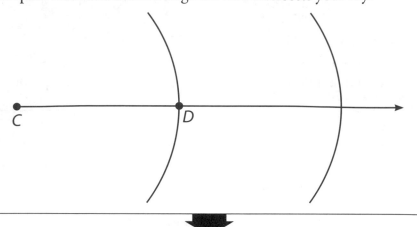

6. Mark the point of intersection as point E.

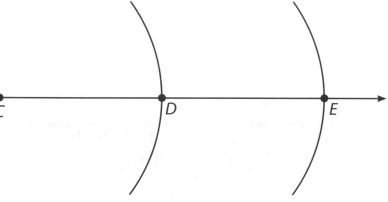

Do not erase any of your markings.

$CE = 2AB$

Example 4

Use the given angle to construct a new angle equal to $\angle A + \angle A$.

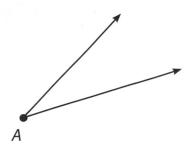

---

1. Follow the steps from Example 2 to copy $\angle A$. Label the vertex of the copied angle G.

2. Put the sharp point of the compass on vertex A of the original angle. Set the compass to any width that will cross both sides of the original angle.

3. Draw an arc across both sides of $\angle A$. Label where the arc intersects the angle as points B and C.

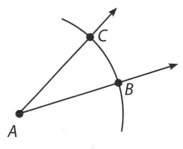

4. Without changing the compass setting, put the sharp point of the compass on *G*. Draw a large arc that intersects one side of your newly constructed angle. Label the point of intersection *H*.

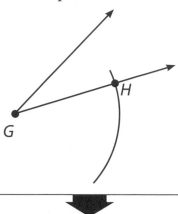

5. Put the sharp point of the compass on *C* of the original angle and set the width of the compass so it touches *B*.

6. Without changing the compass setting, put the sharp point of the compass on point *H* and make an arc that intersects the arc created in step 4. Label the point of intersection as *J*.

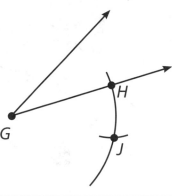

7. Draw a ray from point G to point J.

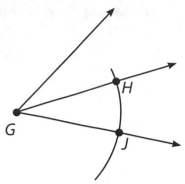

Do not erase any of your markings.

$\angle G = \angle A + \angle A$

Example 5

Use the given segments to construct a new segment equal to $AB - CD$.

1. Draw a ray longer than that of $\overline{AB}$. Label the endpoint M.

2. Follow the steps from Example 3 to copy $\overline{AB}$ onto the ray. Label the second endpoint P.

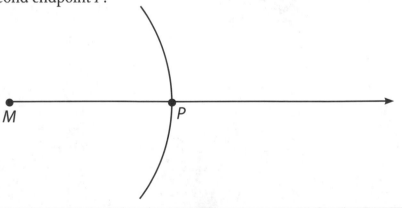

3. Put the sharp point of the compass on endpoint M of the ray. Copy segment $\overline{CD}$ onto the same ray. Label the endpoint N.

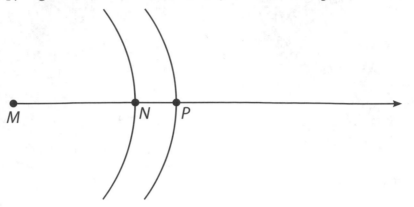

Do not erase any of your markings.

$NP = AB - CD$

Angles can be subtracted in the same way.

Practice 5.3.1: Copying Segments and Angles

Copy the following segments using a straightedge and a compass.

1.

A B

2.

C

D

3.

F

E

Use the line segments from problems 1–3 to construct the line segments described in problems 4 and 5.

4. $CD + AB$

5. $3AB - EF$

UNIT 5 • CONGRUENCE, PROOF, AND CONSTRUCTIONS
Lesson 3: Constructing Lines, Segments, and Angles

Copy the following angles using a straightedge and a compass.

6.

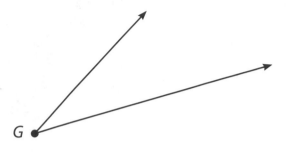

7.

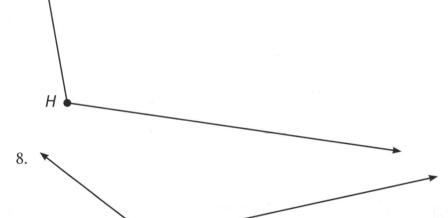

8.

Use the angles from problems 6–8 to construct the angles described in problems 9 and 10.

9. $\angle H - \angle G$

10. $\angle G + \angle J$

Lesson 5.3.2: Bisecting Segments and Angles

Introduction

Segments and angles are often described with measurements. Segments have lengths that can be measured with a ruler. Angles have measures that can be determined by a protractor. It is possible to determine the midpoint of a segment. The **midpoint** is a point on the segment that divides it into two equal parts. When drawing the midpoint, you can measure the length of the segment and divide the length in half. When constructing the midpoint, you cannot use a ruler, but you can use a compass and a straightedge (or patty paper and a straightedge) to determine the midpoint of the segment. This procedure is called bisecting a segment. To **bisect** means to cut in half. It is also possible to bisect an angle, or cut an angle in half using the same construction tools. A **midsegment** is created when two midpoints of a figure are connected. A triangle has three midsegments.

Key Concepts

Bisecting a Segment

- . A segment bisector cuts a segment in half.

- Each half of the segment measures exactly the same length.

- A point, line, ray, or segment can bisect a segment.

- A point on the bisector is **equidistant**, or is the same distance, from either endpoint of the segment.

- The point where the segment is bisected is called the midpoint of the segment.

Bisecting a Segment Using a Compass

1. To bisect $\overline{AB}$, put the sharp point of your compass on endpoint A. Open the compass wider than half the distance of $\overline{AB}$.

2. Make a large arc intersecting $\overline{AB}$.

3. Without changing your compass setting, put the sharp point of the compass on endpoint B. Make a second large arc. It is important that the arcs intersect each other in two places.

4. Use your straightedge to connect the points of intersection of the arcs.

5. Label the midpoint of the segment C.

Do not erase any of your markings.

$\overline{AC}$ is congruent to $\overline{BC}$.

Bisecting a Segment Using Patty Paper

1. Use a straightedge to construct $\overline{AB}$ on patty paper.

2. Fold the patty paper so point A meets point B. Be sure to crease the paper.

3. Unfold the patty paper.

4. Use your straightedge to mark the midpoint of $\overline{AB}$.

5. Label the midpoint of the segment C.

$\overline{AC}$ is congruent to $\overline{BC}$.

Bisecting an Angle

- An angle bisector cuts an angle in half.

- Each half of the angle has exactly the same measure.

- A line or ray can bisect an angle.

- A point on the bisector is equidistant, or is the same distance, from either side of the angle.

Bisecting an Angle Using a Compass

1. To bisect $\angle A$, put the sharp point of the compass on the vertex of the angle.

2. Draw a large arc that passes through each side of the angle.

3. Label where the arc intersects the angle as points B and C.

4. Put the sharp point of the compass on point B. Open the compass wider than half the distance from B to C.

5. Make a large arc.

6. Without changing the compass setting, put the sharp point of the compass on C.

7. Make a second large arc. It is important that the arcs intersect each other in two places.

8. Use your straightedge to create a ray connecting the points of intersection of the arcs with the vertex of the angle, A.

9. Label a point, D, on the ray.

Do not erase any of your markings.

$\angle CAD$ is congruent to $\angle BAD$.

Bisecting an Angle Using Patty Paper

1. Use a straightedge to construct $\angle A$ on patty paper.

2. Fold the patty paper so the sides of $\angle A$ line up. Be sure to crease the paper.

3. Unfold the patty paper.

4. Use your straightedge to mark the crease line with a ray.

5. Label a point, D, on the ray.

$\angle CAD$ is congruent to $\angle BAD$.

Guided Practice 5.3.2

Example 1

Use a compass and straightedge to find the midpoint of $\overline{CD}$. Label the midpoint of the segment M.

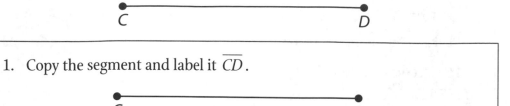

C   D

---

1. Copy the segment and label it $\overline{CD}$.

C   D

---

2. Make a large arc intersecting $\overline{CD}$.

   Put the sharp point of your compass on endpoint C. Open the compass wider than half the distance of $\overline{CD}$. Draw the arc.

C   D

---

3. Make a second large arc.

   Without changing your compass setting, put the sharp point of the compass on endpoint D, then make the second arc.

   It is important that the arcs intersect each other in two places.

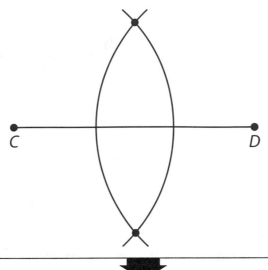

4. Connect the points of intersection of the arcs.

   Use your straightedge to connect the points of intersection.

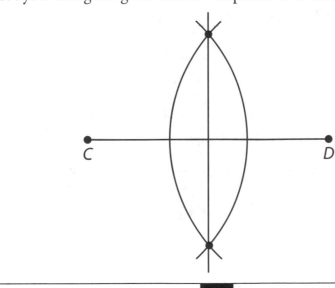

5. Label the midpoint of the segment M.

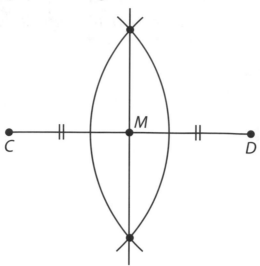

Do not erase any of your markings.

$\overline{CM}$ is congruent to $\overline{MD}$.

Example 2

Construct a segment whose measure is $\dfrac{1}{4}$ the length of $\overline{PQ}$.

1. Copy the segment and label it $\overline{PQ}$.

2. Make a large arc intersecting $\overline{PQ}$.

   Put the sharp point of your compass on endpoint P. Open the compass wider than half the distance of $\overline{PQ}$. Draw the arc.

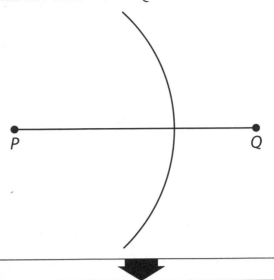

3. Make a second large arc.

   Without changing your compass setting, put the sharp point of the compass on endpoint Q, then make the second arc.

   It is important that the arcs intersect each other in two places.

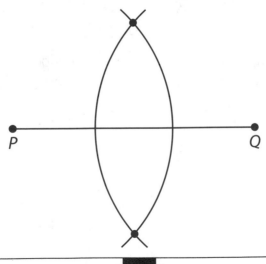

4. Connect the points of intersection of the arcs.

   Use your straightedge to connect the points of intersection.

   Label the midpoint of the segment M.

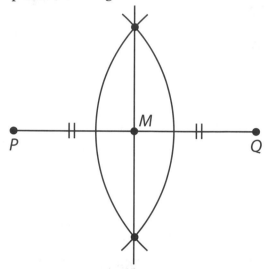

   $\overline{PM}$ is congruent to $\overline{MQ}$.

   $\overline{PM}$ and $\overline{MQ}$ are both $\dfrac{1}{2}$ the length of $\overline{PQ}$.

5. Find the midpoint of $\overline{PM}$.

   Make a large arc intersecting $\overline{PM}$.

   Put the sharp point of your compass on endpoint P. Open the compass wider than half the distance of $\overline{PM}$. Draw the arc.

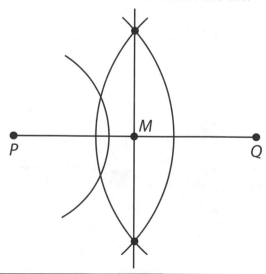

6. Make a second large arc.

Without changing your compass setting, put the sharp point of the compass on endpoint M, and then draw the second arc.

It is important that the arcs intersect each other in two places.

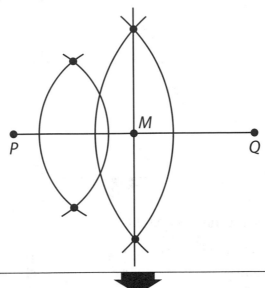

7. Connect the points of intersection of the arcs.

Use your straightedge to connect the points of intersection.

Label the midpoint of the smaller segment N.

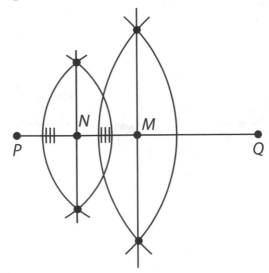

Do not erase any of your markings.

$\overline{PN}$ is congruent to $\overline{NM}$.

$\overline{PN}$ is $\dfrac{1}{4}$ the length of $\overline{PQ}$.

Example 3

Use a compass and a straightedge to bisect an angle.

1. Draw an angle and label the vertex *J*.

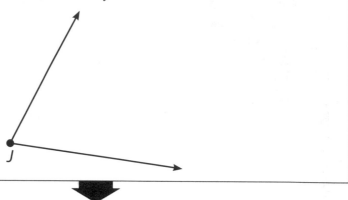

2. Make a large arc intersecting the sides of $\angle J$.

   Put the sharp point of the compass on the vertex of the angle and swing the compass so that it passes through each side of the angle.

   Label where the arc intersects the angle as points *L* and *M*.

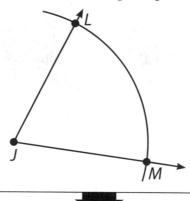

3. Find a point that is equidistant from both sides of $\angle J$.

Put the sharp point of the compass on point L.

Open the compass wider than half the distance from L to M.

Make an arc beyond the arc you made for points L and M.

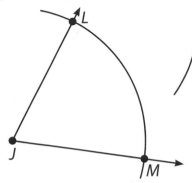

Without changing the compass setting, put the sharp point of the compass on M.

Make a second arc that crosses the arc you just made. It is important that the arcs intersect each other.

Label the point of intersection N.

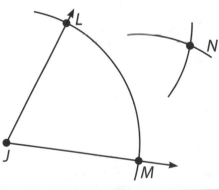

4. Draw the angle bisector.

Use your straightedge to create a ray connecting the point *N* with the vertex of the angle, *J*.

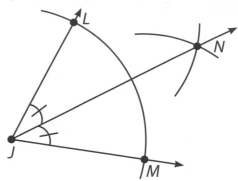

Do not erase any of your markings.

∠*LJN* is congruent to ∠*NJM* .

Example 4

Construct an angle whose measure is $\dfrac{3}{4}$ the measure of ∠*S* .

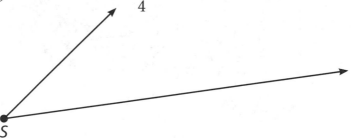

1. Copy the angle and label the vertex *S*.

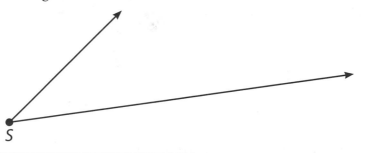

2. Make a large arc intersecting the sides of ∠S.

   Put the sharp point of the compass on the vertex of the angle and swing the compass so that it passes through each side of the angle.

   Label where the arc intersects the angle as points *T* and *U*.

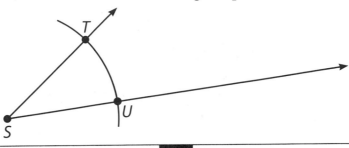

3. Find a point that is equidistant from both sides of ∠S.

   Put the sharp point of the compass on point *T*.

   Open the compass wider than half the distance from *T* to *U*.

   Make an arc beyond the arc you made for points *T* and *U*.

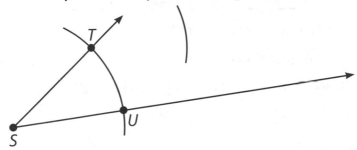

   Without changing the compass setting, put the sharp point of the compass on *U*.

   Make a second arc that crosses the arc you just made. It is important that the arcs intersect each other.

   Label the point of intersection *W*.

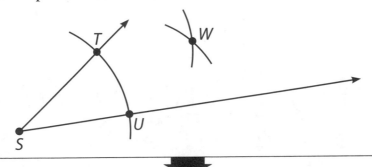

4. Draw the angle bisector.

   Use your straightedge to create a ray connecting the point W with the vertex of the angle, S.

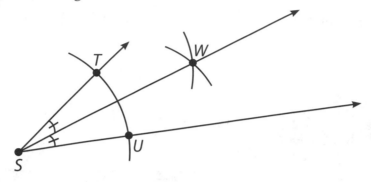

   $\angle TSW$ is congruent to $\angle WSU$.

   The measure of $\angle TSW$ is $\dfrac{1}{2}$ the measure of $\angle S$.

   The measure of $\angle WSU$ is $\dfrac{1}{2}$ the measure of $\angle S$.

5. Find a point that is equidistant from both sides of $\angle WSU$.

   Label the intersection of the angle bisector and the initial arc as X.

   Put the sharp point of the compass on point X.

   Open the compass wider than half the distance from X to U.

   Make an arc.

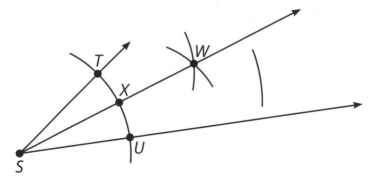

(*continued*)

Without changing the compass setting, put the sharp point of the compass on U.

Make a second arc. It is important that the arcs intersect each other.

Label the point of intersection Z.

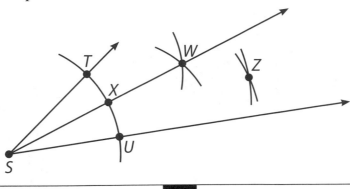

6. Draw the angle bisector.

Use your straightedge to create a ray connecting point Z with the vertex of the original angle, S.

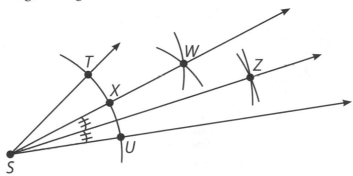

Do not erase any of your markings.

$\angle XSZ$ is congruent to $\angle ZSU$.

$\angle TSZ$ is $\dfrac{3}{4}$ the measure of $\angle TSU$.

UNIT 5 • CONGRUENCE, PROOF, AND CONSTRUCTIONS
Lesson 3: Constructing Lines, Segments, and Angles

Practice 5.3.2: Bisecting Segments and Angles

Use a compass and straightedge to copy each segment, and then construct the bisector of each segment.

1.

    A ●————————● B

2.

    C ●

    D ●

3.

    E ●————————● F

Use a compass and straightedge to construct each segment as specified.

4. Construct a segment whose measure is $\dfrac{3}{4}$ the length of $\overline{AB}$ in problem 1.

5. Construct a segment whose measure is $\dfrac{1}{4}$ the length of $\overline{CD}$ in problem 2.

continued

UNIT 5 • CONGRUENCE, PROOF, AND CONSTRUCTIONS
Lesson 3: Constructing Lines, Segments, and Angles

Use a compass and straightedge to copy each angle, and then construct the bisector of each angle.

6.

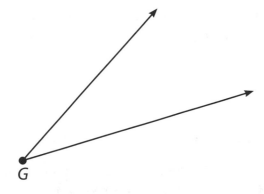

7.

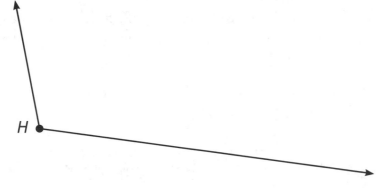

8.

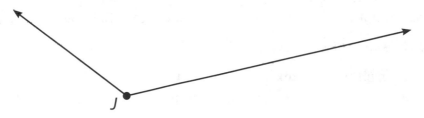

Use a compass and straightedge to construct each angle as specified.

9. Construct an angle whose measure is $\dfrac{3}{4}$ the measure of $\angle H$ in problem 7.

10. Construct an angle whose measure is $\dfrac{1}{4}$ the measure of $\angle J$ in problem 8.

Lesson 5.3.3: Constructing Perpendicular and Parallel Lines

Introduction

Geometry construction tools can also be used to create perpendicular and parallel lines. While performing each construction, it is important to remember that the only tools you are allowed to use are a compass and a straightedge, a reflective device and a straightedge, or patty paper and a straightedge. You may be tempted to measure angles or lengths, but in constructions this is not allowed. You can adjust the opening of your compass to verify that lengths are equal.

Key Concepts

Perpendicular Lines and Bisectors

- **Perpendicular lines** are two lines that intersect at a right angle (90˚).

- A perpendicular line can be constructed through the midpoint of a segment. This line is called the **perpendicular bisector** of the line segment.

- It is impossible to create a perpendicular bisector of a line, since a line goes on infinitely in both directions, but similar methods can be used to construct a line perpendicular to a given line.

- It is possible to construct a perpendicular line through a point on the given line as well as through a point not on a given line.

Constructing a Perpendicular Bisector of a Line Segment Using a Compass

1. To construct a perpendicular bisector of $\overline{AB}$, put the sharp point of your compass on endpoint A. Open the compass wider than half the distance of $\overline{AB}$.

2. Make a large arc intersecting $\overline{AB}$.

3. Without changing your compass setting, put the sharp point of the compass on endpoint B. Make a second large arc. It is important that the arcs intersect each other.

4. Use your straightedge to connect the points of intersection of the arcs.

5. Label the new line m.

Do not erase any of your markings.

$\overline{AB}$ is perpendicular to line m.

Constructing a Perpendicular Bisector of a Line Segment Using Patty Paper

1. Use a straightedge to construct $\overline{AB}$ onto patty paper.

2. Fold the patty paper so point A meets point B. Be sure to crease the paper.

3. Unfold the patty paper.

4. Use your straightedge to mark the creased line.

5. Label the new line *m*.

$\overline{AB}$ is perpendicular to line *m*.

Constructing a Perpendicular Line Through a Point on the Given Line Using a Compass

1. To construct a perpendicular line through the point, A, on a line, put the sharp point of your compass on point A. The opening of the compass does not matter, but try to choose a setting that isn't so large or so small that it's difficult to make markings.

2. Make an arc on either side of point A on the line. Label the points of intersection C and D.

3. Place the sharp point of the compass on point C. Open the compass so it extends beyond point A.

4. Create an arc on either side of the line.

5. Without changing your compass setting, put the sharp point of the compass on endpoint D. Make a large arc on either side of the line. It is important that the arcs intersect each other.

6. Use your straightedge to connect the points of intersection of the arcs.

7. Label the new line *m*.

Do not erase any of your markings.

$\overline{CD}$ is perpendicular to line *m* through point A.

Constructing a Perpendicular Line Through a Point on the Given Line Using Patty Paper

1. Use a straightedge to construct a line, ℓ, on the patty paper. Label a point on the line A.

2. Fold the patty paper so the line folds onto itself through point A. Be sure to crease the paper.

3. Unfold the patty paper.

4. Use your straightedge to mark the creased line.

5. Label the new line m.

Line ℓ is perpendicular to line m through point A.

Constructing a Perpendicular Line Through a Point Not on the Given Line Using a Compass

1. To construct a perpendicular line through the point, G, not on the given line ℓ, put the sharp point of your compass on point G. Open the compass until it extends farther than the given line.

2. Make a large arc that intersects the given line in exactly two places. Label the points of intersection C and D.

3. Without changing your compass setting, put the sharp point of the compass on point C. Make a second arc below the given line.

4. Without changing your compass setting, put the sharp point of the compass on point D. Make a third arc below the given line. The third arc must intersect the second arc.

5. Label the point of intersection E.

6. Use your straightedge to connect points G and E. Label the new line m.

Do not erase any of your markings.

Line ℓ is perpendicular to line m through point G.

Constructing a Perpendicular Line Through a Point Not on the Given Line Using Patty Paper

1. Use a straightedge to construct a line, ℓ, on the patty paper. Label a point not on the line, G.

2. Fold the patty paper so the line folds onto itself through point G. Be sure to crease the paper.

3. Unfold the patty paper.

4. Use your straightedge to mark the creased line.

5. Label the new line m.

Line ℓ is perpendicular to line m through point G.

Parallel Lines

- **Parallel lines** are lines that either do not share any points and never intersect, or share all points.

- Any two points on one parallel line are equidistant from the other line.

- There are many ways to construct parallel lines.

- One method is to construct two lines that are both perpendicular to the same given line.

Constructing a Parallel Line Using a Compass

1. To construct a parallel line through a point, A, not on the given line ℓ, first construct a line perpendicular to ℓ.

2. Put the sharp point of your compass on point A. Open the compass until it extends farther than line ℓ.

3. Make a large arc that intersects the given line in exactly two places. Label the points of intersection C and D.

4. Without changing your compass setting, put the sharp point of the compass on point C. Make a second arc below the given line.

5. Without changing your compass setting, put the sharp point of the compass on point D. Make a third arc below the given line. The third arc must intersect the second arc.

6. Label the point of intersection E.

7. Use your straightedge to connect points A and E. Label the new line m. Line m is perpendicular to line ℓ.

8. Construct a second line perpendicular to line m.

9. Put the sharp point of your compass on point A. Open the compass until it extends farther than line m.

10. Make a large arc that intersects line m in exactly two places. Label the points of intersection F and G.

11. Without changing your compass setting, put the sharp point of the compass on point F. Make a second arc to the right of line m.

12. Without changing your compass setting, put the sharp point of the compass on point G. Make a third arc to the right of line m. The third arc must intersect the second arc.

13. Label the point of intersection H.

14. Use your straightedge to connect points A and H. Label the new line n.

Do not erase any of your markings.

Line n is perpendicular to line m.

Line ℓ is parallel to line n.

Constructing a Parallel Line Using Patty Paper

1. Use a straightedge to construct line ℓ on the patty paper. Label a point not on the line A.

2. Fold the patty paper so the line folds onto itself through point A. Be sure to crease the paper.

3. Unfold the patty paper.

4. Fold the new line onto itself through point A.

5. Unfold the patty paper.

6. Use your straightedge to mark the second creased line.

7. Label the new line m.

Line m is parallel to line ℓ.

Guided Practice 5.3.3

Example 1

Use a compass and a straightedge to construct the perpendicular bisector of $\overline{AB}$.

1. Make a large arc intersecting $\overline{AB}$.

   Put the sharp point of your compass on endpoint A. Open the compass wider than half the distance of $\overline{AB}$. Draw the arc.

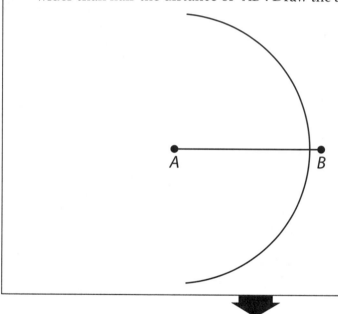

2. Make a second large arc.

   Without changing your compass setting, put the sharp point of the compass on endpoint *B*.

   Make a second large arc.

   It is important that the arcs intersect each other in two places.

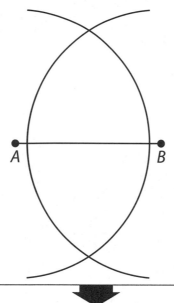

3. Connect the points of intersection of the arcs.

   Use your straightedge to connect the points of intersection of the arcs.

   Label the new line *m*.

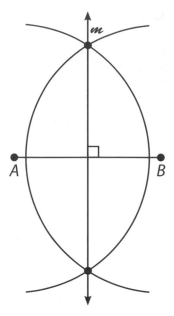

   Do not erase any of your markings.

   Line *m* is the perpendicular bisector of $\overline{AB}$.

Example 2

Use a compass and a straightedge to construct a line perpendicular to line ℓ through point A.

<table>
<tr><td>

1. Draw line ℓ with point A on the line.

</td></tr>
<tr><td>

2. Make an arc on either side of point A.

   Put the sharp point of your compass on point A.

   Make arcs on either side of point A through line ℓ.

   Label the points of intersection C and D.

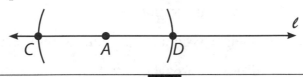

</td></tr>
<tr><td>

3. Make a set of arcs on either side of line ℓ.

   Place the sharp point of the compass on point C.

   Open the compass so it extends beyond point A.

   Create an arc on either side of the line.

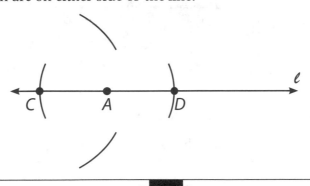

</td></tr>
</table>

4. Make a second set of arcs on either side of line ℓ.

Without changing your compass setting, put the sharp point of the compass on point D.

Make an arc on either side of the line.

It is important that the arcs intersect each other.

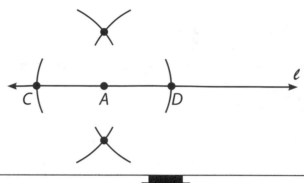

5. Connect the points of intersection.

Use your straightedge to connect the points of intersection of the arcs.

This line should also go through point A.

Label the new line m.

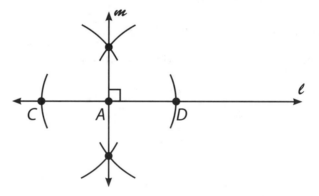

Do not erase any of your markings.

Line ℓ is perpendicular to line m through point A.

Example 3

Use a compass and a straightedge to construct a line perpendicular to line *m* through point *B* that is not on the line.

1. Draw line *m* with point *B* not on the line.

    m

    • *B*

2. Make a large arc that intersects line *m*.

    Put the sharp point of your compass on point *B*.

    Open the compass until it extends farther than line *m*.

    Make a large arc that intersects the given line in exactly two places.

    Label the points of intersection *F* and *G*.

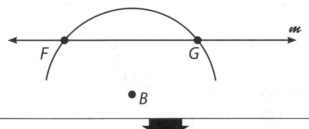

3. Make a set of arcs above line *m*.

   Without changing your compass setting, put the sharp point of the compass on point *F*. Make a second arc above the given line.

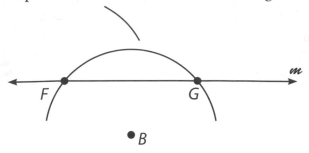

   Without changing your compass setting, put the sharp point of the compass on point *G*. Make a third arc above the given line. The third arc must intersect the second arc.

   Label the point of intersection *H*.

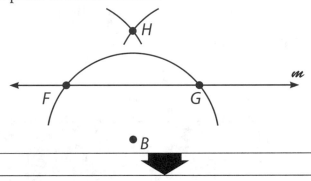

4. Draw the perpendicular line.

   Use your straightedge to connect points *B* and *H*.

   Label the new line *n*.

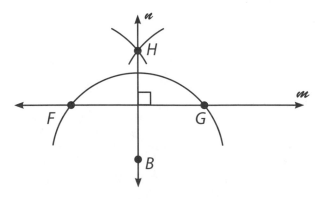

   Do not erase any of your markings.

   Line *n* is perpendicular to line *m*.

Example 4

Use a compass and a straightedge to construct a line parallel to line *n* through point *C* that is not on the line.

1. Draw line *n* with point *C* not on the line.

2. Construct a line perpendicular to line *n* through point *C*.

   Make a large arc that intersects line *n*.

   Put the sharp point of your compass on point *C*.

   Open the compass until it extends farther than line *n*.

   Make a large arc that intersects the given line in exactly two places.

   Label the points of intersection *J* and *K*.

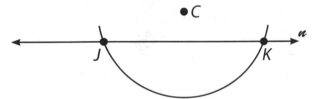

   Make a set of arcs below line *n*.

   Without changing your compass setting, put the sharp point of the compass on point *J*. Make a second arc below the given line.

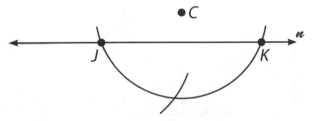

   Without changing your compass setting, put the sharp point of the compass on point *K*. Make a third arc below the given line.

   Label the point of intersection *R*.

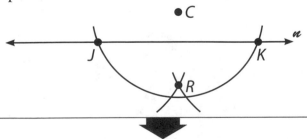

3. Draw the perpendicular line.

   Use your straightedge to connect points *C* and *R*.

   Label the new line *p*.

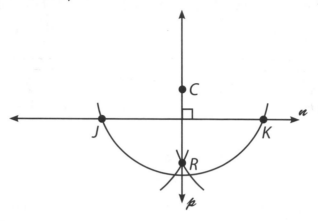

   Do not erase any of your markings.

   Line *n* is perpendicular to line *p*.

4. Construct a second line perpendicular to line *p*.

   Put the sharp point of your compass on point *C*.

   Make a large arc that intersects line *p* on either side of point *C*.

   Label the points of intersection *X* and *Y*.

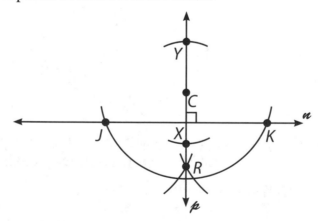

(continued)

Make a set of arcs to the right of line p.

Put the sharp point of your compass on point X.

Open the compass so that it extends beyond point C.

Make an arc to the right of line p.

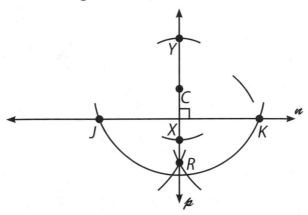

Without changing your compass setting, put the sharp point of the compass on point Y. Make another arc to the right of line p.

Label the point of intersection S.

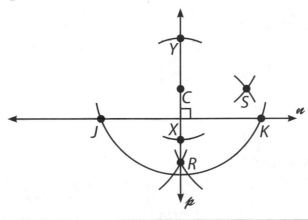

5. Draw the perpendicular line.

   Use your straightedge to connect points *C* and *S*.

   Label the new line *g*.

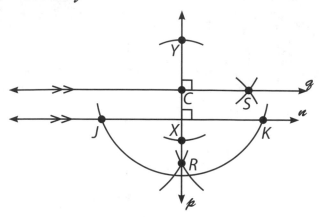

   Do not erase any of your markings.

   Line *g* is perpendicular to line *p*.

   Line *g* is parallel to line *n*.

UNIT 5 • CONGRUENCE, PROOF, AND CONSTRUCTIONS
Lesson 3: Constructing Lines, Segments, and Angles

Practice 5.3.3: Constructing Perpendicular and Parallel Lines

Use a compass and a straightedge to copy each segment, and then construct the perpendicular bisector of each.

1.

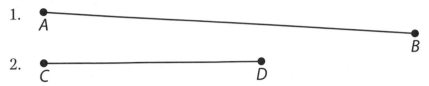

    A   B

2.   C   D

Use a compass and a straightedge to copy each segment, place a point on the segment, and then construct a perpendicular line through the point.

3.

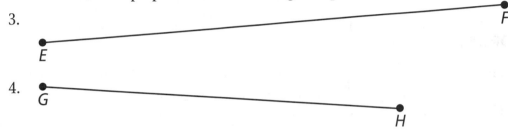

4.

Use a compass and a straightedge to copy each segment, place a point not on the segment, and then construct a perpendicular line through the point.

5.

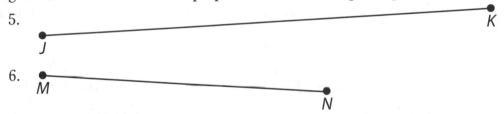

6.

Use a compass and a straightedge to copy each segment, place a point not on the segment, and then construct a parallel line through the point.

7.

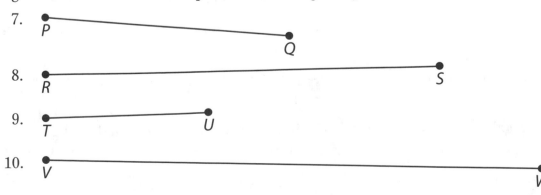

8.

9.

10.

Lesson 4: Constructing Polygons

Common Core State Standard

G–CO.13   Construct an equilateral triangle, a square, and a regular hexagon inscribed in a circle.

Essential Questions

1. How can you justify that a construction was done correctly?

2. How can a polygon be constructed given a circle?

3. How are basic constructions used to construct regular polygons?

WORDS TO KNOW

circle	the set of all points that are equidistant from a reference point, the center. The set of points forms a two-dimensional curve that measures 360˚.
congruent	having the same shape, size, or angle
construction	a precise representation of a figure using a straightedge and compass, patty paper and a straightedge, or a reflecting device and a straightedge
diameter	a straight line passing through the center of a circle connecting two points on the circle; twice the radius
equilateral triangle	a triangle with all three sides equal in length
inscribe	to draw one figure within another figure so that every vertex of the enclosed figure touches the outside figure
radius	a line segment that extends from the center of a circle to a point on the circle. Its length is half the diameter.
regular hexagon	a six-sided polygon with all sides equal and all angles measuring 120˚
regular polygon	a two-dimensional figure with all sides and all angles congruent

square	a four-sided regular polygon with all sides equal and all angles measuring 90°
triangle	a three-sided polygon with three angles

Recommended Resources

- DePaul University. "Inscribing Regular Polygons."

  http://www.walch.com/rr/00007

  This site includes overviews and graphics demonstrating how to construct various regular polygons in a given circle.

- Math Open Reference. "Hexagon inscribed in a circle."

  http://www.walch.com/rr/00008

  This site provides animated step-by-step instructions for constructing a regular hexagon inscribed in a given circle.

- Zef Damen. "Equilateral Triangle."

  http://www.walch.com/rr/00009

  This site gives step-by-step instructions for constructing an equilateral triangle inscribed in a given circle.

Lesson 5.4.1: Constructing Equilateral Triangles Inscribed in Circles

Introduction

The ability to copy and bisect angles and segments, as well as construct perpendicular and parallel lines, allows you to construct a variety of geometric figures, including triangles, squares, and hexagons. There are many ways to construct these figures and others. Sometimes the best way to learn how to construct a figure is to try on your own. You will likely discover different ways to construct the same figure and a way that is easiest for you. In this lesson, you will learn two methods for constructing a triangle within a circle.

Key Concepts

Triangles

- A **triangle** is a polygon with three sides and three angles.

- There are many types of triangles that can be constructed.

- Triangles are classified based on their angle measure and the measure of their sides.

- **Equilateral triangles** are triangles with all three sides equal in length.

- The measure of each angle of an equilateral triangle is 60°.

Circles

- A circle is the set of all points that are equidistant from a reference point, the center.

- The set of points forms a two-dimensional curve that is 360°.

- Circles are named by their center. For example, if a circle has a center point, G, the circle is named circle G.

- The **diameter** of a circle is a straight line that goes through the center of a circle and connects two points on the circle. It is twice the radius.

- The **radius** of a circle is a line segment that runs from the center of a circle to a point on the circle.

- The radius of a circle is one-half the length of the diameter.

- There are 360° in every circle.

Inscribing Figures

- To **inscribe** means to draw a figure within another figure so that every vertex of the enclosed figure touches the outside figure.

- A figure inscribed within a circle is a figure drawn within a circle so that every vertex of the figure touches the circle.

- It is possible to inscribe a triangle within a circle. Like with all constructions, the only tools used to inscribe a figure are a straightedge and a compass, patty paper and a straightedge, reflective tools and a straightedge, or technology.

- This lesson will focus on constructions with a compass and a straightedge.

Method 1: Constructing an Equilateral Triangle Inscribed in a Circle Using a Compass

1. To construct an equilateral triangle inscribed in a circle, first mark the location of the center point of the circle. Label the point X.

2. Construct a circle with the sharp point of the compass on the center point.

3. Label a point on the circle point A.

4. Without changing the compass setting, put the sharp point of the compass on A and draw an arc to intersect the circle at two points. Label the points B and C.

5. Use a straightedge to construct $\overline{BC}$.

6. Put the sharp point of the compass on point B. Open the compass until it extends to the length of $\overline{BC}$. Draw another arc that intersects the circle. Label the point D.

7. Use a straightedge to construct $\overline{BD}$ and $\overline{CD}$.

Do not erase any of your markings.

Triangle BCD is an equilateral triangle inscribed in circle X.

- A second method "steps out" each of the vertices.

- Once a circle is constructed, it is possible to divide the circle into 6 equal parts.

- Do this by choosing a starting point on the circle and moving the compass around the circle, making marks that are the length of the radius apart from one another.

- Connecting every other point of intersection results in an equilateral triangle.

Method 2: Constructing an Equilateral Triangle Inscribed in a Circle Using a Compass

1. To construct an equilateral triangle inscribed in a circle, first mark the location of the center point of the circle. Label the point X.

2. Construct a circle with the sharp point of the compass on the center point.

3. Label a point on the circle point A.

4. Without changing the compass setting, put the sharp point of the compass on A and draw an arc to intersect the circle at one point. Label the point of intersection B.

5. Put the sharp point of the compass on point B and draw an arc to intersect the circle at one point. Label the point of intersection C.

6. Continue around the circle, labeling points D, E, and F. Be sure not to change the compass setting.

7. Use a straightedge to connect A and C, C and E, and E and A.

Do not erase any of your markings.

Triangle ACE is an equilateral triangle inscribed in circle X.

Guided Practice 5.4.1

Example 1

Construct equilateral triangle *ACE* inscribed in circle *O* using Method 1.

1. Construct circle *O*.

   Mark the location of the center point of the circle, and label the point *O*. Construct a circle with the sharp point of the compass on the center point.

   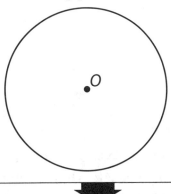

2. Label a point on the circle point *Z*.

   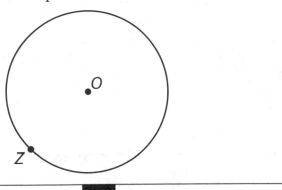

3. Locate vertices *A* and *C* of the equilateral triangle.

   Without changing the compass setting, put the sharp point of the compass on *Z* and draw an arc to intersect the circle at two points. Label the points *A* and *C*.

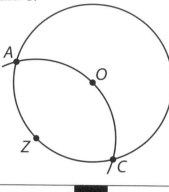

4. Locate the third vertex of the equilateral triangle.

   Put the sharp point of the compass on point *A*. Open the compass until it extends to the length of $\overline{AC}$. Draw another arc that intersects the circle, and label the point *E*.

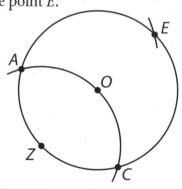

5. Construct the sides of the triangle.

Use a straightedge to connect *A* and *C*, *C* and *E*, and *A* and *E*. Do not erase any of your markings.

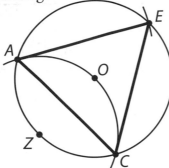

Triangle *ACE* is an equilateral triangle inscribed in circle *O*.

Example 2

Construct equilateral triangle *ACE* inscribed in circle *O* using Method 2.

1. Construct circle *O*.

    Mark the location of the center point of the circle, and label the point *O*. Construct a circle with the sharp point of the compass on the center point.

    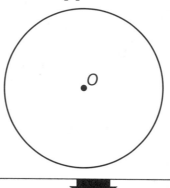

2. Label a point on the circle point *A*.

    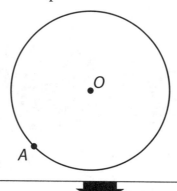

3. Locate vertices *C* and *E*.

Begin by marking the remaining five equidistant points around the circle. Without changing the compass setting, put the sharp point of the compass on *A*. Draw an arc to intersect the circle at one point. Label the point of intersection *B*.

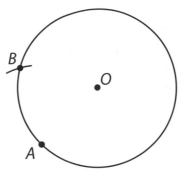

Put the sharp point of the compass on point *B*. Without changing the compass setting, draw an arc to intersect the circle at one point. Label the point of intersection *C*.

Continue around the circle, labeling points *D*, *E*, and *F*. Be sure not to change the compass setting.

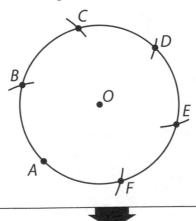

4. Construct the sides of the triangle.

Use a straightedge to connect *A* and *C*, *C* and *E*, and *E* and *A*. Do not erase any of your markings.

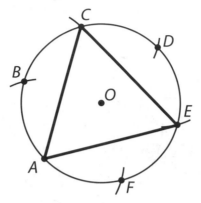

Triangle *ACE* is an equilateral triangle inscribed in circle *O*.

Example 3

Construct equilateral triangle *JKL* inscribed in circle *P* using Method 1. Use the length of $\overline{HP}$ as the radius for circle *P*.

1. Construct circle *P*.

    Mark the location of the center point of the circle, and label the point *P*. Set the opening of the compass equal to the length of $\overline{HP}$. Then, put the sharp point of the compass on point *P* and construct a circle. Label a point on the circle point *G*.

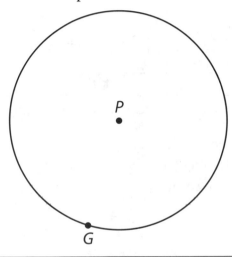

2. Locate vertices *J* and *K* of the equilateral triangle.

   Without changing the compass setting, put the sharp point of the compass on *G*. Draw an arc to intersect the circle at two points. Label the points *J* and *K*.

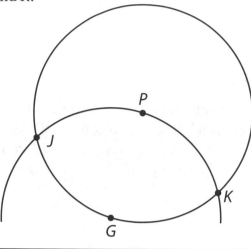

3. Locate the third vertex of the equilateral triangle.

   Put the sharp point of the compass on point *J*. Open the compass until it extends to the length of $\overline{JK}$. Draw another arc that intersects the circle, and label the point *L*.

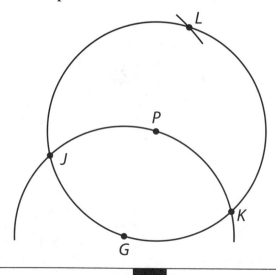

4. Construct the sides of the triangle.

Use a straightedge to connect *J* and *K*, *K* and *L*, and *L* and *J*. Do not erase any of your markings.

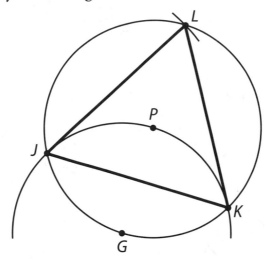

Triangle *JKL* is an equilateral triangle inscribed in circle *P* with the given radius.

Example 4

Construct equilateral triangle *JLN* inscribed in circle *P* using Method 2. Use the length of $\overline{HP}$ as the radius for circle *P*.

1. Construct circle *P*.

    Mark the location of the center point of the circle, and label the point *P*. Set the opening of the compass equal to the length of $\overline{HP}$. Then, put the sharp point of the compass on point *P* and construct a circle. Label a point on the circle point *G*.

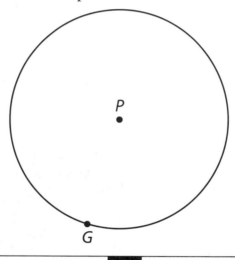

2. Locate vertex *J*.

Without changing the compass setting, put the sharp point of the compass on *G*. Draw an arc to intersect the circle at one point. Label the point of intersection *J*.

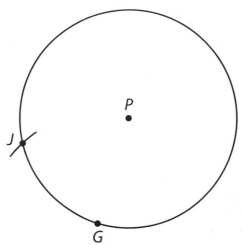

Put the sharp point of the compass on point *J*. Without changing the compass setting, draw an arc to intersect the circle at one point. Label the point of intersection *K*.

Continue around the circle, labeling points *L*, *M*, and *N*. Be sure not to change the compass setting.

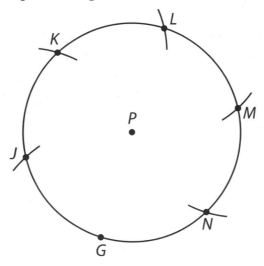

3. Construct the sides of the triangle.

   Use a straightedge to connect *J* and *L*, *L* and *N*, and *J* and *N*. Do not erase any of your markings.

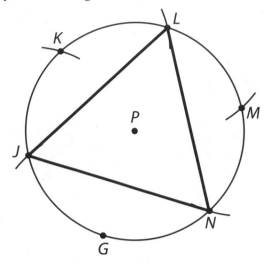

   Triangle *JLN* is an equilateral triangle inscribed in circle *P*.

UNIT 5 • CONGRUENCE, PROOF, AND CONSTRUCTIONS
Lesson 4: Constructing Polygons

Practice 5.4.1: Constructing Equilateral Triangles Inscribed in Circles

Use a compass and a straightedge to construct each equilateral triangle using Method 1.

1. Construct equilateral triangle *ABC* inscribed in circle *D*.

2. Construct equilateral triangle *EFG* inscribed in circle *H* with radius $\overline{MN}$.

3. Construct equilateral triangle *IJK* inscribed in circle *L* with radius $\overline{PQ}$.

4. Construct equilateral triangle *MNO* inscribed in circle *P* with the radius equal to twice $\overline{RS}$.

5. Construct equilateral triangle *QRS* inscribed in circle *T* with the radius equal to one-half $\overline{VW}$.

UNIT 5 • CONGRUENCE, PROOF, AND CONSTRUCTIONS
Lesson 4: Constructing Polygons

Use a compass and a straightedge to construct each equilateral triangle using Method 2.

6. Construct equilateral triangle *ABC* inscribed in circle *D*.

7. Construct equilateral triangle *EFG* inscribed in circle *H* with radius $\overline{MN}$.

8. Construct equilateral triangle *IJK* inscribed in circle *L* with radius $\overline{PQ}$.

9. Construct equilateral triangle *MNO* inscribed in circle *P* with the radius equal to twice $\overline{RS}$.

10. Construct equilateral triangle *QRS* inscribed in circle *T* with the radius equal to one-half $\overline{VW}$.

Lesson 5.4.2: Constructing Squares Inscribed in Circles

Introduction

Triangles are not the only figures that can be inscribed in a circle. It is also possible to inscribe other figures, such as squares. The process for inscribing a square in a circle uses previously learned skills, including constructing perpendicular bisectors.

Key Concepts

- A **square** is a four-sided regular polygon.

- A regular polygon is a polygon that has all sides equal and all angles equal.

- The measure of each of the angles of a square is 90°.

- Sides that meet at one angle to create a 90° angle are perpendicular.

- By constructing the perpendicular bisector of a diameter of a circle, you can construct a square inscribed in a circle.

Constructing a Square Inscribed in a Circle Using a Compass
1. To construct a square inscribed in a circle, first mark the location of the center point of the circle. Label the point X.
2. Construct a circle with the sharp point of the compass on the center point.
3. Label a point on the circle point A.
4. Use a straightedge to connect point A and point X. Extend the line through the circle, creating the diameter of the circle. Label the second point of intersection C.
5. Construct the perpendicular bisector of $\overline{AC}$ by putting the sharp point of your compass on endpoint A. Open the compass wider than half the distance of $\overline{AC}$. Make a large arc intersecting $\overline{AC}$. Without changing your compass setting, put the sharp point of the compass on endpoint C. Make a second large arc. Use your straightedge to connect the points of intersection of the arcs.
6. Extend the bisector so it intersects the circle in two places. Label the points of intersection B and D.
7. Use a straightedge to connect points A and B, B and C, C and D, and A and D.
Do not erase any of your markings.
Quadrilateral $ABCD$ is a square inscribed in circle X.

Guided Practice 5.4.2

Example 1

Construct square *ABCD* inscribed in circle *O*.

1. Construct circle *O*.

   Mark the location of the center point of the circle, and label the point *O*. Construct a circle with the sharp point of the compass on the center point.

   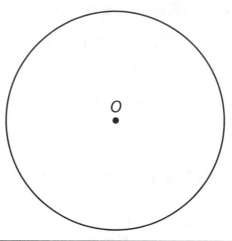

2. Label a point on the circle point *A*.

   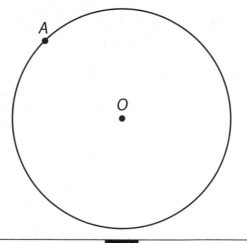

3. Construct the diameter of the circle.

Use a straightedge to connect point *A* and point *O*. Extend the line through the circle, creating the diameter of the circle. Label the second point of intersection *C*.

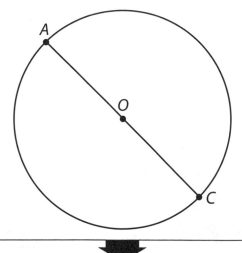

4. Construct the perpendicular bisector of $\overline{AC}$.

Extend the bisector so it intersects the circle in two places. Label the points of intersection *B* and *D*.

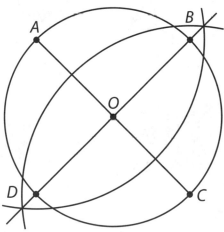

5. Construct the sides of the square.

   Use a straightedge to connect points *A* and *B*, *B* and *C*, *C* and *D*, and *A* and *D*. Do not erase any of your markings.

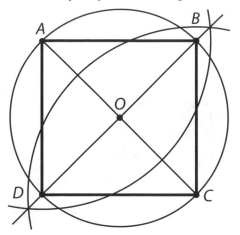

   Quadrilateral *ABCD* is a square inscribed in circle *O*.

Example 2

Construct square *EFGH* inscribed in circle *P* with the radius equal to the length of $\overline{EP}$.

E   P

1. Construct circle *P*.

   Mark the location of the center point of the circle, and label the point *P*. Set the opening of the compass equal to the length of $\overline{EP}$. Construct a circle with the sharp point of the compass on the center point, *P*.

   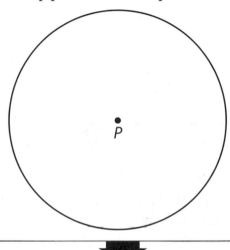

2. Label a point on the circle point *E*.

   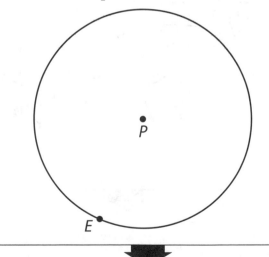

3. Construct the diameter of the circle.

   Use a straightedge to connect point E and point P. Extend the line through the circle, creating the diameter of the circle. Label the second point of intersection G.

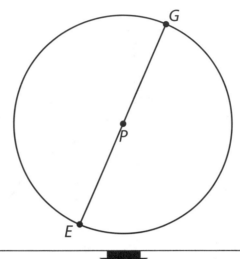

4. Construct the perpendicular bisector of $\overline{EG}$.

   Extend the bisector so it intersects the circle in two places. Label the points of intersection F and H.

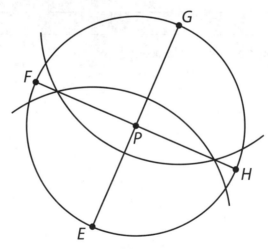

5. Construct the sides of the square.

   Use a straightedge to connect points E and F, F and G, G and H, and H and E. Do not erase any of your markings.

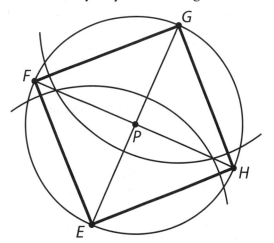

   Quadrilateral *EFGH* is a square inscribed in circle P.

Example 3

Construct square *JKLM* inscribed in circle *Q* with the radius equal to one-half the length of $\overline{JL}$.

1. Construct circle *Q*.

    Mark the location of the center point of the circle, and label the point *Q*. Bisect the length of $\overline{JL}$. Label the midpoint of the segment as point *P*.

    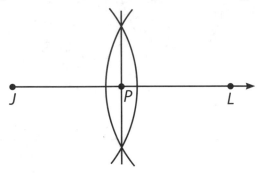

    Next, set the opening of the compass equal to the length of $\overline{JP}$. Construct a circle with the sharp point of the compass on the center point, *Q*.

    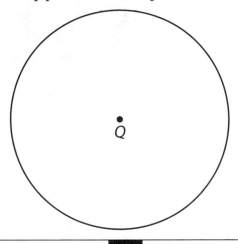

2. Label a point on the circle point *J*.

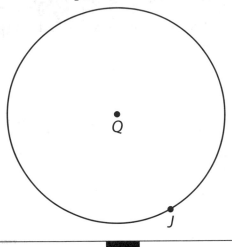

3. Construct the diameter of the circle.

Use a straightedge to connect point *J* and point *Q*. Extend the line through the circle, creating the diameter of the circle. Label the second point of intersection *L*.

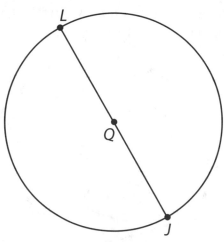

4. Construct the perpendicular bisector of $\overline{JL}$.

   Extend the bisector so it intersects the circle in two places. Label the points of intersection K and M.

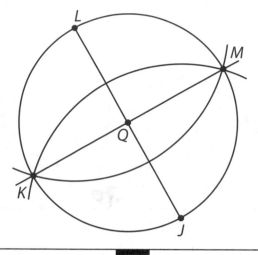

5. Construct the sides of the square.

   Use a straightedge to connect points J and K, K and L, L and M, and M and J. Do not erase any of your markings.

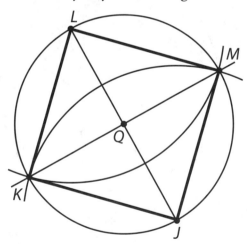

Quadrilateral $JKLM$ is a square inscribed in circle Q.

UNIT 5 • CONGRUENCE, PROOF, AND CONSTRUCTIONS
Lesson 4: Constructing Polygons

Practice 5.4.2: Constructing Squares Inscribed in Circles

Use a compass and a straightedge to construct each square inscribed in a circle.

1. Construct square *BCDE* inscribed in circle *F.*

2. Construct square *GHIJ* inscribed in circle *L.*

3. Construct square *MNOP* inscribed in circle *Q* with radius $\overline{MQ}$.

      M   Q

4. Construct square *RSTU* inscribed in circle *V* with radius $\overline{RV}$.

      R   V

5. Construct square *WXYZ* inscribed in circle *A* with radius $\overline{WA}$.

      W   A

6. Construct square *CDEF* inscribed in circle *G* with radius $\overline{CG}$.

      C   G

7. Construct square *HJKL* inscribed in circle *M* with the radius equal to twice $\overline{AB}$.

      A   B

8. Construct square *NOPQ* inscribed in circle *R* with the radius equal to one-half $\overline{CD}$.

      C   D

9. Construct square *STUV* inscribed in circle *W* with a diameter equal to $\overline{SU}$.

      S   U

10. Construct square *ABCD* inscribed in circle *E* with a diameter equal to $\overline{AC}$.

      A   C

Lesson 5.4.3: Constructing Regular Hexagons Inscribed in Circles

Introduction

Construction methods can also be used to construct figures in a circle. One figure that can be inscribed in a circle is a hexagon. Hexagons are polygons with six sides.

Key Concepts

- **Regular hexagons** have six equal sides and six angles, each measuring 120°.

- The process for inscribing a regular hexagon in a circle is similar to that of inscribing equilateral triangles and squares in a circle.

- The construction of a regular hexagon is the result of the construction of two equilateral triangles inscribed in a circle.

Method 1: Constructing a Regular Hexagon Inscribed in a Circle Using a Compass

1. To construct a regular hexagon inscribed in a circle, first mark the location of the center point of the circle. Label the point X.

2. Construct a circle with the sharp point of the compass on the center point.

3. Label a point on the circle point A.

4. Use a straightedge to connect point A and point X. Extend the line through the circle, creating the diameter of the circle. Label the second point of intersection D.

5. Without changing the compass setting, put the sharp point of the compass on A. Draw an arc to intersect the circle at two points. Label the points B and F.

6. Put the sharp point of the compass on D. Without changing the compass setting, draw an arc to intersect the circle at two points. Label the points C and E.

7. Use a straightedge to connect points A and B, B and C, C and D, D and E, E and F, and F and A.

Do not erase any of your markings.

Hexagon $ABCDEF$ is regular and is inscribed in circle X.

- A second method "steps out" each of the vertices.

- Once a circle is constructed, it is possible to divide the circle into six equal parts.

- Do this by choosing a starting point on the circle and moving the compass around the circle, making marks equal to the length of the radius.

- Connecting every point of intersection results in a regular hexagon.

Method 2: Constructing a Regular Hexagon Inscribed in a Circle Using a Compass

1. To construct a regular hexagon inscribed in a circle, first mark the location of the center point of the circle. Label the point X.

2. Construct a circle with the sharp point of the compass on the center point.

3. Label a point on the circle point A.

4. Without changing the compass setting, put the sharp point of the compass on A. Draw an arc to intersect the circle at one point. Label the point of intersection B.

5. Put the sharp point of the compass on point B. Without changing the compass setting, draw an arc to intersect the circle at one point. Label the point of intersection C.

6. Continue around the circle, labeling points D, E, and F. Be sure not to change the compass setting.

7. Use a straightedge to connect points A and B, B and C, C and D, D and E, E and F, and F and A.

Do not erase any of your markings.

Hexagon $ABCDEF$ is regular and is inscribed in circle X.

Guided Practice 5.4.3

Example 1

Construct regular hexagon *ABCDEF* inscribed in circle *O* using Method 1.

1. Construct circle *O*.

   Mark the location of the center point of the circle, and label the point *O*. Construct a circle with the sharp point of the compass on the center point.

   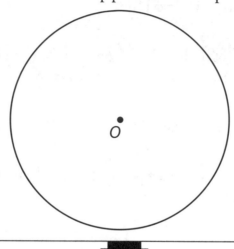

2. Label a point on the circle point *A*.

   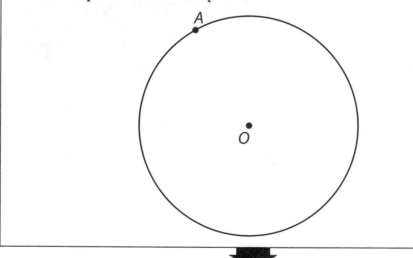

3. Construct the diameter of the circle.

Use a straightedge to connect point *A* and the center point, *O*. Extend the line through the circle, creating the diameter of the circle. Label the second point of intersection *D*.

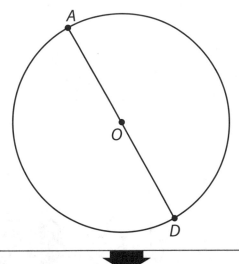

4. Locate two vertices on either side of point *A*.

Without changing the compass setting, put the sharp point of the compass on point *A*. Draw an arc to intersect the circle at two points. Label the points *B* and *F*.

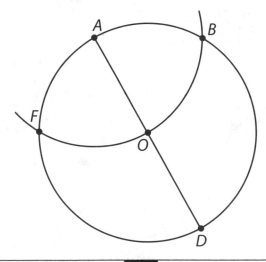

5. Locate two vertices on either side of point *D*.

   Without changing the compass setting, put the sharp point of the compass on point *D*. Draw an arc to intersect the circle at two points. Label the points *C* and *E*.

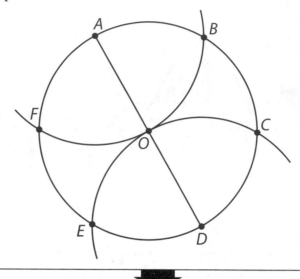

6. Construct the sides of the hexagon.

   Use a straightedge to connect *A* and *B*, *B* and *C*, *C* and *D*, *D* and *E*, *E* and *F*, and *F* and *A*. Do not erase any of your markings.

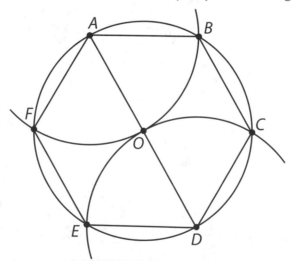

Hexagon *ABCDEF* is a regular hexagon inscribed in circle *O*.

Example 2

Construct regular hexagon *ABCDEF* inscribed in circle *O* using Method 2.

1. Construct circle *O*.

   Mark the location of the center point of the circle, and label the point *O*. Construct a circle with the sharp point of the compass on the center point.

   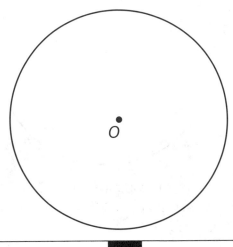

2. Label a point on the circle point *A*.

   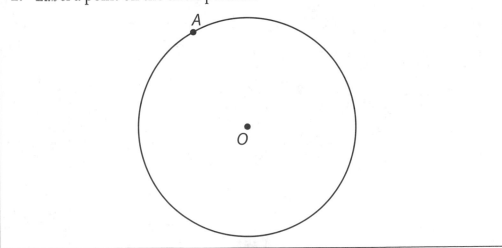

3. Locate the remaining vertices.

Without changing the compass setting, put the sharp point of the compass on *A*. Draw an arc to intersect the circle at one point. Label the point of intersection *B*.

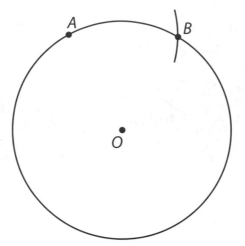

Put the sharp point of the compass on point *B*. Without changing the compass setting, draw an arc to intersect the circle at one point. Label the point of intersection *C*.

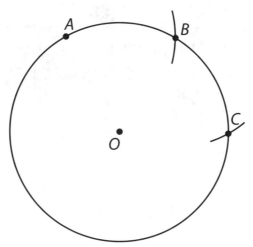

(continued)

Continue around the circle, labeling points *D*, *E*, and *F*. Be sure not to change the compass setting.

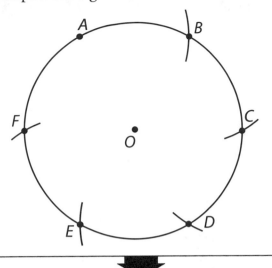

4. Construct the sides of the hexagon.

Use a straightedge to connect *A* and *B*, *B* and *C*, *C* and *D*, *D* and *E*, *E* and *F*, and *F* and *A*. Do not erase any of your markings.

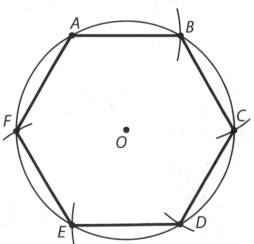

Hexagon *ABCDEF* is a regular hexagon inscribed in circle *O*.

Example 3

Construct regular hexagon *LMNOPQ* inscribed in circle *R* using Method 1. Use the length of $\overline{RL}$ as the radius for circle *R*.

R   L

1. Construct circle *R*.

   Mark the location of the center point of the circle, and label the point *R*. Set the opening of the compass equal to the length of $\overline{RL}$. Put the sharp point of the circle on *R* and construct a circle.

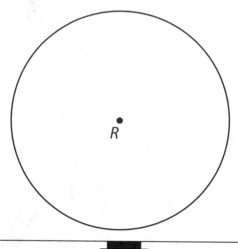

2. Label a point on the circle point *L*.

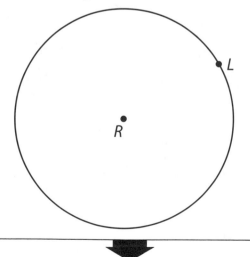

3. Construct the diameter of the circle.

Use a straightedge to connect point L and the center point, R. Extend the line through the circle, creating the diameter of the circle. Label the second point of intersection O.

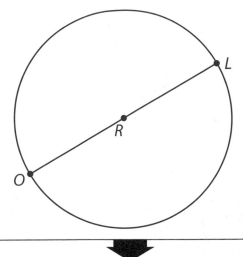

4. Locate two vertices on either side of point L.

Without changing the compass setting, put the sharp point of the compass on point L. Draw an arc to intersect the circle at two points. Label the points M and Q.

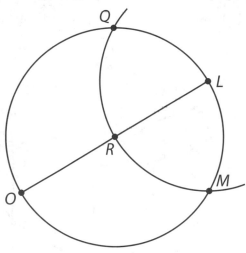

5. Locate two vertices on either side of point O.

   Without changing the compass setting, put the sharp point of the compass on point O. Draw an arc to intersect the circle at two points. Label the points P and N.

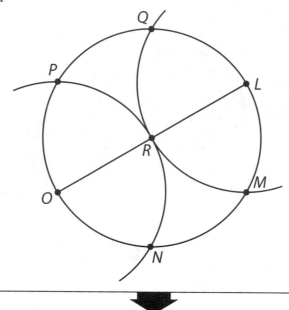

6. Construct the sides of the hexagon.

   Use a straightedge to connect L and M, M and N, N and O, O and P, P and Q, and Q and L. Do not erase any of your markings.

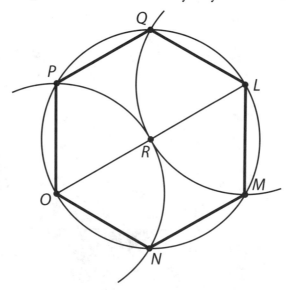

   Hexagon $LMNOPQ$ is a regular hexagon inscribed in circle R.

Example 4

Construct regular hexagon *LMNOPQ* inscribed in circle *R* using Method 2. Use the length of $\overline{RL}$ as the radius for circle *R*.

R   L

1. Construct circle *R*.

   Mark the location of the center point of the circle, and label the point *R*. Set the opening of the compass equal to the length of $\overline{RL}$. Put the sharp point of the circle on *R* and construct a circle.

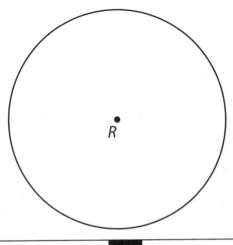

2. Label a point on the circle point *L*.

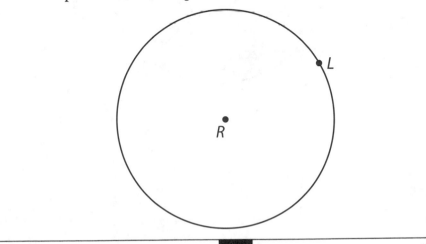

3. Locate the remaining vertices.

   Without changing the compass setting, put the sharp point of the compass on L. Draw an arc to intersect the circle at one point. Label the point of intersection M.

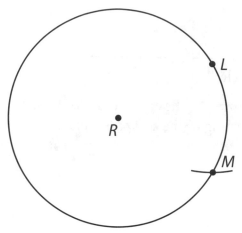

   Put the sharp point of the compass on point M. Without changing the compass setting, draw an arc to intersect the circle at one point. Label the point of intersection N.

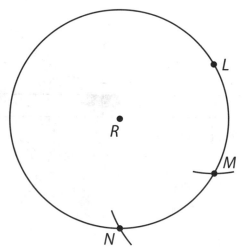

(*continued*)

Continue around the circle, labeling points O, P, and Q. Be sure not to change the compass setting.

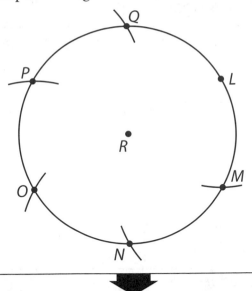

4. Construct the sides of the hexagon.

Use a straightedge to connect L and M, M and N, N and O, O and P, P and Q, and Q and L. Do not erase any of your markings.

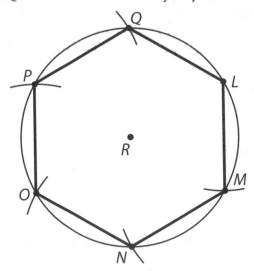

Hexagon $LMNOPQ$ is a regular hexagon inscribed in circle R.

UNIT 5 • CONGRUENCE, PROOF, AND CONSTRUCTIONS
Lesson 4: Constructing Polygons

Practice 5.4.3: Constructing Regular Hexagons Inscribed in Circles

Use a compass and a straightedge to construct each regular hexagon using Method 1.

1. Construct regular hexagon *DEFGHJ* inscribed in circle *A*.

2. Construct regular hexagon *KLMNOP* inscribed in circle *B* with radius $\overline{BC}$.

3. Construct regular hexagon *STUVWX* inscribed in circle *C* with radius $\overline{DE}$.

4. Construct regular hexagon *UVWXYZ* inscribed in circle *D* with the radius equal to twice $\overline{FG}$.

5. Construct regular hexagon *FGHJKL* inscribed in circle *E* with the radius equal to one-half $\overline{HJ}$.

continued

Use a compass and a straightedge to construct each regular hexagon using Method 2.

6. Construct regular hexagon *DEFGHJ* inscribed in circle *A*.

7. Construct regular hexagon *KLMNOP* inscribed in circle *B* with radius $\overline{BC}$.

8. Construct regular hexagon *STUVWX* inscribed in circle *C* with radius $\overline{DE}$.

9. Construct regular hexagon *UVWXYZ* inscribed in circle *D* with the radius equal to twice $\overline{FG}$.

10. Construct regular hexagon *FGHJKL* inscribed in circle *E* with the radius equal to one-half $\overline{HJ}$.

Lesson 5: Exploring Congruence

Common Core State Standard

G–CO.6 Use geometric descriptions of rigid motions to transform figures and to predict the effect of a given rigid motion on a given figure; given two figures, use the definition of congruence in terms of rigid motions to decide if they are congruent.

Essential Questions

1. What are the differences between rigid and non-rigid motions?

2. How do you identify a transformation as a rigid motion?

3. How do you identify a transformation as a non-rigid motion?

WORDS TO KNOW

angle of rotation	the measure of the angle created by the preimage vertex to the point of rotation to the image vertex. All of these angles are congruent when a figure is rotated.
clockwise	rotating a figure in the direction that the hands on a clock move
compression	a transformation in which a figure becomes smaller; compressions may be horizontal (affecting only horizontal lengths), vertical (affecting only vertical lengths), or both
congruency transformation	a transformation in which a geometric figure moves but keeps the same size and shape
congruent	figures are congruent if they have the same shape, size, lines, and angles; the symbol for representing congruency between figures is $\cong$
corresponding angles	angles of two figures that lie in the same position relative to the figure. In transformations, the corresponding vertices are the preimage and image vertices, so $\angle A$ and $\angle A'$ are corresponding vertices and so on.

corresponding sides	sides of two figures that lie in the same position relative to the figure. In transformations, the corresponding sides are the preimage and image sides, so $\overline{AB}$ and $\overline{A'B'}$ are corresponding sides and so on.
counterclockwise	rotating a figure in the opposite direction that the hands on a clock move
dilation	a transformation in which a figure is either enlarged or reduced by a scale factor in relation to a center point
equidistant	the same distance from a reference point
image	the new, resulting figure after a transformation
isometry	a transformation in which the preimage and image are congruent
line of reflection	the perpendicular bisector of the segments that connect the corresponding vertices of the preimage and the image
non-rigid motion	a transformation done to a figure that changes the figure's shape and/or size
point of rotation	the fixed location that an object is turned around; the point can lie on, inside, or outside the figure
preimage	the original figure before undergoing a transformation
rigid motion	a transformation done to a figure that maintains the figure's shape and size or its segment lengths and angle measures
scale factor	a multiple of the lengths of the sides from one figure to the transformed figure. If the scale factor is larger than 1, then the figure is enlarged. If the scale factor is between 0 and 1, then the figure is reduced.

Recommended Resources

- Math Is Fun. "Rotation."

  http://www.walch.com/rr/00010

  This website explains what a rotation is, and then gives the opportunity to experiment with rotating different shapes about a point of rotation and an angle. There are links at the bottom of the page for translations and reflections with similar applets.

- Math Open Reference. "Dilation—of a polygon."

  http://www.walch.com/rr/00011

  This site gives a description of a dilation and provides an applet with a slider, allowing users to explore dilating a rectangle with different scale factors. The website goes on to explain how to create a dilation of a polygon.

- MisterTeacher.com. "Alphabet Geometry: Transformations—Translations."

  http://www.walch.com/rr/00012

  This site explains and animates a translation. It also contains links to descriptions and animations of rotations and reflections.

Lesson 5.5.1: Describing Rigid Motions and Predicting the Effects

Introduction

Think about trying to move a drop of water across a flat surface. If you try to push the water droplet, it will smear, stretch, and transfer onto your finger. The water droplet, a liquid, is not rigid. Now think about moving a block of wood across the same flat surface. A block of wood is solid or rigid, meaning it maintains its shape and size when you move it. You can push the block and it will keep the same size and shape as it moves. In this lesson, we will examine **rigid motions**, which are transformations done to an object that maintain the object's shape and size or its segment lengths and angle measures.

Key Concepts

- Rigid motions are transformations that don't affect an object's shape and size. This means that corresponding sides and corresponding angle measures are preserved.

- When angle measures and sides are preserved they are congruent, which means they have the same shape and size.

- The congruency symbol ($\cong$) is used to show that two figures are congruent.

- The figure before the transformation is called the preimage.

- The figure after the transformation is the image.

- **Corresponding sides** are the sides of two figures that lie in the same position relative to the figure. In transformations, the corresponding sides are the preimage and image sides, so $\overline{AB}$ and $\overline{A'B'}$ are corresponding sides and so on.

- **Corresponding angles** are the angles of two figures that lie in the same position relative to the figure. In transformations, the corresponding vertices are the preimage and image vertices, so $\angle A$ and $\angle A'$ are corresponding vertices and so on.

- Transformations that are rigid motions are translations, reflections, and rotations.

- Transformations that are not rigid motions are dilations, vertical stretches or compressions, and horizontal stretches or compressions.

Translations

- A translation is sometimes called a slide.

- In a translation, the figure is moved horizontally and/or vertically.

- The orientation of the figure remains the same.

- Connecting the corresponding vertices of the preimage and image will result in a set of parallel lines.

Translating a Figure Given the Horizontal and Vertical Shift
1. Place your pencil on a vertex and count over horizontally the number of units the figure is to be translated.
2. Without lifting your pencil, count vertically the number of units the figure is to be translated.
3. Mark the image vertex on the coordinate plane.
4. Repeat this process for all vertices of the figure.
5. Connect the image vertices.

Reflections

- A reflection creates a mirror image of the original figure over a reflection line.

- A reflection line can pass through the figure, be on the figure, or be outside the figure.

- Reflections are sometimes called flips.

- The orientation of the figure is changed in a reflection.

- In a reflection, the corresponding vertices of the preimage and image are equidistant from the line of reflection, meaning the distance from each vertex to the line of reflection is the same.

- The **line of reflection** is the perpendicular bisector of the segments that connect the corresponding vertices of the preimage and the image.

Reflecting a Figure over a Given Reflection Line

1. Draw the reflection line on the same coordinate plane as the figure.

2. If the reflection line is vertical, count the number of horizontal units one vertex is from the line and count the same number of units on the opposite side of the line. Place the image vertex there. Repeat this process for all vertices.

3. If the reflection line is horizontal, count the number of vertical units one vertex is from the line and count the same number of units on the opposite side of the line. Place the image vertex there. Repeat this process for all vertices.

4. If the reflection line is diagonal, draw lines from each vertex that are perpendicular to the reflection line extending beyond the line of reflection. Copy each segment from the vertex to the line of reflection onto the perpendicular line on the other side of the reflection line and mark the image vertices.

5. Connect the image vertices.

Rotations

- A rotation moves all points of a figure along a circular arc about a point. Rotations are sometimes called turns.

- In a rotation, the orientation is changed.

- The **point of rotation** can lie on, inside, or outside the figure, and is the fixed location that the object is turned around.

- The **angle of rotation** is the measure of the angle created by the preimage vertex to the point of rotation to the image vertex. All of these angles are congruent when a figure is rotated.

- Rotating a figure **clockwise** moves the figure in a circular arc about the point of rotation in the same direction that the hands move on a clock.

- Rotating a figure **counterclockwise** moves the figure in a circular arc about the point of rotation in the opposite direction that the hands move on a clock.

Rotating a Figure Given a Point and Angle of Rotation

1. Draw a line from one vertex to the point of rotation.

2. Measure the angle of rotation using a protractor.

3. Draw a ray from the point of rotation extending outward that creates the angle of rotation.

4. Copy the segment connecting the point of rotation to the vertex (created in step 1) onto the ray created in step 3.

5. Mark the endpoint of the copied segment that is not the point of rotation with the letter of the corresponding vertex, followed by a prime mark ('). This is the first vertex of the rotated figure.

6. Repeat the process for each vertex of the figure.

7. Connect the vertices that have prime marks. This is the rotated figure.

Guided Practice 5.5.1

Example 1

Describe the transformation that has taken place in the diagram below.

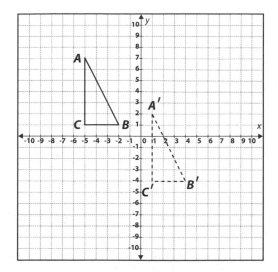

1. Examine the orientation of the figures to determine if the orientation has changed or stayed the same. Look at the sides of the triangle.

Side length	Preimage orientation	Image orientation
Shortest	Bottom of triangle and horizontal	Bottom of triangle and horizontal
Longest	Right side of triangle going from top left to bottom right	Right side of triangle going from top left to bottom right
Intermediate	Left side of triangle and vertical	Left side of triangle and vertical

The orientation of the triangles has remained the same.

2. Connect the corresponding vertices with lines.

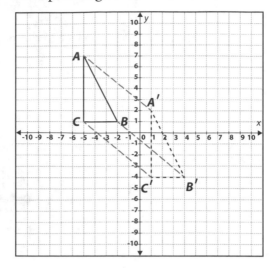

The lines connecting the corresponding vertices appear to be parallel.

3. Analyze the change in position.

Check the horizontal distance of vertex A. To go from A to A' horizontally, the vertex was shifted to the right 6 units. Vertically, vertex A was shifted down 5 units. Check the remaining two vertices. Each vertex slid 6 units to the right and 5 units down.

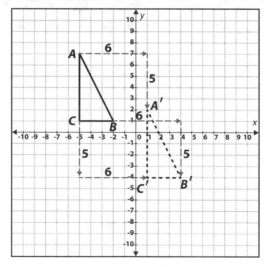

Example 2

Describe the transformation that has taken place in the diagram below.

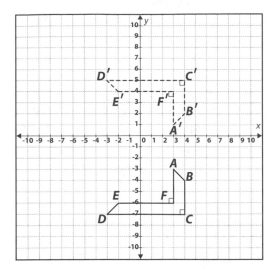

1. Examine the orientation of the figures to determine if the orientation has changed or stayed the same. Look at the sides of the figures and pick a reference point. A good reference point is the outer right angle of the figure. From this point, examine the position of the "arms" of the figure.

Arm	Preimage orientation	Image orientation
Shorter	Pointing upward from the corner of the figure with a negative slope at the end of the arm	Pointing downward from the corner of the figure with a positive slope at the end of the arm
Longer	Pointing to the left from the corner of the figure with a positive slope at the end of the arm	Pointing to the left from the corner of the figure with a negative slope at the end of the arm

(continued)

The orientation of the figures has changed. In the preimage, the outer right angle is in the bottom right-hand corner of the figure, with the shorter arm extending upward. In the image, the outer right angle is on the top right-hand side of the figure, with the shorter arm extending down.

Also, compare the slopes of the segments at the end of the longer arm. The slope of the segment at the end of the arm is positive in the preimage, but in the image the slope of the corresponding arm is negative. A similar reversal has occurred with the segment at the end of the shorter arm. In the preimage, the segment at the end of the shorter arm is negative, while in the image the slope is positive.

2. Determine the transformation that has taken place.

Since the orientation has changed, the transformation is either a reflection or a rotation. Since the orientation of the image is the mirror image of the preimage, the transformation is a reflection. The figure has been flipped over a line.

3. Determine the line of reflection.

Connect some of the corresponding vertices of the figure. Choose one of the segments you created and construct the perpendicular bisector of the segment. Verify that this is the perpendicular bisector for all segments joining the corresponding vertices. This is the line of reflection.

The line of reflection for this figure is $y = -1$.

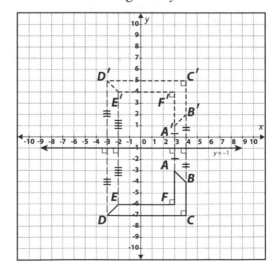

Example 3

Describe the transformation that has taken place in the diagram below.

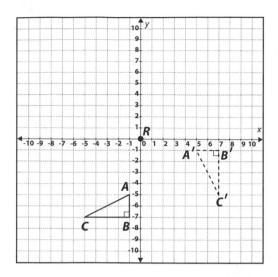

1. Examine the orientation of the figures to determine if the orientation has changed or stayed the same.

   Look at the sides of the triangle.

Side length	Preimage orientation	Image orientation
Shortest	Right side of triangle and vertical	Top of triangle and horizontal
Longest	Diagonal from bottom left to top right of triangle	Diagonal from top left to bottom right of triangle
Intermediate	Bottom side of triangle and horizontal	Right side of triangle and vertical

   The orientation of the triangles has changed.

2. Determine the transformation that has taken place.

Since the orientation has changed, the transformation is either a reflection or a rotation. Since the orientation of the image is NOT the mirror image of the preimage, the transformation is a rotation. The figure has been turned about a point. All angles that are made up of the preimage vertex to the reflection point to the corresponding image vertex are congruent. This means that $\angle ARA' \cong \angle BRB' \cong \angle CRC'$.

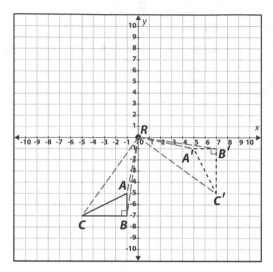

Example 4

Rotate the given figure 45° counterclockwise about the origin.

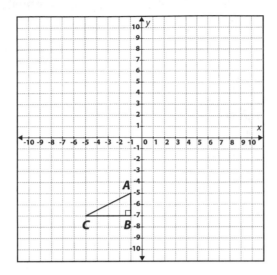

1. Create the angle of rotation for the first vertex.

   Connect vertex A and the origin with a line segment. Label the point of reflection R. Then, use a protractor to measure a 45° angle. Use the segment from vertex A to the point of rotation R as one side of the angle. Mark a point X at 45°. Draw a ray extending out from point R, connecting R and X. Copy $\overline{AR}$ onto $\overrightarrow{RX}$. Label the endpoint that leads away from the origin A'.

   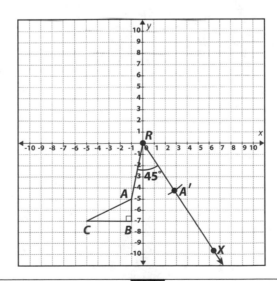

2. Create the angle of rotation for the second vertex.

Connect vertex *B* and the origin with a line segment. The point of reflection is still *R*. Then, use a protractor to measure a 45° angle. Use the segment from vertex *B* to the point of rotation *R* as one side of the angle. Mark a point *Y* at 45°. Draw a ray extending out from point *R*, connecting *R* and *Y*. Copy $\overline{BR}$ onto $\overrightarrow{RY}$. Label the endpoint that leads away from the origin *B'*.

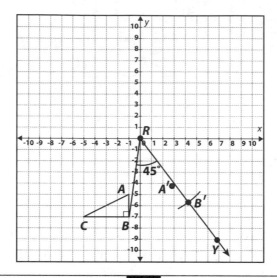

3. Create the angle of rotation for the third vertex.

Connect vertex C and the origin with a line segment. The point of reflection is still R. Then, use a protractor to measure a 45° angle. Use the segment from vertex C to the point of rotation R as one side of the angle. Mark a point Z at 45°. Draw a ray extending out from point R, connecting R and Z and continuing outward from Z. Copy $\overline{CR}$ onto $\overrightarrow{RZ}$. Label the endpoint that leads away from the origin C'.

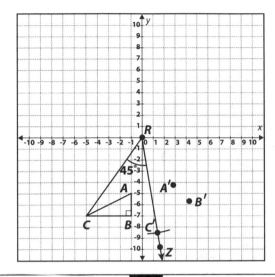

4. Connect the rotated points.

The connected points A', B', and C' form the rotated figure.

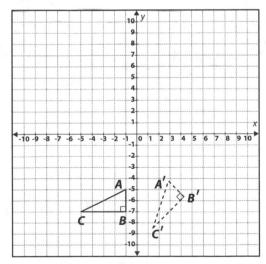

UNIT 5 • CONGRUENCE, PROOF, AND CONSTRUCTIONS
Lesson 5: Exploring Congruence

Practice 5.5.1: Describing Rigid Motions and Predicting the Effects

For problems 1–3, describe the rigid motion used to transform each figure. If the transformation is a translation, state the units and direction(s) the figure was transformed. If the transformation is a reflection, state the line of reflection.

1.

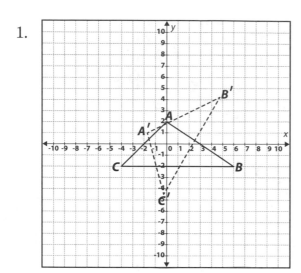

2.

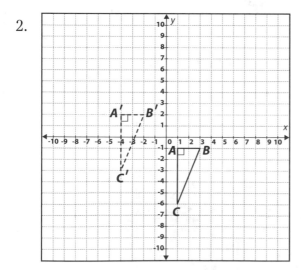

continued

UNIT 5 • CONGRUENCE, PROOF, AND CONSTRUCTIONS
Lesson 5: Exploring Congruence

3.

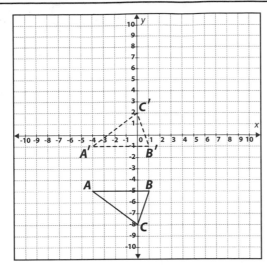

4. Reflect the given triangle over the line $x = -2$.

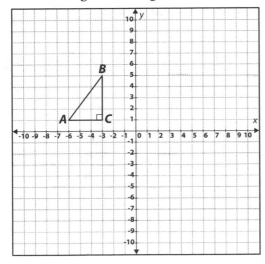

continued

UNIT 5 • CONGRUENCE, PROOF, AND CONSTRUCTIONS
Lesson 5: Exploring Congruence

5. Rotate the given triangle 80° counterclockwise about point *R*.

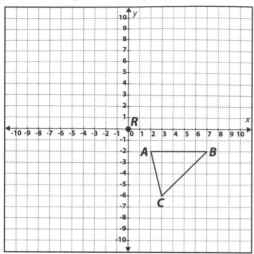

6. Translate the given triangle 8 units to the left and 3 units down.

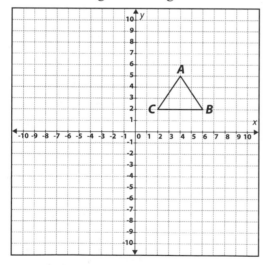

UNIT 5 • CONGRUENCE, PROOF, AND CONSTRUCTIONS
Lesson 5: Exploring Congruence

7. Explorers recovered a necklace pendant in an archeological dig. Parts of the pendant are broken off. Artists have determined that the pendant exhibits a line of symmetry down through the center of the pendant. Recreate the missing portions of the pendant given the line of reflection shown.

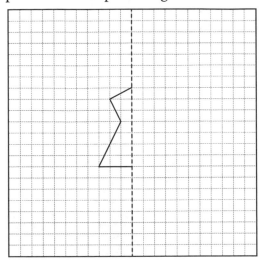

8. Eli's family just switched to using a satellite dish to receive their TV signal. The family has determined that they need to rotate the dish 20° counterclockwise about its anchor, point R. The shape of the dish is modeled by a triangle. What will the final position of the dish be after the rotation?

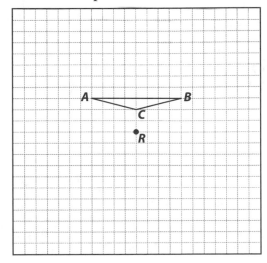

9. For fire safety, there should be a 3-foot radius from the center of the outer wall of a fireplace that is free of furniture. According to the floor plan pictured below, two chairs lie within this area and are considered to be fire hazards. What rigid motions can be performed on the chairs to create a safer space?

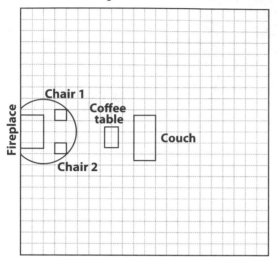

10. The International Space Station uses large solar panels made up of smaller hexagons to bring power to the station. The hexagon labeled *ABCDEF* requires two types of rigid motions to bring it into its proper place at $A''B''C''D''E''F''$. What rigid motions will bring the solar panel into place? Use a diagram to justify your answer.

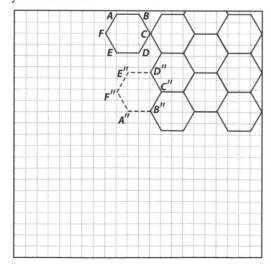

Lesson 5.5.2: Defining Congruence in Terms of Rigid Motions

Introduction

Rigid motions can also be called congruency transformations. A **congruency transformation** moves a geometric figure but keeps the same size and shape. Preimages and images that are congruent are also said to be isometries. If a figure has undergone a rigid motion or a set of rigid motions, the preimage and image are congruent. When two figures are congruent, they have the same shape and size. Remember that rigid motions are translations, reflections, and rotations. Non-rigid motions are dilations, stretches, and compressions. **Non-rigid motions** are transformations done to a figure that change the figure's shape and/or size.

Key Concepts

- To decide if two figures are congruent, determine if the original figure has undergone a rigid motion or set of rigid motions.

- If the figure has undergone only rigid motions (translations, reflections, or rotations), then the figures are congruent.

- If the figure has undergone any non-rigid motions (dilations, stretches, or compressions), then the figures are not congruent. A **dilation** uses a center point and a scale factor to either enlarge or reduce the figure. A dilation in which the figure becomes smaller can also be called a **compression**.

- A **scale factor** is a multiple of the lengths of the sides from one figure to the dilated figure. The scale factor remains constant in a dilation.

- If the scale factor is larger than 1, then the figure is enlarged.

- If the scale factor is between 0 and 1, then the figure is reduced.

- To calculate the scale factor, divide the length of the sides of the image by the lengths of the sides of the preimage.

- A vertical stretch or compression preserves the horizontal distance of a figure, but changes the vertical distance.

- A horizontal stretch or compression preserves the vertical distance of a figure, but changes the horizontal distance.

- To verify if a figure has undergone a non-rigid motion, compare the lengths of the sides of the figure. If the sides remain congruent, only rigid motions have been performed.

- If the side lengths of a figure have changed, non-rigid motions have occurred.

Non-Rigid Motions		
Dilations	**Vertical transformations**	**Horizontal transformations**
Enlargement/reduction	Stretch/compression	Stretch/compression
Compare $\triangle ABC$ with $\triangle DEF$. The size of each side changes by a constant scale factor. The angle measures have stayed the same.	Compare $\triangle ABC$ with $\triangle ADC$. The vertical distance changes by a scale factor. The horizontal distance remains the same. Two of the angles have changed measures.	Compare $\triangle ABC$ with $\triangle ABD$. The horizontal distance changes by a scale factor. The vertical distance remains the same. Two of the angles have changed measures.

Guided Practice 5.5.2

Example 1

Determine if the two figures below are congruent by identifying the transformations that have taken place.

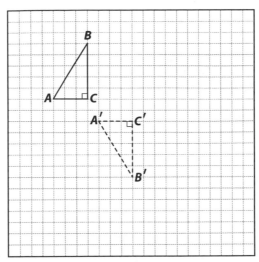

1. Determine the lengths of the sides.

   For the horizontal and vertical legs, count the number of units for the length. For the hypotenuse, use the Pythagorean Theorem, $a^2 + b^2 = c^2$, for which a and b are the legs and c is the hypotenuse.

$AC = 3$	$A'C' = 3$
$CB = 5$	$C'B' = 5$
$AC^2 + CB^2 = AB^2$	$A'C'^2 + C'B'^2 = A'B'^2$
$3^2 + 5^2 = AB^2$	$3^2 + 5^2 = A'B'^2$
$34 = AB^2$	$34 = A'B'^2$
$\sqrt{34} = \sqrt{AB^2}$	$\sqrt{34} = \sqrt{A'B'^2}$
$AB = \sqrt{34}$	$A'B' = \sqrt{34}$

   The sides in the first triangle are congruent to the sides of the second triangle. *Note*: When taking the square root of both sides of the equation, reject the negative value since the value is a distance and distance can only be positive.

2. Identify the transformations that have occurred.

The orientation has changed, indicating a rotation or a reflection.

The second triangle is a mirror image of the first, but translated to the right 4 units.

The triangle has undergone rigid motions: reflection and translation.

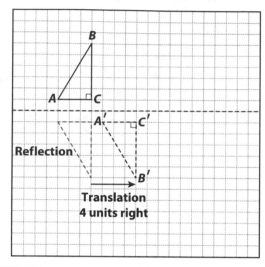

3. State the conclusion.

The triangle has undergone two rigid motions: reflection and translation. Rigid motions preserve size and shape. The triangles are congruent.

Example 2

Determine if the two figures below are congruent by identifying the transformations that have taken place.

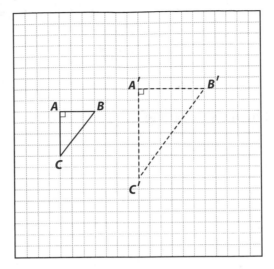

1. Determine the lengths of the sides.

    For the horizontal and vertical legs, count the number of units for the length. For the hypotenuse, use the Pythagorean Theorem, $a^2 + b^2 = c^2$, for which a and b are the legs and c is the hypotenuse.

$AB = 3$	$A'B' = 6$
$AC = 4$	$A'C' = 8$
$AB^2 + AC^2 = CB^2$	$A'B'^2 + A'C'^2 = C'B'^2$
$3^2 + 4^2 = CB^2$	$6^2 + 8^2 = C'B'^2$
$25 = CB^2$	$100 = C'B'^2$
$\sqrt{25} = \sqrt{CB^2}$	$\sqrt{100} = \sqrt{C'B'^2}$
$CB = \sqrt{25}$	$C'B' = \sqrt{100}$
$CB = 5$	$C'B' = 10$

    The sides in the first triangle are not congruent to the sides of the second triangle. They are not the same size.

2. Identify the transformations that have occurred.

The orientation has stayed the same, indicating translation, dilation, stretching, or compression. The vertical and horizontal distances have changed. This could indicate a dilation.

3. Calculate the scale factor of the changes in the side lengths.

Divide the image side lengths by the preimage side lengths.

$$\frac{A'B'}{AB} = \frac{6}{3} = 2$$

$$\frac{A'C'}{AC} = \frac{8}{4} = 2$$

$$\frac{C'B'}{CB} = \frac{10}{5} = 2$$

The scale factor is constant between each pair of sides in the preimage and image. The scale factor is 2, indicating a dilation. Since the scale factor is greater than 1, this is an enlargement.

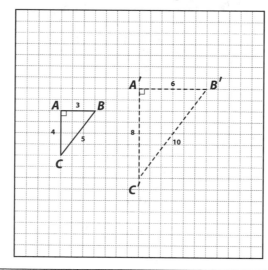

4. State the conclusion.

The triangle has undergone at least one non-rigid motion: a dilation. Specifically, the dilation is an enlargement with a scale factor of 2. The triangles are not congruent because dilation does not preserve the size of the original triangle.

Example 3

Determine if the two figures below are congruent by identifying the transformations that have taken place.

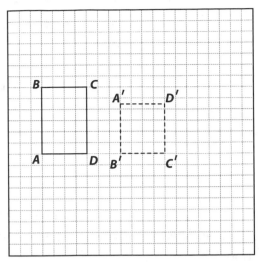

1. Determine the lengths of the sides.

   For the horizontal and vertical sides, count the number of units for the length.

$AB = 6$	$A'B' = 4.5$
$BC = 4$	$B'C' = 4$
$CD = 6$	$C'D' = 4.5$
$DA = 4$	$D'A' = 4$

   Two of the sides in the first rectangle are not congruent to two of the sides of the second rectangle. Two sides are congruent in the first and second rectangles.

2. Identify the transformations that have occurred.

The orientation has changed, and two side lengths have changed. The change in side length indicates at least one non-rigid motion has occurred. Since not all pairs of sides have changed in length, the non-rigid motion must be a horizontal or vertical stretch or compression.

The image has been reflected since $\overline{BC}$ lies at the top of the preimage and $\overline{B'C'}$ lies at the bottom of the image. Reflections are rigid motions. However, one non-rigid motion makes the figures not congruent. A non-rigid motion has occurred since not all the sides in the image are congruent to the sides in the preimage.

The vertical lengths have changed, while the horizontal lengths have remained the same. This means the transformation must be a vertical transformation.

3. Calculate the scale factor of the change in the vertical sides.

Divide the image side lengths by the preimage side lengths.

$$\frac{A'B'}{AB} = \frac{4.5}{6} = 0.75$$

$$\frac{C'D'}{CD} = \frac{4.5}{6} = 0.75$$

The vertical sides have a scale factor of 0.75. The scale factor is between 0 and 1, indicating compression. Since only the vertical sides changed, this is a vertical compression.

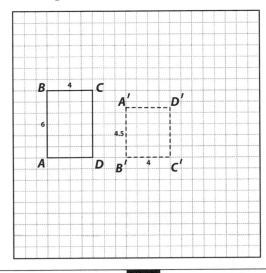

4. State the conclusion.

The vertical sides of the rectangle have undergone at least one non-rigid transformation of a vertical compression. The vertical sides have been reduced by a scale factor of 0.75. Since a non-rigid motion occurred, the figures are not congruent.

Example 4

Determine if the two figures below are congruent by identifying the transformations that have taken place.

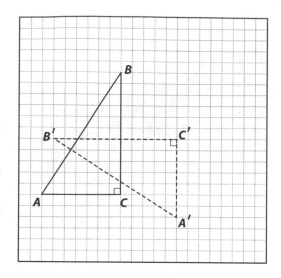

1. Determine the lengths of the sides.

    For the horizontal and vertical sides, count the number of units for the length. For the hypotenuse, use the Pythagorean Theorem, $a^2 + b^2 = c^2$, for which a and b are the legs and c is the hypotenuse.

$BC = 11$	$B'C' = 11$
$CA = 7$	$C'A' = 7$
$BC^2 + CA^2 = AB^2$	$B'C'^2 + C'A'^2 = A'B'^2$
$11^2 + 7^2 = AB^2$	$11^2 + 7^2 = A'B'^2$
$170 = AB^2$	$170 = A'B'^2$
$\sqrt{170} = \sqrt{AB^2}$	$\sqrt{170} = \sqrt{A'B'^2}$
$AB = \sqrt{170}$	$A'B' = \sqrt{170}$

    The sides of the first triangle are congruent to the sides of the second triangle.

2. Identify the transformations that have occurred.

The orientation has changed and all side lengths have stayed the same. This indicates a reflection or a rotation. The preimage and image are not mirror images of each other. Therefore, the transformation that occurred is a rotation.

3. State the conclusion.

Rotations are rigid motions and rigid motions preserve size and shape. The two figures are congruent.

Practice 5.5.2: Defining Congruence in Terms of Rigid Motions

For problems 1–6, determine if the two given figures are congruent by identifying the transformation(s) that occurred. State whether each transformation is rigid or non-rigid.

1.

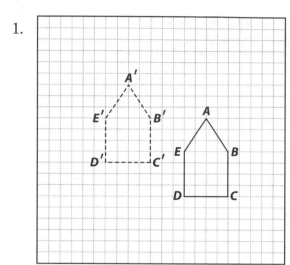

2.

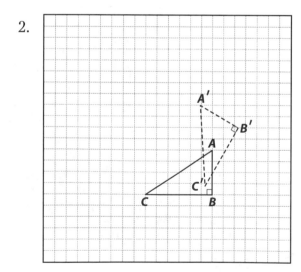

continued

UNIT 5 • CONGRUENCE, PROOF, AND CONSTRUCTIONS
Lesson 5: Exploring Congruence

3.

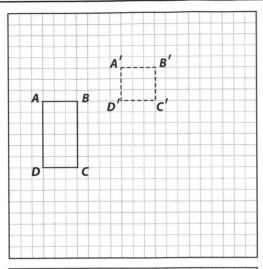

4.

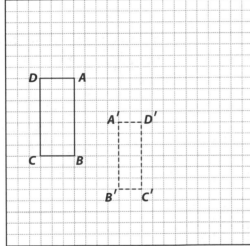

5.

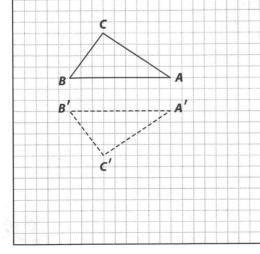

UNIT 5 • CONGRUENCE, PROOF, AND CONSTRUCTIONS
Lesson 5: Exploring Congruence

6.

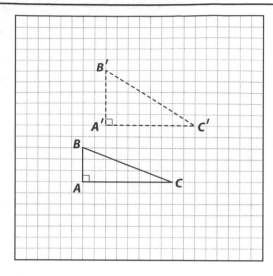

7. A wall bracket is used to hang heavy objects as pictured below. Describe the transformations that have taken place and determine whether the triangles are congruent in terms of rigid and non-rigid motions.

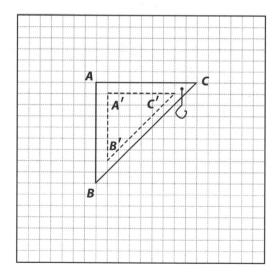

continued

8. A game at a carnival requires the player to throw baseballs at targets represented by $\triangle ABC$, pictured below. $\triangle A'B'C'$ represents the position of the target after it is hit. The point represents the target's hinge. Describe the transformations that have taken place and determine whether the triangles are congruent in terms of rigid and non-rigid motions.

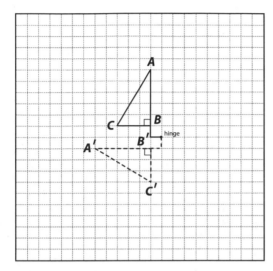

9. Graphic designers often use transformations to create their art. Describe the transformations that have taken place and determine whether the figures are congruent in terms of rigid and non-rigid motions.

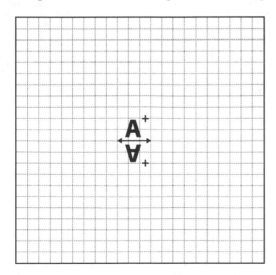

10. A door with windowpanes is pictured below. Describe the transformations of pane 1 that took place to create each of the other 5 panes. Are the panes congruent? Justify your answers in terms of rigid and non-rigid motions.

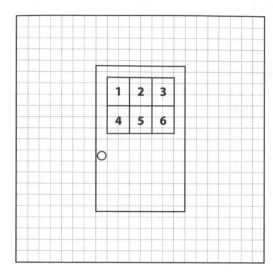

Lesson 6: Congruent Triangles

Common Core State Standards

G–CO.7	Use the definition of congruence in terms of rigid motions to show that two triangles are congruent if and only if corresponding pairs of sides and corresponding pairs of angles are congruent.
G–CO.8	Explain how the criteria for triangle congruence (ASA, SAS, and SSS) follow from the definition of congruence in terms of rigid motions.

Essential Questions

1. Why is it important to know how to mark congruence on a diagram?

2. What does it mean if two triangles are congruent?

3. If two triangles have two sides and one angle that are equivalent, can congruence be determined?

4. How many equivalent measures are needed to determine if triangles are congruent?

WORDS TO KNOW

angle-side-angle (ASA)	if two angles and the included side of one triangle are congruent to two angles and the included side of another triangle, then the two triangles are congruent
congruent angles	two angles that have the same measure
congruent sides	two sides that have the same length
congruent triangles	triangles having the same angle measures and side lengths
corresponding angles	a pair of angles in a similar position
Corresponding Parts of Congruent Triangles are Congruent (CPCTC)	if two or more triangles are proven congruent, then all of their corresponding parts are congruent as well
corresponding sides	the sides of two figures that lie in the same position relative to the figures
included angle	the angle between two sides

included side	the side between two angles of a triangle
postulate	a true statement that does not require a proof
rigid motion	a transformation done to an object that maintains the object's shape and size or its segment lengths and angle measures
side-angle-side (SAS)	if two sides and the included angle of one triangle are congruent to two sides and the included angle of another triangle, then the two triangles are congruent
side-side-side (SSS)	if three sides of one triangle are congruent to three sides of another triangle, then the two triangles are congruent

Recommended Resources

- Illuminations. "Congruence Theorems."

  http://www.walch.com/rr/00013

  This site allows users to investigate congruence postulates by manipulating parts of a triangle.

- Math Open Reference. "Congruent Triangles."

  http://www.walch.com/rr/00014

  This site provides an explanation of congruent triangles, as well as interactive graphics that demonstrate how congruent triangles remain congruent when different transformations are applied.

- Math Warehouse. "Corresponding Sides and Angles: Identify Corresponding Parts."

  http://www.walch.com/rr/00015

  This site explains how to identify corresponding parts of a triangle, and provides interactive questions and answers.

- National Library of Virtual Manipulatives. "Congruent Triangles."

  http://www.walch.com/rr/00016

  This site allows users to construct congruent triangles according to each of the congruence postulates.

Lesson 5.6.1: Triangle Congruency

Introduction

If a rigid motion or a series of rigid motions, including translations, rotations, or reflections, is performed on a triangle, then the transformed triangle is congruent to the original. When two triangles are congruent, the corresponding angles have the same measures and the corresponding sides have the same lengths. It is possible to determine whether triangles are congruent based on the angle measures and lengths of the sides of the triangles.

Key Concepts

- To determine whether two triangles are congruent, you must observe the angle measures and side lengths of the triangles.

- When a triangle is transformed by a series of rigid motions, the angles are images of each other and are called corresponding angles.

- Corresponding angles are a pair of angles in a similar position.

- If two triangles are congruent, then any pair of corresponding angles is also congruent.

- When a triangle is transformed by a series of rigid motions, the sides are also images of each other and are called corresponding sides.

- Corresponding sides are the sides of two figures that lie in the same position relative to the figure.

- If two triangles are congruent, then any pair of corresponding sides is also congruent.

- Congruent triangles have three pairs of corresponding angles and three pairs of corresponding sides, for a total of six pairs of corresponding parts.

- If two or more triangles are proven congruent, then all of their corresponding parts are congruent as well. This postulate is known as **Corresponding Parts of Congruent Triangles are Congruent (CPCTC)**. A **postulate** is a true statement that does not require a proof.

- The corresponding angles and sides can be determined by the order of the letters.

- If $\triangle ABC$ is congruent to $\triangle DEF$, the angles of the two triangles correspond in the same order as they are named.

- Use the symbol → to show that two parts are corresponding.

    Angle A → Angle D; they are equivalent.

    Angle B → Angle E; they are equivalent.

    Angle C → Angle F; they are equivalent.

- The corresponding angles are used to name the corresponding sides.

    $\overline{AB}$ → $\overline{DE}$; they are equivalent.

    $\overline{BC}$ → $\overline{EF}$; they are equivalent.

    $\overline{AC}$ → $\overline{DF}$; they are equivalent.

- Observe the diagrams of $\triangle ABC$ and $\triangle DEF$.

$\triangle ABC \cong \triangle DEF$

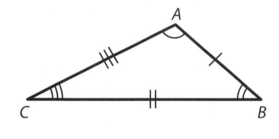

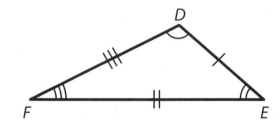

$\angle A \cong \angle D$ $\overline{AB} \cong \overline{DE}$

$\angle B \cong \angle E$ $\overline{BC} \cong \overline{EF}$

$\angle C \cong \angle F$ $\overline{AC} \cong \overline{DF}$

- By observing the angles and sides of two triangles, it is possible to determine if the triangles are congruent.

- Two triangles are congruent if the corresponding angles are congruent and corresponding sides are congruent.

- Notice the number of tick marks on each side of the triangles in the diagram.

- The tick marks show the sides that are congruent.

- Compare the number of tick marks on the sides of $\triangle ABC$ to the tick marks on the sides of $\triangle DEF$.

- Match the number of tick marks on one side of one triangle to the side with the same number of tick marks on the second triangle.

    $\overline{AB}$ and $\overline{DE}$ each have one tick mark, so the two sides are congruent.

    $\overline{BC}$ and $\overline{EF}$ each have two tick marks, so the two sides are congruent.

    $\overline{AC}$ and $\overline{DF}$ each have three tick marks, so the two sides are congruent.

- The arcs on the angles show the angles that are congruent.

- Compare the number of arcs on the angles of $\triangle ABC$ to the number of arcs on the angles of $\triangle DEF$.

- Match the arcs on one angle of one triangle to the angle with the same number of arcs on the second triangle.

    $\angle A$ and $\angle D$ each have one arc, so the two angles are congruent.

    $\angle B$ and $\angle E$ each have two arcs, so the two angles are congruent.

    $\angle C$ and $\angle F$ each have three arcs, so the two angles are congruent.

- If the sides and angles are not labeled as congruent, you can use a ruler and protractor or construction methods to measure each of the angles and sides.

Guided Practice 5.6.1

Example 1

Use corresponding parts to identify the congruent triangles.

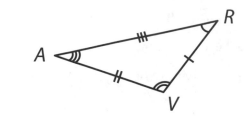

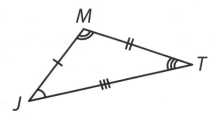

1. Match the number of tick marks to identify the corresponding congruent sides.

    $\overline{RV}$ and $\overline{JM}$ each have one tick mark; therefore, they are corresponding and congruent.

    $\overline{VA}$ and $\overline{MT}$ each have two tick marks; therefore, they are corresponding and congruent.

    $\overline{RA}$ and $\overline{JT}$ each have three tick marks; therefore, they are corresponding and congruent.

2. Match the number of arcs to identify the corresponding congruent angles.

   $\angle R$ and $\angle J$ each have one arc; therefore, the two angles are corresponding and congruent.

   $\angle V$ and $\angle M$ each have two arcs; therefore, the two angles are corresponding and congruent.

   $\angle A$ and $\angle T$ each have three arcs; therefore, the two angles are corresponding and congruent.

3. Order the congruent angles to name the congruent triangles.

   $\triangle RVA$ is congruent to $\triangle JMT$, or $\triangle RVA \cong \triangle JMT$.

   It is also possible to identify the congruent triangles as $\triangle VAR \cong \triangle MTJ$, or even $\triangle ARV \cong \triangle TJM$; whatever order chosen, it is important that the order in which the vertices are listed in the first triangle matches the congruency of the vertices in the second triangle.

   For instance, it is not appropriate to say that $\triangle RVA$ is congruent to $\triangle MJT$ because $\angle R$ is not congruent to $\angle M$.

Example 2

$\triangle BDF \cong \triangle HJL$

Name the corresponding angles and sides of the congruent triangles.

1. Identify the congruent angles.

   The names of the triangles indicate the angles that are corresponding and congruent. Begin with the first letter of each name.

   Identify the first set of congruent angles.

   $\angle B$ is congruent to $\angle H$.

   Identify the second set of congruent angles.

   $\angle D$ is congruent to $\angle J$.

   Identify the third set of congruent angles.

   $\angle F$ is congruent to $\angle L$.

2. Identify the congruent sides.

   The names of the triangles indicate the sides that are corresponding and congruent. Begin with the first two letters of each name.

   Identify the first set of congruent sides.

   $\overline{BD}$ is congruent to $\overline{HJ}$.

   Identify the second set of congruent sides.

   $\overline{DF}$ is congruent to $\overline{JL}$.

   Identify the third set of congruent sides.

   $\overline{BF}$ is congruent to $\overline{HL}$.

Example 3

Use construction tools to determine if the triangles are congruent. If they are, name the congruent triangles and corresponding angles and sides.

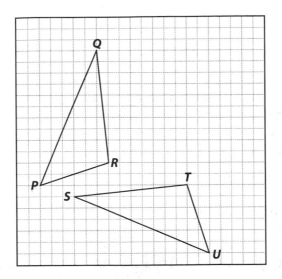

1. Use a compass to compare the length of each side.

    Begin with the shortest sides, $\overline{PR}$ and $\overline{UT}$.

    Set the sharp point of the compass on point P and extend the pencil of the compass to point R.

    Without changing the compass setting, set the sharp point of the compass on point U and extend the pencil of the compass to point T.

    The compass lengths match, so the length of $\overline{UT}$ is equal to $\overline{PR}$; therefore, the two sides are congruent.

    Compare the longest sides, $\overline{PQ}$ and $\overline{US}$.

    Set the sharp point of the compass on point P and extend the pencil of the compass to point Q.

    Without changing the compass setting, set the sharp point of the compass on point U and extend the pencil of the compass to point S.

    The compass lengths match, so the length of $\overline{US}$ is equal to $\overline{PQ}$; therefore, the two sides are congruent.

    (continued)

Compare the last pair of sides, $\overline{QR}$ and $\overline{ST}$.

Set the sharp point of the compass on point Q and extend the pencil of the compass to point R.

Without changing the compass setting, set the sharp point of the compass on point S and extend the pencil of the compass to point T.

The compass lengths match, so the length of $\overline{ST}$ is equal to $\overline{QR}$; therefore, the two sides are congruent.

2. Use a compass to compare the measure of each angle.

Begin with the largest angles, $\angle R$ and $\angle T$.

Set the sharp point of the compass on point R and create a large arc through both sides of $\angle R$.

Without adjusting the compass setting, set the sharp point on point T and create a large arc through both sides of $\angle T$.

Set the sharp point of the compass on one point of intersection and open it so it touches the second point of intersection.

Use this setting to compare the distance between the two points of intersection on the second triangle.

The measure of $\angle R$ is equal to the measure of $\angle T$; therefore, the two angles are congruent.

The measure of $\angle Q$ is equal to the measure of $\angle S$; therefore, the two angles are congruent.

The measure of $\angle P$ is equal to the measure of $\angle U$; therefore, the two angles are congruent.

3. Summarize your findings.

The corresponding and congruent sides include:

$\overline{PR} \cong \overline{UT}$ $\overline{PQ} \cong \overline{US}$ $\overline{QR} \cong \overline{ST}$

The corresponding and congruent angles include:

$\angle R \cong \angle T$ $\angle Q \cong \angle S$ $\angle P \cong \angle U$

Therefore, $\triangle RQP \cong \triangle TSU$.

UNIT 5 • CONGRUENCE, PROOF, AND CONSTRUCTIONS
Lesson 6: Congruent Triangles

Practice 5.6.1: Triangle Congruency

Use the diagrams to correctly name each set of congruent triangles according to their corresponding parts.

1.

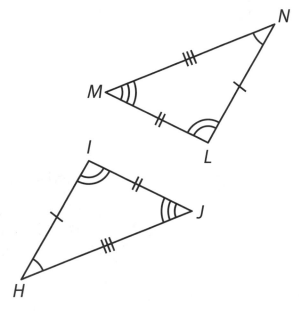

2.

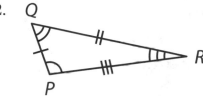

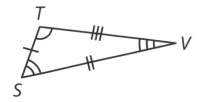

continued

UNIT 5 • CONGRUENCE, PROOF, AND CONSTRUCTIONS
Lesson 6: Congruent Triangles

3.

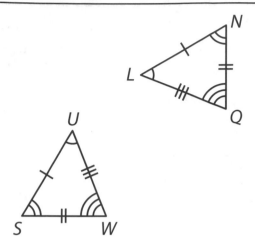

Name the corresponding angles and sides for each pair of congruent triangles.

4. $\triangle HIJ \cong \triangle MNP$

5. $\triangle BDE \cong \triangle HJL$

6. $\triangle NPR \cong \triangle TVX$

Use either a ruler and a protractor or construction tools to determine if the triangles are congruent. If they are, name the congruent triangles and their corresponding angles and sides.

7.   A welder has two pieces of metal to join together. Are the pieces congruent?

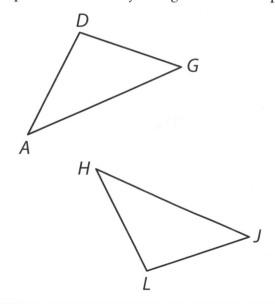

continued

8. The construction of a bridge includes trusses. Two of the trusses are shown below. Are the trusses congruent?

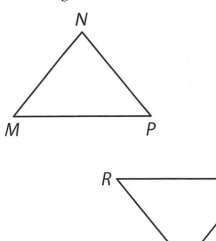

9. Talia is creating a glass mosaic to border her bathroom mirror. She has broken up several pieces of glass, and wants to make sure congruent pieces aren't next to each other. Are the pieces of glass congruent?

continued

UNIT 5 • CONGRUENCE, PROOF, AND CONSTRUCTIONS
Lesson 6: Congruent Triangles

10. A contractor wants to replace a rotted piece of triangular decking with a piece of wood from a recent job. Is the scrap piece of wood congruent to the wood that needs replacement?

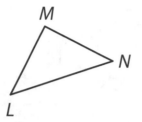

Lesson 5.6.2: Explaining ASA, SAS, and SSS

Introduction

When a series of rigid motions is performed on a triangle, the result is a congruent triangle. When triangles are congruent, the corresponding parts of the triangles are also congruent. It is also true that if the corresponding parts of two triangles are congruent, then the triangles are congruent. It is possible to determine if triangles are congruent by measuring and comparing each angle and side, but this can take time. There is a set of congruence criteria that lets us determine whether triangles are congruent with less information.

Key Concepts

- The criteria for triangle congruence, known as triangle congruence statements, provide the least amount of information needed to determine if two triangles are congruent.

- Each congruence statement refers to the corresponding parts of the triangles.

- By looking at the information about each triangle, you can determine whether the triangles are congruent.

- The **side-side-side (SSS)** congruence statement states that if three sides of one triangle are congruent to three sides of another triangle, then the two triangles are congruent.

- If it is known that the corresponding sides are congruent, it is understood that the corresponding angles are also congruent.

- The **side-angle-side (SAS)** congruence statement states that if two sides and the included angle of one triangle are congruent to two sides and the included angle of another triangle, then the two triangles are congruent.

- The **included angle** is the angle that is between the two congruent sides.

Included angle	Non-included angle
$\angle A$ is included between $\overline{CA}$ and $\overline{AB}$.	$\angle B$ is NOT included between $\overline{CA}$ and $\overline{AB}$.
$\angle D$ is included between $\overline{FD}$ and $\overline{DE}$.	$\angle E$ is NOT included between $\overline{FD}$ and $\overline{DE}$.

- The **angle-side-angle** congruence statement, or **ASA**, states that if two angles and the included side of one triangle are congruent to two angles and the included side of another triangle, then the two triangles are congruent.

- The **included side** is the side that is between the two congruent angles.

Included side	Non-included side
$\overline{AC}$ is included between $\angle C$ and $\angle A$. $\overline{FD}$ is included between $\angle F$ and $\angle D$.	$\overline{CB}$ is NOT included between $\angle C$ and $\angle A$. $\overline{FE}$ is NOT included between $\angle F$ and $\angle D$.

- A fourth congruence statement, angle-angle-side (AAS), states that if two angles and a non-included side of one triangle are congruent to the corresponding two angles and side of a second triangle, then the triangles are congruent.

- This lesson will focus on the first three congruence statements: SSS, SAS, and ASA.

- The following diagram compares these three congruence statements.

Side-Side-Side (SSS)	Side-Angle-Side (SAS)	Angle-Side-Angle (ASA)
$\triangle ABC \cong \triangle XYZ$	$\triangle DEF \cong \triangle TVW$	$\triangle GHJ \cong \triangle QRS$

Guided Practice 5.6.2

Example 1

Determine which congruence statement, if any, can be used to show that $\triangle PQR$ and $\triangle STU$ are congruent.

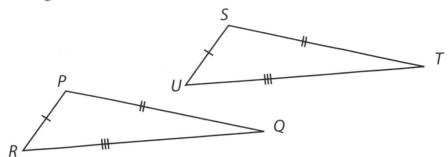

1. Determine which components of the triangles are congruent.

   According to the diagram, $\overline{RP} \cong \overline{US}$, $\overline{PQ} \cong \overline{ST}$, and $\overline{TU} \cong \overline{QR}$.

   Corresponding side lengths of the two triangles are identified as congruent.

2. Determine if this information is enough to state that all six corresponding parts of the two triangles are congruent.

   It is given that all side lengths of the two triangles are congruent; therefore, all their angles are also congruent.

   Because all six corresponding parts of the two triangles are congruent, then the two triangles are congruent.

3. Summarize your findings.

   $\triangle PQR \cong \triangle STU$ because of the congruence statement side-side-side (SSS).

Example 2

Determine which congruence statement, if any, can be used to show that $\triangle ABC$ and $\triangle DEF$ are congruent.

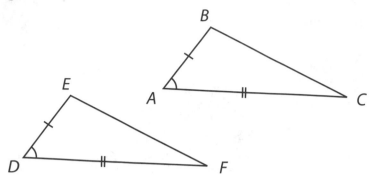

1. Determine which components of the triangles are congruent.

   According to the diagram, $\overline{AB} \cong \overline{DE}$, $\overline{AC} \cong \overline{DF}$, and $\angle A \cong \angle D$.

   Two corresponding side lengths of the two triangles and one corresponding angle are identified as congruent.

2. Determine if this information is enough to state that all six corresponding parts of the two triangles are congruent.

   Notice that the congruent angles are included angles, meaning the angles are between the sides that are marked as congruent.

   It is given that two sides and the included angle are congruent, so the two triangles are congruent.

3. Summarize your findings.

   $\triangle ABC \cong \triangle DEF$ because of the congruence statement side-angle-side (SAS).

Example 3

Determine which congruence statement, if any, can be used to show that $\triangle HIJ$ and $\triangle KLM$ are congruent if $\overline{HI} \cong \overline{KL}$, $\angle H \cong \angle K$, and $\angle I \cong \angle L$.

1. Determine which components of the triangles are congruent.

   One corresponding side length of the two triangles and two corresponding angles are identified as congruent.

   It is often helpful to draw a diagram of the triangles with the given information to see where the congruent side is in relation to the congruent angles.

   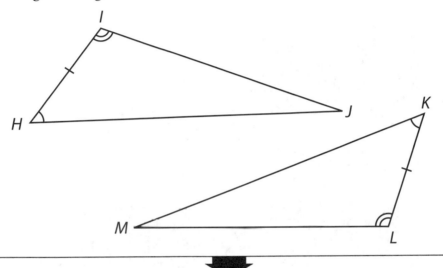

2. Determine if this information is enough to state that all six corresponding parts of the two triangles are congruent.

   Notice that the congruent sides are included sides, meaning the sides are between the angles that are marked as congruent.

   It is given that the two angles and the included side are equivalent, so the two triangles are congruent.

3. Summarize your findings.

   $\triangle HIJ \cong \triangle KLM$ because of the congruence statement angle-side-angle (ASA).

Example 4

Determine which congruence statement, if any, can be used to show that $\triangle PQR$ and $\triangle STU$ are congruent if $\overline{PQ} \cong \overline{ST}$, $\overline{PR} \cong \overline{SU}$, and $\angle Q \cong \angle T$.

1. Determine which components of the triangles are equivalent.

   Two corresponding side lengths of the two triangles and one corresponding angle are identified as congruent.

   Draw a diagram of the triangles with the given information to see where the congruent sides are in relation to the congruent angle.

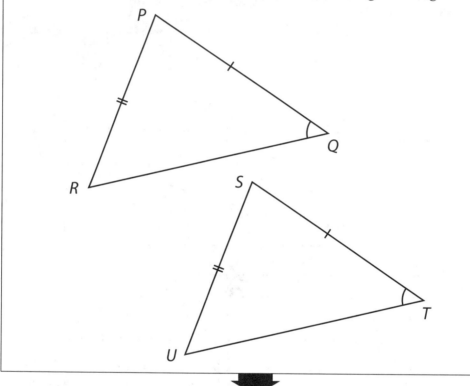

2. Determine if this information is enough to state that all six corresponding parts of the two triangles are congruent.

   Notice that the congruent angles are not included angles, meaning the angles are not between the sides that are marked as congruent.

   There is no congruence statement that allows us to state that the two triangles are congruent based on the given information.

3. Summarize your findings.

   It cannot be determined whether $\triangle PQR$ and $\triangle STU$ are congruent.

Example 5

Determine which congruence statement, if any, can be used to show that $\triangle ABD$ and $\triangle FEC$ are congruent.

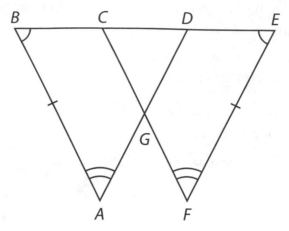

1. Determine which components of the triangles are congruent.

   Notice that the triangles overlap.

   If you have trouble seeing the two triangles, redraw each triangle.

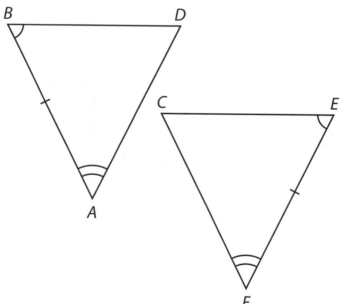

   According to the diagram, $\overline{AB} \cong \overline{FE}$, $\angle A \cong \angle F$, and $\angle B \cong \angle E$.

   One corresponding side length of the two triangles and two corresponding angles are identified as congruent.

2. Determine if this information is enough to state that all six corresponding parts of the two triangles are congruent.

Notice that the congruent sides are included sides, meaning the sides are between the angles that are marked as congruent.

It is given that two angles and the included side are equivalent, so the two triangles are congruent.

3. Summarize your findings.

$\triangle ABD \cong \triangle FEC$ because of the congruence statement angle-side-angle (ASA).

UNIT 5 • CONGRUENCE, PROOF, AND CONSTRUCTIONS
Lesson 6: Congruent Triangles

Practice 5.6.2: Explaining ASA, SAS, and SSS

For each diagram, determine which congruence statement can be used to show that the triangles are congruent. If it is not possible to prove triangle congruence, explain why not.

1.

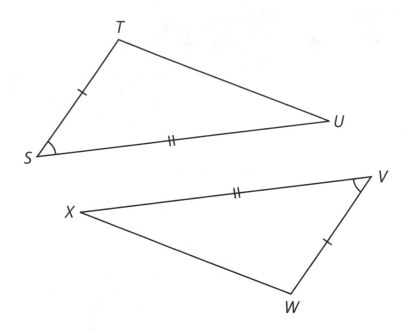

2.

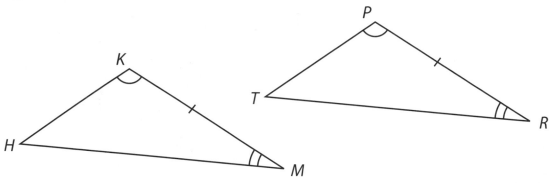

continued

3. Based on the information in the diagram, is $\triangle ABD$ congruent to $\triangle FEC$?

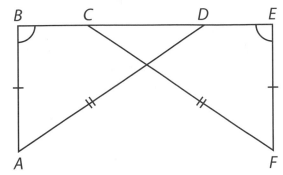

Use the given information to determine which congruence statement can be used to show that the triangles are congruent. If it is not possible to prove triangle congruence, explain why not.

4. $\triangle ABC$ and $\triangle XYZ$: $\angle A \cong \angle X$, $\angle B \cong \angle Y$, and $\overline{AB} \cong \overline{XY}$

5. $\triangle EDF$ and $\triangle GIH$: $\angle F \cong \angle H$, $\overline{ED} \cong \overline{GI}$, and $\overline{EF} \cong \overline{GH}$

6. $\triangle LMN$ and $\triangle PQR$: $\overline{LM} \cong \overline{PQ}$, $\overline{MN} \cong \overline{QR}$, $\overline{LN} \cong \overline{PR}$

7. Nadia is building a model bridge. Based on the information about each truss shown in the diagram below, determine if the triangles are congruent. If so, name the congruent triangles and identify the congruence statement used.

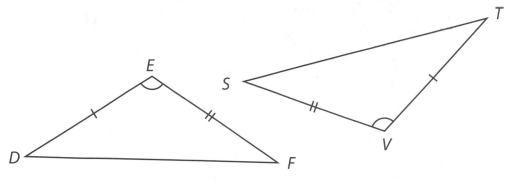

continued

UNIT 5 • CONGRUENCE, PROOF, AND CONSTRUCTIONS
Lesson 6: Congruent Triangles

8. Rashid is constructing a bench and needs two congruent sides. He found two pre-cut pieces of wood, shown in the diagram. Based on the information about each angle, determine if the triangles are congruent. If so, name the congruent triangles and identify the congruence statement used.

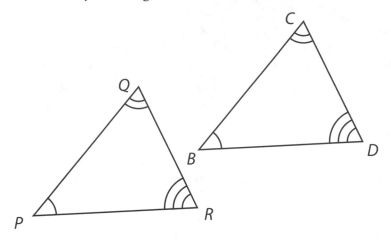

The diagram below represents a quilt design. Before you cut the fabric, you want to determine if certain triangles are congruent. Use the diagram to solve problems 9 and 10.

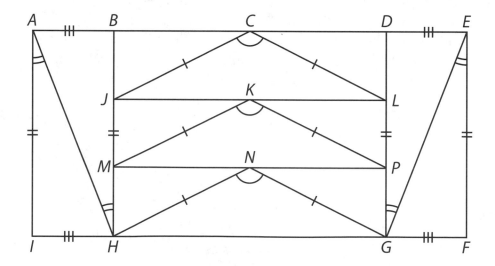

9. Use the information given in the diagram to determine if △HNG and △JCL are congruent. If so, identify the congruence statement used.

10. Use the information given in the diagram to determine if △AIH and △HBA are congruent. If so, identify the congruence statement used.

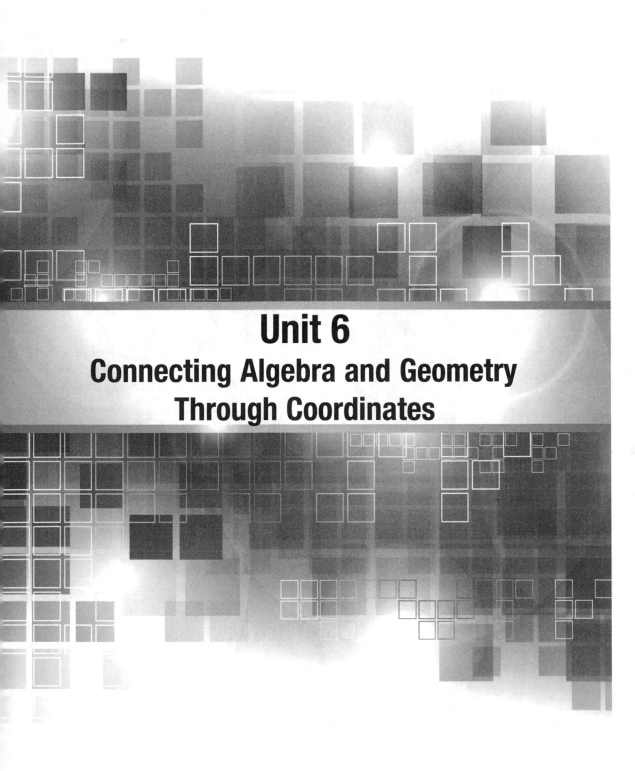

Unit 6
Connecting Algebra and Geometry Through Coordinates

Lesson 1: Slope and Distance

Common Core State Standards

G–GPE.4 Use coordinates to prove simple geometric theorems algebraically. *For example, prove or disprove that a figure defined by four given points in the coordinate plane is a rectangle; prove or disprove that the point $(1, \sqrt{3})$ lies on the circle centered at the origin and containing the point $(0, 2)$.*

G–GPE.5 Prove the slope criteria for parallel and perpendicular lines and use them to solve geometric problems (e.g., find the equation of a line parallel or perpendicular to a given line that passes through a given point).

Essential Questions

1. How is finding the distance between two points in two dimensions similar to finding the distance between two points in one dimension? How is it different?

2. How are the distance formula and the Pythagorean Theorem related?

3. How can algebra be used to explore properties of geometric shapes in the plane?

4. What are real-world applications of slope and the distance formula?

5. Is there a relationship between the slopes of parallel lines?

6. Is there a relationship between the slopes of perpendicular lines?

WORDS TO KNOW

congruent	having the same measure, length, or size
distance formula	a formula that states the distance between points (x_1, y_1) and (x_2, y_2) is equal to $\sqrt{(x_2 - x_1)^2 + (y_2 - y_1)^2}$
parallel	lines that never intersect and have equal slope
parallelogram	a quadrilateral with opposite sides parallel
perpendicular	lines that intersect at a right angle (90°); their slopes are opposite reciprocals
quadrilateral	a polygon with four sides
rectangle	a parallelogram with opposite sides that are congruent and consecutive sides that are perpendicular
rhombus	a parallelogram with four congruent sides

slope	measure of the rate of change of one variable with respect to another variable; $\text{slope} = \dfrac{y_2 - y_1}{x_2 - x_1} = \dfrac{\Delta y}{\Delta x} = \dfrac{\text{rise}}{\text{run}}$
square	a parallelogram with four congruent sides and four right angles

Recommended Resources

- Math Open Reference. "Distance from a point to a line."

  http://walch.com/rr/CAU6L1ShortestDistance

  This site shows how to find the shortest distance from a point to a line, and provides an animation that allows you to manipulate both a point and a line on a coordinate plane to see how the perpendicular distance changes.

- MathsNet. "Interactive Shape."

  http://walch.com/rr/CAU6L1LineRelationships

  Use this animation to determine the relationship between lines.

- Purplemath. "Straight-Line Equations: Parallel and Perpendicular Lines."

  http://walch.com/rr/CAU6L1Straight-LineEquations

  This site summarizes how to write equations that are parallel and perpendicular to a given point.

- University of Puerto Rico. "Practice: Coordinates on the Cartesian Plane."

  http://walch.com/rr/CAU6L1DistancePoints

  Plot coordinates on a Cartesian plane and calculate the distance between the points.

Lesson 6.1.1: Using Coordinates to Prove Geometric Theorems with Slope and Distance

Introduction

It is not uncommon for people to think of geometric figures, such as triangles and quadrilaterals, to be separate from algebra; however, we can understand and prove many geometric concepts by using algebra. In this lesson, you will see how the distance formula originated with the Pythagorean Theorem, as well as how distance between points and the slope of lines can help us to determine specific geometric shapes.

Key Concepts

Calculating the Distance Between Two Points

- To find the distance between two points on a coordinate plane, you have used the Pythagorean Theorem.

    - After creating a right triangle using each point as the end of the hypotenuse, you calculated the vertical height (a) and the horizontal height (b).

    - These lengths were then substituted into the Pythagorean Theorem ($a^2 + b^2 = c^2$) and solved for c.

    - The result was the distance between the two points.

- This is similar to the **distance formula**, which states the distance between points (x_1, y_1) and (x_2, y_2) is equal to $\sqrt{(x_2 - x_1)^2 + (y_2 - y_1)^2}$.

- Using the Pythagorean Theorem:

    - Find the length of a: $|y_2 - y_1|$.

    - Find the length of b: $|x_2 - x_1|$.

    - Substitute these values into the Pythagorean Theorem.

$$c^2 = a^2 + b^2$$
$$c^2 = |y_2 - y_1|^2 + |x_2 - x_1|^2$$
$$c = \sqrt{|y_2 - y_1|^2 + |x_2 - x_1|^2}$$

- Using the distance formula:

$$\text{distance} = \sqrt{(x_2 - x_1)^2 + (y_2 - y_1)^2}$$

- We will see in the Guided Practice an example that proves the calculations will result in the same distance.

Calculating Slope

- To find the **slope**, or steepness of a line, calculate the change in y divided by the change in x using the formula $m = \dfrac{y_2 - y_1}{x_2 - x_1}$.

Parallel and Perpendicular Lines

- **Parallel lines** are lines that never intersect and have equal slope.

  - To prove that two lines are parallel, you must show that the slopes of both lines are equal.

- **Perpendicular lines** are lines that intersect at a right angle (90°). The slopes of perpendicular lines are always opposite reciprocals.

  - To prove that two lines are perpendicular, you must show that the slopes of both lines are opposite reciprocals.

  - When the slopes are multiplied, the result will always be –1.

  - Horizontal and vertical lines are always perpendicular to each other.

Guided Practice 6.1.1

Example 1

Calculate the distance between the points (4, 9) and (–2, 6) using both the Pythagorean Theorem and the distance formula.

1. To use the Pythagorean Theorem, first plot the points on a coordinate system.

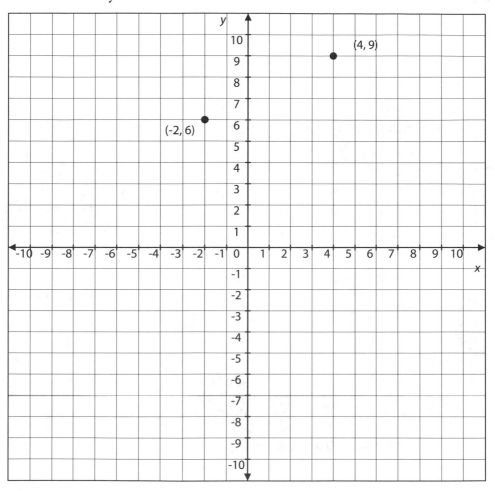

2. Draw lines to form a right triangle, using each point as the end of the hypotenuse.

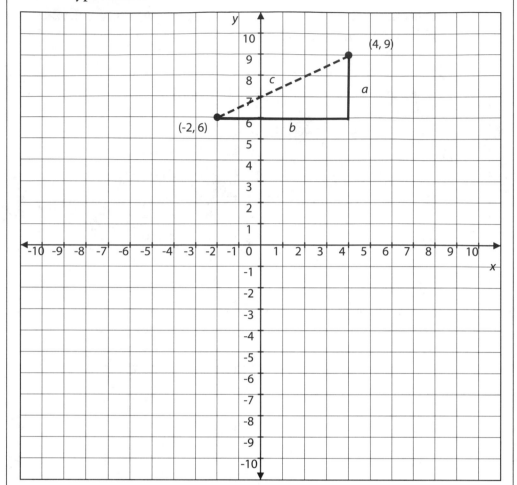

3. Calculate the length of the vertical side, a, of the right triangle.

Let $(x_1, y_1) = (4, 9)$ and $(x_2, y_2) = (-2, 6)$.

$$|y_2 - y_1| = |6 - 9| = |-3| = 3$$

The length of side a is 3 units.

4. Calculate the length of the horizontal side, b, of the right triangle.

$$|x_2 - x_1| = |-2 - 4| = |-6| = 6$$

The length of side b is 6 units.

5. Use the Pythagorean Theorem to calculate the length of the hypotenuse, c.

$a^2 + b^2 = c^2$	Pythagorean Theorem
$3^2 + 6^2 = c^2$	Substitute values for a and b.
$9 + 36 = c^2$	Simplify each term.
$45 = c^2$	Simplify.
$\sqrt{45} = \sqrt{c^2}$	Take the square root of both sides of the equation.
$c = \sqrt{45} \approx 6.7$	

The distance between the points (4, 9) and (–2, 6) is $\sqrt{45}$, or approximately 6.7 units.

6. Now use the distance formula to calculate the distance between the same points, (4, 9) and (–2, 6).

Let $(x_1, y_1) = (4, 9)$ and $(x_2, y_2) = (-2, 6)$.

$\sqrt{(x_2 - x_1)^2 + (y_2 - y_1)^2}$	Distance formula
$\sqrt{(-2 - 4)^2 + (6 - 9)^2}$	Substitute (4, 9) and (–2, 6).
$\sqrt{(-6)^2 + (-3)^2}$	Simplify.
$\sqrt{36 + 9}$	Evaluate squares.
$\sqrt{45}$	Simplify.

The distance between the points (4, 9) and (–2, 6) is $\sqrt{45}$ units, or approximately 6.7 units.

Both calculations will produce the same results each time.

Example 2

Determine if the line through the points (–8, 5) and (–5, 3) is parallel to the line through the points (1, 3) and (4, 1).

1. Plot the lines on a coordinate plane.

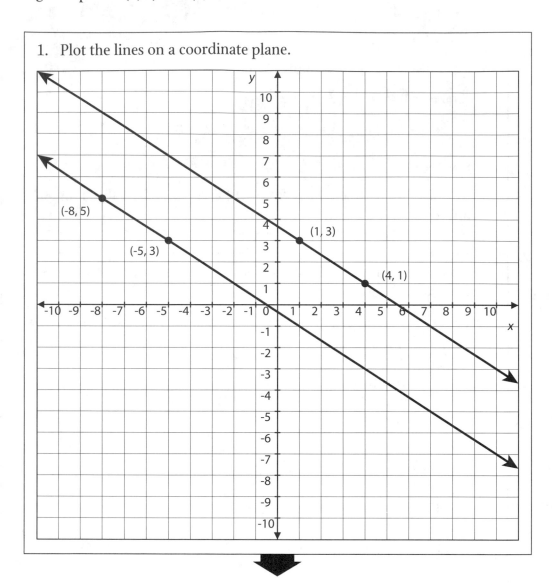

2. Calculate the slope of the line through the points (–8, 5) and (–5, 3).

   Let $(x_1, y_1) = (–8, 5)$ and $(x_2, y_2) = (–5, 3)$.

   Substitute these values into the slope formula.

   $$m = \frac{y_2 - y_1}{x_2 - x_1}$$ Original formula

   $$= \frac{(3) - (5)}{(–5) - (–8)}$$ Substitute (x_1, y_1) and (x_2, y_2).

   $$= -\frac{2}{3}$$ Simplify.

   The slope of the line through the points (–8, 5) and (–5, 3) is $-\frac{2}{3}$.

3. Calculate the slope of the line through the points (1, 3) and (4, 1).

   Let $(x_1, y_1) = (1, 3)$ and $(x_2, y_2) = (4, 1)$.

   Substitute these values into the slope formula.

   $$m = \frac{y_2 - y_1}{x_2 - x_1}$$ Original formula

   $$= \frac{(1) - (3)}{(4) - (1)}$$ Substitute (x_1, y_1) and (x_2, y_2).

   $$= -\frac{2}{3}$$ Simplify.

   The slope of the line through the points (1, 3) and (4, 1) is $-\frac{2}{3}$.

4. Determine if the lines are parallel.

   Parallel lines have equal slope.

   The slope of each line is $-\frac{2}{3}$; therefore, the lines are parallel.

Example 3

Determine if the line through the points (0, 8) and (4, 9) is perpendicular to the line through the points (–9, 10) and (–8, 6).

1. Plot the lines on a coordinate plane.

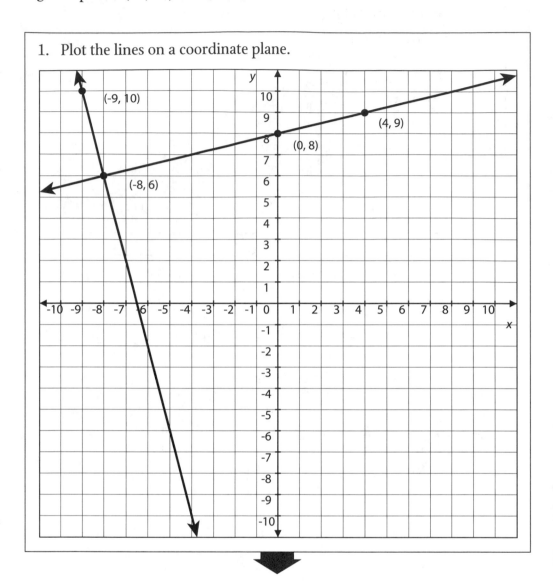

2. Calculate the slope of the line through the points (0, 8) and (4, 9).

   Let $(x_1, y_1) = (0, 8)$ and $(x_2, y_2) = (4, 9)$.

   Substitute these values into the slope formula.

   $m = \dfrac{y_2 - y_1}{x_2 - x_1}$ Original formula

   $= \dfrac{(9) - (8)}{(4) - (0)}$ Substitute (x_1, y_1) and (x_2, y_2).

   $= \dfrac{1}{4}$ Simplify.

   The slope of the line through the points (0, 8) and (4, 9) is $\dfrac{1}{4}$.

3. Calculate the slope of the line through the points (–9, 10) and (–8, 6).

   Let $(x_1, y_1) = (-9, 10)$ and $(x_2, y_2) = (-8, 6)$.

   Substitute these values into the slope formula.

   $m = \dfrac{y_2 - y_1}{x_2 - x_1}$ Original formula

   $= \dfrac{(6) - (10)}{(-8) - (-9)}$ Substitute (x_1, y_1) and (x_2, y_2).

   $= -\dfrac{4}{1} = -4$ Simplify.

   The slope of the line through the points (–9, 10) and (–8, 6) is –4.

4. Determine if the lines are perpendicular.

Perpendicular lines have slopes that are opposite reciprocals.

The slope of the first line is $\dfrac{1}{4}$.

The reciprocal of $\dfrac{1}{4}$ is $\dfrac{4}{1}$ or 4.

The opposite of 4 is –4.

The slope of the second line is –4.

The product of the two slopes is –1.

The slopes of the lines are opposite reciprocals; therefore, the lines are perpendicular.

Example 4

A right triangle is defined as a triangle with 2 sides that are perpendicular. Triangle *ABC* has vertices *A* (–4, 8), *B* (–1, 2), and *C* (7, 6). Determine if this triangle is a right triangle. When disproving a figure, you only need to show one condition is not met.

1. Plot the triangle on a coordinate plane.

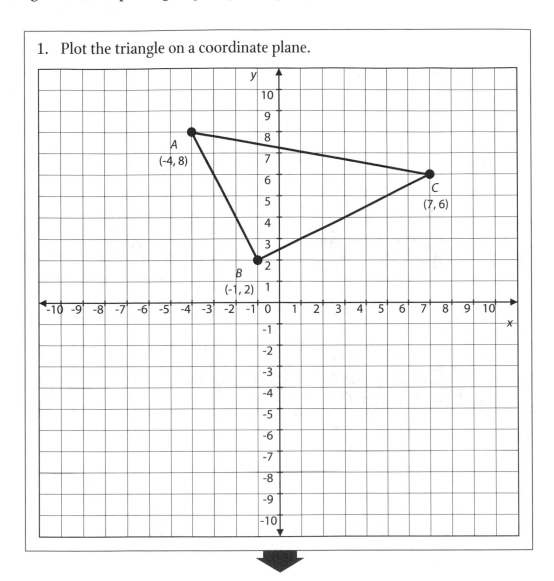

2. Calculate the slope of each side using the general slope formula,
$$m = \frac{y_2 - y_1}{x_2 - x_1}.$$

$$\text{slope of } \overline{AB} = \frac{(2)-(8)}{(-1)-(-4)} = \frac{-6}{3} = -2$$

$$\text{slope of } \overline{BC} = \frac{(6)-(2)}{(7)-(-1)} = \frac{4}{8} = \frac{1}{2}$$

$$\text{slope of } \overline{AC} = \frac{(6)-(8)}{(7)-(-4)} = \frac{-2}{11} = -\frac{2}{11}$$

3. Observe the slopes of each side.

The slope of $\overline{AB}$ is –2 and the slope of $\overline{BC}$ is $\frac{1}{2}$.

These slopes are opposite reciprocals of each other and are perpendicular.

4. Make connections.

Right triangles have two sides that are perpendicular.

Triangle ABC has two sides that are perpendicular; therefore, it is a right triangle.

Example 5

A square is a quadrilateral with two pairs of parallel opposite sides, consecutive sides that are perpendicular, and all sides **congruent**, meaning they have the same length. Quadrilateral $ABCD$ has vertices A (-1, 2), B (1, 5), C (4, 3), and D (2, 0). Determine if this quadrilateral is a square.

1. Plot the quadrilateral on a coordinate plane.

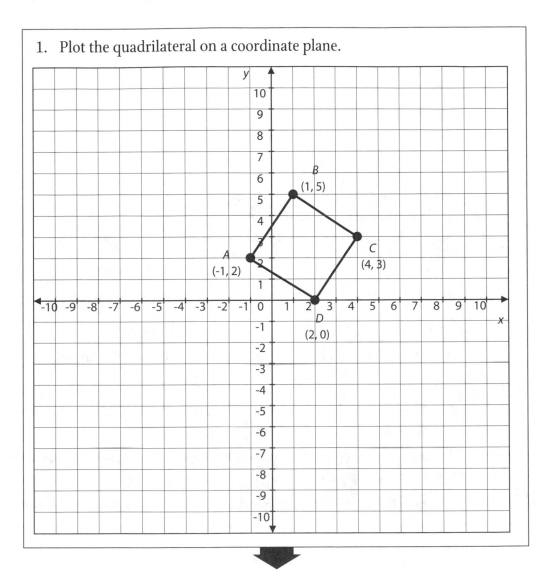

2. First show the figure has two pairs of parallel opposite sides.

    Calculate the slope of each side using the general slope formula,

    $$m = \frac{y_2 - y_1}{x_2 - x_1}.$$

    slope of $\overline{AB} = \dfrac{(5)-(2)}{(1)-(-1)} = \dfrac{3}{2}$

    slope of $\overline{BC} = \dfrac{(3)-(5)}{(4)-(1)} = \dfrac{-2}{3} = -\dfrac{2}{3}$

    slope of $\overline{CD} = \dfrac{(0)-(3)}{(2)-(4)} = \dfrac{-3}{-2} = \dfrac{3}{2}$

    slope of $\overline{AD} = \dfrac{(0)-(2)}{(2)-(-1)} = \dfrac{-2}{3} = -\dfrac{2}{3}$

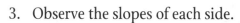

3. Observe the slopes of each side.

    The side opposite $\overline{AB}$ is $\overline{CD}$. The slopes of these sides are the same.

    The side opposite $\overline{BC}$ is $\overline{AD}$. The slopes of these sides are the same.

    The quadrilateral has two pairs of parallel opposite sides.

    $\overline{AB}$ and $\overline{BC}$ are consecutive sides. The slopes of the sides are opposite reciprocals.

    $\overline{BC}$ and $\overline{CD}$ are consecutive sides. The slopes of the sides are opposite reciprocals.

    $\overline{CD}$ and $\overline{AD}$ are consecutive sides. The slopes of the sides are opposite reciprocals.

    $\overline{AB}$ and $\overline{AD}$ are consecutive sides. The slopes of the sides are opposite reciprocals.

    Consecutive sides are perpendicular.

4. Show that the quadrilateral has four congruent sides.

Find the length of each side using the distance formula,

$$d=\sqrt{(x_2-x_1)^2+(y_2-y_1)^2} \; .$$

length of $\overline{AB}=\sqrt{(1-(-1))^2+(5-2)^2}=\sqrt{(2)^2+(3)^2}=\sqrt{4+9}=\sqrt{13}$

length of $\overline{BC}=\sqrt{(4-1)^2+(3-5)^2}=\sqrt{(3)^2+(-2)^2}=\sqrt{9+4}=\sqrt{13}$

length of $\overline{CD}=\sqrt{(2-4)^2+(0-3)^2}=\sqrt{(-2)^2+(-3)^2}=\sqrt{4+9}=\sqrt{13}$

length of $\overline{AD}=\sqrt{(2-(-1))^2+(0-2)^2}=\sqrt{(3)^2+(-2)^2}=\sqrt{9+4}=\sqrt{13}$

The lengths of all 4 sides are congruent.

5. Make connections.

A square is a quadrilateral with two pairs of parallel opposite sides, consecutive sides that are perpendicular, and all sides congruent.

Quadrilateral $ABCD$ has two pairs of parallel opposite sides, the consecutive sides are perpendicular, and all the sides are congruent. It is a square.

UNIT 6 • CONNECTING ALGEBRA AND GEOMETRY THROUGH COORDINATES

Lesson 1: Slope and Distance

Practice 6.1.1: Using Coordinates to Prove Geometric Theorems with Slope and Distance

Use the distance formula to calculate the distance between the points indicated.

1. $(2, 3)$ and $(-2, 5)$

2. $(7, -2)$ and $(8, -9)$

A right triangle has two perpendicular sides. Graph each triangle and then determine if each one is a right triangle. Use the slope formula and/or distance formula to justify your answer.

3. $A (0, -1)$, $B (1, 4)$, and $C (3, 1)$

4. $A (-3, -3)$, $B (4, 1)$, and $C (3, -4)$

A parallelogram is a quadrilateral with opposite sides parallel. Graph each quadrilateral and then determine if each one is a parallelogram. Use the slope formula and/or distance formula to justify your answer.

5. $A (0, 0)$, $B (1, 5)$, $C (4, 6)$, and $D (3, 0)$

6. $A (-1, 1)$, $B (1, 3)$, $C (4, -2)$, and $D (2, -4)$

A rectangle is a parallelogram with opposite sides that are congruent and consecutive sides that are perpendicular. Graph each quadrilateral and then determine if each one is a rectangle. Use the slope formula and/or distance formula to justify your answer.

7. $A (-3, -4)$, $B (-1, -2)$, $C (4, -7)$, and $D (2, -9)$

8. $A (-2, -3)$, $B (-4, 2)$, $C (6, 6)$, and $D (3, -1)$

A square is a parallelogram with four congruent sides and four right angles. Graph each quadrilateral and then determine if each one is a square. Use the slope formula and/or distance formula to justify your answer.

9. $A (1, 0)$, $B (4, 4)$, $C (8, 1)$, and $D (5, -3)$

10. $A (-2, 5)$, $B (2, 6)$, $C (4, -2)$, and $D (0, -3)$

Lesson 6.1.2: Working with Parallel and Perpendicular Lines

Introduction

The slopes of parallel lines are always equal, whereas the slopes of perpendicular lines are always opposite reciprocals. It is important to be able to determine whether lines are parallel or perpendicular, but the creation of parallel and perpendicular lines is also important. In this lesson, you will write the equations of lines that are parallel and perpendicular to a given line through a given point.

Key Concepts

- You can write the equation of a line through a given point that is parallel to a given line if you know the equation of the given line. It is necessary to identify the slope of the given equation before trying to write the equation of the line that is parallel or perpendicular.

- Writing the given equation in slope-intercept form allows you to quickly identify the slope, m, of the equation.

- If the given equation is not in slope-intercept form, take a few moments to rewrite it.

Writing Equations Parallel to a Given Line Through a Given Point
1. Rewrite the given equation in slope-intercept form if necessary.
2. Identify the slope of the given line.
3. Write the general point-slope form of a linear equation: $y - y_1 = m(x - x_1)$.
4. Substitute the slope of the given line for m in the general equation.
5. Substitute x and y from the given point into the general equation for x_1 and y_1.
6. Simplify the equation.
7. Rewrite the equation in slope-intercept form if necessary.

- Writing the equation of a line perpendicular to a given line through a given point is similar to writing equations of parallel lines.

- The slopes of perpendicular lines are opposite reciprocals.

Writing Equations Perpendicular to a Given Line Through a Given Point

1. Rewrite the given equation in slope-intercept form if necessary.

2. Identify the slope of the given line.

3. Find the opposite reciprocal of the slope of the given line.

4. Write the general point-slope form of a linear equation:
   $y - y_1 = m(x - x_1)$.

5. Substitute the opposite reciprocal of the given line for m in the general equation.

6. Substitute x and y from the given point into the general equation for x_1 and y_1.

7. Simplify the equation.

8. Rewrite the equation in slope-intercept form if necessary.

- The shortest distance between two points is a line.

- The shortest distance between a given point and a given line is the line segment that is perpendicular to the given line through the given point.

Finding the Shortest Distance Between a Given Point and a Given Line

1. Follow the steps outlined previously to find the equation of the line that is perpendicular to the given line through the given point.

2. Find the intersection between the two lines by setting the given equation and the equation of the perpendicular line equal to each other.

3. Solve for x.

4. Substitute the x-value into the equation of the given line to find the y-value.

5. Find the distance between the given point and the point of intersection of the given line and the perpendicular line using the distance formula,
   $\sqrt{(x_2 - x_1)^2 + (y_2 - y_1)^2}$.

Guided Practice 6.1.2

Example 1

Write the slope-intercept form of an equation for the line that passes through the point $(5, -2)$ and is parallel to the graph of $8x - 2y = 6$.

1. Rewrite the given equation in slope-intercept form.

$8x - 2y = 6$	Given equation
$-2y = 6 - 8x$	Subtract $8x$ from both sides.
$y = -3 + 4x$	Divide both sides by -2.
$y = 4x - 3$	Write the equation in slope-intercept form.

2. Identify the slope of the given line.

   The slope of the line $y = 4x - 3$ is 4.

3. Substitute the slope of the given line for m in the point-slope form of a linear equation.

$y - y_1 = m(x - x_1)$	Point-slope form
$y - y_1 = 4(x - x_1)$	Substitute m from the given equation.

4. Substitute x and y from the given point into the equation for x_1 and y_1.

$y - y_1 = 4(x - x_1)$	Equation
$y - (-2) = 4(x - 5)$	Substitute $(5, -2)$ for x_1 and y_1.

5. Simplify the equation.

$$y - (-2) = 4(x - 5) \qquad \text{Equation with substituted values for } x_1 \text{ and } y_1$$

$$y - (-2) = 4x - 20 \qquad \text{Distribute 4 over } (x - 5).$$

$$y + 2 = 4x - 20 \qquad \text{Simplify.}$$

$$y = 4x - 22 \qquad \text{Subtract 2 from both sides.}$$

The equation of the line through the point (5, −2) that is parallel to the equation $8x - 2y = 6$ is $y = 4x - 22$.

This can be seen on the following graph.

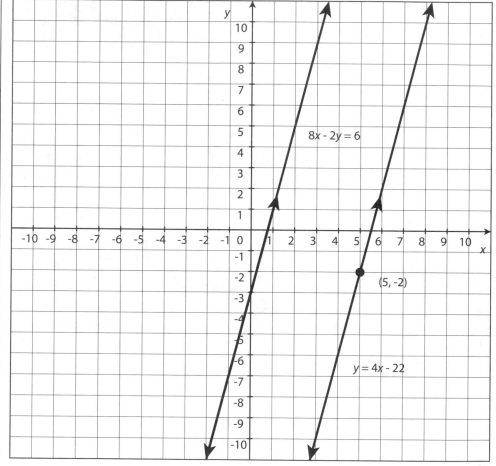

Example 2

Write the slope-intercept form of an equation for the line that passes through the point (–1, 6) and is perpendicular to the graph of $-10x + 5y = 20$.

1. Rewrite the given equation in slope-intercept form.

$-10x + 5y = 20$	Given equation
$5y = 20 + 10x$	Add $10x$ to both sides.
$y = 4 + 2x$	Divide both sides by 5.
$y = 2x + 4$	Write the equation in slope-intercept form.

2. Identify the slope of the given line.

   The slope of the line $y = 2x + 4$ is 2.

3. Find the opposite reciprocal of the slope of the given line.

   The slope of the given line is 2.

   The opposite of 2 is –2.

   The reciprocal of –2 is $-\dfrac{1}{2}$.

4. Substitute the opposite reciprocal for m in the point-slope form of a linear equation.

$y - y_1 = m(x - x_1)$	Point-slope form
$y - y_1 = -\dfrac{1}{2}(x - x_1)$	Substitute m from the given equation.

5. Substitute x and y from the given point into the equation for x_1 and y_1.

$y - y_1 = -\dfrac{1}{2}(x - x_1)$	Equation
$y - 6 = -\dfrac{1}{2}(x - (-1))$	Substitute (–1, 6) for x_1 and y_1.

6. Simplify the equation.

$$y-6=-\frac{1}{2}(x-(-1))$$ Equation with substituted values for x_1 and y_1

$$y-6=-\frac{1}{2}x-\frac{1}{2}$$ Distribute $-\frac{1}{2}$ over $(x-(-1))$.

$$y=-\frac{1}{2}x+\frac{11}{2}$$ Add 6 to both sides.

The equation of the line through the point (–1, 6) that is perpendicular to the graph of $-10x+5y=20$ is $y=-\frac{1}{2}x+\frac{11}{2}$.

This can be seen on the following graph.

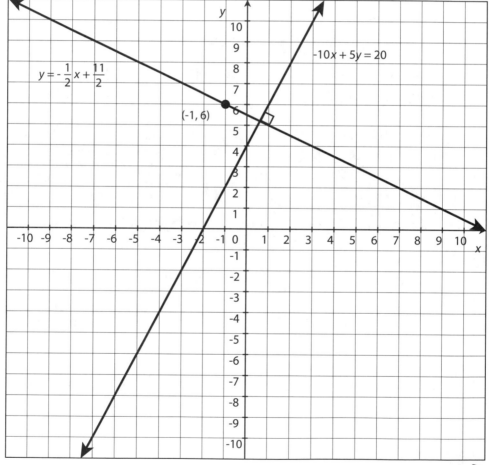

Example 3

Find the point on the line $y = 4x + 1$ that is closest to the point $(-2, 8)$.

1. Find the line perpendicular to the given line, $y = 4x + 1$, that passes through the point $(-2, 8)$.

2. Identify the slope of the given line.

   The slope of the line $y = 4x + 1$ is 4.

3. Find the opposite reciprocal of the slope of the given line.

   The opposite of 4 is -4.

   The reciprocal of -4 is $-\dfrac{1}{4}$.

4. Substitute the opposite reciprocal for m in the point-slope form of a linear equation.

   $y - y_1 = m(x - x_1)$ Point-slope form

   $y - y_1 = -\dfrac{1}{4}(x - x_1)$ Substitute m from the given equation.

5. Substitute x and y from the given point into the equation for x_1 and y_1.

   $y - y_1 = -\dfrac{1}{4}(x - x_1)$ Equation

   $y - 8 = -\dfrac{1}{4}(x - (-2))$ Substitute $(-2, 8)$ for x_1 and y_1.

6. Simplify the equation.

$$y - 8 = -\frac{1}{4}(x - (-2))$$ Equation with substituted values for x_1 and y_1

$$y - 8 = -\frac{1}{4}x - \frac{1}{2}$$ Distribute $-\frac{1}{4}$ over $(x - (-2))$.

$$y = -\frac{1}{4}x + \frac{15}{2}$$ Add 8 to both sides.

The equation of the line through the point (–2, 8) that is perpendicular to the graph of $y = 4x + 1$ is $y = -\frac{1}{4}x + \frac{15}{2}$.

This can be seen on the following graph.

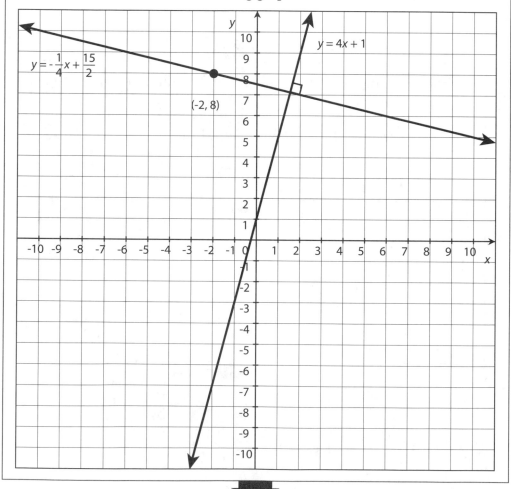

7. Find the intersection between the two lines by setting the given equation equal to the equation of the perpendicular line, then solve for x.

$$4x+1=-\frac{1}{4}x+\frac{15}{2}$$ Set both equations equal to each other.

$$4x=-\frac{1}{4}x+\frac{13}{2}$$ Subtract 1 from both sides.

$$\frac{17}{4}x=\frac{13}{2}$$ Add $\frac{1}{4}x$ to both sides.

$$x=\frac{26}{17}$$ Divide both sides by $\frac{17}{4}$.

8. Substitute the value of x back into the given equation to find the value of y.

$$y = 4x + 1 \qquad \text{Given equation}$$

$$y = 4\left(\frac{26}{17}\right) + 1 \qquad \text{Substitute } \frac{26}{17} \text{ for } x.$$

$$y = \frac{121}{17} \qquad \text{Simplify.}$$

The point on the line closest to $(-2, 8)$ is the point $\left(\dfrac{26}{17}, \dfrac{121}{17}\right)$.

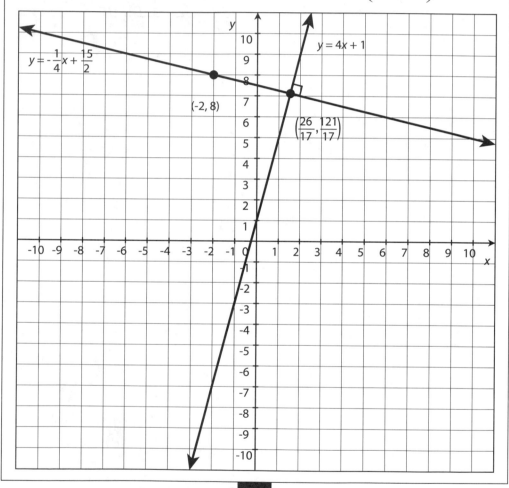

9. Calculate the distance between the two points using the distance formula.

$$\sqrt{(x_2 - x_1)^2 + (y_2 - y_1)^2}$$ Distance formula

$$\sqrt{\left(\frac{26}{17} - (-2)\right)^2 + \left(\frac{121}{17} - 8\right)^2}$$ Substitute values for (x_1, y_1) and (x_2, y_2) using the points $(-2, 8)$ and $\left(\frac{26}{17}, \frac{121}{17}\right)$.

$$\sqrt{\left(\frac{60}{17}\right)^2 + \left(\frac{-15}{17}\right)^2}$$ Simplify.

$$\sqrt{\left(\frac{3600}{289}\right) + \left(\frac{225}{289}\right)}$$ Evaluate squares.

$$\sqrt{\frac{3825}{289}}$$ Simplify.

$$\sqrt{\frac{225}{17}}$$ Reduce to lowest terms.

The distance between the point of intersection and the given point is $\sqrt{\dfrac{225}{17}}$ units or approximately 3.6 units.

UNIT 6 • CONNECTING ALGEBRA AND GEOMETRY THROUGH COORDINATES

Lesson 1: Slope and Distance

Practice 6.1.2: Working with Parallel and Perpendicular Lines

Write the slope-intercept form of an equation for the line that passes through the given point and is parallel to the graph of the given equation.

1. $(1, -5)$ and $6x - 2y = -8$

2. $(-8, 2)$ and $x + 4y = -2$

Write the slope-intercept form of an equation for the line that passes through the given point and is perpendicular to the graph of the given equation.

3. $(0, 7)$ and $9x + 3y = 12$

4. $(3, -4)$ and $5x - 10y = 30$

Calculate the shortest distance from the given point to the line indicated.

5. $(2, 1)$ to $-2x + y = 1$

For questions 6–10, refer to the following map. Each unit represents 100 yards.

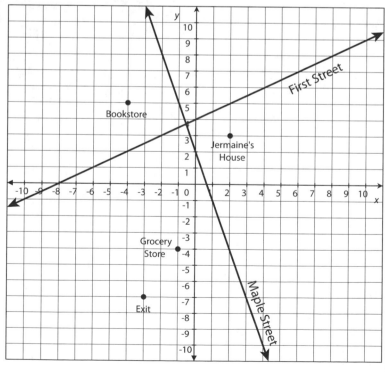

continued

6. First Street is given by the equation $y = \dfrac{1}{2}x + 4$. The grocery store is located on Second Street at the point (–1, –4). What is the equation of the line that represents Second Street that runs parallel to First Street through the point (–1, –4)?

7. Jermaine's house is located at the point (2, 3). His driveway is perpendicular to Maple Street, which is represented by the equation $y = -3x + 2$. What is the equation of the line that represents Jermaine's driveway?

8. The highway runs parallel to Maple Street. There is an exit located at the point (–3, –7). What is the equation of the line that represents the highway?

9. A bookstore is located at the point (–4, 5). The street the bookstore is located on is perpendicular to First Street. What is the equation of the line that represents the street that leads from the bookstore to First Street?

10. What is the shortest distance from the grocery store to Maple Street?

Lesson 2: Lines and Line Segments

Common Core State Standard

G–GPE.7   Use coordinates to compute perimeters of polygons and areas of triangles and rectangles, e.g., using the distance formula.★

Essential Questions

1. How can the midpoint of a line segment be found without measuring?

2. How are the midpoint formula and the distance formula related?

3. How can the distance formula be used to find the area and perimeter of figures on a coordinate plane?

WORDS TO KNOW

area   the amount of space inside the boundary of a two-dimensional figure

distance formula   formula that states the distance between (x_1, y_1) and (x_2, y_2) is equal to $\sqrt{(x_2 - x_1)^2 + (y_2 - y_1)^2}$

perimeter   the distance around a two-dimensional figure

polygon   two-dimensional figure with at least three sides

Recommended Resources

- Math Open Reference. "Midpoint of a Line Segment (Coordinate Geometry)."

  http://walch.com/rr/CAU6L2Midpoint

  Users can adjust a line segment by dragging the endpoints around a coordinate plane to see how the midpoint changes. The equations for each set of endpoints are displayed off to the side of the plane and change as the points are dragged.

- Math Open Reference. "Rectangle Area and Perimeter (Coordinate Geometry)."

  http://walch.com/rr/CAU6L2RectanglePerimeter

  Drag the vertices of a rectangle around different points on a coordinate plane and watch as the coordinates, area, and perimeter change.

- Purplemath. "The Midpoint Formula."

  http://walch.com/rr/CAU6L2MidpointFormula

  This site explains why finding the midpoint can be useful and includes worked examples. A widget on the second page allows users to enter problems, view the steps to the solution, and then view a graph of the solution.

Lesson 6.2.1: Calculating Perimeter and Area

Introduction

The distance formula can be used to find solutions to many real-world problems. In the previous lesson, the distance formula was used to find the distance between two given points. In this lesson, the distance formula will be applied to perimeter and area problems.

A **polygon** is a two-dimensional figure formed by three or more segments. Sometimes we need to calculate the **perimeter** or distance around a polygon, as well as find the **area** or the amount of space inside the boundary of a polygon. The distance formula is a valuable tool for both of these calculations.

Key Concepts

- Situations where you would need to calculate perimeter include finding the amount of linear feet needed to fence a yard or a garden, determining the amount of trim needed for a room, or finding the amount of concrete needed to edge a statue.

- Perimeter is the sum of the lengths of all the sides of a polygon.

- The final answer must include the appropriate label (units, feet, inches, meters, centimeters, etc.).

- Sometimes the answer is not a whole number. If it is not, you must simplify the radical and then approximate the value.

Calculating the Perimeter of a Polygon

1. Calculate the length of each side of the polygon using the distance formula: $\sqrt{(x_2 - x_1)^2 + (y_2 - y_1)^2}$.

2. Add all the lengths of the polygon to find the perimeter.

3. Simplify and approximate the value if necessary.

Be sure to include the appropriate label in your answer.

- Calculating area is necessary when finding the amount of carpeting needed for a room in your home, or to determine how large a garden will be.

- The area of a triangle is found using the formula $Area = \frac{1}{2}(base)(height)$.

- The height of a triangle is the perpendicular distance from the third vertex to the base of the triangle.

- It may be necessary to determine the equation of the line that represents the height of the triangle before calculating the area. For an example of this, see Example 3 in the Guided Practice.

- Determining the lengths of the base and the height is necessary if these lengths are not stated in the problem.

- The final answer must include the appropriate label (units^2, feet^2, inches^2, meters^2, centimeters^2, etc.).

Calculating the Area of a Triangle

1. Find the equation of the line that represents the base of the triangle.

2. Find the equation of the line that represents the height of the triangle.

3. Find the point of intersection of the line representing the height of the triangle and the line representing the base of the triangle.

4. Calculate the length of the base of the triangle using the distance formula: $\sqrt{(x_2 - x_1)^2 + (y_2 - y_1)^2}$.

5. Calculate the length of the height of the triangle using the distance formula: $\sqrt{(x_2 - x_1)^2 + (y_2 - y_1)^2}$.

6. Calculate the area using the formula $Area = \frac{1}{2}(base)(height)$.

Be sure to include the appropriate label in your answer.

- By definition, rectangles have adjacent sides that are perpendicular.

- The area of a rectangle is found using the formula $Area = (base)(height)$.

- The lengths of the base and height are found using the distance formula.

- The final answer must include the appropriate label (units^2, feet^2, inches^2, meters^2, centimeters^2, etc.).

Calculating the Area of a Rectangle

1. Calculate the length of the base of the rectangle using the distance formula: $\sqrt{(x_2 - x_1)^2 + (y_2 - y_1)^2}$.

2. Calculate the length of the height of the rectangle using the distance formula: $\sqrt{(x_2 - x_1)^2 + (y_2 - y_1)^2}$.

3. Calculate the area using the formula: $Area = (base)(height)$.

Be sure to include the appropriate label in your answer.

Guided Practice 6.2.1

Example 1

Triangle *ABC* has vertices *A* (−3, 1), *B* (1, 3), and *C* (2, −4). Calculate the perimeter of the triangle.

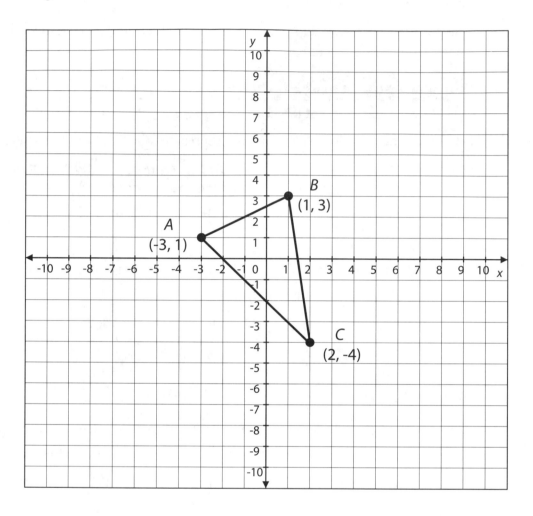

1. Calculate the length of each side of the triangle . Use the distance formula.

    Calculate the length of $\overline{AB}$.

    $\sqrt{(x_2-x_1)^2+(y_2-y_1)^2}$ Distance formula

    $\sqrt{((1)-(-3))^2+((3)-(1))^2}$ Substitute (–3, 1) and (1, 3).

    $\sqrt{(4)^2+(2)^2}$ Simplify as needed.

    $\sqrt{16+4}$

    $\sqrt{20}$

    $2\sqrt{5}$

    The length of $\overline{AB}$ is $2\sqrt{5}$ units.

    Calculate the length of $\overline{BC}$.

    $\sqrt{(x_2-x_1)^2+(y_2-y_1)^2}$ Distance formula

    $\sqrt{((2)-(1))^2+((-4)-(3))^2}$ Substitute (1, 3) and (2, –4).

    $\sqrt{(1)^2+(-7)^2}$ Simplify as needed.

    $\sqrt{1+49}$

    $\sqrt{50}$

    $5\sqrt{2}$

    The length of $\overline{BC}$ is $5\sqrt{2}$ units.

    Calculate the length of $\overline{CA}$.

    $\sqrt{(x_2-x_1)^2+(y_2-y_1)^2}$ Distance formula

    $\sqrt{((-3)-(2))^2+((1)-(-4))^2}$ Substitute (2, –4) and (–3, 1).

    $\sqrt{(-5)^2+(5)^2}$ Simplify as needed.

    $\sqrt{25+25}$

    $\sqrt{50}$

    $5\sqrt{2}$

    The length of $\overline{CA}$ is $5\sqrt{2}$ units.

2. Calculate the perimeter of triangle *ABC*.

Find the sum of the sides of the triangle.

perimeter $= AB + BC + CA$

$= 2\sqrt{5} + 5\sqrt{2} + 5\sqrt{2}$

$= 2\sqrt{5} + 10\sqrt{2}$

≈ 18.6

The perimeter of triangle *ABC* is $2\sqrt{5} + 10\sqrt{2} \approx 18.6$ units.

Example 2

Quadrilateral *ABCD* has vertices *A* (–3, 0), *B* (2, 4), *C* (3, 1), and *D* (–4, –3). Calculate the perimeter of the quadrilateral.

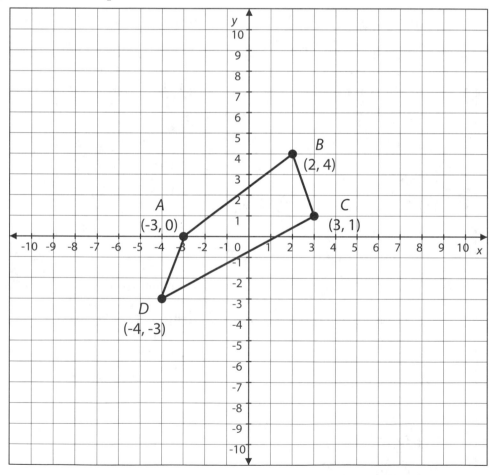

1. Calculate the length of each side of the quadrilateral using the distance formula.

Calculate the length of $\overline{AB}$.

$$\sqrt{(x_2 - x_1)^2 + (y_2 - y_1)^2}$$ Distance formula

$$\sqrt{((2) - (-3))^2 + ((4) - (0))^2}$$ Substitute (–3, 0) and (2, 4).

$$\sqrt{(5)^2 + (4)^2}$$ Simplify as needed.

$$\sqrt{25 + 16}$$

$$\sqrt{41}$$

The length of $\overline{AB}$ is $\sqrt{41}$ units.

Calculate the length of $\overline{BC}$.

$$\sqrt{(x_2 - x_1)^2 + (y_2 - y_1)^2}$$ Distance formula

$$\sqrt{((3) - (2))^2 + ((1) - (4))^2}$$ Substitute (2, 4) and (3, 1).

$$\sqrt{(1)^2 + (-3)^2}$$ Simplify as needed.

$$\sqrt{1 + 9}$$

$$\sqrt{10}$$

The length of $\overline{BC}$ is $\sqrt{10}$ units.

Calculate the length of $\overline{CD}$.

$$\sqrt{(x_2 - x_1)^2 + (y_2 - y_1)^2}$$ Distance formula

$$\sqrt{((-4) - (3))^2 + ((-3) - (1))^2}$$ Substitute (3, 1) and (–4, –3).

$$\sqrt{(-7)^2 + (-4)^2}$$ Simplify as needed.

$$\sqrt{49 + 16}$$

$$\sqrt{65}$$

The length of $\overline{CD}$ is $\sqrt{65}$ units.

(continued)

Calculate the length of $\overline{DA}$.

$\sqrt{(x_2 - x_1)^2 + (y_2 - y_1)^2}$ Distance formula

$\sqrt{((-3)-(-4))^2 + ((0)-(-3))^2}$ Substitute (–4, –3) and (–3, 0).

$\sqrt{(1)^2 + (3)^2}$ Simplify as needed.

$\sqrt{1 + 9}$

$\sqrt{10}$

The length of $\overline{DA}$ is $\sqrt{10}$ units.

2. Calculate the perimeter of quadrilateral $ABCD$.

Find the sum of the sides of the quadrilateral.

perimeter $= AB + BC + CD + DA$

$= \sqrt{41} + \sqrt{10} + \sqrt{65} + \sqrt{10}$

$= 2\sqrt{10} + \sqrt{41} + \sqrt{65}$

≈ 20.8

The perimeter of quadrilateral $ABCD$ is
$2\sqrt{10} + \sqrt{41} + \sqrt{65} \approx 20.8$ units.

Example 3

Triangle *ABC* has vertices *A* (1, −1), *B* (4, 3), and *C* (5, −3). Calculate the area of triangle *ABC*.

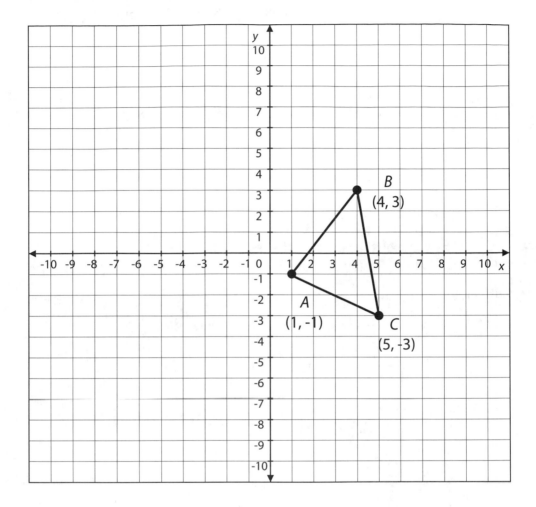

1. Find the equation of the line that represents the base of the triangle.

   Let $\overline{AC}$ be the base.

   Calculate the slope of the equation that represents side $\overline{AC}$.

   $$m = \frac{y_2 - y_1}{x_2 - x_1}$$ Slope formula

   $$= \frac{(-3)-(-1)}{(5)-(1)}$$ Substitute $(1, -1)$ and $(5, -3)$.

   $$= \frac{-2}{4}$$ Simplify as needed.

   $$= -\frac{1}{2}$$

   The slope of the equation that represents side $\overline{AC}$ is $-\frac{1}{2}$.

   Write the equation of the line that represents side $\overline{AC}$.

   $$y - y_1 = m(x - x_1)$$ Point-slope form

   $$y - y_1 = -\frac{1}{2}(x - x_1)$$ Substitute $-\frac{1}{2}$ for m.

   $$y - (-1) = -\frac{1}{2}(x - (1))$$ Substitute $(1, -1)$ for (x_1, y_1).

   $$y + 1 = -\frac{1}{2}(x - 1)$$ Simplify.

   $$y + 1 = -\frac{1}{2}x + \frac{1}{2}$$ Distribute $-\frac{1}{2}$ over $(x - 1)$.

   $$y = -\frac{1}{2}x - \frac{1}{2}$$ Subtract 1 from both sides.

   The equation of the line that represents the base of the triangle is
   $$y = -\frac{1}{2}x - \frac{1}{2}.$$

2. Find the equation of the line that represents the height of the triangle.

The equation of the line that represents the height is perpendicular to the base; therefore, the slope of this line is the opposite reciprocal of the base.

The slope of the line representing the height is 2.

$y - y_1 = m(x - x_1)$ Point-slope form

$y - y_1 = 2(x - x_1)$ Substitute 2 for m.

$y - (3) = 2(x - (4))$ Substitute (4, 3) for (x_1, y_1).

$y - 3 = 2(x - 4)$ Simplify.

$y - 3 = 2x - 8$ Distribute 2 over $(x - 4)$.

$y = 2x - 5$ Add 3 to both sides.

The equation of the line that represents the height of the triangle is $y = 2x - 5$.

3. Find the point of intersection of the line representing the height and the line representing the base of the triangle.

Set the equation of the line representing the base and the equation of the line representing the height equal to each other to determine the point of intersection.

$$-\frac{1}{2}x - \frac{1}{2} = 2x - 5 \qquad \text{Set the equations equal to each other.}$$

$$-\frac{1}{2}x = 2x - \frac{9}{2} \qquad \text{Add } \frac{1}{2} \text{ to both sides.}$$

$$-\frac{5}{2}x = -\frac{9}{2} \qquad \text{Subtract } 2x \text{ from both sides.}$$

$$x = \frac{9}{5} \qquad \text{Divide both sides by } -\frac{5}{2}.$$

The point of intersection has an x-value of $\frac{9}{5}$.

Substitute $\frac{9}{5}$ into either equation to find the y-value.

$$y = 2x - 5 \qquad \text{Equation of the line representing height}$$

$$y = 2\left(\frac{9}{5}\right) - 5 \qquad \text{Substitute } \frac{9}{5} \text{ for } x.$$

$$y = \frac{18}{5} - 5 \qquad \text{Simplify.}$$

$$y = -\frac{7}{5} \qquad \text{Solve for } y.$$

The point of intersection has a y-value of $-\frac{7}{5}$.

The point of intersection is $\left(\frac{9}{5}, -\frac{7}{5}\right)$.

4. Calculate the length of the base, $\overline{AC}$, of the triangle.

$\sqrt{(x_2-x_1)^2+(y_2-y_1)^2}$ Distance formula

$\sqrt{((5)-(1))^2+((-3)-(-1))^2}$ Substitute $(1, -1)$ and $(5, -3)$.

$\sqrt{(4)^2+(-2)^2}$ Simplify as needed.

$\sqrt{16+4}$

$\sqrt{20}$

$2\sqrt{5}$

The length of $\overline{AC}$ is $2\sqrt{5}$ units.

5. Calculate the length of the height from point B to the point of intersection.

$\sqrt{(x_2-x_1)^2+(y_2-y_1)^2}$ Distance formula

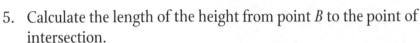

$\sqrt{\left(\left(\dfrac{9}{5}\right)-(4)\right)^2+\left(\left(-\dfrac{7}{5}\right)-(3)\right)^2}$ Substitute $(4, 3)$ and $\left(\dfrac{9}{5}, -\dfrac{7}{5}\right)$.

$\sqrt{\left(-\dfrac{11}{5}\right)^2+\left(-\dfrac{22}{5}\right)^2}$ Simplify as needed.

$\sqrt{\dfrac{121}{25}+\dfrac{484}{25}}$

$\sqrt{\dfrac{605}{25}}$

$\dfrac{\sqrt{605}}{\sqrt{25}}$

$\dfrac{11\sqrt{5}}{5}$

The length of the height is $\dfrac{11\sqrt{5}}{5}$ units.

6. Calculate the area of triangle ABC.

$$Area = \frac{1}{2}(base)(height)$$ Area formula for triangles

$$= \frac{1}{2}\left(2\sqrt{5}\right)\left(\frac{11\sqrt{5}}{5}\right)$$ Substitute the lengths of the height and the base of the triangle.

$$= \frac{1}{2}\left(\frac{\left(2\sqrt{5}\right)\left(11\sqrt{5}\right)}{5}\right)$$ Simplify as needed.

$$= \frac{1}{2}\left(\frac{22\left(\sqrt{5}\right)\left(\sqrt{5}\right)}{5}\right)$$

$$= \frac{1}{2}\left(\frac{22(5)}{5}\right)$$

$$= \frac{1}{2}(22)$$

$$= 11$$

The area of triangle ABC is 11 square units.

Example 4

Rectangle $ABCD$ has vertices A (–3, –4), B (–1, 2), C (2, 1), and D (0, –5). Calculate the area of the rectangle.

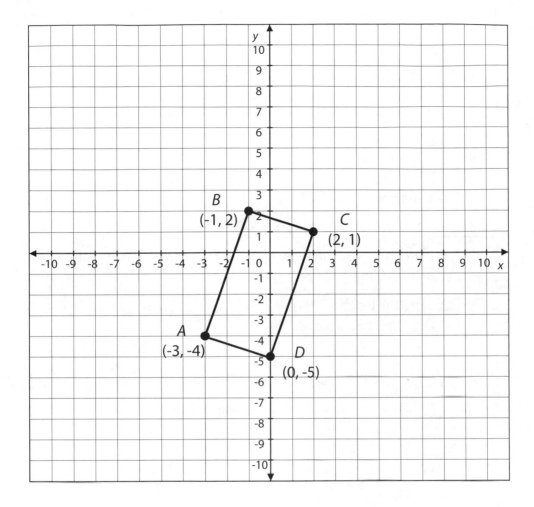

1. Calculate the length of the base of the rectangle. Use the distance formula.

   Calculate the length of $\overline{AB}$.

$\sqrt{(x_2-x_1)^2+(y_2-y_1)^2}$	Distance formula
$\sqrt{((-1)-(-3))^2+((2)-(-4))^2}$	Substitute (−3, −4) and (−1, 2).
$\sqrt{(2)^2+(6)^2}$	Simplify as needed.
$\sqrt{4+36}$	
$\sqrt{40}$	
$2\sqrt{10}$	

   The length of $\overline{AB}$ is $2\sqrt{10}$ units.

2. Calculate the length of the height of rectangle $ABCD$ using the distance formula.

   Calculate the length of $\overline{BC}$.

$\sqrt{(x_2-x_1)^2+(y_2-y_1)^2}$	Distance formula
$\sqrt{((2)-(-1))^2+((1)-(2))^2}$	Substitute (−1, 2) and (2, 1).
$\sqrt{(3)^2+(-1)^2}$	Simplify as needed.
$\sqrt{9+1}$	
$\sqrt{10}$	

   The length of $\overline{BC}$ is $\sqrt{10}$ units.

3. Calculate the area of rectangle $ABCD$.

$Area = base \bullet height$	Area formula for a rectangle
$=\left(2\sqrt{10}\right)\left(\sqrt{10}\right)$	Substitute the lengths of the height and base of the triangle.
$= (2)(10)$	Simplify.
$= 20$	

   The area of rectangle $ABCD$ is 20 square units.

UNIT 6 • CONNECTING ALGEBRA AND GEOMETRY THROUGH COORDINATES

Lesson 2: Lines and Line Segments

Practice 6.2.1: Perimeter and Area

Calculate the perimeter of each of the polygons below.

1. Triangle *ABC* has vertices *A* (0, 3), *B* (5, 1), and *C* (2, –2).

2. Rectangle *ABCD* has vertices *A* (–4, –4), *B* (–2, 0), *C* (4, –3), and *D* (2, –7).

3. Rhombus *ABCD* has vertices *A* (–3, 3), *B* (0, 5), *C* (3, 3), and *D* (0, 1).

4. Quadrilateral *ABCD* has vertices *A* (–2, –3), *B* (1, 1), *C* (7, 1), and *D* (6, –3).

5. Quadrilateral *ABCD* has vertices *A* (–1, 5), *B* (3, 6), *C* (5, –2), and *D* (1, –3).

Calculate the area of each of the polygons below.

6. Rectangle *ABCD* has vertices *A* (–1, 5), *B* (3, 5), *C* (3, –4), and *D* (–1, –4).

7. Rectangle *ABCD* has vertices *A* (–2, –3), *B* (0, 3), *C* (3, 2), and *D* (1, –4).

8. Right triangle *ABC* has vertices *A* (–3, 3), *B* (–3, –1), and *C* (5, –1).

9. Triangle *ABC* has vertices *A* (–1, 1), *B* (–1, –6), and *C* (–4, –6).

10. Triangle *ABC* has vertices *A* (3, 0), *B* (1, 8), and *C* (2, 10).

Answer Key

Answer Key

Unit 1: Relationships Between Quantities

Lesson 1: Interpreting Structure in Expressions

Practice 1.1.1: Identifying Terms, Factors, and Coefficients, pp. 7–8

1. terms: $14x^2$, $2x$, -9
   factors: 14 and x^2, 2 and x
   coefficients: 14, 2
   constant: -9

3. terms: $(4x^3)/5$, $9x$
   factors: 4/5 and x^3, 9 and x
   coefficient: 4/5
   constants: there are none

5. expression: $x^6 + 3x$
   terms: x^6, $3x$
   factors: 3 and x
   coefficient: 3
   constants: there are none

7. expression: $2x + 0.05(x) = 2.05x$
   terms: $2.05x$
   factors: 2.05 and x
   coefficient: 2.05
   constants: there are none

9. expression: $x + x + (x - 4) + (x - 4) = 2(x) + 2(x - 4) = 4x - 8$
   terms: $4x$, -8
   factors: 4 and x
   coefficient: 4
   constant: -8

Practice 1.1.2: Interpreting Complicated Expressions, pp. 12–13

1. The order of operations indicates that exponents must be applied before multiplying.
3. The number of books does not affect the value of m; the number of books is a constant and remains unchanged by the number of magazines.
5. The value of the expression will be greater than 9.
7. The amount will be increased.
9. The values of $(1 + r)$ would be less than 1.

Lesson 2: Creating Equations and Inequalities in One Variable

Practice 1.2.1: Creating Linear Equations in One Variable, pp. 28–29

1. Answers may vary. Possible answers:
   a. miles per hour
   b. inches per minute or miles per hour
   c. meters per second or feet per second
   d. dollars per pound

3. 287.88 ft²

5. $15

7. $17 per lunch

9. 76,800 square feet

Practice 1.2.2: Creating Linear Inequalities in One Variable, pp. 36–37

1. $x \leq 8$

3. $w \leq 2400$

5. $15x \geq 950$; $x \geq 63\ 1/3$; You must work at least 63 1/3 hours.

7. $22x + 9 \leq 75$; $x \leq 3$; Arianna can buy up to 3 computer games.

9. $25,000 - 3000x \geq 4000$; $x \leq 7$ days. The giveaway should end in 7 days or less in order to have $4,000 or more to give away for the grand prize.

Practice 1.2.3: Creating Exponential Equations, pp. 47–48

1. a. linear; b. exponential

3. a. exponential; b. linear

5. $4800 = a(2)^3$; $600

7. $y = 100(0.5)^8$; 0.39 grams

9. $y = 63,000(1.01)^4$; about 65,559 people

Lesson 3: Creating and Graphing Equations in Two Variables

Practice 1.3.1: Creating and Graphing Linear Equations in Two Variables, p. 79

1.

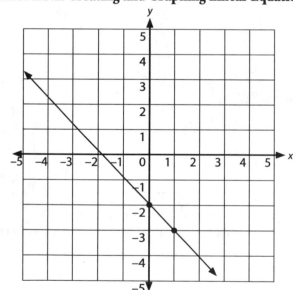

3.

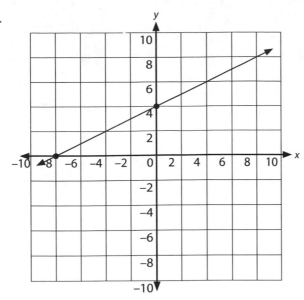

5. $y = 5/9(x - 32)$; slope = $5/9$; y-intercept: $(0, -17\ 7/9)$

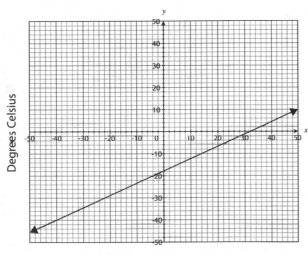

Degrees Fahrenheit

7. $y = 65x + 100$; slope = 65; y-intercept: (0, 100)

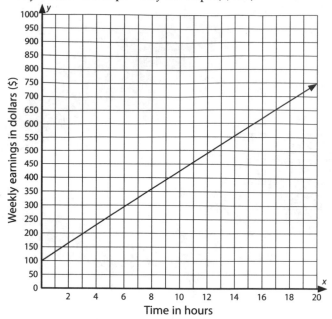

9. $y = -15x + 500$; slope = -15; y-intercept: (0, 500)

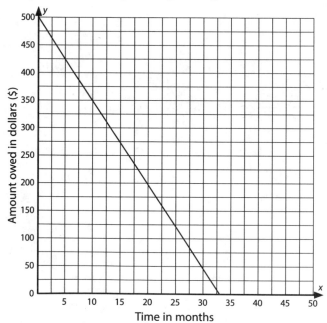

Practice 1.3.2: Creating and Graphing Exponential Equations, p. 92

1.

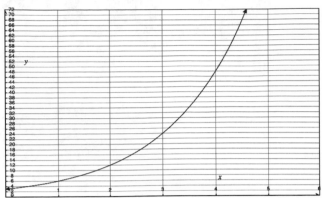

3.

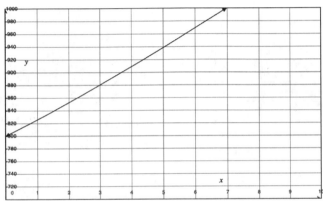

5. $y = 16(2)^{24x/36} = 16(2)^{2x/3}$, for which x is in days

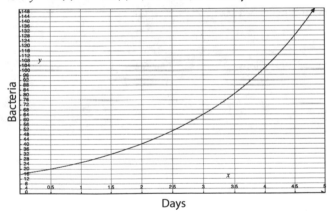

7. $y = 15{,}000(0.978)^x$

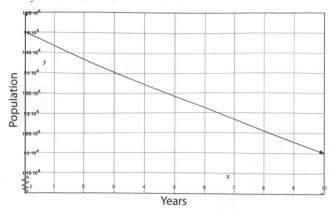

9. $y = 300(1.0006)^{52x}$

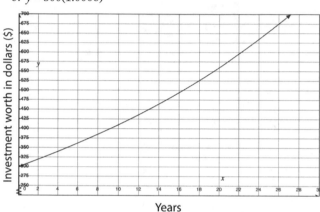

Lesson 4: Representing Constraints

Practice 1.4.1: Representing Constraints, pp. 99–100

  1. no

  3. no

  5. a. $y = 2.60x + 7.90$; b. $x = 8.5$; maximum = 8,500 gallons

  7. $\begin{cases} y = 7x + 15 \\ y = 5x + 20 \\ x \geq 1 \end{cases}$

  9. $\begin{cases} x + y \leq 32 \\ y \leq 6 \\ x \geq 0 \\ y \geq 0 \end{cases}$

Lesson 5: Rearranging Formulas

Practice 1.5.1: Rearranging Equations and Formulas, p. 107

  1. $y = 10x - 6$

  3. $y = 3x - 9$

  5. $d = C/\pi$

  7. $t = I/pr$

  9. $F = (9/5)C + 32$

Unit 2: Linear and Exponential Relationships

Lesson 1: Graphs As Solution Sets and Function Notation

Practice 2.1.1: Graphing the Set of All Solutions, pp. 10–12

1.

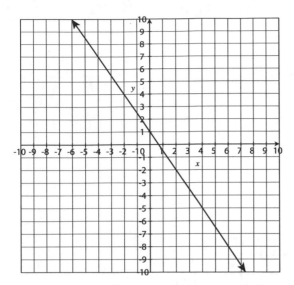

3.

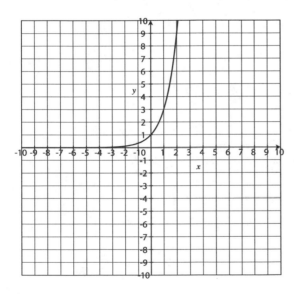

5. {(0, 2); (2, 5); (4, 8)}

7. The painter will have 35 gallons remaining after 6 hours.

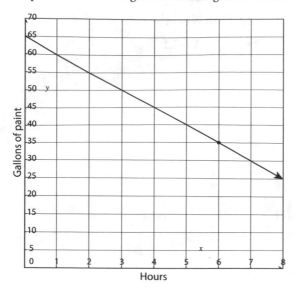

9. Enrico would have to ride 49 miles on the fifth day.

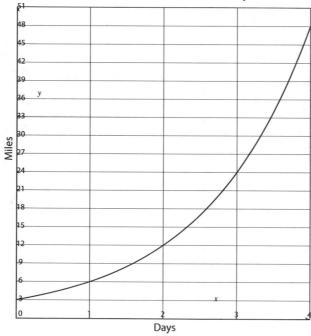

Practice 2.1.2: Intersecting Graphs, pp. 19–20

1. If $f(x) = g(x)$ for some value of x, then the point $(x, f(x))$ will be on the curve f and the point $(x, g(x))$ will be on the curve g. Since $f(x) = g(x)$ $(x, f(x))$ and $(x, g(x))$ are the same point.

3. The graphs will not cross between the values of x in the table.

5. The graphs intersect where $x \approx 2$.

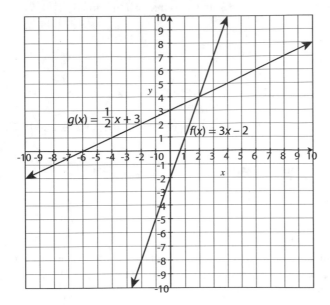

7. $x = 6$

x	$r(x) = x - 6$	$s(x) = \left(\dfrac{1}{4}\right)^x$	$r(x) - s(x)$
3	−3	0.02	−3.02
4	−2	0.003	−2.003
5	−1	0	−1
6	0	0	0
7	1	0	1
8	2	0	2

9. It will take Josiah about 50 minutes to catch up with Alanna. They will be about 75 nautical miles from the airport.

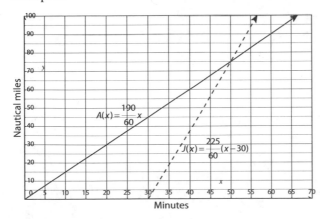

Practice 2.1.3: Domain and Range, pp. 30–33

1. No; 10 is mapped to 1 and 4, 20 is mapped to 2 and 5, and 30 is mapped to 3 and 6.
3. Yes; the graph passes the vertical line test.
5. Yes; each x is paired to only one y.
7. domain: {all reals}; range: {all reals}
9. domain:

   {0, 1, 2, 3, 4, 5, 6, 7, 8, 9, 10, 11, 12, 13, 14, 15, 16, 17, 18, 19, 20, 21, 22, 23, 24, 25};
   range:
   {–100, –88, –76, –64, –52, –40, –28, –16, –4, 8, 20, 32, 44, 56, 68, 80, 92, 104, 116, 128, 140, 152, 164, 176, 188, 200}

Practice 2.1.4: Function Notation and Evaluating Functions, pp. 38–40

1. {10, 28, 46, 82}
3. {3.25, 4, 7, 67}
5. $f(–4) = 7$
7. Evaluating the function over the domain results in the range of {50, 44, 20, 8}. After 3 months, the store is down to 50 employees. After 6 months, the store is down to 44 employees. After 18 months, the store is down to 20 employees, and after 24 months the store is down to 8 employees. The following are all points on the function of $g(x) = –2x + 56$:

   $g(3) = 50$

   $g(6) = 44$

   $g(18) = 20$

   $g(24) = 8$

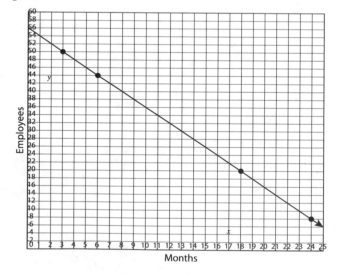

9. $d(3) = 300$; $d(5) = 420$; $d(8) = 600$. After 3 hours, Carlos will have driven a total of 300 miles. After 5 hours, he will have driven a total of 420 miles. After 8 hours, he will have driven a total of 600 miles.

Lesson 2: Solving Linear Inequalities in Two Variables and Systems of Inequalities

Practice 2.2.1: Solving Linear Inequalities in Two Variables, p. 57

1.

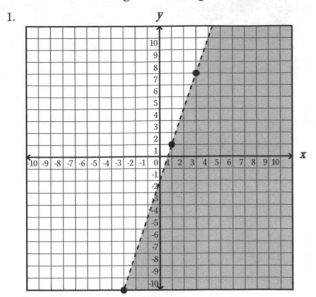

3.

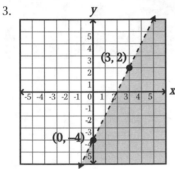

5.

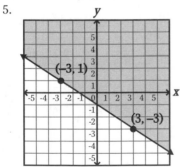

7.

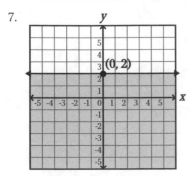

9. $x + y > 200$

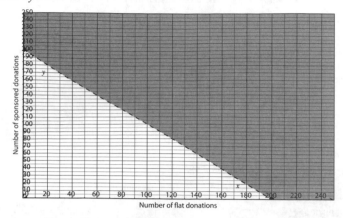

Practice 2.2.2: Solving Systems of Linear Inequalities, pp. 67–68

1.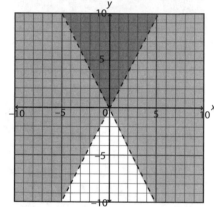

3.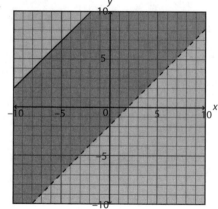

5.

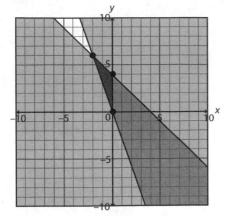

7.

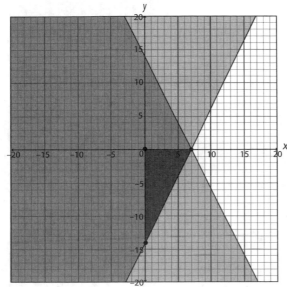

9. a. $\begin{cases} x+5y<15 \\ 3x+2y\le12 \\ x\ge0 \\ y\ge0 \end{cases}$; b. Graph:

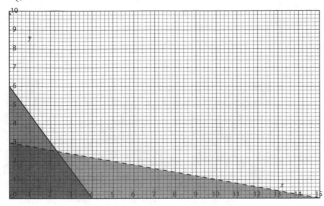

Lesson 3: Sequences As Functions

Practice 2.3.1: Sequences As Functions, p. 80

1. 32
3. 53

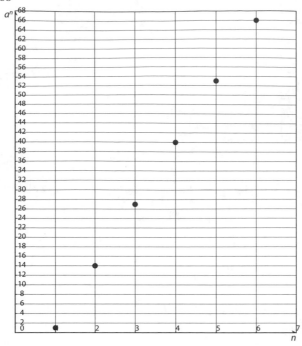

5. 32

7. $a_5 = 21$, $a_6 = 25$

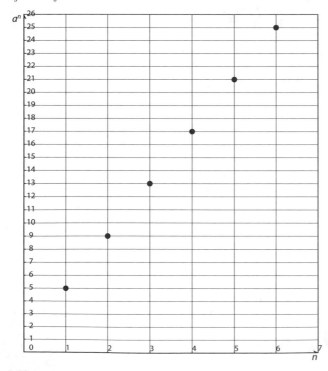

9. 5:53 A.M.

Lesson 4: Interpreting Graphs of Functions

Practice 2.4.1: Identifying Key Features of Linear and Exponential Graphs, pp. 97–102

1. domain: whole numbers

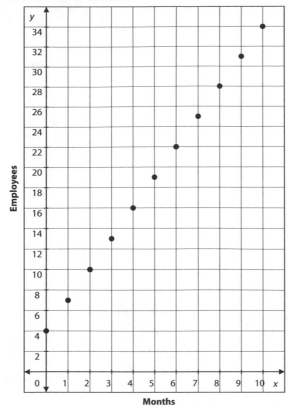

3. x-intercept: none; y-intercept: (0, 30); the function is decreasing; the function is positive for $0 \le x \le 4$; minimum: 18; maximum: 30; asymptote: there is no asymptote; domain: $0 \le x \le 4$, where x is a whole number

5. x-intercept: (0, 0); y-intercept: (0, 0); the function is increasing; the function is positive for $x \ge 0$; minimum: 0; maximum: there is no maximum; asymptote: there is no asymptote; domain: $x \ge 0$

7. x-intercept: none; y-intercept: (0, 32); the function is decreasing; the function is positive for $x \ge 0$; minimum: 1; maximum: 32; asymptote: there is no asymptote; domain: $0 \le x \le 5$, where x is a whole number

9. x-intercept: none; y-intercept: (0, 1500); the function is increasing; the function is positive for $x \ge 0$; minimum: 1500; maximum: there is no maximum; asymptote: $y = 0$; domain: $x \ge 0$

Practice 2.4.2: Proving Average Rate of Change, pp. 109–111

1. -0.02
3. 30.72
5. 2.54
7. 0.13
9. 144.83

Practice 2.4.3: Recognizing Average Rate of Change, pp. 120–123

1. ≈ 0.06 gallons per door
3. ≈ 0.97 Australian dollars per U.S. dollar
5. Yes, a prediction is possible. Sample prediction: The rate of change would be the same as the rate of change in questions 3 and 4 because the function is linear.
7. ≈ 150 campers per year
9. ≈ -65 people per year

Lesson 5: Analyzing Linear and Exponential Functions

Practice 2.5.1: Graphing Linear Functions, pp. 136–137

1. x-intercept: $(-6, 0)$; y-intercept: $(0, -4)$

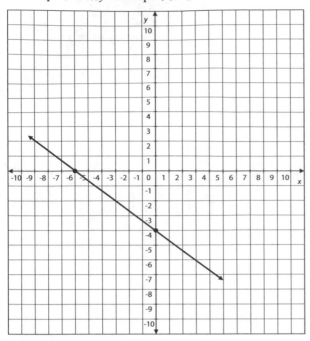

3. x-intercept: $(-5, 0)$; y-intercept: $(0, 15)$

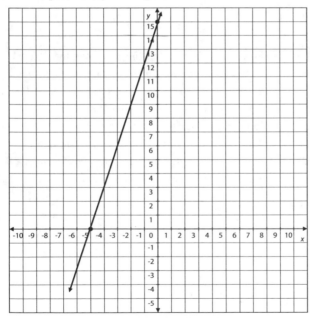

5. *x*-intercept: (–3, 0); *y*-intercept: (0, 7)

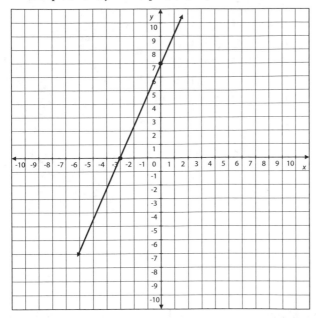

7. 5 bags of bottles, 6 bags of cans

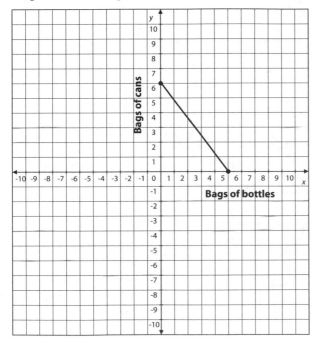

9. 9 acres of corn, 3 acres of wheat

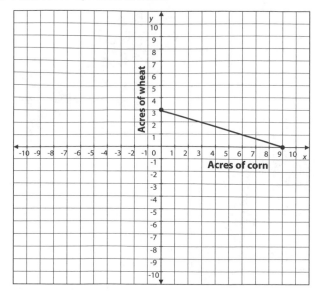

Practice 2.5.2: Graphing Exponential Functions, pp. 150–151

1. y-intercept: $(0, -2)$; growth, with a horizontal asymptote of $y = 3$

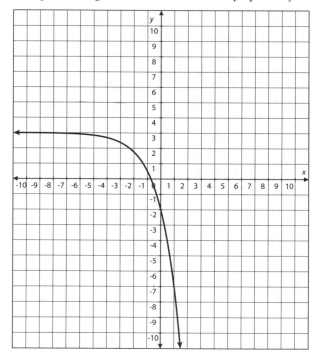

3. *y*-intercept: (0, 6); decay, with a horizontal asymptote of *y* = 2

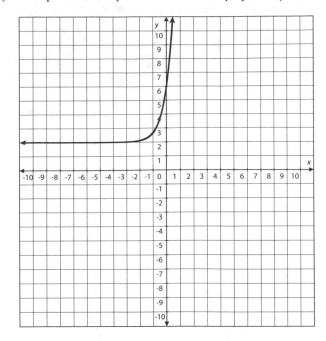

5. *y*-intercept: (0, 7); decay, with a horizontal asymptote of *y* = –5

7. $f(x) = 55\left(\dfrac{1}{2}\right)^x$; 6.875 grams

9. *f*(*x*) = 250(1.037)^x; $278.79

Lesson 6: Comparing Functions

Practice 2.6.1: Comparing Linear Functions, pp. 162–166

1. Function A has a rate of change of 3 and a *y*-intercept of –5. Function B has a rate of change of 2 and a *y*-intercept of 1. Function A has a greater rate of change because 3 is greater than 2. Function B has a greater *y*-intercept because 1 is greater than –5.

3. Function A has a rate of change of 2/3 and a *y*-intercept of 9. Function B has a rate of change of 0 and a *y*-intercept of 2. Function A has a greater rate of change and a greater *y*-intercept.

5. Function A has a rate of change of 0.23 and a *y*-intercept of 0. Function B has a rate of change of 0.20 and a *y*-intercept of 0. Function A has a greater rate of change. Both functions share the same *y*-intercept.

7. Function A has a rate of change of 2.00 and a *y*-intercept of 1. Function B has a rate of change of 2.50 and a *y*-intercept of 3.50. The initial cost to rent a game is higher with Function B. Function B has the higher rate of change, meaning the charge for each extra night is higher than for Function A.

9. Function A has a rate of change of –0.32 and a *y*-intercept of 12.5. Function B has a rate of change of –0.32 and a *y*-intercept of 10. Function A has a greater *y*-intercept, meaning that this container of cat food initially held more food. Functions A and B have the same rate of change, meaning that the cat is being fed the same amount every time in each scenario.

Practice 2.6.2: Comparing Exponential Functions, pp. 178–182

1. Function A has a greater rate of change because the slope of the function over the interval is 33,600, compared to 933.333 for Function B. Function B has a greater *y*-intercept of 50, compared to 25 for Function A.

3. Function A has the greater rate of change, 17.755, compared to 15.882 for Function B. Function B has the greater *y*-intercept of 300, compared to 250 for Function A.

5. Function A has a greater rate of change and y-intercept than Function B. Function A's rate of change is −2,781.40 and its y-intercept is at 25,000. Function B's rate of change is −1,638.04 and its y-intercept is at 20,000.

7. Function A has a lower rate of change than Function B, but a greater y-intercept. Function A has a rate of change of 13.70 and a y-intercept of 930. Function B has a rate of change of 35.4 and a y-intercept of 875.

9. Function A has a greater rate of change and y-intercept than Function B. Function A has a rate of change of −4,723.25 and a y-intercept of 32,000. Function B has a rate of change of −3,286.25 and a y-intercept of 27,500.

Practice 2.6.3: Comparing Linear to Exponential Functions, pp. 190–191

1. Check the students' graphs for accuracy. $g(x)$ will eventually grow faster than $f(x)$.

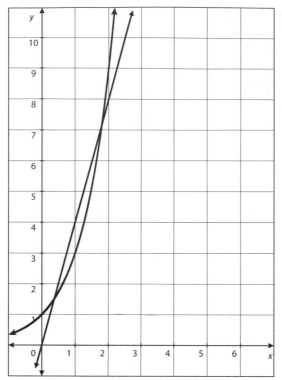

3. Check the students' graphs for accuracy. $f(x)$ decreases faster than $g(x)$.

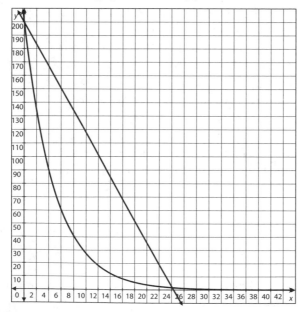

5. Check the students' graphs for accuracy. The approximate point is (5, 17).

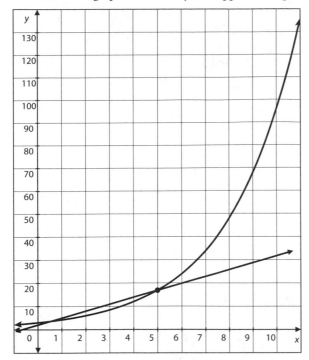

7. $g(x)$ eventually increases faster than $f(x)$.

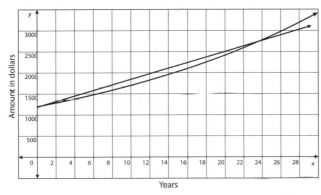

9. Choose $f(x)$ if investing for less than 10 years because the value of $f(x)$ is greater than the value of $g(x)$ during the first 24 years.

Lesson 7: Building Functions

Practice 2.7.1: Building Functions from Context, pp. 203–204

1. $f(x) = 15x$
3. $f(x) = 7 + 9x$
5. $f(x) = 60 \cdot (0.9)^x$
7. $f(x) = 4x - 3$
9. $f(x) = 10 + 0.25x$

Practice 2.7.2: Constructing Functions from Graphs and Tables, pp. 214–215

1. $f(x) = 6 \cdot \left(\dfrac{1}{3}\right)^x$
3. $f(x) = 5x - 2$

5. $f(x) = 0.5 \cdot 4^x$

7. $f(x) = 22x - 18$

9. $f(x) = (-0.5) \cdot 6^x$

Lesson 8: Operating on Functions and Transformations

Practice 2.8.1: Operating on Functions, p. 222

1. $8x - 1$

3. $3(2^x)$

5. $-4x + 19$

7. $-28x + 84$

9. $f(x) = 100(1.02)^x$; $f(x) = 100(1.02)^x + 200$; 200 is added to the first function.

Practice 2.8.2: Transformations of Linear and Exponential Functions, pp. 228–232

1.

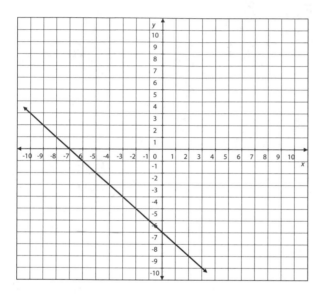

3.

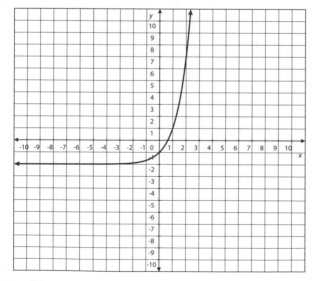

5. $g(x) = f(x) + 13$

7. $g(x) = f(x) - 4$

9. 13

Lesson 9: Arithmetic and Geometric Sequences

Practice 2.9.1: Arithmetic Sequences, p. 239

1. $a_n = 1.8n + 2.4$

3. $a_n = 43n - 280$

5. 12.3, 12.9, 13.5, 14.1, 14.7

7. $a_n = 12n + 3$

9. $a_n = \dfrac{1}{4}n + \dfrac{1}{4}$, 6 days

Practice 2.9.2: Geometric Sequences, p. 244

1. $a_n = 3^{n-1}$

3. $a_n = 16\left(-\dfrac{1}{2}\right)^{n-1}$

5. $48, -16, \dfrac{16}{3}, -\dfrac{16}{9}, \dfrac{16}{27}$

7. $448.75

9. 3 years

Lesson 10: Interpreting Parameters

Practice 2.10.1: Interpreting Parameters, p. 255

1. slope = 3; y-intercept = 12

3. slope = −6; y-intercept = 13

5. growth factor = 4; starting amount = 2; vertical shift = 9

7. slope = 2.5; y-intercept = 7

9. Kendall picks 35 strawberries per minute and started with 20 strawberries in his basket.

Unit 3: Reasoning with Equations

Lesson 1: Solving Equations and Inequalities

Practice 3.1.1: Properties of Equality, pp. 9–10

1. subtraction property of equality
3. division property of equality
5. addition property of equality; $x = 2$
7. addition property of equality; multiplication property of equality; division property of equality
9.

Equation	Steps
$\dfrac{4x}{9} = 20$	Original equation
$4x = 180$	Multiplication property of equality
$x = 45$	Division property of equality

Practice 3.1.2: Solving Linear Equations, p. 20

1. $x = 4$
3. $t = 3$
5. all real numbers
7. $a = 20$
9. $a = 5Kn + k$

Practice 3.1.3: Solving Linear Inequalities, p. 26

1. $x < -2$
3. $x > -3$
5. $x > 2$
7. $x > 3/19$
9. $x < 9/8$

Practice 3.1.4: Solving Exponential Equations, p. 34

1. $x = 4$
3. $x = -2$
5. $x = -3$
7. $x = 4$
9. $x = 3$

Lesson 2: Solving Systems of Equations

Practice 3.2.1: Proving Equivalencies, pp. 43–44

1. $(-18, 82)$
3. infinitely many solutions
5. $(-5, 2)$
7. $\begin{cases} x + y = 10 \\ 1.10x + 1.35y = 12 \end{cases}$; $(6, 4)$; 6 muffins and 4 bottles of milk

9. $\begin{cases} x+y=1750 \\ 0.035x+0.047y=73.85 \end{cases}$; (700, 1050);

$700 was invested at 3.5% and $1,050 was invested at 4.7%.

Practice 3.2.2: Solving Systems of Linear Equations, p. 55

1. one solution: (3, 4)

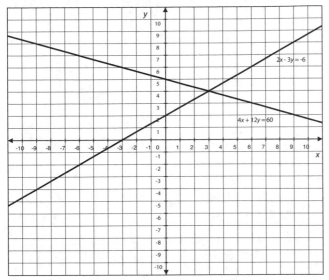

3. infinitely many solutions

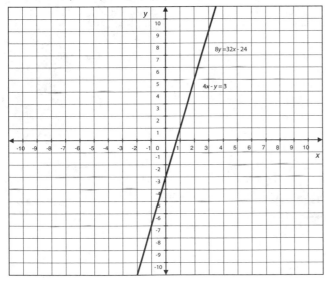

5. $\begin{cases} x+y=10 \\ 1.25x+0.50y=9.50 \end{cases}$; (6, 4); 6 candy bars and 4 chips

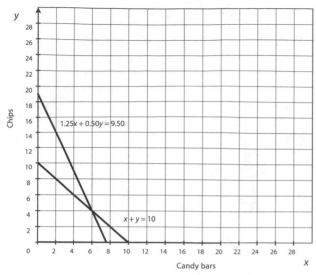

7. $\begin{cases} x+y=14 \\ 5x+15y=100 \end{cases}$; (11, 3);

11 short-answer questions and 3 essay questions

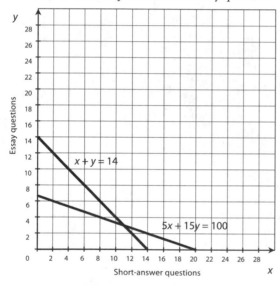

9. $\begin{cases} 0.50x + 1.25y = 29 \\ x + y = 37 \end{cases}$; (23, 14);

Abe sold 23 lollipops and 14 chocolate bars.

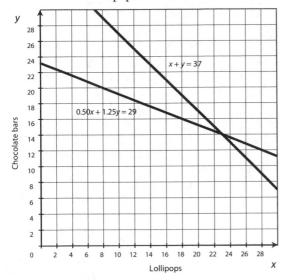

Unit 4: Descriptive Statistics

Lesson 1: Working with a Single Measurement Variable

Practice 4.1.1: Representing Data Sets, pp. 15–17

1. minimum: 58; maximum: 77; median: 69

3.

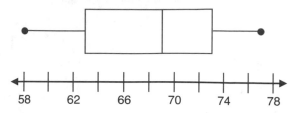

5. Dot plot:

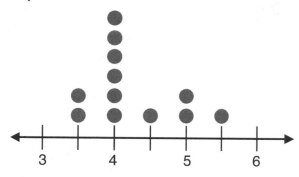

Box plot:

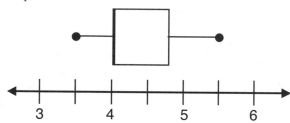

7.

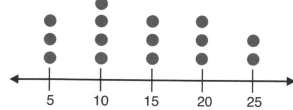

9.

Practice 4.1.2: Comparing Data Sets, pp. 27–29

1. There are not any data values in either data set that are very small or very large, so either measure of center would be appropriate for this data set. We can use the mean.

3. Class 1: 2.43; Class 2: 3.87

5. Tuesday: minimum = 5.00, maximum = 21.40, first quartile = 12.40, median = 15.00, third quartile = 17.10
   Wednesday: minimum = 5.60, maximum = 33.70, first quartile = 8.60, median = 23.50, third quartile: 29.90

7. Chloe's commissions on Tuesday have less variation, and a lower median than her commissions on Wednesday. Her sales are more consistent Tuesday than on Wednesday.

9. It appears that Florida's school lunch prices have a higher mean than South Carolina's school lunch prices. This is seen in the graph by the clustering of data points around a higher value in Florida's dot plot, from 2.25 to 2.75. South Carolina's school lunch prices cluster around the values 1.75 to 2.25.

Practice 4.1.3: Interpreting Data Sets, pp. 39–41

1. Q_1: 2.5, Q_3: 9.5, IQR: 7; 1.5(IQR) = 10.5; $Q_1 - 1.5$(IQR) = 2.5 – 10.5 = –8. There are no data values less than this, so there are no outliers in the lower half of the data. $Q_3 + 1.5$(IQR) = 9.5 + 10.5 = 20. There are no values greater than this value, so there are also no outliers in the upper half of the data.

3. Median: 4.5; mean: 6.05

5. Q_1: 17.5, Q_3: 35, IQR: 17.5; 1.5(IQR) = 26.25; $Q_1 - 1.5$(IQR) = 17.4 – 26.25 = –8.75. There are no data values less than this, so there are no outliers in the lower half of the data. $Q_3 + 1.5$(IQR) = 35 + 26.25 = 61.25. The greatest data value, 65, is greater than this value and is therefore an outlier.

7. Due to the outlier, the data is skewed to the right. The overall range of the data is greater due to the outlier.

9. Because there are no outliers, Jackson can use either the mean or median to estimate his score. Mean: 1,033.33; median: 1,000.

Lesson 2: Working with Two Categorical and Quantitative Variables

Practice 4.2.1: Summarizing Data Using Two-Way Frequency Tables, pp. 50–52

1. Frequency table:

Location	Library	Playground	Recreation center
North	10	8	5
South	9	5	13

3. Conditional frequencies, total number of people:

Location	Library	Playground	Recreation center	Total
North	0.2	0.16	0.1	0.46
South	0.18	0.1	0.26	0.54
Total	0.38	0.26	0.36	1

5. Using the conditional frequencies relative to the total number of people surveyed, the preference for a recreation center by those from the southern part of town has the highest value, followed closely by northern town residents' preference for a library. Northern town residents preferred a library, and southern town residents preferred a recreation center.

7. Marginal frequencies:

Gender	Pizza	Hamburger	Hot dog	Spaghetti	Total
Male	18	17	9	12	56
Female	14	7	13	19	53
Total	32	24	22	31	109

9. Conditional frequencies relative to the total number of people surveyed:

Gender	Pizza	Hamburger	Hot dog	Spaghetti	Total
Male	0.17	0.16	0.08	0.11	0.51
Female	0.13	0.06	0.12	0.17	0.49
Total	0.29	0.22	0.20	0.28	1.00

Practice 4.2.2: Solving Problems Given Functions Fitted to Data, pp. 65–66

1.

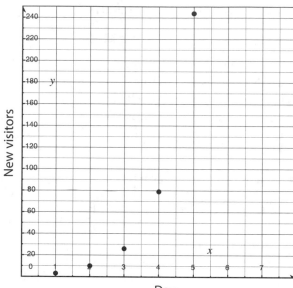

3.

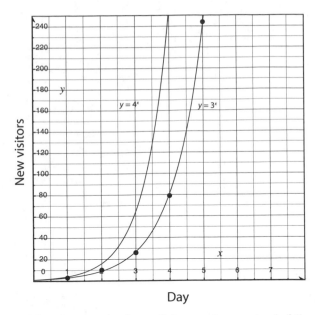

Day

The function $y = 3^x$ is a better fit because it more closely follows the data trend.

5. approximately 2,187 visitors

7. The scatter plot could be estimated using a straight line. A linear function is a better fit for the data.

9. approximately 98 sandwiches

Practice 4.2.3: Analyzing Residuals, pp. 80–82

1.

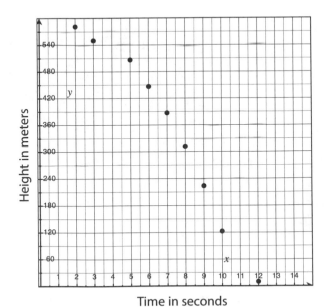

Time in seconds

3. It comes close to the data, but the line does not follow the shape of the data.

5.

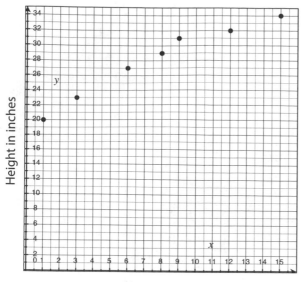

Age in months

7. Yes; it follows the shape of the data set.

9.

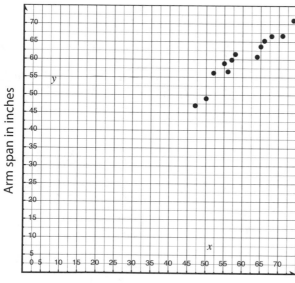

Height in inches

Practice 4.2.4: Fitting Linear Functions to Data, pp. 93–96

1.

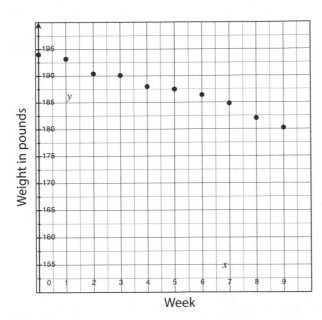

3.

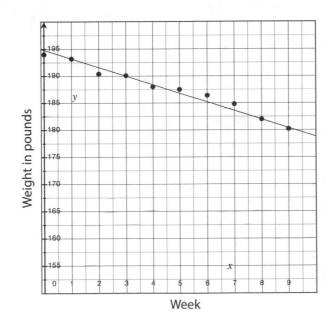

5.

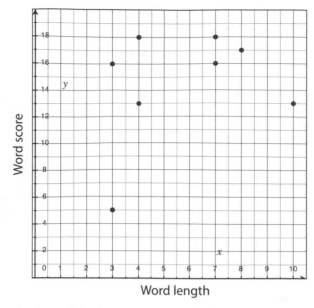

The shape of the data is neither linear nor exponential.

7.

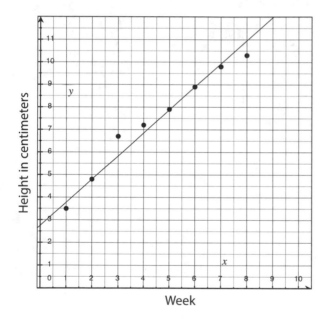

9.

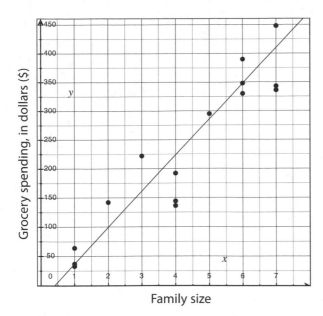

Family size

Lesson 3: Interpreting Linear Models

Practice 4.3.1: Interpreting Slope and *y*-intercept, pp. 108–111

1.

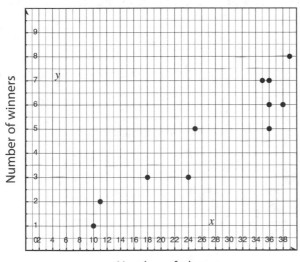

Number of players

3. A player wins the game approximately 19% of the time. In this case, when there are no players, there would be no winners; when $x = 0$, then y should equal 0. The y-intercept is not relevant in this context.

5. Answers may vary; equations should be close to $y = 0.87x + 29.9$.

7. Answers may vary; equations should be close to $y = 18.25x - 6.8$.

9. Answers may vary; equations should be close to $y = 1.80x + 51.21$.

Practice 4.3.2: Calculating and Interpreting the Correlation Coefficient, pp. 122–124

1. weak negative linear correlation

3. no correlation

5.

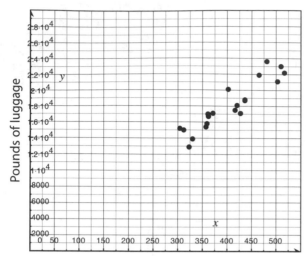

Number of passengers

7. $r = 0.92$; there is a very strong positive linear correlation between the data.

9. There does not appear to be a relationship between the data.

Practice 4.3.3: Distinguishing Between Correlation and Causation, pp. 135–137

1.

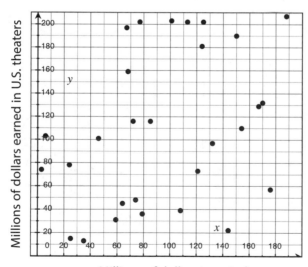

Millions of dollars invested

3. $r = 0.342$; this indicates that there is a weak positive linear correlation between dollars invested and dollars earned by a movie.

5.

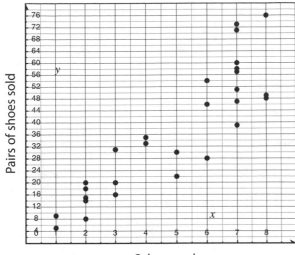

Salespeople

7. $r = 0.892$; this indicates that there is a strong positive linear correlation between number of salespeople and pairs of shoes sold.

9. As the age of cell phone users increases, the number of apps decreases. The graph follows approximately a linear shape with a negative slope.

Unit 5: Congruence, Proof, and Constructions

Lesson 1: Introducing Transformations

Practice 5.1.1: Defining Terms, p. 11
1. circle
3. segment AB
5. point
7. 90°
9. the set of points between two points and the infinite number of points that continue beyond them

Practice 5.1.2: Transformations As Functions, p. 24
1. yes
3. that the image is congruent to the preimage
5. 4
7. $S_{8,-3}$
9. $P(x-3, y+2); h = 3, k = -2$

Practice 5.1.3: Applying Lines of Symmetry, p. 33
1. an infinite number
3. when a right angle is not present
5. 3
7. $360/5 = 72; 72°$
9. 8 inches

Lesson 2: Defining and Applying Rotations, Reflections, and Translations

Practice 5.2.1: Defining Rotations, Reflections, and Translations, p. 41
1. rotation
3. reflection
5. $A'(1,1)$
7. $B''(-2,-5)$
9. $P''(-9,3)$

Practice 5.2.2: Applying Rotations, Reflections, and Translations, p. 49
For problems 1, 2, 8, and 9, check students' graphs for the coordinates and labels listed below.
1. $A''(9,2)$, $B''(14,3)$, and $C''(8,5)$
3. Quadrant I
5. $A'(-2,-2)$, $B'(-5,-2)$, $C'(-5,1)$, and $D'(-2,1)$
7. $r_{y\text{-axis}}$
9. $D''(2,4)$, $E''(1,8)$, and $F''(-2,2)$

Lesson 3: Constructing Lines, Segments, and Angles

Practice 5.3.1: Copying Segments and Angles, pp. 67–68

1–9. Check with your teacher to verify accuracy.

Practice 5.3.2: Bisecting Segments and Angles, pp. 84–85

1–9. Check with your teacher to verify accuracy.

Practice 5.3.3: Constructing Perpendicular and Parallel Lines, p. 103

1–9. Check with your teacher to verify accuracy.

Lesson 4: Constructing Polygons

Practice 5.4.1: Constructing Equilateral Triangles Inscribed in Circles, pp. 121–122

1. Check with your teacher to verify accuracy. Be sure each of the vertices lies on the circle.
3. Check with your teacher to verify accuracy. Be sure each of the vertices lies on the circle.
5. Check with your teacher to verify accuracy. Be sure each of the vertices lies on the circle and the radius of the circle is equal to half the length of the given segment.
7. Check with your teacher to verify accuracy. Be sure each of the vertices lies on the circle.
9. Check with your teacher to verify accuracy. Be sure each of the vertices lies on the circle and the radius of the circle is twice the length of the given segment.

Practice 5.4.2: Constructing Squares Inscribed in Circles, p. 133

1. Check with your teacher to verify accuracy. Be sure each of the vertices lies on the circle.
3. Check with your teacher to verify accuracy. Be sure each of the vertices lies on the circle and the radius of the circle is equal to the length of the given segment.
5. Check with your teacher to verify accuracy. Be sure each of the vertices lies on the circle and the radius of the circle is equal to the length of the given segment.
7. Check with your teacher to verify accuracy. Be sure each of the vertices lies on the circle and the radius of the circle is equal to twice the length of the given segment.
9. Check with your teacher to verify accuracy. Be sure each of the vertices lies on the circle and the radius of the circle is equal to half the length of the given segment.

Practice 5.4.3: Constructing Regular Hexagons Inscribed in Circles, pp. 148–149

1. Check with your teacher to verify accuracy. Be sure each of the vertices lies on the circle.
3. Check with your teacher to verify accuracy. Be sure each of the vertices lies on the circle and the radius of the circle is equal to the length of the given segment.
5. Check with your teacher to verify accuracy. Be sure each of the vertices lies on the circle and the radius of the circle is equal to half the length of the given segment.
7. Check with your teacher to verify accuracy. Be sure each of the vertices lies on the circle and the radius of the circle is equal to the length of the given segment.
9. Check with your teacher to verify accuracy. Be sure each of the vertices lies on the circle and the radius of the circle is equal to twice the length of the given segment.

Lesson 5: Exploring Congruence

Practice 5.5.1: Describing Rigid Motions and Predicting the Effects, pp. 166–170

1. Rotation; the orientation changed, but the images are not mirror reflections of each other.

3. Reflection; the line of reflection is $y = -3$; the orientation changed and the preimage and image are mirror reflections of each other; the line of reflection is the perpendicular bisector of the segments connecting the vertices of the preimage and image.

5.

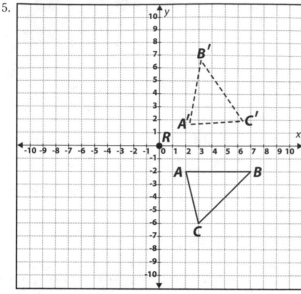

7.

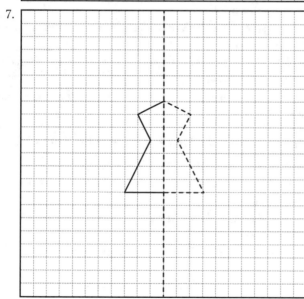

9. Answers may vary. Sample answer: Translate both chairs 2 units to the right.

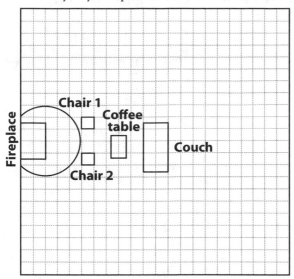

Practice 5.5.2: Defining Congruence in Terms of Rigid Motions, pp. 182–186

1. Congruent; a translation occurred 7 units to the left and 3 units up. Translations are rigid motions.
3. Not congruent; a vertical compression has occurred with a scale factor of 1/2. Compressions are non-rigid motions.
5. Congruent; a reflection has occurred. Reflections are rigid motions.
7. The outer triangle has been dilated by a scale factor of 2/3. Since dilations are non-rigid motions, the triangles are not congruent.
9. The art is a reflection. Since reflections are rigid motions, the A+ on top is congruent to the A+ on the bottom.

Lesson 6: Congruent Triangles

Practice 5.6.1: Triangle Congruency, pp. 197–200

1. Sample answer: $\triangle NLM \cong \triangle HIJ$
3. Sample answer: $\triangle USW \cong \triangle LNQ$
5. $\angle B \cong \angle H$, $\angle D \cong \angle J$, $\angle E \cong \angle L$, $\overline{BD} \cong \overline{HJ}$, $\overline{DE} \cong \overline{JL}$, $\overline{BE} \cong \overline{HL}$
7. Yes, the triangles are congruent; $\triangle DGA \cong \triangle LJH$.
9. Yes, the triangles are congruent; $\triangle BCD \cong \triangle FGE$.

Practice 5.6.2: Explaining ASA, SAS, and SSS, pp. 210–212

1. SAS
3. Congruency cannot be determined; the identified congruent parts form SSA, which is not a triangle congruence statement.
5. Congruency cannot be determined; the identified congruent parts form SSA, which is not a triangle congruence statement.
7. $\triangle DEF \cong \triangle TVS$; SAS
9. The pieces of fabric are congruent; SAS

Unit 6: Connecting Algebra and Geometry Through Coordinates

Lesson 1: Slope and Distance

Practice 6.1.1: Using Coordinates to Prove Geometric Theorems with Slope and Distance, p. 18

1. $\sqrt{20} \approx 4.5$ units

3. Triangle ABC is a right triangle. The slope of $\overline{AB} = 5$, the slope of $\overline{BC} = -\dfrac{3}{2}$, and the slope of $\overline{AC} = \dfrac{2}{3}$. The slopes of $\overline{BC}$ and $\overline{AC}$ are opposite reciprocals of each other; therefore, they are perpendicular and create a right triangle. The distance between points A and B is equal to the square of the lengths of the remaining sides.

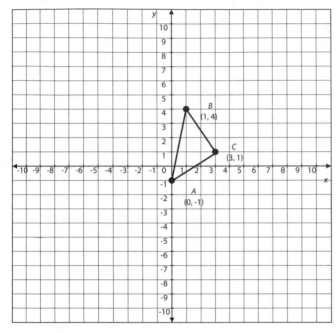

5. Quadrilateral $ABCD$ is not a parallelogram. The slope of $\overline{AB} = 5$, the slope of $\overline{CD} = 6$, the slope of $\overline{BC} = \dfrac{1}{3}$, and the slope of $\overline{AD} = 0$. Opposite sides do not have equal slopes and are therefore not parallel.

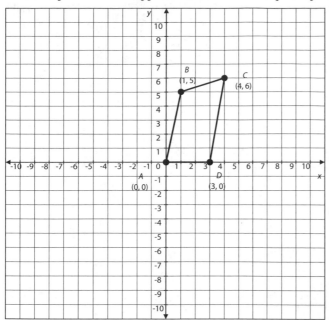

7. Quadrilateral $ABCD$ is a rectangle. $\overline{AB}$ and $\overline{CD}$ are opposite sides and both have a slope of 1. $\overline{BC}$ and $\overline{AD}$ are opposite sides and both have a slope of -1. The slopes of the opposite sides are equal and are therefore parallel. The slope of $\overline{AB}$ is the opposite reciprocal of the slope of sides $\overline{BC}$ and $\overline{AD}$; therefore, they are perpendicular. $\overline{CD}$ is also the opposite reciprocal of the slope of $\overline{BC}$ and $\overline{AD}$; therefore, $\overline{CD}$ is perpendicular to $\overline{BC}$ and $\overline{AD}$. $\overline{AB}$ and $\overline{CD}$ are both $\sqrt{8}$ units long, and $\overline{BC}$ and $\overline{AD}$ are both $\sqrt{50}$ units long; therefore, opposite sides are congruent.

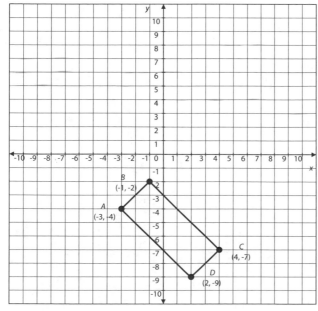

9. Quadrilateral $ABCD$ is a square. The length of each side is 5 units and opposite sides do have the same slope, so they are parallel. $\overline{AB}$ and $\overline{DC}$ are opposite and both have a slope of $\dfrac{4}{3}$, and $\overline{AD}$ and $\overline{BC}$ are opposite and both have a slope of $-\dfrac{3}{4}$. $\dfrac{4}{3}$ and $-\dfrac{3}{4}$ are opposite reciprocals; therefore, the sides are perpendicular and the angles are 90°.

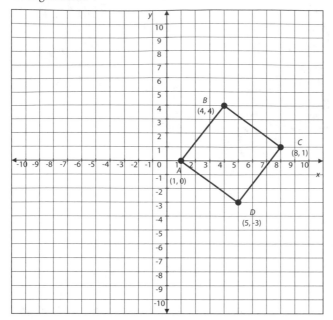

Practice 6.1.2: Working with Parallel and Perpendicular Lines, pp. 30–31

1. $y = 3x - 8$

3. $y = \dfrac{1}{3}x + 7$

5. $\sqrt{\dfrac{80}{25}}$ or ≈ 1.79 units

7. $y = \dfrac{1}{3}x + \dfrac{7}{3}$

9. $y = -2x - 3$

Lesson 2: Lines and Line Segments

Practice 6.2.1: Perimeter and Area, p. 49

1. $3\sqrt{2} + 2\sqrt{29} \approx 15.0$ units

3. $4\sqrt{13} \approx 14.4$ units

5. $6\sqrt{17} \approx 24.7$ units

7. 20 units^2

9. 10.5 units^2

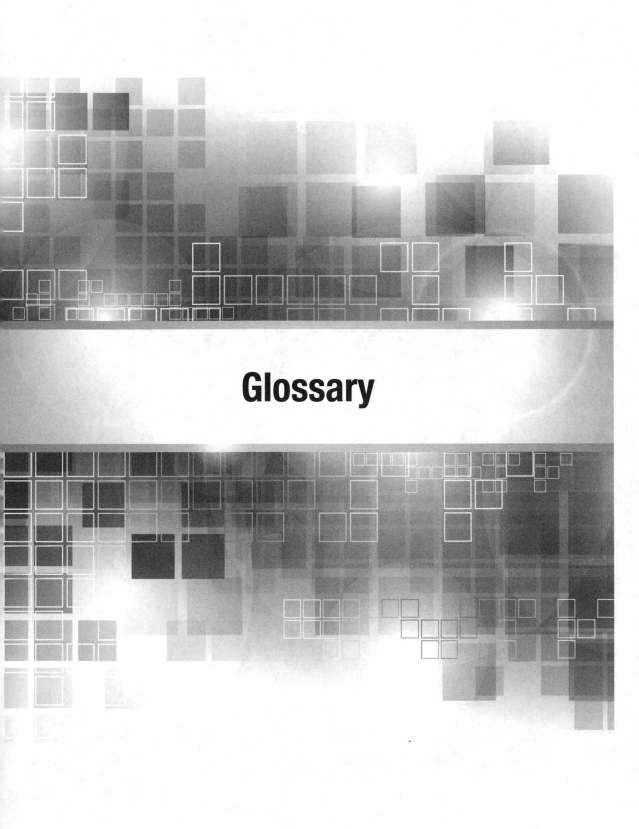

Glossary

Glossary

English		Español
A		
acute angle an angle measuring less than 90° but greater than 0°	U5-1	**ángulo agudo** ángulo que mide menos de 90° pero más de 0°
algebraic expression a mathematical statement that includes numbers, operations, and variables to represent a number or quantity	U1-1	**expresión algebraica** declaración matemática que incluye números, operaciones y variables para representar un número o una cantidad
algebraic inequality an inequality that has one or more variables and contains at least one of the following symbols: $<, >, \leq, \geq,$ or $\neq$	U1-93	**desigualdad algebraica** desigualdad que tiene una o más variables y contiene al menos uno de los siguientes símbolos: $<, >,$ $\leq, \geq, o \neq$
altitude the perpendicular line from a vertex of a figure to its opposite side; height	U5-50	**altitud** línea perpendicular desde un vértice de una figura hasta su lado opuesto; altura
angle two rays or line segments sharing a common endpoint; the symbol used is $\angle$	U5-1 U5-50	**ángulo** dos semirrectas o segmentos de línea que comparten un extremo común; el símbolo utilizado es $\angle$
angle of rotation the measure of the angle created by the preimage vertex to the point of rotation to the image vertex. All of these angles are congruent when a figure is rotated.	U5-150	**ángulo de rotación** medida del ángulo creada por el vértice del preimagen hasta el punto de rotación del vértice del imagen. Todos estos ángulos son congruentes cuando una figura está rotada.
angle-side-angle (ASA) if two angles and the included side of one triangle are congruent to two angles and the included side of another triangle, then the two triangles are congruent	U5-187	**ángulo-lado-ángulo (ASA)** si dos ángulos y el lado incluido de un triángulo son congruentes con los dos ángulos y el lado incluido de otro triángulo, entonces los dos triángulos son congruentes

English		Español
arc length the distance between the endpoints of an arc; written as $d\left(\overset{\frown}{ABC}\right)$	U5-1	**longitud de arco** distancia entre los extremos de un arco; se expresa como $d\left(\overset{\frown}{ABC}\right)$
area the amount of space inside the boundary of a two-dimensional figure	U6-32	**área** cantidad de espacio dentro del límite de una figura bidimensional
arithmetic sequence a linear function with a domain of positive consecutive integers in which the difference between any two consecutive terms is equal	U2-233	**secuencia aritmética** función lineal con dominio de enteros consecutivos positivos, en la que la diferencia entre dos términos consecutivos es equivalente
asymptote a line that a graph gets closer and closer to, but never crosses or touches	U2-82 U2-124	**asíntota** línea a la que se acerca cada vez más un gráfico, pero sin cruzarlo ni tocarlo

B

base the factor being multiplied together in an exponential expression; in the expression a^b, a is the base	U1-1	**base** factor que se multiplica en forma conjunta en una expresión exponencial; en la expresión a^b, a es la base
bisect to cut in half	U5-50	**bisecar** cortar por la mitad
box plot a plot showing the minimum, maximum, first quartile, median, and third quartile of a data set; the middle 50% of the data is indicated by a box. Example:	U4-1	**diagrama de caja** diagrama que muestra el mínimo, máximo, primer cuartil, mediana y tercer cuartil de un conjunto de datos; se indica con una caja el 50% medio de los datos. Ejemplo:

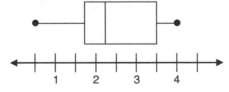

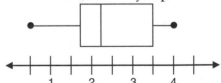

C

causation a relationship between two events where a change in one event is responsible for a change in the second event	U4-97	**causalidad** relación entre dos eventos en la que un cambio en un evento es responsable por un cambio en el segundo evento

English		Español
conditional relative frequency the percentage of a joint frequency as compared to the total number of respondents, total number of people with a given characteristic, or the total number of times a specific response was given	U4-42	**frecuencia condicional relativa** porcentaje de una frecuencia conjunta en comparación con la cantidad total de respondedores, cantidad total de personas con una determinada característica, o cantidad total de veces que se dio una respuesta específica
congruency transformation a transformation in which a geometric figure moves but keeps the same size and shape	U5-150	**transformación de congruencia** transformación en la que se mueve una figura geométrica pero se mantiene el mismo tamaño y la misma forma
congruent figures are congruent if they have the same shape, size, lines, and angles; the symbol for representing congruency between figures is ≅	U5-2 U5-50 U5-104 U5-150 U6-1	**congruente** las figuras son congruentes si tienen la misma forma, tamaño, rectas y ángulos; el símbolo para representar la congruencia entre figuras es ≅
congruent angles two angles that have the same measure	U5-187	**ángulos congruentes** dos ángulos con la misma medida
congruent sides two sides that have the same length	U5-187	**lados congruentes** dos lados con la misma longitud
congruent triangles triangles having the same angle measures and side lengths	U5-187	**triángulos congruentes** triángulos con las mismas medidas de ángulos y longitudes de lados
consistent a system of equations with at least one ordered pair that satisfies both equations	U3-35	**consistente** sistema de ecuaciones con al menos un par ordenado que satisface ambas ecuaciones
constant a quantity that does not change	U1-1	**constante** cantidad que no cambia
constant ratio the number each consecutive term is multiplied by in a geometric sequence	U2-233	**proporción constante** el número que cada término esta multiplicado por en una secuencia geométrica
constraint a restriction or limitation on either the input or output values	U1-93	**limitación** restricción o límite en los valores de entrada o salida

English		Español
circle the set of points on a plane at a certain distance, or radius, from a single point, the center. The set of points forms a two-dimensional curve that measures 360°.	U5-1 U5-104	**círculo** conjunto de punt plano a determinada di: o radio, de un único pui centro. El conjunto de p forma una curva bidime que mide 360°.
circular arc on a circle, the unshared set of points between the endpoints of two radii	U5-2	**arco circular** en un círcul conjunto de puntos no compartidos entre los ex de dos radios
clockwise rotating a figure in the direction that the hands on a clock move	U5-34 U5-150	**sentido horario** rotación figura en la dirección en mueven las agujas de un
coefficient the number multiplied by a variable in an algebraic expression	U1-1	**coeficiente** número multi por una variable en una e algebraica
common difference the number added to each consecutive term in an arithmetic sequence	U2-233	**diferencia común** númerc sumado a cada término consecutivo en una secuei aritmética
compass an instrument for creating circles or transferring measurements that consists of two pointed branches joined at the top by a pivot	U5-50	**compás** instrumento utiliza crear círculos o transferir r que consiste en dos brazos terminados en punta y uni la parte superior por un piv
compression a transformation in which a figure becomes smaller; compressions may be horizontal (affecting only horizontal lengths), vertical (affecting only vertical lengths), or both	U5-150	**compresión** transformación la que una figura se hace má pequeña; las compresiones ser horizontales (cuando afe sólo la longitud horizontal), verticales (cuando afectan só la longitud vertical), o en am sentidos

English		Español
construct to create a precise geometric representation using a straightedge along with either patty paper (tracing paper), a compass, or a reflecting device	U5-50	**construir** crear una representación geométrica precisa mediante regla de borde recto y papel encerado (papel para calcar), compás o un dispositivo de reflexión
construction a precise representation of a figure using a straightedge and a compass, patty paper and a straightedge, or a reflecting device and a straightedge	U5-51 U5-104	**construcción** representación precisa de una figura mediante regla de borde recto y compás, papel encerado y una regla de borde recto, o un dispositivo de reflexión y una regla de borde recto
continuous having no breaks	U2-82	**continuo** sin interrupciones
coordinate plane a set of two number lines, called the axes, that intersect at right angles	U1-49	**plano de coordenadas** conjunto de dos rectas numéricas, denominadas ejes, que se cortan en ángulos rectos
correlation a relationship between two events, where a change in one event is related to a change in the second event. A correlation between two events does not imply that the first event is responsible for the change in the second event; the correlation only shows how likely it is that a change also took place in the second event.	U4-97	**correlación** relación entre dos eventos en la que el cambio en un evento se relaciona con un cambio en el segundo evento. Una correlación entre dos eventos no implica que el primero sea responsable del cambio en el segundo; la correlación sólo demuestra cuán probable es que también se produzca un cambio en el segundo evento.

English		Español
correlation coefficient a quantity that assesses the strength of a linear relationship between two variables, ranging from −1 to 1; a correlation coefficient of −1 indicates a strong negative correlation, a correlation coefficient of 1 indicates a strong positive correlation, and a correlation coefficient of 0 indicates a very weak or no linear correlation	U4-98	**coeficiente de correlación** cantidad que evalúa la fuerza de una relación lineal entre dos variables, que varía de −1 a 1; un coeficiente de correlación de −1 indica una fuerte correlación negativa, un coeficiente de correlación de 1 indica una fuerte correlación positiva, y un coeficiente de correlación de 0 indica una correlación muy débil o no lineal
corresponding angles angles of two figures that lie in the same position relative to the figure. In transformations, the corresponding vertices are the preimage and image vertices, so $\angle A$ and $\angle A'$ are corresponding vertices and so on.	U5-150 U5-187	**ángulos correspondientes** ángulos de dos figuras que se ubican en la misma posición relativa a la figura. En las transformaciones, los vértices correspondientes son los vértices de preimagen e imagen, de manera que $\angle A$ y $\angle A'$ son los vértices correspondientes, etc.
Corresponding Parts of Congruent Triangles are Congruent (CPCTC) if two or more triangles are proven congruent, then all of their corresponding parts are congruent as well	U5-187	**Las partes correspondientes de triángulos congruentes son congruentes (CPCTC)** si se comprueba que dos o más triángulos son congruentes, entonces todas sus partes correspondientes son también congruentes
corresponding sides sides of two figures that lie in the same position relative to the figure. In transformations, the corresponding sides are the preimage and image sides, so $\overline{AB}$ and $\overline{A'B'}$ are corresponding sides and so on.	U5-151 U5-187	**lados correspondientes** lados de dos figuras que están en la misma posición relativa a la figura. En las transformaciones, los lados correspondientes son los de preimagen e imagen, entonces $\overline{AB}$ y $\overline{A'B'}$ son los lados correspondientes, etc.

English		Español
counterclockwise rotating a figure in the opposite direction that the hands on a clock move	U5-34 U5-151	**en sentido antihorario** rotación de una figura en la dirección opuesta a la que se mueven las agujas de un reloj
curve the graphical representation of the solution set for $y = f(x)$; in the special case of a linear equation, the curve will be a line	U2-1	**curva** representación gráfica del conjunto de soluciones para $y = f(x)$; en el caso especial de una ecuación lineal, la curva será una recta

D

English		Español
dependent a system of equations that has an infinite number of solutions; lines coincide when graphed	U3-35	**dependiente** sistema de ecuaciones con una cantidad infinita de soluciones; las rectas coinciden cuando se grafican
dependent variable labeled on the y-axis; the quantity that is based on the input values of the independent variable; the output variable of a function	U1-49 U2-1	**variable dependiente** designada en el eje y; cantidad que se basa en los valores de entrada de la variable independiente; variable de salida de una función
diameter a straight line passing through the center of a circle connecting two points on the circle; twice the radius	U5-104	**diámetro** línea recta que pasa por el centro de un círculo y conecta dos puntos en el círculo; dos veces el radio
dilation a transformation in which a figure is either enlarged or reduced by a scale factor in relation to a center point	U5-151	**dilatación** transformación en la que una figura se amplía o se reduce por un factor de escala en relación con un punto central
discrete individually separate and distinct	U2-69	**discreto** individualmente aparte y distinto
distance along a line the linear distance between two points on a given line; written as $d(PQ)$	U5-2	**distancia a lo largo de una recta** distancia lineal entre dos puntos de una determinada línea; se expresa como $d(PQ)$

English		Español

distance formula formula that
states the distance between points
(x_1, y_1) and (x_2, y_2) is equal to
$\sqrt{(x_2 - x_1)^2 + (y_2 - y_1)^2}$

U6-1
U6-32

fórmula de distancia fórmula
que establece la distancia entre los
puntos (x_1, y_1) y (x_2, y_2) equivale a
$\sqrt{(x_2 - x_1)^2 + (y_2 - y_1)^2}$

domain the set of all inputs of a
function; the set of x-values that
are valid for the function

U2-2
U2-82

dominio conjunto de todas
las entradas de una función;
conjunto de valores x que son
válidos para la función

dot plot a frequency plot that
shows the number of times a
response occurred in a data
set, where each data value is
represented by a dot. Example:

U4-2

diagrama de puntos diagrama de
frecuencia que muestra la cantidad de
veces que se produjo una respuesta en
un conjunto de datos, en el que cada
valor de dato está representado por
un punto. Ejemplo:

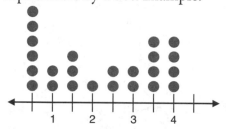

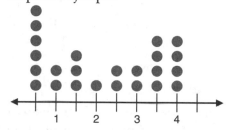

drawing a precise representation
of a figure, created with
measurement tools such as a
protractor and a ruler

U5-51

dibujo representación precisa
de una figura, creada con
herramientas de medición tales
como transportador y regla

E

elimination method adding or
subtracting the equations in
the system together so that one
of the variables is eliminated;
multiplication might be necessary
before adding the equations
together

U3-35

método de eliminación suma
o sustracción conjunta de
ecuaciones en el sistema de
manera de eliminar una de las
variables; podría requerirse
multiplicación antes de la suma
conjunta de las ecuaciones

end behavior the behavior of the
graph as x approaches positive
infinity and as x approaches
negative infinity

U2-124

comportamiento final el
comportamiento de la gráfica al
aproximarse x a infinito positivo
o a infinito negativo

English		Español
endpoint either of two points that mark the ends of a line segment; a point that marks the end of a ray	U5-51	**extremo** uno de los dos puntos que marcan el final de un segmento de recta; punto que marca el final de una semirrecta
equation a mathematical sentence that uses an equal sign (=) to show that two quantities are equal	U1-14 U2-192	**ecuación** declaración matemática que utiliza el signo igual (=) para demostrar que dos cantidades son equivalentes
equidistant the same distance from a reference point	U5-51 U5-151	**equidistante** a la misma distancia de un punto de referencia
equilateral triangle a triangle with all three sides equal in length	U5-104	**triángulo equilátero** triángulo con sus tres lados de la misma longitud
explicit equation an equation describing the nth term of a pattern	U2-192	**ecuación explícita** ecuación que describe el *enésimo* término de un patrón
explicit formula a formula used to find the nth term of a sequence; the explicit formula for an arithmetic sequence is $a_n = a_1 + (n-1)d$; the explicit formula for a geometric sequence is $a_n = a_1 \bullet r^{n-1}$	U2-69 U2-233	**fórmula explícita** fórmula utilizada para encontrar el *enésimo* término de una secuencia; la fórmula explícita para una secuencia aritmética es $a_n = a_1 + (n-1)d$; la fórmula explícita para una secuencia geométrica es $a_n = a_1 \bullet r^{n-1}$
exponent the number of times a factor is being multiplied together in an exponential expression; in the expression a^b, b is the exponent	U1-1	**exponente** cantidad de veces que se multiplica un factor en forma conjunta en una expresión exponencial; en la expresión a^b, b es el exponente
exponential decay an exponential equation with a base, b, that is between 0 and 1 ($0 < b < 1$); can be represented by the formula $y = a(1 - r)^t$, where a is the initial value, $(1 - r)$ is the decay rate, t is time, and y is the final value	U1-14 U1-49	**decaimiento exponencial** ecuación exponencial con una base, b, que está entre 0 y 1 ($0 < b < 1$); puede representarse con la fórmula $y = a(1 - r)^t$, en la que a es el valor inicial, $(1 - r)$ es la tasa de decaimiento, t es el tiempo, y y es el valor final

English		Español

exponential equation an equation that has a variable in the exponent; the general form is $y = a \bullet b^x$, where a is the initial value, b is the base, x is the time, and y is the final output value. Another form is $y = ab^{\frac{x}{t}}$, where t is the time it takes for the base to repeat.

U1-14
U1-49
U2-192

ecuación exponencial ecuación con una variable en el exponente; la forma general es $y = a \bullet b^x$, en la que a es el valor inicial, b es la base, x es el tiempo, y y es el valor final de salida. Otra forma es $y = ab^{\frac{x}{t}}$, en la que t es el tiempo que tarda la base en repetirse.

exponential function a function that has a variable in the exponent:

U2-124
U2-152
U2-245

función exponencial función con una variable en el exponente:

- the general form is $f(x) = ab^x$, where a is the initial value, b is the growth or decay factor, x is the time, and $f(x)$ is the final output value
- can also be written in the form $f(x) = b^x + k$, where b is a positive integer not equal to 1 and k can equal 0; the parameters are b and k. b is the growth factor and k is the vertical shift.

- la forma general es $f(x) = ab^x$, en la que a es el valor inicial, b es el factor de crecimiento o decaimiento, x es el tiempo, y $f(x)$ es el valor de salida
- también puede expresarse en la forma $f(x) = b^x + k$, en donde b es un entero positivo diferente de 1 y k puede ser igual a 0; los parámetros son b y k. b es el factor de crecimiento y k es el desplazamiento vertical.

exponential growth an exponential equation with a base, b, greater than 1 ($b > 1$); can be represented by the formula $y = a(1 + r)^t$, where a is the initial value, $(1 + r)$ is the growth rate, t is time, and y is the final value

U1-14
U1-50

crecimiento exponencial ecuación exponencial con una base, b, mayor que 1 ($b > 1$); puede representarse con la fórmula $y = a(1 + r)^t$, en la que a es el valor inicial, $(1 + r)$ es la tasa de crecimiento, t es el tiempo, y y es el valor final

English		Español
expression a combination of variables, quantities, and mathematical operations; 4, 8x, and $b + 10^2$ are all expressions.	U2-192	**expresión** combinación de variables, cantidades y operaciones matemáticas; 4, 8x, y $b + 10^2$ son todas expresiones.
extrema the minima and maxima of a function	U2-82	**extremos** los mínimos y máximos de una función

F

factor one of two or more numbers or expressions that when multiplied produce a given product	U1-1 U2-152	**factor** uno de dos o más números o expresiones que cuando se multiplican generan un producto determinado
first quartile the value that identifies the lower 25% of the data; the median of the lower half of the data set; written as Q_1	U4-2	**primer cuartil** valor que identifica el 25% inferior de los datos; mediana de la mitad inferior del conjunto de datos; se expresa Q_1
formula a literal equation that states a specific rule or relationship among quantities	U1-101	**fórmula** ecuación literal que establece una regla específica o relación entre cantidades
function a relation in which every element of the domain is paired with exactly one element of the range; that is, for every value of x, there is exactly one value of y.	U2-2 U2-192 U2-216 U4-42	**función** relación en la que cada elemento de un dominio se combina con exactamente un elemento del rango; es decir, para cada valor de x, existe exactamente un valor de y.
function notation a way to name a function using $f(x)$ instead of y	U2-2	**notación de función** forma de nombrar una función con el uso de $f(x)$ en lugar de y

G

geometric sequence an exponential function that results in a sequence of numbers separated by a constant ratio	U2-233	**secuencia geométrica** función exponencial que produce como resultado una secuencia de números separados por una proporción constante

English		Español
graphing method solving a system by graphing equations on the same coordinate plane and finding the point of intersection	U3-35	**método de representación gráfica** resolución de un sistema mediante graficación de ecuaciones en el mismo plano de coordenadas y hallazgo del punto de intersección
growth factor the multiple by which a quantity increases or decreases over time	U2-152	**factor de crecimiento** múltiplo por el que aumenta o disminuye una cantidad con el tiempo

H

English		Español
half plane a region containing all points that has one boundary, a straight line that continues in both directions infinitely	U2-41	**semiplano** región que contiene todos los puntos y que tiene un límite, una línea recta que continúa en ambas direcciones de manera infinita
histogram a frequency plot that shows the number of times a response or range of responses occurred in a data set. Example:	U4-2	**histograma** diagrama de frecuencia que muestra la cantidad de veces que se produce una respuesta o rango de respuestas en un conjunto de datos. Ejemplo:

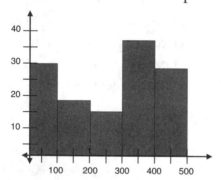   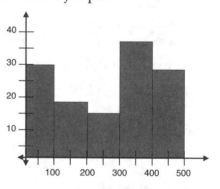

I

English		Español
image the new, resulting figure after a transformation	U5-2 U5-151	**imagen** nueva figura resultante después de una transformación
included angle the angle between two sides	U5-187	**ángulo incluido** ángulo entre dos lados
included side the side between two angles of a triangle	U5-188	**lado incluido** lado entre dos ángulos de un triángulo

English		Español
inclusive a graphed line or boundary is part of an inequality's solution	U2-41	**inclusivo** línea graficada o límite que forma parte de una solución de desigualdad
inconsistent a system of equations with no solutions; lines are parallel when graphed	U3-35	**inconsistente** sistema de ecuaciones sin soluciones; las líneas son paralelas cuando se las grafica
independent a system of equations with exactly one solution	U3-36	**independiente** sistema de ecuaciones con una solución exacta
independent variable labeled on the x-axis; the quantity that changes based on values chosen; the input variable of a function	U1-50 U2-2	**variable independiente** designada en el eje x; cantidad que cambia según valores seleccionados; variable de entrada de una función
inequality a mathematical sentence that shows the relationship between quantities that are not equivalent	U1-15 U1-93	**desigualdad** declaración matemática que demuestra la relación entre cantidades que no son equivalentes
inscribe to draw one figure within another figure so that every vertex of the enclosed figure touches the outside figure	U5-104	**inscribir** dibujar una figura dentro de otra de manera que cada vértice de la figura interior toque la exterior
integer a number that is not a fraction or a decimal	U2-82	**entero** número que no es una fracción ni un decimal
intercept the point at which a line intersects the x- or y-axis	U2-41 U2-82	**intersección** punto en el que una recta corta el eje x o y
interquartile range the difference between the third and first quartiles; 50% of the data is contained within this range	U4-2	**rango intercuartílico** diferencia entre el tercer y primer cuartil; el 50% de los datos está contenido dentro de este rango
interval a continuous series of values	U2-82 U2-152	**intervalo** serie continua de valores
inverse a number that when multiplied by the original number has a product of 1	U1-101	**inverso** número que cuando se lo multiplica por el número original tiene un producto de 1

English		Español
irrational numbers numbers that cannot be written as $\dfrac{a}{b}$, where a and b are integers and $b \neq 0$; any number that cannot be written as a decimal that ends or repeats	U2-82	**números irracionales** números que no pueden expresarse como $\dfrac{a}{b}$, en los que a y b son enteros y $b \neq 0$; cualquier número que no puede expresarse como decimal finito o periódico
isometry a transformation in which the preimage and image are congruent	U5-2 U5-151	**isometría** transformación en la que la preimagen y la imagen son congruentes

J

English		Español
joint frequency the number of times a specific response is given by people with a given characteristic; the cell values in a two-way frequency table	U4-42	**frecuencia conjunta** cantidad de veces que personas con una determinada característica brindan una respuesta específica; valores de celdas en una tabla de frecuencia de doble entrada

L

English		Español
laws of exponents rules that must be followed when working with exponents	U3-1	**leyes de los exponentes** normas que deben cumplirse cuando se trabaja con exponentes
like terms terms that contain the same variables raised to the same power	U1-1	**términos semejantes** términos que contienen las mismas variables elevadas a la misma potencia
line the set of points between two points P and Q in a plane and the infinite number of points that continue beyond those points; written as $\overleftrightarrow{PQ}$	U5-2 U5-51	**línea recta** conjunto de puntos entre dos puntos P y Q en un plano y cantidad infinita de puntos que continúan más allá de esos puntos; se expresa como $\overleftrightarrow{PQ}$
line of reflection the perpendicular bisector of the segments that connect the corresponding vertices of the preimage and the image	U5-151	**línea de reflexión** bisectriz perpendicular de los segmentos que conectan los vértices correspondientes de la preimagen y la imagen

English		Español
line of symmetry a line separating a figure into two halves that are mirror images; written as ℓ	U5-2	**línea de simetría** línea que separa una figura en dos mitades que son imágenes en espejo; se expresa como ℓ
line segment a line with two endpoints; written as $\overline{PQ}$	U5-2	**segmento de recta** recta con dos extremos; se expresa como $\overline{PQ}$
line symmetry exists for a figure if for every point on one side of the line of symmetry, there is a corresponding point the same distance from the line	U5-2	**simetría lineal** la que existe en una figura si para cada punto a un lado de la línea de simetría, hay un punto correspondiente a la misma distancia de la línea
linear equation an equation that can be written in the form $ax + by = c$, where a, b, and c are rational numbers; can also be written as $y = mx + b$, in which m is the slope, b is the y-intercept, and the graph is a straight line. The solutions to the linear equation are the infinite set of points on the line.	U1-15 U1-50 U2-2 U2-193	**ecuación lineal** ecuación que puede expresarse en la forma $ax + by = c$, en la que a, b, y c son números racionales; también puede escribirse como $y = mx + b$, en donde m es la pendiente, b es el intercepto de y, y la gráfica es una línea recta. Las soluciones de la ecuación lineal son el conjunto infinito de puntos en la recta.
linear fit (or linear model) an approximation of data using a linear function	U4-98	**ajuste lineal (o modelo lineal)** aproximación de datos con el uso de una función lineal
linear function a function that can be written in the form $f(x) = mx + b$, in which m is the slope, b is the y-intercept, and the graph is a straight line	U2-124 U2-193 U2-245	**función lineal** función que puede expresarse en la forma $f(x) = mx + b$, en la que m es la pendiente, b es el intercepto de y, y la gráfica es una línea recta
literal equation an equation that involves two or more variables	U1-101	**ecuación literal** ecuación que incluye dos o más variables

M

marginal frequency the total number of times a specific response is given, or the total number of people with a given characteristic	U4-43	**frecuencia marginal** cantidad total de veces que se da una respuesta específica, o cantidad total de personas con una determinada característica

English		Español
mean the average value of a data set, found by summing all values and dividing by the number of data points	U4-2	**media** valor promedio de un conjunto de datos, que se determina al sumar todos los valores y dividirlos por la cantidad de puntos de datos
mean absolute deviation the average absolute value of the difference between each data point and the mean; found by summing the absolute value of the difference between each data point and the mean, then dividing this sum by the total number of data points	U4-2	**desviación media absoluta** valor promedio absoluto de la diferencia entre cada punto de datos y la media; se determina mediante la suma del valor absoluto de la diferencia entre cada punto de datos y la media, y luego se divide esta suma por la cantidad total de puntos de datos
measures of center values that describe expected and repeated data values in a data set; the mean and median are two measures of center	U4-3	**medidas de centro** valores que describen los valores de datos esperados y repetidos de un conjunto de datos; la media y la mediana son dos medidas de centro
measures of spread a measure that describes the variance of data values, and identifies the diversity of values in a data set	U4-3	**medidas de dispersión** medidas que describen la varianza de los valores de datos e identifican la diversidad de valores en un conjunto de datos
median 1. the middle-most value of a data set; 50% of the data is less than this value, and 50% is greater than it 2. the segment joining the vertex to the midpoint of the opposite side	U4-3 U5-51	**mediana** 1. valor medio exacto de un conjunto de datos; el 50% de los datos es menor que ese valor, y el otro 50% es mayor 2. segmento que une el vértice con el punto medio del lado opuesto
midpoint a point on a line segment that divides the segment into two equal parts	U5-51	**punto medio** punto en un segmento de recta que lo divide en dos partes iguales
midsegment a line segment joining the midpoints of two sides of a figure	U5-51	**segmento medio** segmento de recta que une los puntos medios de dos lados de una figura

English		Español
N		
natural numbers the set of positive integers {1, 2, 3, ..., *n*}	U2-69 U2-82	**números naturales** conjunto de enteros positivos {1, 2, 3, ..., *n*}
negative function a portion of a function where the *y*-values are less than 0 for all *x*-values	U2-82	**función negativa** porción de una función en la que los valores *y* son menores que 0 para todos los valores *x*
non-inclusive a graphed line or boundary is not part of an inequality's solution	U2-41	**no inclusivo** línea graficada o límite que no forma parte de una solución de desigualdad
non-rigid motion a transformation done to a figure that changes the figure's shape and/or size	U5-151	**movimiento no rígido** transformación hecha a una figura que cambia su forma o tamaño
O		
obtuse angle an angle measuring greater than 90° but less than 180°	U5-2	**ángulo obtuso** ángulo que mide más de 90° pero menos de 180°
one-to-one a relationship wherein each point in a set of points is mapped to exactly one other point	U5-2	**unívoca** relación en la que cada punto de un conjunto de puntos se corresponde con otro con exactitud
order of operations the order in which expressions are evaluated from left to right (grouping symbols, evaluating exponents, completing multiplication and division, completing addition and subtraction)	U1-2	**orden de las operaciones** orden en el que se evalúan las expresiones de izquierda a derecha (con agrupación de símbolos, evaluación de exponentes, realización de multiplicaciones y divisiones, sumas y sustracciones)
ordered pair a pair of values (x, y) where the order is significant	U2-2	**par ordenado** par de valores (x, y), en los que el orden es significativo

English		Español
outlier a data value that is much greater than or much less than the rest of the data in a data set; mathematically, any data less than $Q_1 - 1.5(IQR)$ or greater than $Q_3 + 1.5(IQR)$ is an outlier	U4-3	**valor atípico** valor de datos que es mucho mayor o mucho menor que el resto de los datos de un conjunto de datos; en matemática, cualquier dato menor que $Q_1 - 1,5(IQR)$ o mayor que $Q_3 + 1,5(IQR)$ es un valor atípico

	P	
parallel lines that never intersect and have equal slope	U6-1	**paralelas** líneas que nunca llegan a cortarse y tienen la misma pendiente
parallel lines lines in a plane that either do not share any points and never intersect, or share all points; written as $\overleftrightarrow{AB} \parallel \overleftrightarrow{PQ}$	U5-2 U5-51	**líneas paralelas** líneas en un plano que no comparten ningún punto y nunca se cortan, o que comparten todos los puntos; se expresan como $\overleftrightarrow{AB} \parallel \overleftrightarrow{PQ}$
parallelogram a quadrilateral with opposite sides parallel	U6-1	**paralelogramo** cuadrilátero con lados opuestos paralelos
parameter a term in a function that determines a specific form of a function but not the nature of the function	U2-245	**parámetro** término en una función que determina una forma específica de una función pero no su naturaleza
perimeter the distance around a two-dimensional figure	U6-32	**perímetro** distancia alrededor de una figura bidimensional
perpendicular lines that intersect at a right angle (90°); their slopes are opposite reciprocals	U6-1	**perpendiculares** líneas que se cortan en ángulo recto (90°); sus pendientes son recíprocas opuestas
perpendicular bisector a line constructed through the midpoint of a segment	U5-51	**bisectriz perpendicular** línea que se construye a través del punto medio de un segmento
perpendicular lines two lines that intersect at a right angle (90°); written as $\overleftrightarrow{AB} \perp \overleftrightarrow{PQ}$	U5-2 U5-51	**líneas perpendiculares** dos líneas que se cortan en ángulo recto (90°); se expresan como $\overleftrightarrow{AB} \perp \overleftrightarrow{PQ}$

English		Español
point an exact position or location in a given plane	U5-2	**punto** posición o ubicación exacta en un plano determinado
point of intersection the point at which two lines cross or meet	U3-36	**punto de intersección** punto en que se cruzan o encuentran dos líneas
point of rotation the fixed location that an object is turned around; the point can lie on, inside, or outside the figure	U5-151	**punto de rotación** ubicación fija en torno a la que gira un objeto; el punto puede estar encima, dentro o fuera de la figura
polygon two-dimensional figure with at least three sides	U6-32	**polígono** figura bidimensional con al menos tres lados
positive function a portion of a function where the y-values are greater than 0 for all x-values	U2-82	**función positiva** porción de una función en la que los valores y son mayores que 0 para todos los valores x
postulate a true statement that does not require a proof	U5-188	**postulado** afirmación verdadera que no requiere prueba
preimage the original figure before undergoing a transformation	U5-2 U5-151	**preimagen** figura original antes de sufrir una transformación
properties of equality rules that allow you to balance, manipulate, and solve equations	U3-1	**propiedades de igualdad** normas que permiten equilibrar, manipular y resolver ecuaciones
properties of inequality rules that allow you to balance, manipulate, and solve inequalities	U3-1	**propiedades de desigualdad** normas que permiten equilibrar, manipular y resolver desigualdades

Q

quadrant the coordinate plane is separated into four sections:	U5-34	**cuadrante** plano de coordenadas que se divide en cuatro secciones:
• In Quadrant I, x and y are positive.		• En el cuadrante I, x y y son positivos.
• In Quadrant II, x is negative and y is positive.		• En el cuadrante II, x es negativo y y es positivo.
• In Quadrant III, x and y are negative.		• En el cuadrante III, x y y son negativos.
• In Quadrant IV, x is positive and y is negative.		• En el cuadrante IV, x es positivo y y es negativo.

English		Español
quadrilateral a polygon with four sides	U6-1	**cuadrilátero** polígono con cuatro lados
quantity something that can be compared by assigning a numerical value	U1-15	**cantidad** algo que puede compararse al asignarle un valor numérico

R

English		Español
radius a line segment that extends from the center of a circle to a point on the circle. Its length is half the diameter.	U5-104	**radio** segmento de línea que se extiende desde el centro de un círculo hasta un punto de la circunferencia del círculo. Su longitud es la mitad del diámetro.
range the set of all outputs of a function; the set of y-values that are valid for the function	U2-2	**rango** conjunto de todas las salidas de una función; conjunto de valores y válidos para la función
rate a ratio that compares different kinds of units	U1-15	**tasa** proporción en que se comparan distintos tipos de unidades
rate of change a ratio that describes how much one quantity changes with respect to the change in another quantity; also known as the slope of a line	U2-82 U2-152	**tasa de cambio** proporción que describe cuánto cambia una cantidad con respecto al cambio de otra cantidad; también se la conoce como pendiente de una recta
ratio the relation between two quantities; can be expressed in words, fractions, decimals, or as a percent	U2-82	**proporción** relación entre dos cantidades; puede expresarse en palabras, fracciones, decimales o como porcentaje
rational number a number that can be written as $\frac{a}{b}$, where a and b are integers and $b \neq 0$; any number that can be written as a decimal that ends or repeats	U2-82	**número racional** número que puede expresarse como $\frac{a}{b}$, en los que a y b son enteros y $b \neq 0$; cualquier número que puede escribirse como decimal finito o periódico
ray a line with only one endpoint; written as $\overrightarrow{PQ}$	U5-2 U5-51	**semirrecta** línea con un solo extremo; se expresa como $\overrightarrow{PQ}$

English		Español
real numbers the set of all rational and irrational numbers	U2-82	**números reales** conjunto de todos los números racionales e irracionales
reciprocal a number that when multiplied by the original number has a product of 1	U1-101	**recíproco** número que cuando se lo multiplica por el número original tiene un producto de 1
rectangle a parallelogram with opposite sides that are congruent and consecutive sides that are perpendicular	U6-1	**rectángulo** paralelogramo con lados opuestos congruentes y lados consecutivos que son perpendiculares
recursive formula a formula used to find the next term of a sequence when the previous term or terms are known; the recursive formula for an arithmetic sequence is $a_n = a_{n-1} + d$; the recursive formula for a geometric sequence is $a_n = a_{n-1} \bullet r$	U2-69 U2-234	**fórmula recursiva** fórmula que se utiliza para encontrar el término siguiente de una secuencia cuando se conoce el o los términos anteriores; la fórmula recursiva de una secuencia aritmética es $a_n = a_{n-1} + d$; la fórmula recursiva para una secuencia geométrica es $a_n = a_{n-1} \bullet r$
reflection a transformation where a mirror image is created; also called a flip; an isometry in which a figure is moved along a line perpendicular to a given line called the line of reflection	U5-2 U5-34	**reflexión** transformación por la cual se crea una imagen en espejo; isometría en la que se mueve una figura a lo largo de una línea perpendicular hacia una recta determinada llamada línea de reflexión
regular hexagon a six-sided polygon with all sides equal and all angles measuring 120°	U5-104	**hexágono regular** polígono de seis lados con todos los lados iguales y en el que todos los ángulos miden 120°
regular polygon a two-dimensional figure with all sides and all angles congruent	U5-104 U5-2	**polígono regular** figura bidimensional con todos los lados y todos los ángulos congruentes
relation a relationship between two sets of elements	U2-2	**relación** conexión entre dos conjuntos de elementos

English		Español
relative maximum the greatest value of a function for a particular interval of the function	U2-82	**máximo relativo** el mayor valor de una función para un intervalo particular de la función
relative minimum the least value of a function for a particular interval of the function	U2-82	**mínimo relativo** el menor valor de una función para un intervalo particular de la función
residual the vertical distance between an observed data value and an estimated data value on a line of best fit	U4-43	**residual** distancia vertical entre un valor de datos observado y un valor de datos estimado sobre una línea de ajuste óptimo
residual plot provides a visual representation of the residuals for a set of data; contains the points (*x*, residual for *x*)	U4-43	**diagrama residual** brinda una representación visual de los residuales para un conjunto de datos; contiene los puntos (*x*, residual de *x*)
rhombus a parallelogram with four congruent sides	U6-1	**rombo** paralelograma con cuatro lados congruentes
right angle an angle measuring 90°	U5-3	**ángulo recto** ángulo que mide 90°
rigid motion a transformation done to a figure that maintains the figure's shape and size or its segment lengths and angle measures	U5-151 U5-188	**movimiento rígido** transformación que se realiza a una figura que mantiene su forma y tamaño o las longitudes de sus segmentos y las medidas de ángulos
rotation a transformation that turns a figure around a point; also called a turn; an isometry where all points in the preimage are moved along circular arcs determined by the center of rotation and the angle of rotation	U5-3 U5-35	**rotación** transformación que hace girar una figura alrededor de un punto; isometría en la que todos los puntos de la preimagen se mueven a lo largo de arcos circulares determinados por el centro de rotación y el ángulo de rotación

English		Español
	S	
scale factor a multiple of the lengths of the sides from one figure to the transformed figure. If the scale factor is larger than 1, then the figure is enlarged. If the scale factor is between 0 and 1, then the figure is reduced.	U5-151	**factor de escala** múltiplo de las longitudes de los lados de una figura a la figura transformada. Si el factor de escala es mayor que 1, entonces la figura se agranda. Si el factor de escala se encuentra entre 0 y 1, entonces la figura se reduce.
scatter plot a graph of data in two variables on a coordinate plane, where each data pair is represented by a point	U4-43	**diagrama de dispersión** gráfica de datos en dos variables en un plano de coordenadas, en la que cada par de datos está representado por un punto
segment a part of a line that is noted by two endpoints	U5-51	**segmento** parte de una recta comprendida entre dos extremos
sequence an ordered list of numbers	U2-69	**secuencia** lista ordenada de números
side-angle-side (SAS) if two sides and the included angle of one triangle are congruent to two sides and the included angle of another triangle, then the two triangles are congruent	U5-188	**lado-ángulo-lado (SAS)** si dos lados y el ángulo incluido de un triángulo son congruentes con dos lados y el ángulo incluido de otro triángulo, entonces los dos triángulos son congruentes
side-side-side (SSS) if three sides of one triangle are congruent to three sides of another triangle, then the two triangles are congruent	U5-188	**lado-lado-lado (SSS)** si los tres lados de un triángulo son congruentes con los tres lados de otro triángulo, entonces los dos triángulos son congruentes
sketch a quickly done representation of a figure; a rough approximation of a figure	U5-51	**bosquejo** representación de una figura realizada con rapidez; aproximación imprecisa de una figura

English		Español

skewed to the left data concentrated on the higher values in the data set, which has a tail to the left. Example:

U4-3

desviados hacia la izquierda datos concentrados en los valores más altos del conjunto de datos, que tiene una cola hacia la izquierda. Ejemplo:

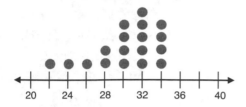 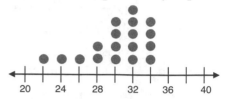

skewed to the right data concentrated on the lower values in the data set, which has a tail to the right. Example:

U4-3

desviados hacia la derecha datos concentrados en los valores más bajos del conjunto de datos, que tiene una cola hacia la derecha. Ejemplo:

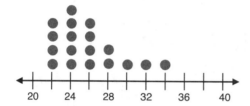 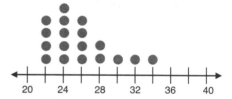

slope the measure of the rate of change of one variable with respect to another variable; slope $= \dfrac{y_2 - y_1}{x_2 - x_1} = \dfrac{\Delta y}{\Delta x} = \dfrac{\text{rise}}{\text{run}}$; the slope in the equation $y = mx + b$ is m.

U1-50
U2-83
U2-153
U2-193
U4-98
U6-2

pendiente medida de la tasa de cambio de una variable con respecto a otra; pendiente $= \dfrac{y_2 - y_1}{x_2 - x_1} = \dfrac{\Delta y}{\Delta x}$; la pendiente en la ecuación $y = mx + b$ es m

slope-intercept method the method used to graph a linear equation; with this method, draw a line using only two points on the coordinate plane

U2-83

método pendiente-intercepto método utilizado para graficar una ecuación lineal; con este método, se dibuja una línea con sólo dos puntos en un plano de coordenadas

solution a value that makes the equation true

U1-15

solución valor que hace verdadera la ecuación

English		Español
solution set the value or values that make a sentence or statement true; the set of ordered pairs that represent all of the solutions to an equation or a system of equations	U1-15 U1-93 U2-2	**conjunto de soluciones** valor o valores que hacen verdadera una afirmación o declaración; conjunto de pares ordenados que representa todas las soluciones para una ecuación o sistema de ecuaciones
solution to a system of linear inequalities the intersection of the half planes of the inequalities; the solution is the set of all points that make all the inequalities in the system true	U2-41	**solución a un sistema de desigualdades lineales** intersección de los medios planos de las desigualdades; la solución es el conjunto de todos los puntos que hacen verdaderas todas las desigualdades de un sistema
square a parallelogram with four congruent sides and four right angles	U5-105 U6-2	**cuadrado** paralelograma con cuatro lados congruentes y cuatro ángulos rectos
straightedge a bar or strip of wood, plastic, or metal having at least one long edge of reliable straightness	U5-51	**regla de borde recto** barra o franja de madera, plástico o metal que tiene, al menos, un borde largo de rectitud confiable
substitution method solving one of a pair of equations for one of the variables and substituting that into the other equation	U3-36	**método de sustitución** solución de un par de ecuaciones para una de las variables y sustitución de eso en la otra ecuación
symmetric situation in which data is concentrated toward the middle of the range of data; data values are distributed in the same way above and below the middle of the sample. Example:	U4-3	**simétrico** situación en la que los datos se concentran hacia el medio del rango de datos; los valores de datos se distribuyen de la misma manera por encima y por debajo del medio de la muestra. Ejemplo:

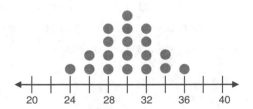

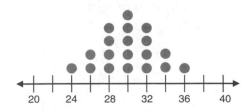

English		Español
system a set of more than one equation	U2-2	**sistema** conjunto de más de una ecuación
system of equations a set of equations with the same unknowns	U1-93 U3-36	**sistema de ecuaciones** conjunto de ecuaciones con las mismas incógnitas
system of inequalities two or more inequalities in the same variables that work together	U1-93 U2-42	**sistema de desigualdades** dos o más desigualdades en las mismas variables que operan juntas

T

English		Español
term a number, a variable, or the product of a number and variable(s)	U1-2	**término** número, variable o producto de un número y una o más variables
third quartile value that identifies the upper 25% of the data; the median of the upper half of the data set; 75% of all data is less than this value; written as Q_3	U4-3	**tercer cuartil** valor que identifica el 25% superior de los datos; mediana de la mitad superior del conjunto de datos; el 75% de los datos es menor que este valor; se expresa como Q_3
transformation a change in a geometric figure's position, shape, or size	U2-216 U5-3	**transformación** cambio en la posición, la forma o el tamaño de una figura geométrica
translation moving a graph either vertically, horizontally, or both, without changing its shape; a slide; an isometry where all points in the preimage are moved parallel to a given line	U2-216 U5-3 U5-35	**traslación** movimiento de un gráfico en sentido vertical, horizontal, o en ambos, sin modificar su forma; deslizamiento; isometría en la que todos los puntos de la preimagen se mueven en paralelo a una línea determinada
trend a pattern of behavior, usually observed over time or over multiple iterations	U4-43	**tendencia** patrón de comportamiento, que se observa por lo general en el tiempo o en múltiples repeticiones

English		Español
triangle a three-sided polygon with three angles	U5-105	**triángulo** polígono de tres lados con tres ángulos
two-way frequency table a table that divides responses into categories, showing both a characteristic in the table rows and a characteristic in the table columns; values in cells are a count of the number of times each response was given by a respondent with a certain characteristic	U4-43	**tabla de frecuencia de doble entrada** tabla que divide las respuestas en dos categorías, y muestra una característica en las filas y una en las columnas; los valores de las celdas son un conteo de la cantidad de veces que un respondedor da una respuesta con una determinada característica

U

English		Español
undefined slope the slope of a vertical line	U2-83	**pendiente indefinida** pendiente de una línea vertical
unit rate a rate per one given unit	U1-15	**tasa unitaria** tasa de una unidad determinada

V

English		Español
variable a letter used to represent a value or unknown quantity that can change or vary	U1-2 U1-15 U2-193	**variable** letra utilizada para representar un valor o una cantidad desconocida que puede cambiar o variar
vertical shift number of units the graph of the function is moved up or down; a translation	U2-216 U2-245	**desplazamiento vertical** cantidad de unidades que el gráfico de la función se desplaza hacia arriba o hacia abajo; traslación

W

English		Español
whole numbers the set of natural numbers that also includes 0: {0, 1, 2, 3, ...}	U2-83	**números enteros** conjunto de números naturales que incluye el 0: {0, 1, 2, 3, ...}

X

English		Español
x-intercept the point at which the line intersects the x-axis at $(x, 0)$	U1-50 U2-42 U2-83 U2-153	**intercepto de x** punto en el que una recta corta el eje x en $(x, 0)$

English		Español
	Y	
***y*-intercept** the point at which a line or curve intersects the *y*-axis at (0, *y*); the *y*-intercept in the equation $y = mx + b$ is *b*.	U1-50 U2-42 U2-124 U2-153 U2-193 U4-98	**intercepto de *y*** punto en el que una recta o curva corta el eje *y* en (0, *y*); el intercepto de *y* en la ecuación $y = mx + b$ es *b*.

Formulas

Formulas

ALGEBRA

General

(x, y)	Ordered pair
$(x, 0)$	x-intercept
$(0, y)$	y-intercept

Symbols

$\approx$	Approximately equal to
$\neq$	Is not equal to
$|a|$	Absolute value of a
$\sqrt{a}$	Square root of a

Linear Equations

$m = \dfrac{y_2 - y_1}{x_2 - x_1}$	Slope
$ax + b = c$	One variable
$y = mx + b$	Slope-intercept form
$ax + by = c$	General form
$y - y_1 = m(x - x_1)$	Point-slope form

Arithmetic Sequences

$a_n = a_1 + (n - 1)d$	Explicit formula
$a_n = a_{n-1} + d$	Recursive formula

Geometric Sequences

$a_n = a_1 \cdot r^{n-1}$	Explicit formula
$a_n = a_{n-1} \cdot r$	Recursive formula

Exponential Equations

$y = ab^x$	General form
$y = ab^{\frac{x}{t}}$	Exponential equation
$y = a(1 + r)^t$	Exponential growth
$y = a(1 - r)^t$	Exponential decay

$A = P\left(1 + \dfrac{r}{n}\right)^{nt}$	Compounded interest formula
Compounded...	n (number of times per year)
Yearly/annually	1
Semi-annually	2
Quarterly	4
Monthly	12
Weekly	52
Daily	365

Functions

$f(x)$	Notation, "f of x"
$f(x) = mx + b$	Linear function
$f(x) = b^x + k$	Exponential function
$(f + g)(x) = f(x) + g(x)$	Addition
$(f - g)(x) = f(x) - g(x)$	Subtraction
$(f \cdot g)(x) = f(x) \cdot g(x)$	Multiplication
$(f \div g)(x) = f(x) \div g(x)$	Division

Formulas

Properties of Equality

Property	In symbols
Reflexive property of equality	$a = a$
Symmetric property of equality	If $a = b$, then $b = a$.
Transitive property of equality	If $a = b$ and $b = c$, then $a = c$.
Addition property of equality	If $a = b$, then $a + c = b + c$.
Subtraction property of equality	If $a = b$, then $a - c = b - c$.
Multiplication property of equality	If $a = b$ and $c \neq 0$, then $a \bullet c = b \bullet c$.
Division property of equality	If $a = b$ and $c \neq 0$, then $a \div c = b \div c$.
Substitution property of equality	If $a = b$, then b may be substituted for a in any expression containing a.

Properties of Operations

Property	General rule
Commutative property of addition	$a + b = b + a$
Associative property of addition	$(a + b) + c = a + (b + c)$
Commutative property of multiplication	$a \bullet b = b \bullet a$
Associative property of multiplication	$(a \bullet b) \bullet c = a \bullet (b \bullet c)$
Distributive property of multiplication over addition	$a \bullet (b + c) = a \bullet b + a \bullet c$

Properties of Inequality

Property
If $a > b$ and $b > c$, then $a > c$.
If $a > b$, then $b < a$.
If $a > b$, then $-a < -b$.
If $a > b$, then $a \pm c > b \pm c$.
If $a > b$ and $c > 0$, then $a \bullet c > b \bullet c$.
If $a > b$ and $c < 0$, then $a \bullet c < b \bullet c$.
If $a > b$ and $c > 0$, then $a \div c > b \div c$.
If $a > b$ and $c < 0$, then $a \div c < b \div c$.

Laws of Exponents

Law	General rule
Multiplication of exponents	$b^m \bullet b^n = b^{m+n}$
Power of exponents	$\left(b^m\right)^n = b^{mn}$ $\left(bc\right)^n = b^n c^n$
Division of exponents	$\dfrac{b^m}{b^n} = b^{m-n}$
Exponents of zero	$b^0 = 1$
Negative exponents	$b^{-n} = \dfrac{1}{b^n}$ and $\dfrac{1}{b^{-n}} = b^n$

Formulas

DATA ANALYSIS

$IQR = Q_3 - Q_1$	Interquartile range
$Q_1 - 1.5(IQR)$	Lower outlier formula
$Q_3 + 1.5(IQR)$	Upper outlier formula
$y - y_0$	Residual formula

GEOMETRY

Symbols	
$d\left(\overset{\frown}{ABC}\right)$	Arc length
$\angle$	Angle
$\odot$	Circle
$\cong$	Congruent
$\overleftrightarrow{PQ}$	Line
$\overline{PQ}$	Line Segment
$\overrightarrow{PQ}$	Ray
$\parallel$	Parallel
$\perp$	Perpendicular
$\bullet$	Point
$\triangle$	Triangle
A'	Prime
$\circ$	Degrees

Translations	
$T_{(h,k)} = (x + h, y + k)$	Translation

Reflections	
$r_{x\text{-axis}}(x, y) = (x, -y)$	Through the x-axis
$r_{y\text{-axis}}(x, y) = (-x, y)$	Through the y-axis
$r_{y=x}(x, y) = (y, x)$	Through the line $y = x$

Rotations	
$R_{90}(x, y) = (-y, x)$	Counterclockwise 90° about the origin
$R_{180}(x, y) = (-x, -y)$	Counterclockwise 180° about the origin
$R_{270}(x, y) = (y, -x)$	Counterclockwise 270° about the origin

Congruent Triangle Statements

Side-Side-Side (SSS)	Side-Angle-Side (SAS)	Angle-Side-Angle (ASA)
$\triangle ABC \cong \triangle XYZ$	$\triangle DEF \cong \triangle TVW$	$\triangle GHJ \cong \triangle QRS$

Formulas

Pythagorean Theorem
$a^2 + b^2 = c^2$

Distance Formula	
$d = \sqrt{(x_2 - x_1)^2 + (y_2 - y_1)^2}$	Distance formula

Area	
$A = lw$	Rectangle
$A = \dfrac{1}{2}bh$	Triangle

MEASUREMENTS

Length
Metric
1 kilometer (km) = 1000 meters (m)
1 meter (m) = 100 centimeters (cm)
1 centimeter (cm) = 10 millimeters (mm)
Customary
1 mile (mi) = 1760 yards (yd)
1 mile (mi) = 5280 feet (ft)
1 yard (yd) = 3 feet (ft)
1 foot (ft) = 12 inches (in)

Volume and Capacity
Metric
1 liter (L) = 1000 milliliters (mL)
Customary
1 gallon (gal) = 4 quarts (qt)
1 quart (qt) = 2 pints (pt)
1 pint (pt) = 2 cups (c)
1 cup (c) = 8 fluid ounces (fl oz)

Weight and Mass
Metric
1 kilogram (kg) = 1000 grams (g)
1 gram (g) = 1000 milligrams (mg)
1 metric ton (MT) = 1000 kilograms (kg)
Customary
1 ton (T) = 2000 pounds (lb)
1 pound (lb) = 16 ounces (oz)